project WILD

PRINCIPAL SPONSORS

Project WILD is co-sponsored by the Western Association of Fish and Wildlife Agencies and the Council for Environmental Education.

ORGANIZATIONAL SPONSORS

American Fisheries Society
Defenders of Wildlife
National Wildlife Federation
U.S. Environmental Protection Agency
U.S. Fish and Wildlife Service
The Wildlife Society

INTERNATIONAL ORGANIZATIONAL SPONSORS

Canadian Wildlife Federation
Czech Junak, Czech Republic
Centre for Environment Education,
    Ahmedabad, India
National Centre for Educational Materials,
    Iceland
Umea University, Sweden

AWARDS AND RECOGNITION

Project WILD, its sponsors and many of its participants—including students and teachers—have received a variety of awards and recognition.

Project WILD was honored at the White House in 1991 as one of the first recipients of a Gold Medal for Education and Communications in the President's Environment and Conservation Challenge Award program. This award was bestowed "for excellence in developing innovative solutions to the nation's environmental challenges."

Project WILD has also received the Conservation Education Award from The Wildlife Society. These materials have been endorsed by the National Council for the Social Studies and are consistent with recommendations of the National Science Teachers Association.

Project WILD
5430 Grosvenor Lane, Suite 230
Bethesda, MD 20814-2142
Phone (301) 493-5447
Fax (301) 493-5627
Email natpwild@igc.apc.org
Web http://eelink.umich.edu/wild/

Printing History
FIRST EDITION
PROJECT WILD ELEMENTARY
AND SECONDARY ACTIVITY GUIDES

	Elementary	Secondary
1st Printing, 1983	25,000	12,500
2nd Printing, 1984	51,434	27,828
3rd Printing, 1985	50,000	25,000
4th Printing, 1986	37,900	12,647
5th Printing, 1987	35,309	15,302
6th Printing, 1988	50,223	15,960
7th Printing, 1989	56,117	23,425
8th Printing, 1990	52,520	22,751
9th Printing, 1991	56,813	19,480
Total, First Edition	415,316	174,893

SECOND EDITION
PROJECT WILD ACTIVITY GUIDE

1st Printing, 1992	70,000
2nd Printing, 1993	60,000
3rd Printing, 1994	50,000
4th Printing, 1995	50,000
5th Printing, 1996	50,000
6th Printing, 1997	42,000

project WILD

K–12 Activity Guide

Project WILD is an interdisciplinary, supplementary conservation and environmental education program for educators of kindergarten through high school age young people.

PARTICIPATING MEMBERS AND STATE SPONSORS

Alabama Department of Conservation and Natural Resources

Alaska Department of Education

Alaska Department of Fish and Game

Arizona Department of Education

Arizona Game and Fish Department

Arkansas Game and Fish Commission

California Department of Education

California Department of Fish and Game

Colorado Department of Education

Colorado Division of Wildlife

Connecticut Department of Environmental Protection

Delaware Department of Natural Resources
and Environmental Control

District of Columbia Environmental Regulation Administration

Florida Game and Freshwater Fish Commission

Georgia Department of Natural Resources,
Wildlife Resources Division

Georgia Chapter, Safari Club International

University of Georgia, Extension Service

Hawaii Department of Education

Hawaii Department of Land and Natural Resources,
Division of Aquatic Resources

Idaho Department of Education

Idaho Department of Fish and Game

Illinois Board of Education

Illinois Department of Natural Resources, Education
Services Section

Northern Illinois University

Indiana Department of Natural Resources,
Division of Fish and Wildlife

Iowa Association of County Conservation Boards

Iowa Conservation Education Council

Iowa Department of Education

Iowa Department of Natural Resources

Geary County, Kansas Unified School District

Kansas Department of Wildlife and Parks

Kentucky Department of Fish and Wildlife Resources

Louisiana Department of Wildlife and Fisheries

Maine Department of Inland Fisheries and Wildlife

Maryland Department of Natural Resources, Wildlife and
Heritage Division

Massachusetts Audubon Society

Massachusetts Division of Fisheries and Wildlife

Michigan Alliance for Outdoor and Environmental Education

Michigan State University

Minnesota Department of Education

Minnesota Department of Natural Resources

Minnesota Environmental Education Board

Mississippi Department of Wildlife, Fisheries
and Parks

Missouri Department of Conservation

Saint Louis Zoo, Missouri

School District of Kansas City, Missouri

Montana Department of Fish, Wildlife and Parks

Montana Office of Public Instruction

Nebraska Game and Parks Commission

Nevada Department of Education

Nevada Division of Wildlife

New Hampshire Fish and Game Department

New Hampshire Wildlife Trust

New Jersey Division of Fish, Game and Wildlife

New Mexico Department of Education

New Mexico Department of Game and Fish

New York State Department of Environmental Conservation

North Carolina Wildlife Resources Commission

North Dakota Department of Game and Fish

Ohio Department of Education
Ohio Division of Wildlife
Oklahoma Conservation Commission
Oklahoma Department of Wildlife Conservation
Oregon Department of Education
Oregon Department of Fish and Wildlife
Pennsylvania Fish and Boat Commission
Pennsylvania Game Commission
Puerto Rico Department of Natural and Environmental Resources
Rhode Island Division of Fish and Wildlife
South Carolina Department of Natural Resources
South Dakota Department of Game, Fish and Parks
Tennessee Conservation League
Tennessee Department of Education
Tennessee Wildlife Resources Agency

Texas Parks and Wildlife Department
Dallas Safari Club, Texas
Houston Safari Club, Texas
Utah Division of Wildlife Resources
Utah State Board of Education
Vermont Department of Fish and Wildlife
Virginia Department of Game and Inland Fisheries
Virginia Division, Izaak Walton League of America
Washington Department of Fish and Wildlife
Washington State Office of the Superintendent of Public Instruction
West Virginia Department of Natural Resources
Wisconsin Department of Natural Resources
Wyoming Department of Education
Wyoming Game and Fish Department

PREFACE

Project WILD is an interdisciplinary, supplementary conservation and environmental education program emphasizing wildlife.

For instructional purposes in Project WILD, wildlife is defined as any non-domesticated animal. Wildlife may be small organisms only visible to people if seen through a microscope, or as large as a great blue whale. Wildlife includes, but is not limited to, insects, spiders, birds, reptiles, fish, amphibians and mammals, if non-domesticated.

Project WILD's primary audience is teachers of kindergarten through high school students. This does not limit the usefulness of the Project to formal educational settings, however. Volunteers working with young people in pre-school and after-school programs; representatives of private conservation, industry and other community groups who are interested in providing instructional programs for young people or their teachers; and personnel involved in preparation of future teachers are all among those who effectively use the instructional resources of this program.

Project WILD is based on the premise that young people and their teachers have a vital interest in learning about the earth as home for people and wildlife. The program emphasizes wildlife—because of its intrinsic, ecological and other values, as well as its importance as a basis for understanding the fragile grounds upon which all life rests. Project WILD is designed to prepare young people for decisions affecting people, wildlife and their shared home, earth. In the face of pressures of all kinds affecting the quality and sustainability of life on earth as we know it, Project WILD addresses the need for human beings to develop as responsible members of the ecosystem.

In the decade since Project WILD began, more than 600,000 educators in the U.S. have participated in Project WILD workshops. These educators in turn have provided instruction using Project WILD to more than 38 million youth.

The goal of Project WILD is to assist learners of any age in developing awareness, knowledge, skills and commitment to result in informed decisions, responsible behavior and constructive actions concerning wildlife and the environment upon which all life depends.

Project WILD is a joint project of the Western Association of Fish and Wildlife Agencies (WAFWA) and the Council for Environmental Education (CEE) (formerly the Western Regional Environmental Education Council, Inc. [WREEC]). These two organizations are the founding sponsors. The Western Association is a group comprised of the directors of the state agencies in western states and western Canadian provinces who are responsible for management of wildlife in their respective jurisdictions. WREEC was founded in 1970 in a unique and visionary effort to create a partnership between education and natural resource professionals in the 13 western states. Through the years, as support for WREEC's co-sponsored programs expanded beyond the western states, WREEC's network for environmental education continued to grow. In 1996, WREEC officially changed its name to the Council for Environmental Education (CEE) to more accurately reflect its national network of state department of education and natural

resource agency professionals. The purposes of the Council are to support environmental education through the management and development of environmental education programs, to publish and disseminate environmental education materials, and to facilitate the development and maintenance of partnerships for environmental education.

Agreements between the two sponsoring organizations allow for additional sponsorship by other interested organizations and agencies.

The Project WILD Program Committee, CEE staff, WAFWA members and all associate organizational and state sponsors, as well as others associated with the program, are dedicated to achieving the highest possible standards of professional quality, factual accuracy and objectivity in all programs, activities and materials bearing the WILD name. Project WILD has adopted policies and guidelines which state the program's commitment to neutrality on controversial issues, treating such issues fairly and honestly without advocating any one particular point of view, recognizing that people need information from a variety of sources to make their own informed decisions. Project WILD programs, activities and materials are not to be used to promote agency or organizational policies or political points of view.

ASSOCIATE AND CONTRIBUTING SPONSORSHIP

It is possible for an agency or organization to become an associate or contributing sponsor of Project WILD, with appropriate credit given for that organization's involvement in the program. Each printing of the project materials will reflect the complete list of sponsors.

FOR ADDITIONAL INFORMATION

For additional information about participation in Project WILD as an associate or contributing sponsor, please contact the Project WILD National Office: 5430 Grosvenor Lane, Suite 230, Bethesda, MD 20814-2142, *phone* (301) 493-5447, *email* natpwild@igc.apc.org.

Or contact CEE at 5555 Morningside Drive, Suite 212, Houston, TX 77005-3216, 713-520-1936.

CEE STAFF
Josetta Hawthorne
Executive Director
CEE

Donna Asbury
Director
Project WILD

Michele Campbell
Administrative Coordinator
Project WILD

Mike Kaspar
EETAP Coordinator
Project WILD

INTRODUCTION

A concern for the land and its resources is basic to our survival, both as individuals and as a nation, for we cannot live apart from our planetary home. Environmental quality and human health and well-being are interdependent.

What will our land be like 20, 40 or 100 years from now? No one can really be certain, but we are gaining in our knowledge of environmental cause and effect. We can be sure, however, that our environmental future is to a large degree in our hands. We have our technologies, and we are gaining in our ability to manipulate the physical environment and its resources—for better or for worse. The directions we take with our technologies are very much dependent upon the values we hold and the choices we make, individually and socially.

Two elements of society play key roles in shaping future environments: resource managers and educators. Both are concerned with the future. The goal of education is the highest and best use—or conservation—of the human resource. The goal of resource management is the highest and best use—or conservation—of natural resources. These goals are interdependent.

Project WILD is a joint effort involving representatives of these two key elements of society to do something together which might have a beneficial effect on future environments as well as on the lives and well-being of humans and wildlife who will share them. Much has been accomplished thus far; much remains to be done.

Other programs co-sponsored by CEE

Project Learning Tree (PLT)
1111 Nineteenth St., NW, Suite 780
Washington, DC 20036
Phone: (202) 463-2462
Web: http://www.nceet.snre.umich.edu/plt.html

Project WET (Water Education for Teachers)
Culbertson Hall
Montana State University
Bozeman, MT 59717
Phone: (406) 994-5392
Email: rwwet@msu.oscs.montana.edu

The commitment is there, however, and steady progress is being made. How might we describe what has been accomplished thus far?

Some might say that Project WILD is an excellent set of teaching materials bound in an attractive format. Professional educators could describe these materials as a supplementary, interdisciplinary, educational program directed at providing learning experiences for students in kindergarten through grade twelve.

WILD is these things, and more. These descriptions fall short of capturing the essence of the program. Quite simply, Project WILD is people—educators, resource managers, citizen conservationists and others—doing something together which they believe is important for children, and for the land and its resources, now and for the future.

The original movers in Project WILD were resource management professionals and education administrators with state-level responsibilities from 13 western states working through the Council for Environmental Education (CEE) and the Western Association of Fish and Wildlife Agencies (WAFWA). These people put together the basic
concept and plan of action for the program and secured the necessary resources to get it underway. Organizationally, CEE was responsible for the materials and program development while WAFWA provided technical expertise and program resources. Other agencies and organizations have since joined as sponsors.

CEE provided a means for its members to develop and coordinate state-level conservation and environmental education programs on a regional basis for more than 25 years. The organization began as a federal project through a U.S. Office of Education grant in 1970, and became an independent nonprofit educational corporation in 1976.

One of the most visible accomplishments of the Council for Environmental Education (formerly WREEC) is Project Learning Tree (PLT), also a supplementary, interdisciplinary educational program for educators working with students in kindergarten through grade twelve. Project Learning Tree was produced through a grant from the American Forest Institute and is cosponsored by CEE and the American Forest Foundation. Project Learning Tree provides materials and support services with an emphasis on effectively teaching youngsters about forest resources and our interdependence with the natural world.

The experience gained over ten years of working with Project Learning Tree proved to be of great value in developing Project WILD. The same general procedure was followed in developing the materials. A content outline or framework was developed cooperatively with input from a great number of people—educators, preservationists, conservationists, wildlife managers, business and industry representatives and others. The basic materials to teach the concepts in the outline were developed by teachers in five writing workshops held in western states, and were extensively field-tested and edited before being assembled in final form. As with Project Learning Tree, the materials are available to those who attend instructional workshops offered by certified leaders. In the sponsoring states, the wildlife agencies typically are responsible for the statewide implementation program, working with the state education agency, citizen groups, local school personnel and others. Evaluation, revision of the materials, and other services are offered through the Project WILD National Office.

As with all good teaching materials, Project WILD is concerned with providing information and helping students evaluate choices and thereby make reasonable decisions. In short, our mission is to help youngsters learn **how** to think, not **what** to think.

We are proud of the fact that our strict efforts at balance and objectivity, as well as the technical validity and educational value of the materials, have gained sponsors for the project from a number of organizations representing a wide range of views on wildlife and its management.

As noted, Project WILD is a people program. Its overall purpose is to motivate youngsters to take intelligent and constructive action to conserve wildlife and natural resources. Much has been accomplished so far: framework and materials produced, field testing and evaluation completed; implementation plans developed and initiated; updates completed; new program materials developed; services expanded. However, the process will not be complete until the learning activities reach a significant number of youngsters—in classrooms, through youth groups and as individuals.

That is why we consider you—the person now reading this volume—to be so important. You are a key part of the people process, and it is you who must take WILD on the next step in its journey to the youngsters. We will help you all we can, but the final success of the program depends upon your skill in using these materials and resources. And, in so doing, you become part of us—and we become part of you: people who care about children, about our land and its resources, about the present and the future, and who are willing to do something about it.

Welcome to Project WILD!

Rudolph J.H. Schafer

Founder
Western Regional Environmental Education, Inc.
Board Member
Council for Environmental Education

HOW TO USE THIS BOOK

Thanks for your interest in Project WILD! Project WILD has been designed to be an instructional resource for people who care about natural resources and the environment—beginning with the recognition that the earth is home for people and wildlife.

A SUPPLEMENT TO EXISTING COURSES AND PROGRAMS

Instructional activities within the Project WILD materials are designed for easy integration into school subject and skill areas—especially science, social studies, language arts, mathematics and art—so that classroom teachers may use the materials as a means by which to teach required concepts and skills. . .at the same time teaching about people, wildlife and the environment. Educators in non-school settings, such as scout leaders, outdoor education camp personnel, park naturalists and others also find the materials of use.

Instructors may use one or many Project WILD activities. The activities may be integrated into existing courses of study, or the entire set of activities may serve quite effectively as the basis for a course of study.

ORGANIZATION OF THE MATERIALS

Because these materials are supplementary—designed for integration into existing courses of study—instructors may pick and choose from the activities. Each activity is designed to stand alone, without other Project WILD activities. There is no need to do the activities in order, nor to do all activities, even for a given grade level. However the activities have been placed in a thematic and developmental order that can serve as an aid to their use. They are organized to allow students to acquire knowledge, information and skills to assist them in making informed and responsible decisions affecting wildlife, people and our shared environments.

The activities are organized into seven major sections, corresponding to the Conceptual Framework which can be found in the back of this guide. By looking at the Table of Contents—or reading the Conceptual Framework—you can see the conceptual development: from awareness and appreciation. . .to responsible human actions.

Section One: Awareness and Appreciation

Activities in this section are introductory. They are designed to establish a foundation for most of the activities which follow. For example, beginning the school year or an instructional unit involving wildlife with either "What's Wild?" or "Animal Charades" establishes a definition of wildlife and distinguishes between wild and domesticated animals. Other activities in this section examine similar survival needs of people, domesticated animals and wildlife, including a basic introduction into the components of habitat.

Section Two: Diversity of Wildlife Values

Activities in this section provide students an opportunity to consider the range of contributions by wildlife to people and the environment—including aesthetic, ecological, scientific, political, commercial, economic, recreational and intrinsic values.

Section Three: Ecological Principles

Activities in this section provide a good foundation for understanding the characteristics of environments, how they work, who and what inhabits them and specific implications for understanding these principles as they affect wildlife. If the students have limited or no background in ecological principles, it is best to select a few introductory activities from Sections One and Three before tackling some of the more complex activities found in later sections of the Project WILD materials.

Section Four: Management and Conservation

This section builds on the general principles established in Sections One and Three, and provides an opportunity for more depth in understanding how wildlife and other natural resources can be managed and conserved.

Section Five: People, Culture and Wildlife

The major emphasis of activities in this section is to examine the influence of ways that human cultures affect people's attitudes toward and treatment of wildlife and other natural resources—from music to advertisements to cartoons and bumper stickers.

Section Six: Trends, Issues and Consequences

Activities in this section are most effective when students have some background in wildlife and ecological principles. A range of difficult issues is addressed. Students are given opportunities to apply knowledge they have gained in earlier activities by consideration of difficult issues and their consequences.

Section Seven: Responsible Human Actions

Activities in this section are designed to serve as a way for students to recognize, evaluate and make responsible choices in their own lives—reflecting the knowledge and skills they have acquired in earlier activities. Solutions are not prescribed for students. Instead, students are provided opportunities to consider and take constructive actions as thoughtful, informed and responsible inhabitants of our shared home.

ORGANIZATION OF EACH ACTIVITY

Each activity includes a statement of the instructional objective; a brief description of the instructional method employed; background information for the instructor; a list of any materials needed; step-by-step procedures; a few limited examples of ways in which to evaluate student learning; indication of recommended grade level; subjects from which concepts are drawn; skills; duration; recommended group size; setting (indoors or outdoors); and key vocabulary. In every case, an instructor is encouraged to adapt activities for different ages, subjects, skills, group sizes, etc. Finally, each activity includes a listing of points in the Conceptual Framework outline to which the activity either corresponds directly, i.e., the activity is designed to teach the concepts specifically; or, indirectly, i.e., the points noted are useful additional background information for the instructor.

APPENDICES

The Appendices include a list of agencies and organizations which are referenced in one or more Project WILD activities; a glossary of terms for use by the instructor; a complete listing of the Conceptual Framework in outline form; an alphabetical listing of activities by title; a set of guidelines for study of live animals in classrooms; and cross references by subject area, skills, grade levels and topics for use in creating instructional units. Additional appendices are included to provide a variety of kinds of background information.

We hope you find these materials of use. Let us hear from you at any time with suggestions as to how to improve them, requests for additional information and assistance—and any news of your experiences and those of your students as you "do something WILD!"

TABLE OF CONTENTS

The time is overdue in developing a long-term approach to the problems of people, wildlife, and habitat . . . The earth is home to us all.

SECTION ONE
AWARENESS AND APPRECIATION

WHAT'S WILD

OBJECTIVES
Students will: 1) distinguish between wildlife and domesticated animals; and 2) recognize that wildlife occurs in a variety of forms.

METHOD
Students find and classify pictures of wild and domesticated animals, and construct collages.

BACKGROUND
An animal is generally referred to as any living organism other than a plant. Wildlife is any animal that lives in a basically free condition, providing for its own food, shelter, and other needs in an environment that serves as a suitable habitat. Wildlife refers to animals that are not tamed or domesticated. Wildlife may be small organisms only visible to humans if seen through a microscope, or as large as a whale. Wildlife includes, but is not limited to, insects, spiders, birds, reptiles, fish, amphibians, and mammals, if non-domesticated. Domesticated animals are those which humans have tamed, kept in captivity, and bred for special purposes. The process of domestication takes place over a long period of time and has involved genetic manipulation through selective breeding. All domesticated animals have their origins in wild ancestors. Cattle used for food and other products; sheep for wool and other products, as well as dogs, cats, birds, and fish commonly kept as pets are all examples of domesticated animals.

Confusion can arise about animals that sometimes may be wild, sometimes may be tamed, and sometimes may be domesticated. If the animal, or population of animals, can live on its own, survive, and even reproduce, it is probably wild. Individual animals may be tamed—like some animals in zoos—while most of their numbers remain wild. A wild animal may appear to be tame, but still should be considered wild unless it is both tamed and domesticated. Some animals that are usually considered domesticated—like dogs, cats, horses, and goats—may become wild. When they do, the term "feral" is used. For example, there are feral goats on Catalina Isle, and feral horses and burros in some areas of western states in the U.S.

Where it is difficult to distinguish whether an animal is wild or domesticated, encourage the students to think in terms of what is **usually** the case. Remember that wild animals basically take care of themselves, as long as they have a suitable environment or habitat in which to live. Domesticated or tamed animals basically depend on people to feed and take care of them, and are typically used by people; for example, as a source of products and as pets. Whereas domesticated animals like cats and dogs are normally considered suitable pets, wild animals—even if tamed—are nearly always unsuitable, inappropriate, and frequently illegal pets.

The major purpose of this activity is for students to be able to distinguish between wild and domesticated animals.

Age: Grades K-3
Subjects: Science, Language Arts, Art
Skills: classification, media construction, observation
Duration: 60 minutes
Group Size: any
Setting: indoors
Conceptual Framework Reference: I., I.B.3, I.B.4, V.A.1
Key Vocabulary: animal, wild, domesticated
Appendices: none

MATERIALS
magazine or newspaper pictures of a wide variety of animals; poster board or heavy construction paper; glue

PROCEDURE

1. Ask students to bring pictures to class of as many animals as they can find in magazines or newspapers at home (or get them from magazines and newspapers available in school, if any). Ask the students to look for pictures of as many different animals as they can, telling them that animals are any living things except plants.

2. Once the students have assembled a collection of animal pictures, it is time to classify them. Students may work alone or in small groups. Talk with the students about wild animals and domesticated animals (like pets, farm animals, etc.) before they get started with their classifying.

3. Once the students have put their animals into two categories—either wild or domesticated—get out the poster board or construction paper and glue and ask the students to make two collages...one of wildlife, and one of domesticated animals. You can make a classroom gallery out of the products.

EXTENSIONS

1. Make a master list of the wildlife and domesticated animals. Use the words for spelling, and talk about the variety of animals found.

2. Younger students can take cut-outs of animals and put them where they fit—like birds in the sky, whales in the ocean, a deer in the forest.

3. Make mobiles that show "layers" of animals—in the sea, on land, and in the air. Build one huge mobile with an animal for each student that shows deserts, forests, mountains, seas, and the skies. Different colors of brightly-colored yarn can be used to hang the different animals in the mobile according to the ecosystem in which they live.

AQUATIC EXTENSIONS

1. Aquatic wildlife occurs in a variety of forms. Create a collage of aquatic animals, including many different kinds.

2. Create posters or collages of aquatic wildlife according to the habitat in which it lives. For example, there are a variety of possible freshwater as well as marine environments in which aquatic wildlife might live. Freshwater: stream or brook, lake, pond, river. Marine: ocean.

EVALUATION

Which animals have been domesticated: goldfish, horses, cows, ducks, boa constrictors, mosquitoes, bats, chickens, lions, eagles?

ANIMAL CHARADES

OBJECTIVES
Students will define wildlife, as well as to distinguish between domesticated and non-domesticated animals.

METHOD
Students use "charades" to distinguish between wild and domesticated animals.

BACKGROUND
An animal is generally referred to as any living organism other than a plant. Wildlife is any animal that lives in a basically free condition, providing for its own food, shelter, and other needs in an environment that serves as a suitable habitat. Wildlife refers to animals that are not tamed or domesticated. Wildlife may be small organisms only visible to humans if seen through a microscope, or as large as a whale. Wildlife includes, but is not limited to, insects, spiders, birds, reptiles, fish, amphibians, and mammals, if non-domesticated. Domesticated animals are those which humans have tamed, kept in captivity and bred for special purposes. The process of domestication takes place over a long period of time and has involved genetic manipulation through selective breeding. All domesticated animals have their origins in wild ancestors. Cattle used for food and other products, sheep for wool and other products, as well as dogs, cats, birds and fish commonly kept as pets are all examples of domesticated animals.

Confusion can arise about animals that sometimes may be wild, sometimes may be tamed, and sometimes may be domesticated. If the animal, or population of animals, can live on its own, survive, and even reproduce, it is probably wild. Individual animals may be tamed—like some animals in zoos—while most of their numbers remain wild. A wild animal may appear to be tame, but still should be considered wild unless it is both tamed and domesticated. Some animals that are usually considered domesticated—like dogs, cats, horses and goats—may become wild. When they do, the term "feral" is used. For example, there are feral goats on Catalina Isle, and feral horses and burros in some areas of western states in the U.S.

Where it is difficult to distinguish whether an animal is wild or domesticated, encourage the students to think in terms of what is **usually** the case. Remember that wild animals basically take care of themselves, as long as they have a suitable environment or habitat in which to live. Domesticated or tamed animals basically depend on people to feed and take care of them, and are typically used by people; for example, as a source of products and as pets. Whereas domesticated animals like cats and dogs are normally considered suitable pets, wild animals—even if tamed—are nearly always unsuitable, inappropriate and frequently illegal pets.

The major purpose of this activity is for students to be able to distinguish between wildlife and domesticated animals.

MATERIALS
chalkboard for use by the teacher or student recorder; small pieces of writing paper; container (e.g., box, hat, wastebasket)

PROCEDURE
1. This is charades—with an instructional purpose! In order to begin this activity, first create a space in the classroom that provides room for individual students to act out an animal and room for the other students to observe the charade and guess which animal is being portrayed.

Age: Grades 4-12
Subjects: Language Arts, Science, Drama
Skills: physical interpretation of concepts, observation, analysis
Duration: 30 minutes
Group Size: 30-40 students, or fewer
Setting: indoors or outdoors
Conceptual Framework Reference: I.B.4., V.A.1.
Vocabulary: animal, wild, domesticated
Appendices: Simulations

---

2. Once the stage and audience areas have been established, each student should take a small piece of paper. On this paper, the student should write **his or her name, the name of the animal the student is going to portray and whether the animal is domesticated or wild.** The teacher will collect the slips of paper before the charades begin.

3. The teacher drops the slips of paper into a container. The charades are played in the order the teacher pulls the names from the container. When a student's name is called, he or she goes to the designated stage area. A student timekeeper says, "Begin," and the performing student dramatizes the chosen animal. (As an alternative procedure, students pick a paper out of the container and act out the charade for someone else's animal. The student who wrote the animal's name is stated and that person cannot guess during that round.) A charade should be guessed by the audience—who may call out their guesses—within a ten-second time limit.

4. Follow the charades with a summary discussion, asking the students to clarify their definitions of **wildlife and domesticated animals.** Encourage their identification of the range of forms found in wild and domesticated species. For example, they should recognize that wildlife may be microscopic in size, like an amoeba, or longer than most houses, like some whales. Determining whether an animal is wild or domesticated can sometimes be difficult. Students may recognize that animals in zoos might fit the definition of domesticated animals. Taking lions, for example, you might note two things: most lions are not in zoos, therefore the species is still found most commonly in the wild; and, lions are not commonly bred for special purposes in zoos, nor usually tamed, and thus might fit only one of the three criteria within the definition of domesticated—that of being captive. Raising trout for stocking and food is an example of another confusing issue. Such trout are captive and bred for special purposes. However, most species of trout exist in the wild, and even those captive are not considered tame. In assisting students to establish definitions for what may be considered wild and domesticated

species, both lions and trout can be considered wild. However, it is useful and important for the students to consider what appear to be and may be exceptions, as they refine their understanding of distinctions between wild and domesticated animals.

EXTENSIONS
1. One or more "animals" which coexist can mime together, representing the animals, their relationships and the ecosystem within which they live.
2. Classify animals into appropriate and inappropriate pets, with reasons for the classifications.

AQUATIC EXTENSIONS
List several kinds of aquatic environments. For example, stream or brook, lake, pond, river (freshwater environments); ocean (marine environment). Announce the general name of the aquatic environment in which the organism you will portray could live. Pantomime the organism's characteristics. Those watching need to identify the aquatic animal you are portraying and match it to the appropriate aquatic environment in which it could live.

EVALUATION
1. Define wildlife.
2. Explain, using examples, how a species can be considered "wild" and "domesticated."

BEARLY BORN

OBJECTIVES

Students will identify similar survival needs of black bears and human babies.

METHOD

Students illustrate, compute and graph differences between people and black bears at various stages of maturity.

BACKGROUND

There are similarities in basic survival needs of black bear cubs and human babies. Both are mammals, born from their mother's body. Although humans sometimes substitute soy or other products for mother's milk, bear cubs and most humans survive solely on mother's milk in the first months of life.

The major purpose of this activity is for students to recognize similarities between bear cubs and human babies as well as to develop mathematics skills.

The additional information on page 7 about bear cubs and their families may be of assistance.

NOTE: Your students may ask where the male, or father, bears are during the time the young cubs are growing. Male bears may kill cubs, so the mother bear keeps the cubs out of contact with males and will fight to protect them if provoked. Under good conditions, a bear may live as long as 30 or more years.

MATERIALS

graph paper and drawing paper
OPTIONAL: yardsticks; 36 inch sewing tapes

Age: Grades 4-7
Subjects: Mathematics, Science
Skills: analysis, comparing similarities and differences, graphing, estimation, prediction with ratio and averaging (optional), discussion, drawing, generalization, media construction, reading, writing
Duration: two 30-minute periods
Group Size: any
Setting: indoors
Conceptual Framework Reference: I.A.
Key Vocabulary: similarities, differences, survival needs, omnivore
Appendices: Local Resources, Metric Chart

PROCEDURE

1. Begin a discussion with the students about black bears. Ask them to guess how much a cub (baby bear) might weigh when it is born. Every student can write down a guess on a piece of paper. Call for their guesses. Ask for their ideas about how long mother bears are pregnant, what baby bears eat when they are born, how much they might weigh when they are a year old, how many brothers and sisters they might have who are their same age, how much they weigh when they are full grown, and how long they live.

2. Following the discussion, post this information or provide it as a "hand-out."

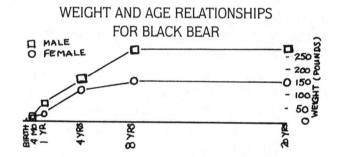

WEIGHT AND AGE RELATIONSHIPS FOR BLACK BEAR

(Data are characteristic of black bear in the southwestern United States. There will be regional variation.)

3. Ask the students to "fill in the blanks" with their own weight at the same ages as the information shows for the black bears. They will be required to estimate for years past their present age. Ask the students to:

   a. graph both sets of data
   b. draw a picture of the bear at each age
   c. draw a picture of themselves at each age

One student's comparative data might look like this:

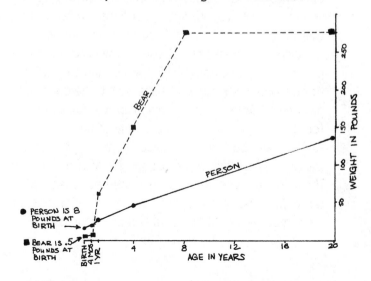

BLACK BEAR CUBS AND THEIR FAMILIES

A baby bear is called a cub. An adult female bear is called a sow. An adult male bear is called a boar. A sow is usually impregnated by a boar in May or June. Interestingly, the fertile egg does not begin active development until around October. In this way, the mother bear's body naturally slows down the development process so that birth can take place around January 1. Contrasted with human fetal development of nine months, the mother bear is pregnant for about seven months. The fetus actively develops for only about three months.

The sow has her cub or cubs in the shelter or den where she spends the winter months. A mother black bear usually has one or two cubs, although she may have as many as four. However, she won't have any cubs until she is four or five years of age, and then only every other year. From the time of birth, the mother's milk is the first food source for the young animals. At birth, a young cub has hair and weighs about eight ounces—about the size of a guinea pig. The bear cubs stay in the den with their mother until they are able to move around very actively. The bear cubs and their mother usually stay in the den until late April or early May. Boars and sows without cubs usually leave their dens a month earlier.

At the time the cubs leave the den with their mother, they are extremely dependent upon her. They still nurse, depending on mother's milk as a food source until the middle of summer, around six months. However, once out of the den, they quickly learn about additional food sources.

Black bears are omnivores. That means they eat plant and animal material. They tend to eat grass, nuts, berries in late summer, insects, grubs—and fish and rodents when they can catch them! Although they do not normally eat carrion, they will turn over dead and decaying animals to find and eat the protein-rich maggots.

When black bear cubs reach one year of age, female cubs weigh about 30 to 50 pounds. Males weigh about 50 to 70 pounds. A mature female bear will weigh about 150 to 185 pounds, and a male will weigh about 275 pounds.

4. Ask the students to compute the following, and include their results with their graph and drawing:

    a. How much weight did the black bear gain at each interval; that is, from birth to four months, four months to one year, etc.?

    b. How much weight did you gain during the same intervals?

    c. How many times more weight did the bear gain during each period?

5. In discussion, ask the students to comment on similarities and differences between bears and people. (For example, both are mammals. Describe their characteristics.) Ask students to identify clearly similarities in basic survival needs of bear cubs and babies.

EXTENSIONS

1. Find a few volunteers and get out your measuring tape! Researchers can estimate the weight of a bear by measuring the bear's girth (the distance around a bear's chest). Given the following data, students can measure the girth of a person's chest and estimate how much they would weigh if they were black bears!

    22" girth: weight of 50 pounds
    30" girth: weight of 100 pounds
    35" girth: weight of 150 pounds
    39" girth: weight of 200 pounds
    45" girth: weight of 300 pounds
    52" girth: weight of 400 pounds

Or: Have the students find a few volunteers to weigh themselves and measure their chest girth. Graph or chart their weight and girth. Graph or chart the weight and girth of black bears. Compare! Weigh and measure girth of older students, teachers and family members. Graph or chart the results. Possible questions:

    a. How much does a four-year-old bear weigh per inch of girth? Ten-year-old? Twenty-year-old?

    b. How much do various age groups of children weigh per inch of girth?

    c. Are bears or children heavier per inch? How about adults versus bears?

2. Calculate how fast a given bear population, if unchecked by limiting factors, can increase over a specific period of time, assuming that: a sow will have two cubs (one of each sex) in her fifth year of life; the total time frame is ten years, from July 1 to June 30; the initial bear population is one five-year-old boar and two six-year-old sows, one with two cubs. Graph or chart the results.

AQUATIC EXTENSIONS

Identify a variety of kinds of aquatic wildlife. Find out the average life span of each organism, how much it weighs at birth and how much it weighs at maturity.

EVALUATION

1. List three survival needs which are similar for bears and humans.

2. Use the following data to construct a graph which compares the growth of catfish from Lake Erie and the growth of catfish from the Ohio River.

	AGE IN YEARS									
	1	2	3	4	5	6	7	8	9	
Lake Erie Catfish	69	115	160	205	244	278	305	336	366	SIZE (in mm)
Ohio River Catfish	56	101	161	227	285	340	386	433	482	

a. Which catfish grew the most between the ages of four and five years?

b. How many times larger is the Ohio catfish at nine years of age than at one year of age?

ANTS ON A TWIG

OBJECTIVES
Students will: 1) identify similarities and differences in basic needs of ants and humans; and 2) generalize that humans and wildlife have similar basic needs.

METHOD
Students go outside to observe and demonstrate ant behavior.

BACKGROUND
Humans, domesticated animals and wildlife have similar basic needs. All depend upon the appropriate distribution or arrangement of food, water, shelter and space. All animals require these elements that comprise habitat.

Sometimes we forget that all living things share the same environment and basic needs. We don't always remember that every creature—from ants to people—needs food, water, shelter and space to survive.

Ants are common social insects. Their colonies may range in population size from less than 100 animals to hundreds of thousands of animals. Most colonies have one queen ant, although some will have several queens. Queens lay the colony's eggs after mating with one of the colony's few males. A queen ant might live for more than 12 years, yet she typically mates only once. Queens may lay more than 100 eggs a day. Most of a colony's members are workers and do not breed.

Ants consume a variety of foods. Not all ants eat all foods. Ants can be herbivores, carnivores or omnivores. The location of an ant colony does not necessarily indicate its food source. Carpenter ants dig elaborate tunnels in wood, but they do not eat wood. In the carpenter ant's case, wood serves as shelter, not food. Most of a carpenter ant's diet is comprised of aphid secretions. These ants "milk" the aphid secretions much like a dairy farmer milks a cow. Some ants also collect leaves that they use in a way similar to farming. They take the leaves to a nest where a fungus grows on them. The ants harvest the fungus and eat it for food.

Some ants are ground dwellers. You may see these ants in neighborhoods and city environments. The nests of these ants can go several feet into the ground and spread out over several thousand square feet.

Ants, like all animals, need water as well as food, shelter and space in which to live, all suitably arranged to meet their needs. Ants will drink free-standing water. The moisture content in their food can also satisfy some of their water needs. Many ants can survive for a day or more of being completely submerged in water.

The major purpose of this activity is for students to learn that humans and all animals have the same basic survival needs.

Age: Grades 3-9
Subjects: Science (Modified: English, Drama)
Skills: analysis, classification, comparing similarities and differences, description, discussion, generalization, kinesthetic concept development, observation, small group work, writing
Duration: two 30-minute class periods; one 50 to 60-minute class period
Group Size: teams of three to six; approximately 30 students total
Setting: outdoors
Conceptual Framework Reference: I.A., I.A.4., I.C.1., I.C.2.
Key Vocabulary: basic or survival needs, observation, evidence
Appendices: Animals In Schools, Field Ethics, Simulations, Observation and Inferences

MATERIALS
note pads and pens or pencils

PROCEDURE

1. Go outside and find some ants—or even inside, if you can find some in school buildings. Check sidewalks, near the cafeteria, around windows. Look on trees, in flower beds, in vacant lots. Working in teams of three to six, ask the students to observe the ants' behavior. At least one student in each group should serve as a recorder, noting the students' observations. Included in their observations should be:

- evidence of how ants take care of their basic needs;
- description of what their basic needs are; and
- description of ant behavior, including how ants move in a line. (This is important for a later phase of the activity!) CAUTION: Remind the students to make their observations without harming the ants or their habitat.

2. After approximately 20 minutes of observation time, bring the teams of students to a central location outside. Ask the students to report their findings. Close the discussion with a sharing of descriptions of ant behavior.

3. Now it's time to demonstrate ant behavior. The students need to get into two lines of equal length facing each other in a narrow area—like on top of a fallen log, between two lines drawn with chalk on a sidewalk, or on a low wall about one foot wide. The two lines of ants must pass each other without falling off! The students should simulate ant behavior based on their earlier observations. Their arms and hands can serve as antennae; for example, touching as they pass each other. NOTE: Physical dramatization of concepts—in this case, ant behavior—is an excellent way to facilitate retention of concept understanding.

4. The log or wall can now serve as a seating space. Having investigated the ways that ants meet their basic needs for **food, water, shelter** and **space,** in a suitable **arrangement,** ask the students to describe similarities and differences between basic needs of ants and humans. Assist the students in generalizing that humans, ants and other animals—both wild and tame—have similar basic needs. Summarize the discussion by noting that, although humans and ants are obviously different, both species share the same basic needs shared by all animal species—the fundamental needs for food, water, shelter, space and the appropriate arrangement of these.

EXTENSIONS

1. Find resources for ant information. Do the student observations match the printed references? Verify accuracy of observations and check any discrepancies.

2. Commercial ant farms are available. One can be established in the classroom for additional observation.

3. Various humane experiments, stressing scientific observation, can be undertaken by the students. For example:

- Map the space used by an ant colony—from the ants' shelter, through their travels, and back to their shelter again.
- Observe how ants find and use water. (Ants get most of their water from their food.) Put water out in various forms for a colony of ants; e.g., in a dish, in chunks of bread soaked in water, in smaller chunks. Observe and record what happens.
- Find ants moving in a line. Drop a small piece of food near the line. Record whether the ants will move off the line to get the food. Repeat this process several times, varying the distance from the ant line and the food that is dropped.

AQUATIC EXTENSIONS

1. Humans and aquatic wildlife have similar basic needs. That is, each needs food, water, shelter and space in a suitable arrangement. Pick an aquatic insect, spider, bird, reptile, fish, amphibian and mammal. List the common name for each; its typical habitat; and the food, kind of water, shelter and space each needs in order to survive.

2. Many aquatic insects have fascinating means of locomotion. Find one, observe it and demonstrate its movement to someone else!

EVALUATION

1. Describe three ant behaviors you have observed.

2. For one of these behaviors, describe why the ants behaved that way. How does the behavior help the ant to survive?

3. What five basic needs do humans and ants share?

COLOR CRAZY

OBJECTIVE
Students will generalize that wildlife occurs in a wide variety of colors.

METHOD
Students create representations of colorful wild animals.

BACKGROUND
Nature is rich with color. Animal coloring has a wide variety of survival implications. For example, wildlife benefits from color for protection and as a way to attract mates. The colors that we see are not the same colors that all animals see. An animal's bright colors may not be visible to its primary predators.

Camouflage, or the ability to blend with surroundings, can determine whether a prey species, like a rabbit, remains hidden from a predator or is easily identified, killed and eaten. Many predators, such as leopards and trout, have camouflaged bodies so that their prey will not see them. Some animals go through seasonal color changes to remain camouflaged. For example, ptarmigans are ground-dwelling tundra birds. In winter, they are white and blend with the color of snow. In summer, they turn mottled brown and resemble their environment.

Many animals are brightly colored. The eastern newt in its land-dwelling juvenile, or eft stage, is a bright red salamander. That color warns predators because the newt's skin contains a toxin. A predator that eats a newt and finds it distasteful learns to avoid newts in the future. Unusual animal coloring can serve as a warning to predators much like a flashing yellow highway light advises motorists of a road hazard to avoid.

Bright colors or other markings may also serve as a defense. Some animals use color to appear to be something that they are not. Polyphemus moths have giant eye spots that create the impression that the animal is larger than it really is. Some caterpillars have spots that make them look like they have two heads.

It is often theorized that color plays a role in animal mating. The brightly colored male scarlet tanager and peacock are two birds that are often given as examples of bright coloration used to attract mates. Female Anolis lizards have been shown to be more likely to approach red throated males than males with green painted throats.

We can see that wildlife occurs in a wide variety of colors. We do not know all the reasons and ways that color affects the lives of animals. No matter what the reasons, nature's colors can be interesting and inspirational. For wildlife, this variety is linked to survival.

The major purpose of this activity is for students to recognize that wildlife exists in a variety of colors.

MATERIALS
pictures of brightly colored animals such as coral reef fish, tropical birds and insects; crayons; paint; chalk; construction paper; scissors; glue
OPTIONAL: other brightly colored art construction material, like artificial feathers, tissue paper, acorn shells, uncooked noodles

PROCEDURE
1.   Lead a discussion by asking students to name and describe real, brightly colored animals. Show students photographs of a variety of brightly colored animals. Discuss how the animals' colors and markings might help them survive.

Age: Grades K-6
Subjects: Science, Language Arts, Art
Skills: description, drawing, generalization, invention, media construction, observation, reading, writing
Duration: 45 minutes
Group Size: any
Setting: indoors
Conceptual Framework Reference: I.B.4.
Key Vocabulary: color, wildlife
Appendices: Local Resources

2. This is a "Make A Colorful Wild Animal" project! Get out brightly colored crayons, paint, chalk, construction paper, scissors, and glue. Other brightly colored materials would also be helpful. With these materials, ask the students to draw, paint, or construct a colorful creature—one that could be a real, wild animal. They can make birds, reptiles, amphibians, insects, fish, mammals—whatever real, wild animal they would like. Have the students describe how the coloring on the animal they created would help it to survive.

3. Make a "Colorful Wildlife Gallery." Display the animal creations in the classroom.

4. Develop a vocabulary list based on the children's descriptions of the animals.

5. OPTIONAL: Bring in wildlife reference books. Let the students look to see if they can find real animals like those they created.

6. Ask the students what they have learned about wild animals. Encourage the generalization that wild animals occur in a wide variety of colors and that animals' colors and markings help them survive.

EXTENSIONS

1. Make a "Museum of Color." Match the students' invented animals with pictures of real animals. Find the primary colors of red, yellow and blue. Look for "rainbow" animals that have three or more distinct colors on their bodies.

2. Make a "Colors from Nature" exhibit, and include colors from plants, rocks and soil—as well as wildlife.

3. Put the pictures of animals with pictures of their natural surroundings. Look for animals that blend and those that stand out brightly.

AQUATIC EXTENSIONS

1. Make a colorful, wild, aquatic animal!

2. A coral reef is one of the most colorful places in the world. Find pictures of reef fish or other reef animals. A look at tropical fish tanks in a pet store or aquarium would also show the diversity of colors found in coral reef animals. Pick a picture of a colorful animal that lives in a coral reef. Think of at least one way this bright color might help the animal survive in its environment. Using bright-colored crayons or other art materials, create a colorful reef animal and draw a picture of it in its habitat.

3. Research light extinction in water. Find out, for example, why bright red fish are camouflaged. Then design a fish based on the depth of its aquatic habitat. View the fish through appropriately colored cellophane or plastic to simulate the effect of its camouflage.

EVALUATION

1. Name a wild animal that has red for a color. Name two wild animals that have brown for a color. Name one that has yellow, one that has blue, and two that have green for a color.

2. Create a model or picture of a colorful butterfly or moth and place it in the classroom. Explain how the colors you gave it will help it survive. Explain where in the classroom its chances for survival would probably be best.

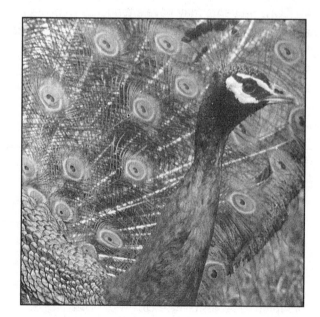

INTERVIEW A SPIDER

OBJECTIVE
Students will generalize that wildlife ranges in size and occurs in a variety of forms, colors and adaptations.

METHOD
Students use interview techniques, research and write to develop natural history information about wildlife species.

BACKGROUND
Wildlife is diverse. Although many people just think of mammals and perhaps birds as wildlife they may not realize that wildlife includes fish, reptiles and amphibians. Wildlife also includes insects, spiders, worms and other invertebrates.

The major purpose of this activity is for students to establish a working definition of wildlife which recognizes that wildlife ranges from microscopic forms, like amoebas, to species many tons in size, like whales, and occurs in a variety of forms, colors and adaptations.

CAUTION: Students may have a tendency to project inapplicable human characteristics to animals, especially because the "interview" format puts the "animals" in a human situation. Assist the students in avoiding anthropomorphism. Stress that they should try to see the world from the animals' perspective.

MATERIALS
writing and research materials

Age: Grades 5-8
Subjects: Language Arts, Science
Skills: description, discussion, generalization, interview, reading, research, writing (creative writing, grammar, punctuation, vocabulary development)
Duration: three classroom periods of 30 minutes each or longer; some research and writing done by students at home
Group Size: any
Setting: indoors and outdoors
Conceptual Framework Reference: I.B.4.
Key Vocabulary: interview, reporting, anthropomorphism
Appendices: Field Ethics, Local Resources

PROCEDURE
1. OPTIONAL: Invite a local newspaper reporter to talk with your students. Ask him or her to describe what a reporter does and especially talk about the techniques of interviewing and writing used.
2. Have the students brainstorm a list of wildlife species. Check the list to make sure it includes many different types of wildlife. OPTIONAL: Make available to the students a list of native species to help them focus on nearby animals they might not have readily classified as "wildlife."
3. Work with the students to establish a research, interview and reporting format for their use as reporters. For example:

Research
- Each team of two students should:
- Decide what animal to "interview."
- Write a list of questions to ask.
- Use reference materials to take notes for appropriate responses to the questions.

Interview
It's time to conduct the interview! Each team of reporters selects an animal to study. The team will first need to gather information about the animal. They can do that by actually observing the animal, consulting resource materials or both! One student

asks questions while the other student assumes the role of the wild animal and responds to the interviewer's questions. Students then switch roles. Remind the students to convey the perspective of the interviewed animal without projecting inapplicable human attributes.

Reporting

Now it's time to organize the information gathered through the process of researching and interviewing the animal. Each team should use its notes as the basis for writing a newspaper article about the wild animal they interviewed.

4.   Talk about the diversity of wildlife. Finally, ask each student to define wildlife in some way that shows his or her understanding of the term—including that wildlife ranges from microscopic forms to those many tons in size and occurs in a variety of forms, colors and adaptation.

VARIATION

Each team can conduct its interview in front of the other students, emphasizing public-speaking skills.

EXTENSION

With the newspaper articles complete, either:
- publish a wildlife newspaper for everyone to read and keep a copy; or
- read the articles aloud for everyone to hear.

AQUATIC EXTENSION

Just as on land, wildlife in aquatic habitats ranges from microscopic forms to those some tons in size, and occurs in a variety of forms, colors and adaptations. From plankton to pelicans, from water striders to the great blue whale, from mollusks to manatees, from shrimp to salmon—the variety is incredible! Do "Interview a Spider" with everyone picking an aquatic animal to research, interview and report about.

EVALUATION

Choose three animals that were interviewed by your classmates. Which of the following words can be used to describe each animal: invertebrate, vertebrate, predator, prey, herbivore, carnivore, insectivore, omnivore, mammal, bird, amphibian, reptile, insect, spider, fish, aquatic, terrestrial, colorful, dull, striped, spotted, runner, flyer, hopper, slider, gigantic, large, small, microscopic. What other words might describe each of the animals?

GRASSHOPPER GRAVITY!

OBJECTIVES
Students will: 1) describe a relationship between structure and function; 2) generalize that wildlife ranges from small to large and occurs in a variety of forms; and 3) recognize that people have power to affect other animals and with that power comes responsibility.

METHOD
Students observe, handle and describe live grasshoppers or crickets.

BACKGROUND
The major purpose of this activity is for students to recognize that wildlife occurs in a variety of forms and that people have power to affect animals. In the process of participating in this activity, students develop important observation skills—and an increased appreciation for grasshoppers!

MATERIALS
one plastic container; hand lens; live grasshopper or cricket for every two students; chalkboard

PROCEDURE
1. People don't often think of insects as animals and they hardly ever think of grasshoppers as wildlife. But a grasshopper is wildlife, too! Either send a small group of students out to collect grasshoppers in plastic jars or send pairs of students out with a plastic jar. (A clear, plastic sheet pulled to the ground by two students usually traps grasshoppers safely!) You need one grasshopper for every two students. (Crickets can also be studied and can sometimes be purchased from pet and sporting goods stores.) Caution the students not to harm the grasshoppers. When you are through studying the grasshoppers, please release them. Tell the students they are going to be like some scientists who carefully observe wildlife with as little impact as possible on the animals. Be prepared, however, for an accidental mishap that a grasshopper doesn't survive. Deal with such accidents on a case-by-case basis, encouraging the students to be careful—but also not to feel guilty if a grasshopper accidentally dies.
2. The following questions may be written out in some form for the students to use in observing the grasshoppers, or you might offer questions to the students aloud as they examine the grasshoppers. (This list can be shortened, and different questions used.) You may want to define some of the vocabulary before using the questions—like antennae, appendage. (For older students, see "Wild Words—A Journal-Making Activity" that could precede this activity.)

3. Finally, remind the students that a grasshopper is only one kind of animal. Animals, including wildlife, are all sizes and shapes. Some are smaller than a grasshopper, and some—like the whale—are much, much bigger.

Age: Grades 2-7 (and older)
Subjects: Science, Language Arts, Social Studies
Skills: analysis, classification, comparing similarities and differences, computation, description, discussion, generalization, listing, observation, reading, writing
Duration: 45 minutes, or longer if all questions are used; can serve as basis for two-week unit of study
Group Size: any
Setting: outdoors and indoors
Conceptual Framework Reference: I.B.4., I.D., II.A.3., II.B., II.F.
Key Vocabulary: wildlife, compound, antennae, appendage, estimate, habitat, responsibility
Appendices: Outdoors, Field Ethics, Animals In Schools

GRASSHOPPERS!

INTERESTING FEATURES What are some of the most outstanding features of the grasshopper?

LEGS How many legs does it have? Are they alike or different? Which legs are the jumping legs? Notice where the legs are attached to the grasshopper's body.

WINGS Look at the wings, if they are present. (Adults have wings. Immature grasshoppers show pads or stumps.) How many wings are there? Notice where they attach to the body.

HEAD Look at the head. How many eyes do you see? Why do you think they have so many eyes? Do they look like your eyes? Check carefully in front and below the large, compound eyes for three smaller, simpler eyes. These eyes probably see light but may not be able to see shapes, sizes and colors.

MOUTH Do you see a mouth? Does the grasshopper have lips? Try to feed the grasshopper a leaf to watch the mouth parts move. Try to describe the mouth parts and how they move.

ANTENNAE Where are the antennae? Are they each a long, string-like, single appendage, or are they made up of many parts? Can you count the parts? Do they all look alike in size, shape and color? Why do you think a grasshopper needs the antennae? For what? Think about radio and television antennae.

MOTION We usually think that grasshoppers "hop." Do they also walk? How do they walk on the ground or floor? If possible, watch the grasshopper climb a small stick, weed stem, or blade of grass. Does it use all of its legs? Without hurting your grasshopper, place it on the ground and make it jump. (If it is an adult with wings, it may fly instead!) Follow it and make it hop or jump several times (at least five times). Does it hop the same distance each time? Measure or estimate the distance of each hop of flight. Does the grasshopper seem to get tired? What makes you think so?

NOISE Do grasshoppers make noises? If your grasshopper makes a noise, try to learn if it does it with its mouth or with some other part of its body.

COLORS Look at the whole grasshopper carefully. Is it the same color all over? Are the colors, shapes and sizes the same on both sides? What is attractive about your grasshopper? Is it clean? Watch to see what the grasshopper does to clean or groom itself.

HABITAT Where does the grasshopper live? What does it eat? Do grasshoppers live in your neighborhood year-round? Suggest two reasons that grasshoppers might not be seen where winters are cold (freezing temperature, not enough food).

CONCLUSIONS Did you think there were so many interesting things about a grasshopper? Do you think other insects might be as interesting? What other insects or small animals might be interesting to look at and learn more about?

4. Ask the students to take the grasshoppers outside and let them go. Some of the students may want to keep the grasshoppers as pets. Talk with the students about how difficult it is for a grasshopper to live very long in a captive state. How much space does a grasshopper need to live? Can you supply that in captivity? Tell the students that by studying grasshoppers, they have done what some scientists do. They have studied something very carefully to learn more about it. People have power over other animals in many circumstances. The students exercised power over the grasshoppers while they studied them. With that power comes important responsibility. In this case, the students exercised their power by making an effort to be careful in handling the grasshoppers and releasing them safely. Ask the students about other situations in which they feel a responsibility for their actions affecting animals. Examples: Taking care of pets, not leaving litter outside that can hurt wild animals. (See "Litter We Know.")

EXTENSIONS

1. Find out what contributions grasshoppers make to ecological systems. What animals use grasshoppers as a food source?
2. Some farmers and gardeners consider grasshoppers a nuisance. Find out why. Find out what actions, if any, are taken to reduce crop damage from grasshoppers in your region. Do the actions seem appropriate? Why or why not? See "Deadly Links" for a related activity about pesticides in the environment.

AQUATIC EXTENSION

Do this activity with a water-related insect, if possible. Adjust the specific questions as needed to suit the insect's characteristics, still using these general categories: Interesting Features, Legs, Wings, Head, Mouth, Antennae, Motion, Noise, Colors, Habitat, Conclusions.

EVALUATION

1. If you were a biologist studying wildlife, which of these could you study and call it wildlife: tigers in India, deer in the forest, cows on a farm, foxes in Iowa, sparrows in the city, spiders in the forest, ants in a building, rats in a garbage dump, white mice in a laboratory cage? (Probably all except the cows in a farm and the white mice in a laboratory cage.)
2. Name three wild animals that are smaller than a grasshopper.
3. Name three wild animals that are larger than a grasshopper.
4. Name three types of wildlife that have one of the same colors as your grasshoppers but aren't insects.
5. Create a simulation that shows how grasshoppers protect themselves from predators. This could be done in a kinesthetic activity format. In the simulation show how a grasshopper's body is adapted for survival.
6. Create several guidelines that people should follow when studying wildlife. Explain why those rules are important. When, if ever, is it acceptable for people studying wildlife to damage or kill wildlife?

WILDLIFE IS EVERYWHERE!

OBJECTIVES
Students will: 1) state that humans and wildlife share environments; and 2) generalize that wildlife is present in areas all over the earth.

METHOD
Students search their environment for evidence of wildlife.

BACKGROUND
People often think of wildlife only as large animals like those they see in pictures of Africa with lions and elephants. They might think of creatures of the North American forests that they have seen like deer and elk. But wildlife includes all animals that have not been domesticated by people.

Domesticated animals are those which have been tamed, made captive and bred for special purposes. Farm animals and pets are considered domesticated animals. (See "What's Wild?" and "Animal Charades.")

Wild animals are all the rest. What may be surprising is that wildlife includes the smallest animal organisms—even those that can be seen only through a microscope. Spiders, insects, reptiles, amphibians and most species of fish, birds and mammals may be considered wildlife. Wildlife occurs in a tremendous variety of forms and colors. And wildlife can be found all around us. Even when we think we can see or hear no animals at all, they exist somewhere around us— maybe even under our feet! There are even tens of thousands of lifeforms on our skin, in our hair and inside our bodies! In fact, each of us would die if all

the organisms that inhabit our bodies were to disappear. People are never truly alone in an environment. Some form of wildlife is near.

The major purpose of this activity is for students to understand that people and wildlife share environments. By investigating microenvironments or microhabitats, the students should be encouraged to generalize from the information they acquire to the entire planet, coming to the understanding that wildlife exists in some form in all areas of the earth. In the deserts of the southern hemisphere; the oceans, tropical jungles and cities of the earth; from the Antarctic snow fields to the glaciers of the Arctic region, wildlife exists in a variety of forms.

MATERIALS
OPTIONAL: string

PROCEDURE
CAUTION: Ask students to observe but not touch or disturb animals they see.

1. Invite your students to explore the classroom, looking for signs of wildlife. Even in the most cleanly-swept classrooms, you can usually find some signs of life—either past or present. It might be a spider web, dead insects near lights or insect holes along baseboards and behind books. After the search and a discussion with the students about what—if anything—

Age: Grades K-3 (and older)
Subjects: Science, Language Arts
Skills: analysis, discussion, generalization, observation
Duration: 30 to 45 minutes
Group Size: any
Setting: indoors and outdoors
Conceptual Framework Reference: I.B., I.B.1., I.B.3.
Key Vocabulary: wildlife, wild, domesticated, environment, evidence
Appendices: Field Ethics, Observations and Inferences

they found, introduce the idea that people and other animals share environments. Sometimes we don't even notice that we are sharing our environment with other living things, but we are.

2. Expand the search for other animals to the out-of-doors. Take the students on the school grounds and give everyone, working in pairs, five minutes to find an animal or some sign that an animal has been there. Look for indirect evidence, such as tracks, webs, droppings, feathers and nests. (Be sure not to harm or seriously disturb anything.) After five minutes, sit down and talk about what everyone found.

Or, in advance, create a wildlife trail for your students to follow—looking for signs of animals along the way—by placing a long piece of string around an area of the school grounds and "salting" the path along the string with evidence of animals: bones, feathers, etc. The students can explore the trail in a "follow the leader" fashion. The students should remain quiet, observing to themselves. At the end of the trail, ask everyone to sit and discuss what they saw.

3. Talk with the children about what they learned. Emphasize that they have seen that people and wildlife share environments. They have seen evidence of wildlife at their school. Ask the children to guess whether they think different kinds of animals are found all over the earth—in the deserts, oceans, mountains and cities. They may draw from their own experiences and talk about places they have been and have seen animals. Encourage the students to make the generalization that wildlife is present all over the earth.

EXTENSIONS

1. Survey your yard, kitchen, neighborhood or city park—looking for wildlife!

2. Search magazines and books for wildlife from all over the planet.

3. "Invent" names and descriptions for the wildlife found outside during searches. Older students can observe the animals, write a written description—and then check their invented names and descriptions against the scientific names and information found in reference materials.

4. Use state maps. Look up names of towns, cities and counties with wild animal names!

AQUATIC EXTENSION

Survey your school grounds or neighborhood for any possible aquatic habitats for wildlife. Check puddles, sprinkler systems and, if possible, streams, beaches, ponds, etc. Look for evidence—direct or indirect—of any wildlife that lives in or near these water-related areas. Tell someone what you find—or show them, taking care not to damage any wildlife you find or its habitat!

EVALUATION

1. In which of the following places would you be likely to find animals living? in a forest; in a hot, dry, desert; in a lake; at the top of a mountain; at the North Pole; in New York City. What kinds of animals might you find in these places? Name any areas on earth where you couldn't find any animals.

2. Name the things you saw, heard or smelled which showed you that wildlife lives in the classroom and on the school grounds.

3. Draw a picture of a place with many different animals living there. Explain your picture.

4. Identify and describe three things that people could do to increase the numbers and kinds of wildlife living in an area that has little evidence of wildlife.

MICROTREK TREASURE HUNT

OBJECTIVES

Students will: 1) state that humans and wildlife share environments; 2) demonstrate that humans do not have exclusive use of environments; and 3) generalize that wildlife can be all around us even if we do not actually see or hear it.

METHOD

Students go outside on a "treasure hunt" for wildlife.

BACKGROUND

See "Wildlife is Everywhere." By investigating microenvironments or microhabitats, the students should be encouraged to generalize from the information they acquire to the whole of the planet, coming to the understanding in general terms that wildlife exists in all areas of the planet, in some form. In the deserts of the southern hemisphere; the oceans, tropical jungles and cities of the earth; from the Antarctic snow fields to the glaciers of the Arctic region, wildlife exists in a variety of forms.

The major purpose of this activity is for students to understand that people and wildlife share environments.

MATERIALS

hand lens; digging tool; pencil and mimeographed instruction sheet for each group of two to five students

Age: Grades 4-6 (and older)
Subjects: Science, Language Arts, Social Studies
Skills: analysis, application, classification, description, discussion, generalization, listing, observation, problem solving, reading, small group work, writing
Duration: 30 minutes to two hours
Group Size: small groups working simultaneously; any number
Setting: outdoors and indoors
Conceptual Framework Reference: I.B., I.B.1., I.B.2., I.B.3., I.B.4.
Key Vocabulary: evidence, environments, wildlife
Appendices: Field Ethics, Observations and Inferences, Ecosystem

PROCEDURE

1. This is a wildlife treasure hunt! The students will be given a list of things to find, and they will go outside and find different kinds of evidence that wildlife exists—even at school! (This activity can be done almost anywhere, with supervision—from city centers to parks to outdoor education sites. It is especially effective where students would not expect to find much wildlife.) Review the concept that wildlife is diverse. Wildlife includes insects, spiders, reptiles, amphibians and most species of fish, birds and mammals.

2. Divide the students into groups of two to five. Provide each group with a small hand lens, small digging tool, pencil, and instruction sheet. The instruction sheet could look something like the following:

WILDLIFE TREASURE HUNT

This is a treasure hunt to look for evidence of wildlife!

CAUTION: Be careful not to kill any animals or damage their homes!

Find evidence that:
1. Humans and wildlife share environments.
2. Humans and wildlife must adjust to their environment, move to a more suitable environment, or perish.
3. Wildlife is all around us even if we don't see or hear it.
4. Wildlife ranges from small in size to very big.
5. People and wildlife experience some of the same problems.
6. Both people and wildlife need places to live.

---

3. Establish a length of time that the students may be outside. This depends on how many things they are asked to look for. Go outside with them to supervise. You can use 15-minute blocks of time, with 15 minutes for every one or two things the students are looking for. For example, the six-item treasure hunt

WILDLIFE TREASURE HUNT

This is a treasure hunt to look for evidence of wildlife!

CAUTION: Be careful not to kill any animals or damage their homes!

Find evidence that:
1. Humans and wildlife share environments.
2. Humans and wildlife must adjust to their environment, move to a more suitable environment, or perish.
3. Wildlife is all around us even if we don't see or hear it.
4. Wildlife ranges from small in size to very big.
5. People and wildlife experience some of the same problems.
6. Both people and wildlife need places to live.

WILDLIFE TREASURE HUNT

This is a treasure hunt to look for evidence of wildlife!

CAUTION: Be careful not to kill any animals or damage their homes!

Find evidence that:
1. Humans and wildlife share environments.
2. Humans and wildlife must adjust to their environment, move to a more suitable environment, or perish.
3. Wildlife is all around us even if we don't see or hear it.
4. Wildlife ranges from small in size to very big.
5. People and wildlife experience some of the same problems.
6. Both people and wildlife need places to live.

WILDLIFE TREASURE HUNT

This is a treasure hunt to look for evidence of wildlife!

CAUTION: Be careful not to kill any animals or damage their homes!

Find evidence that:
1. Humans and wildlife share environments.
2. Humans and wildlife must adjust to their environment, move to a more suitable environment, or perish.
3. Wildlife is all around us even if we don't see or hear it.
4. Wildlife ranges from small in size to very big.
5. People and wildlife experience some of the same problems.
6. Both people and wildlife need places to live.

WILDLIFE TREASURE HUNT

This is a treasure hunt to look for evidence of wildlife!

CAUTION: Be careful not to kill any animals or damage their homes!

Find evidence that:
1. Humans and wildlife share environments.
2. Humans and wildlife must adjust to their environment, move to a more suitable environment, or perish.
3. Wildlife is all around us even if we don't see or hear it.
4. Wildlife ranges from small in size to very big.
5. People and wildlife experience some of the same problems.
6. Both people and wildlife need places to live.

used in the sample given in this activity could take anywhere from 15 to 45 minutes for the students to find their evidence. You could ask all of the students to find evidence for all of the items. Or, especially with younger students, you could assign each group just one of the things to find. Every group should return with some evidence. Evidence can be such things as small drawings on the mimeographed sheet or on extra paper the students take along. It can be word descriptions of what they see. It can be small samples they bring back to class, if they can bring samples without doing significant damage to the environment. You should provide paper sacks for evidence if they are going to bring things back.

4. Before sending the students outside, make sure the instructions are clear. Talk with the students about what wildlife is, contrasted with other animals like pets. Go through the list of things for which they are trying to find evidence to make sure they have an understanding of what they will be looking for. Don't be too specific with your examples. (The most creative and conceptually solid solutions often come up in the face of ambiguity. The students are apt to find delightfully inventive and appropriate evidence if allowed to be responsibly resourceful!) With the time limits established, open the door and begin "trekking."

5. At the end of the designated time period, everyone should meet back at the classroom. Ask the groups to report on what they found.

6. What are some of the most interesting things the students felt they learned? Encourage the students to come to the generalizations that people and wildlife share environments, that wildlife is all around us, and in fact that wildlife in some form is in areas all over the planet.

EXTENSIONS

1. Do some creative writing!
2. Classify the types of wildlife found.
3. Tally the types of wildlife found and the numbers of each kind of wildlife. (You can develop this tally into a pyramid of numbers to demonstrate that such a concept is real.)
4. Do microscope work with some of the samples found; for example, the underside of leaves with insect eggs, soil with a lot of plant matter, water, larvae, the inside of insect galls, bark and a hollow plant stem.
5. See "Wild Words" and add drawings and descriptions to personal journals!

AQUATIC EXTENSION

Adjust the "Wildlife Treasure Hunt" instructions to apply specifically to aquatic wildlife and aquatic habitats. For example, find evidence that humans and aquatic wildlife share environments, etc.

EVALUATION

1. Name three things you saw, heard, or smelled which showed you that wildlife lives in the school areas.
2. Define "evidence." Give examples of how evidence can be used to interpret environments.
3. Create a continuum showing the range of sizes of wildlife for which you found evidence.

STORMY WEATHER

OBJECTIVE

Students will generalize that humans and wildlife share environments and experience some of the same natural phenomena.

METHOD

Students go on a simulated field trip to experience a storm.

BACKGROUND

The major purpose of this activity is for students to recognize that people and wildlife co-exist and sometimes experience the same natural phenomena. During a storm, for example, most people, pets and wildlife need to seek shelter.

MATERIALS

none needed

PROCEDURE

NOTE: This activity makes use of an instructional technique we call a simulated field trip. Brain researchers and learning theorists tell us that the technique provides access to ways of processing information that facilitate long-term memory and comprehension of concepts. As a teacher using this technique, you read or describe in your own words a series of pictures for your students, with their eyes closed, to see in their minds. Leave time between the phrasing of your words for the students to visualize the images you are suggesting. Some teachers use the technique as a regular part of each teaching day. It is not necessary to use the technique frequently; however, it is a powerful and helpful instructional tool for both teachers and students.

1.   Provide the students with the following instructions:
"You are to try to picture in your mind the things you will hear me describing. I won't put in all the details— so you must try to see and feel as clearly as you can the things that I describe. Before we begin, I want you to decide who you will be during this activity. You may either be yourself, or an animal. If you are an animal, you may either be a wild animal, a pet or a farm animal. You don't have to do anything special if you choose to be an animal. It is just that you will be picturing things in your mind from the point of view of the animal you pick. Any questions? Okay, let's see by a show of hands how many people and how many animals we will have for this activity. How many of you are going to be farm animals? Pets? Wild animals? Yourselves?"

NOTE: You don't want to find out which animals the students have selected to be. You only want to be sure that you have some variety—some of them seeing things from their own perspective, some from the perspective of a domesticated animal and some from the perspective of a wild animal.

OPTIONAL: Grand Canyon Suite might be played at this point to set the mood and get an idea of the storm or other music with a "storm" or natural environment theme.

Age: Grades 4-9 (and older)
Subjects: Language Arts, Science, Social Studies
Skills: comparing similarities and differences, description, generalization, visualization
Duration: 20-40 minutes
Group Size: any
Setting: indoors or outdoors
Conceptual Framework Reference: I.A., I.A.2., I.B., I.B.3., I.C., I.C.4.
Key Vocabulary: environment
Appendices: Simulated Field Trips

"Now, we are ready to begin. Get yourselves in a comfortable place. Don't worry about who is sitting next to you. All of you will have your eyes closed. Just be comfortable, and do your best to picture the things I will describe. Okay, close your eyes and picture this...

It is a late summer's night. There is a coolness in the air...You hear the sounds of summer...Somehow, you can feel some changes coming in the weather...In the distance, the dark sky is broken by bright flashes of lightning...The light is far away...After a long wait, a rolling rumble is heard...The lightning gets closer...The rumbles are louder....Suddenly, the lightning flashes and lights up the whole sky...You need to find shelter, to find a safe place.

The brilliant flashes of lightning pop and crackle all around you. The noise of thunder is crashing so that the earth seems to shake...There are no longer times of quiet between the rumbles of thunder and flashes of lightning...It becomes still...You notice scents in the air, things you can smell and feel...You begin to hear a new sound....You are not sure what it is...You again have to find shelter, if you had come out thinking the storm was gone...You need to find a place to stay dry...Suddenly, the rain is pouring down with a loud, rich sound...It rains, and rains...and rains...And then stillness...The storm has passed."

NOTE: Here is an alternative or additional version of the simulated field trip.

"It is a late winter's night. There is a stillness in the air...Bright stars twinkle in the cold, crisp, winter sky...

Somehow, you can feel some changes coming in the weather...A gentle breeze begins to stir the leafless trees...A quiet snow begins to fall...The wind floats the snowflakes through the air...around and around and down....The snow touches you....The wind grows stronger...You can hear the rustle of the branches...You feel the snow pelt you as it swirls faster through the sky.

The snow falls heavier...The wind blows colder...Suddenly a gust of wind kicks up and blows a huge, dead tree down to the ground...It crashes down beside you with a loud BOOM!...and shakes the earth beneath your feet. The wind whips faster...You need to find shelter, a safe place.

Now the snow makes slapping sounds as the wind hurls it against the swaying trees...Branches creak and crackle all around you...Twigs and branches snap off...They strike the ground below...and are covered by the deepening snow...There is whiteness all around you as the blizzard fills the sky...It snows...and it snows...and it snows...And then there is stillness...The storm has passed."

NOTE: Wait a few seconds, and then tell the students, "Open your eyes."

2. Now it is time to find out what the students saw and felt during the simulated field trip. There is no need to hear from every student, nor any reason for them to feel pressured to share. Most often, they are eager to describe what they experienced. Let the students volunteer, being sure to include who they were—that is, wild or domesticated animal of some kind, or themselves. Find out what shelter they found, and where, and what happened to them throughout the storm.

3. After the students have shared their descriptions, turn the discussion to the idea that many animals—including people, pets and wildlife—share a common environment. Whether we live in the cities, in the country, in the desert, or on a mountaintop, people are not the only forms of life that live in those environments. Even if we don't see many animals where we live, they are there in some form—from the ant on the sidewalk to the spider in the garden. It is useful to remember that we are not the only inhabitants of our environment. Events like summer storms, a strong wind and a light or heavy snowfall can all serve as special reminders. Had the students been on a field trip to the actual locations where this storm took place, every animal would have experienced some of the same things, although not in exactly the same ways. Any animals who were out that night likely had to find some kind of protection. Remind the students—next time they see the lightning, hear the thunder and feel the rain—to wonder where the birds are, the spiders, the cats and dogs, the fox and the bear. Where are the other animals who might be feeling this storm?

EXTENSIONS
1. Draw pictures of what you saw in your mind.
2. Pantomime the actions the animals took during the storm.

AQUATIC EXTENSION
Storms can affect aquatic wildlife too. What happens to the fish in a stream during heavy rains? (Many tend to seek shelter near rocks or among underwater plants. Sometimes the storm washes large amounts of soil and rocks into the stream, making it difficult for the fish to breathe.) What about the fish and mammals in ocean waters during hurricanes? Sometimes we know even less about what these aquatic animals do than those on land because we cannot easily see them under water—but they experience storms too. Imagine yourself as an underwater animal in a storm and describe what happens to you and your behavior.

EVALUATION
Write a story that compares the ways a child and a wild animal might experience any of these: drought, snowstorm, flood, tornado, fire, earthquake.

THE BEAUTIFUL BASICS

OBJECTIVE
Students will be able to identify five basic survival needs shared by people and all other animals, including pets and wildlife.

METHOD
Students list and organize needs of people, pets and wildlife.

BACKGROUND
All animals, either directly or indirectly, depend upon plants, sunlight, water, soil and air.

All animals—including people, pets and wildlife—need food, water, shelter and space in which to live. These must be in the quality and quantity required by the particular animal. Because animals need **food, water, shelter** and **space** to be available in a way that is suitable to their needs, we say that these things must be available in a suitable **"arrangement."**

The major purpose of this activity is for students to identify the basic survival needs of all living things and to recognize that people and all animals—including pets—have similar basic needs.

MATERIALS
chalkboard

Age: Grade 2 (and older)
Subjects: Science, Language Arts, Health
Skills: analysis, classification, comparing similarities and differences, discussion, listing, reading
Duration: 20 minutes
Group Size: any
Setting: indoors
Conceptual Framework Reference: I.A., I.A.1., I.A.4, I.C.1., I.C.2.
Key Vocabulary: pets, wildlife, survival needs

PROCEDURE
1. Put three words on a chalk board, so that a column of words can be listed under each: People—Pets—Wildlife. Ask the students, "What do people need in order to be able to live?" List the students' ideas in a column under the word, "People." Do the same for pets and wildlife. (Remember to do the activity, "What's Wild?" before this one, so that students know the major differences between pets and wildlife.)

2. After the lists are made, ask the students to look to see which ideas seem to go together into larger ideas. For example, warmth might be combined with physical comfort and both might fit within the concept of shelter. See if the students can narrow down the lists and come up with the essential survival needs for people, pets and wildlife. The most basic survival needs will be the same for each of the three groups. The lists, when reduced, could include and be limited to:

People	Pets	Wildlife
food	food	food
water	water	water
shelter	shelter	shelter
space	space	space
arrangement	arrangement	arrangement
sunlight	sunlight	sunlight
soil	soil	soil
air	air	air

EVALUATION
1. List at least four things plants and animals need for survival.
2. How do plant needs differ from animal needs?

EVERYBODY NEEDS A HOME

OBJECTIVE
Students will generalize that people and other animals share a basic need to have a home.

METHOD
Students draw pictures of homes and compare their needs with those of other animals.

BACKGROUND
Humans and other animals—including pets, farm animals and wildlife—have some of the same basic needs. Every animal needs a home. But that home is not just a "house" like those in which people live. Home, for many animals, is a much bigger place—and it's outdoors. The scientific term for an animal's home is "habitat." An animal's habitat includes **food, water, shelter** or cover and **space**. Because animals need the food, water, shelter and space to be available in a way that meets the animals' needs, we say that these things must be available in a suitable **arrangement.**

Homes are not just houses. A house may be considered shelter. People build houses, apartments, trailers, houseboats and other kinds of shelter in which to live. Animals don't need a home that looks like a house—but they do need some kind of shelter. The shelter might be underground, in a bush, in the bark of a tree, or in some rocks.

Animals need a place in which to find food and water. They also need enough space in which to live and find the food, water and shelter they need. Everybody needs a home! And "home" is bigger than a "house."

Age: Grade K-3
Subjects: Science, Language Arts, Art
Skills: analysis, comparing similarities and differences, discussion, drawing, generalization, visualization
Duration: 30 minutes or longer
Group Size: any; however, no more than 25 students is recommended
Setting: indoors or outdoors
Conceptual Framework Reference: I.A., I.A.4., I.C.1., I.C.2.
Key Vocabulary: differences, similarities, survival needs, habitat

Home is more like a "neighborhood" that has everything in it that is needed for survival.

The major purpose of this activity is for students to generalize that animals need a home.

MATERIALS
drawing paper; crayons or chalk

PROCEDURE
1. Ask the students to draw a picture of where they live—or to draw a picture of the place where a person they know lives. Ask the students to include pictures in their drawing of the things they need to live where they do; for example, a place to cook and keep food, a place to sleep, a neighborhood.
2. Once the drawings are finished, have a discussion with the students about what they drew. Ask the students to point out the things they need to live that they included in their drawings.
3. Make a "gallery of homes" out of the drawings. Point out to the students that everyone has a home.
4. Ask the students to close their eyes and imagine: a bird's home, an ant's home, a beaver's home, the President's home, their home.
OPTIONAL: Show the students pictures of different places that animals live.
5. Discuss the differences and similarities among the different homes with the students. Talk about the things every animal needs in its home: food, water, shelter and space in which to live, arranged in a way that the animal can survive. Summarize the discussion by emphasizing that although the homes are different, every animal—people, pets, farm animals and wildlife—needs a home. Talk about the idea that a home is actually bigger than a house. In some ways, it is more like a neighborhood. For animals, we can call that neighborhood where all the survival needs are met a "habitat." People go outside their homes to get food at a store, for example. Birds, ants, beavers and other animals have to go out of their "houses" (places of shelter) to get the things they need to live.

EXTENSIONS

1. Draw animal homes. Compare them to places where people live.
2. Go outside and look for animal homes. Be sure not to bother the animals—or the homes—in the process!

AQUATIC EXTENSION

Draw the "homes" of some kinds of aquatic wildlife. Fish, aquatic reptiles, amphibians, aquatic insects and aquatic mammals—just like all other kinds of wildlife—need food, water, shelter and space in a suitable arrangement.

EVALUATION

1. Name three reasons why people need homes and three reasons why animals need homes.
2. Draw a picture of a suitable habitat for an animal. Write a paragraph to describe how the habitat meets the animal's needs for survival.

HABITAT LAP SIT

OBJECTIVES

Students will: 1) identify the components of habitat; 2) recognize how humans and other animals depend upon habitat; and 3) interpret the significance of loss or change in habitat in terms of people and wildlife.

METHOD

Students physically form an interconnected circle to demonstrate components of habitat.

BACKGROUND

See "The Beautiful Basics," "Everybody Needs A Home," "What's That, Habitat?," "Habitracks" and "Habitat Rummy" for activities with similar purposes. People and other animals share some basic needs. Every animal needs a place in which to live. The environment in which an animal lives is called "habitat." An animal's habitat includes **food, water, shelter** and **space** in an **arrangement** appropriate to the animal's needs.

If any of these components of habitat is missing or is affected significantly so that the arrangement for the individual animal or population of animals is no longer suitable, there will be an impact. The impact will not necessarily be catastrophic, but can be. There are a great many additional limiting factors beyond those of suitable food, water, shelter and space. For example, disease, predation, pollution, accidents and climatic conditions are among other factors which can have impact.

All things are interrelated. When we look at a biological community, we find interrelationships and interdependencies between plants and plants, plants and animals, as well as animals and animals. These interrelationships and interdependencies are important.

The major purpose of this activity is for students to become familiar with the **components of habitat,** and to recognize that it is not sufficient for there to be **food, water, shelter** and **space** in order for animals to survive—those components of habitat must be in a suitable **arrangement.**

NOTE: This activity was inspired by a "New Game," and adapted to teach concepts related to wildlife.

MATERIALS

none needed

PROCEDURE

1. This activity takes very little time—but has a lot of impact! Ask the students to number off from "one" to "four." All the "ones" go to one corner of the room, the "twos" to another, etc.
2. As the students move to their corners, clear a space in the center of the room. Better still, go outside to a clear, grassy area. The "ones" should sit or stand together, "twos" together, etc.
3. Assign each group a concept as follows: "ones"=food, "twos"=water, "threes"=shelter, "fours"=space.
4. Now, it's time to form a circle! This is done by building the circle in chains of food, water, shelter and space. A student from each of the four groups walks toward the cleared area. The four students stand next to each other, facing in toward what will be the center of the circle. Four more students—one from each group—join the circle. Keep adding to the circle in sets of four until all the students are in the circle.
5. All students should now be standing shoulder to shoulder, facing the center of the circle.
6. Ask the students to turn toward their **right,** at the same time taking one step toward the center of the circle. They should be standing close together, with each student looking at the back of the head of the student in front of him or her.
7. Don't panic—this **will** work! **Ask everyone to listen carefully.** Students should place their hands on the shoulders of the person in front of them. Students slowly sit down as you count to three. At the point of three, you want the students to sit down—on the knees of the person behind them, keeping their own knees together to support the person in front of them. You then say, **"Food, water, shelter and space**—in the proper **arrangement** (represented by the students' intact, "lap-sit" circle)—are what is needed to have a suitable (good) **habitat."**
8. The students at this point may either fall or sit down. When their laughter has subsided, talk with

Age: Grades 4-9 (also younger and older)
Subjects: Science, Physical Education
Skills: discussion, generalization, kinesthetic concept development, small group work
Duration: 20 minutes
Group Size: 15 to 45 students
Setting: outdoors preferred; indoors possible
Conceptual Framework Reference: I.A., I.A.2., I.A.4., I.C., I.C.1., I.C.2., I.C.3., I.C.4., I.D., III.B.
Key Vocabulary: habitat, food, water, shelter, space, arrangement
Appendices: Simulations

them about the necessary components of suitable habitat for people and wildlife.

9. After the students understand the major point—that food, water, shelter and space are necessary for any animal's survival, and in their appropriate arrangement comprise a suitable habitat—let the students try the circle activity again! This time ask them to hold their lap sit posture. As the students lap-sit-still representing food, water, shelter and space in their appropriate arrangement—identify a student who represents "water." Then say, "It is a drought year. The water supply is reduced by the drought conditions." At this point, have the student who was identified as representing "water" remove himself or herself from the lap-sit circle—and watch the circle collapse, or at least suffer some disruption in arrangement. You could try this in several ways—removing one or more students from the circle. Conditions could vary: pollution of water supply, urban sprawl limiting availability of all components, soil erosion impacting food and water supplies, etc. Since animals' habitat needs depend upon food, water, shelter and space, in their appropriate arrangement, "removal" of any will have an impact.

10. Ask the students to talk about what this activity means to them. Ask the students to summarize the main ideas they have learned. They could include: a) food, water, shelter and space, in their appropriate arrangement, can be called habitat; b) humans and other animals depend upon habitat; c) loss of any of these elements of habitat will have impact on the animals living there; and d) the components of habitat must be in an arrangement suitable to the needs of the individual animals or populations of animals in order for the animals to survive.

VARIATION

Have the students form a circle, holding hands. Walk around the circle, first naming one student as an animal of a particular ecosystem. Name the next four students in the circle as food, water, shelter and space for that animal. Repeat the process until all the students are involved. Any "extras" can be identified as elements of habitat, e.g., resulting from a particularly good year

for habitat needs for the last animal named. When all of the students have been designated as an animal or as components of an animal's habitat, comment on the fact that they are holding hands. This represents the idea that all things in an ecosystem are interrelated. Briefly discuss the idea of interrelationships. Then move the students into position to the "lap sit" described in the Procedure above. Remind the students that they noticed all elements of the ecosystem were interrelated when they were holding hands. Now they are going to find out that they all are dependent upon one another as well. Do the "lap sit." Discuss interrelationships and interdependencies in ecological systems.

AQUATIC EXTENSIONS

Do the "Variation" to "Habitat Lap Sit" from an aquatic perspective. Start it like this:

Have students form a circle, holding hands. Name one student as an animal in an aquatic ecosystem. Name the next four students in the circle as food, water, shelter and space for that animal. Repeat the process until all the students are involved. That is, name another student as an animal in the same aquatic ecosystem, and then name the next four students in the circle as food, water, shelter and space for that animal, etc. Finish the procedure as it is described in the "Variation." Do the activity more than once, picking a different aquatic ecosystem each time—to emphasize that all aquatic animals, in any aquatic ecosystem, need food, water, shelter and space in a suitable arrangement in order to survive.

EVALUATION

1. What are the five essential components of habitat?
2. Explain how the arrangement of food, water, shelter and space is important to humans and other animals.
3. What would probably have the greater long-term impact on the wildlife living on a farm in Iowa? A severe winter which killed many animals or the development of part of the farm into a commercial shopping center?

HABITRACKS

OBJECTIVES

Students will 1) identify the basic components of habitat as food, water, shelter and space in a suitable arrangement; and 2) generalize that these components of habitat are needed by all animals—including people and wildlife.

METHOD

Students identify the components of habitat by using a map and exploring their schoolgrounds.

BACKGROUND

People and other animals share some basic needs. Every animal needs a place in which to live. The environment in which an animal lives is called **habitat**. An animal's habitat includes **food, water, shelter** and adequate **space** in an **arrangement** appropriate to the animal's needs.

The major purpose of this activity is for students to understand that all animals—including people—share some of the same basic needs.

NOTE: This activity may serve as an extension to "Everybody Needs A Home" for students in Grades 2 and 3.

MATERIALS

habitat maps; task cards; and habitat components (see below); glue or tape; scissors; pencils; chalkboard; and small paper bags

Age: Grades 2-5
Subjects: Science, Language Arts, Social Studies
Skills: analysis, classification, comparing similarities and differences, discussion, math (shape recognition and matching), generalization, mapping, observation, reading, small group work, synthesis
Duration: 30 to 60 minutes
Group Size: three to ten groups of three students in each group
Setting: outdoors and indoors
Conceptual Framework Reference: I.A., I.A.4., I.C.1., I.C.2.
Key Vocabulary: habitat, track, survival needs, food, water, shelter, space, arrangement
Appendices: Outdoors

PROCEDURE

ADVANCE PREPARATION BY TEACHER

1. Draw a simple map of the school grounds, including sidewalk, buildings, and playgrounds. Make enough copies of the map—saving your original to use another time—so that you have a map for every group of three students.
2. Choose different animals for which you can draw "tracks." For example: bird, cat, dog, bear, mouse, child, deer and horse.
3. On each map, mark the travels of the animal you have chosen for that map. Try to map the travel as realistically as possible—however, you can begin from the classroom and end back at the classroom. Write the name of the animal, with the word "HABITAT," at the top of each map. For example: "BIRD HABITAT: WHAT BIRDS NEED TO SURVIVE."
4. Make one task card for each animal whose tracks you have mapped. Each task card should look the same, but be a different color. Each card needs to have a shape drawn to represent "food," "water," "shelter" and "space." For example:

5. Make a set of food, water, shelter and space pieces which will fit over the shapes on each task card. Again, these "habitat component" pieces need to be the same color as the task card they go with. For example, if you chose brown for the bear task card, the habitat pieces should also be brown. Just before the activity begins, go outside on the schoolgrounds and place the habitat component pieces along the trail for the appropriate animals. (Be certain to tell other teachers and students about the trail, and ask their cooperation in not disturbing it.) For example, food in the "BEAR HABITAT" might be found at a bush, water in a puddle near the drinking fountain, and space on the playground. Several habitat pieces for different animals will need to be in the same general area—for safety

and convenience as you watch the children. The color-coding works well to minimize confusion—since each group of children with a map and a task card is only looking for the color that matches the task cards.

PROCEDURES WITH STUDENTS

1. Divide the class into teams of three students each.
2. Give each team a "habitat map" that indicates the name of the animal they are tracking. Tell the students that they have ten minutes to track the animal they have been given, looking for the things their animal needs to survive. Give each team the task card for their animal. Also give each team a paper sack to put their habitat pieces in as they find them.
3. Tell the students that to track the animals, they have to be quiet. Being very quiet, all the teams are to go outside and—using their maps—track their animals. To share responsibilities, one student could hold the map, another the task card, and another the sack for the habitat pieces. Tell the students that they are going to find things that represent what their animals need to survive. When they find something that is the color of the task card they are holding, they should put it in their sack. They should find pieces that match what they see on their task cards.
4. Within ten minutes, the students should all follow their maps back to class.
5. Once back in class, give the students tape or glue so that they can affix their habitat pieces to their task cards.
6. Once the habitat task cards are completed, invite the student groups to report on what they found and where they found it. Ask the students if everyone found "food." When they say, "Yes," write food on the chalkboard. Do the same with "water," "space" and "shelter." Ask one of the students in each group to draw a line connecting the four habitat pieces. For example:

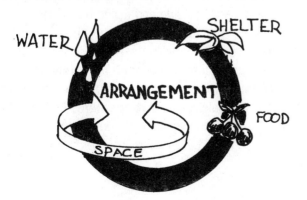

Tell the students that food, water, space and shelter have to go together in a suitable arrangement in order for an animal to live. For example, animals need the right amount of space to survive. A bear needs more space than a small insect. Animals must have the right amount and the right kind of food. Food, water and shelter must be available when needed, etc. (The line connecting food, water, space and shelter represents the idea of a suitable arrangement for the animal in its habitat.)

EXTENSIONS

1. Take a brightly-colored ball of yarn. Each child is labeled either food, water, shelter or space. Connect the "food," "water," "shelter" and "space" by having the children each take hold of part of one long string of the yarn. The children all connected by the yarn represent a suitable arrangement of food, water, shelter and space to meet an animal's needs. First, use a very long piece of yarn that leaves the children standing a distance from each other. This can represent some animals' need for a large habitat in which to live—like a bear or mountain lion. A short length of yarn that has the children standing close to each other can represent some animals' smaller habitat—like an insect.
2. If possible, find real animal tracks! See "Tracks!"
3. Look on the schoolgrounds for components of habitat that meet the needs of some actual wildlife that might live there. Make a map that shows the components and their arrangement. Identify what animals might find this to be a suitable habitat. Look for evidence to see if they do.

AQUATIC EXTENSION

Have a student pick an aquatic animal. Have the student stand in the middle of the other students who are labeled food, water, shelter and space. The student representing the aquatic animal should touch or hold onto the yarn to connect with every other student—indicating the importance of this and every other aquatic animal having a suitable habitat in which to live.

EVALUATION

Draw a picture of an animal in a suitable habitat. Identify and describe what the animal needs to survive, and show where and how its needs are met in the habitat.

WHAT'S THAT, HABITAT?

OBJECTIVES
Students will: 1) identify their own basic needs for food, water, shelter and space in a suitable arrangement; and 2) generalize that wildlife and other animals have similar basic needs.

METHOD
Students draw pictures of people's and animal's homes, comparing basic needs.

BACKGROUND
This activity is similar to "Habitracks." One option is to use "Habitracks" with 4th and 5th grade students, and "What's That, Habitat?" with 2nd and 3rd grade students. Use either activity after "The Beautiful Basics" and "Everybody Needs A Home," especially with 2nd grade students and older. The same drawing used in "Everybody Needs A Home" can be used to start "What's That, Habitat?"

See "The Beautiful Basics" and "Everybody Needs A Home" for more background.

The major purpose of this activity is for students to understand that animals—including people, pets and wildlife—have some of the same basic needs.

MATERIALS
drawing paper; crayons or chalk

Age: Grades 2-3
Subjects: Science, Language Arts, Art, Social Studies
Skills: analysis, comparing similarities and differences, discussion, drawing, generalization, reading, writing
Duration: two 20-minute sessions, or one 40-minute session
Group Size: any
Setting: indoors
Conceptual Framework Reference: I.A., I.A.4., I.C.1., I.C.2.
Key Vocabulary: habitat, survival needs, food, water, shelter, space, arrangement
Appendices: None

PROCEDURE
1. List the following words on a chalkboard: **food, water, shelter, space.**
2. Read each word aloud, asking the students to repeat the words after you. (They may say the letters of the words and use the words for spelling.)
3. Food and water will be easy concepts for the students to understand. They are familiar needs for themselves each day. Shelter and space will be more difficult. Ask the students to explain what shelter and space are. Make sure the meaning of all four words is clear before you proceed.
4. Give the students drawing paper and chalks or crayons. Ask the students to draw a picture of where they live, including pictures of where they find food, water, shelter and space. (NOTE: If the students have made drawings in "Everybody Needs A Home," use those same drawings instead of making new ones!) Ask the students to label the parts of their drawings where they find their food, water, shelter and space. For example:

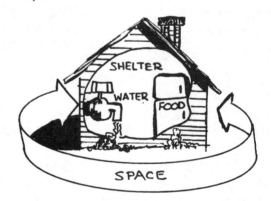

NOTE: Food and water will not be difficult to identify. Shelter could be shown in a number of ways. Here, for example, it is shown by labeling the roof. Space can be shown as the area outside and inside the house or apartment. Shown here, it includes the house and yard. Space can also include the neighborhood. (Space actually includes all the areas used for survival.)
5. Once the drawings are complete, write two more words on the chalkboard: **arrangement, habitat.** Say the words aloud, asking the children to repeat them after you. (Again, these words may be used for spelling.)

6. Tell the students that when **food, water, shelter** and **space** go together in a special way, so that animals—including people—can live, we call that place a **habitat**. The **food, water, shelter** and **space** are in an **arrangement** that makes it possible for animals to live. (OPTIONAL: Ask the children if they could live in a home where the bathroom was four miles north, the kitchen was 12 miles west and the bedroom was nine miles east. The answer, of course, is likely, "No," since the "arrangement" is not suitable for a person. Some animals do travel great distances in their habitat, however.)

7. Ask the students to write the word "habitat" in big letters at the top of their drawings. Talk with them about the meaning of habitat.

8. Give the students another piece of drawing paper. Ask them to think of an animal—any animal. Ask a few students what animal they are thinking of. Identify whether the animals they named are "wild" or "domesticated." You will probably get both. If you don't get both, ask the students to think of the kinds of animals that are missing. It is important to make sure the students are thinking about both wild and domesticated animals.

9. Ask the students to draw a picture of their animal in a place where it lives. Ask the students to make sure they include: food, water, shelter and space in an arrangement that they think would make it possible for the animal to survive.

10. Ask the students to talk about their drawings, pointing out the habitat components they have included.

11. Ask the students to write "habitat" in big letters on the top of this drawing too. Talk with the students about how humans and other animals need food, water, shelter and space. The arrangement is different for each, but all have similar basic needs. When food, water, shelter and space are arranged in a way that is suitable for an animal to survive, we call that place where these things are available a habitat. When the students have an understanding of "habitat," write a few sentences on the chalkboard defining habitat. As much as possible, make use of the ideas the students suggest. For example: **Habitat is a place. It has food, water, shelter and space. These are things that animals need to live.**

Possible sentences for older students: **Food, water and shelter must be within a useable range for each animal. Different kinds of animals need different kinds of food, water and shelter and different amounts of space.**

12. The students may now write these sentences on the back of one of their drawings or on a piece of writing paper. They may also read the words in the sentences you have put on the board, after you. They may also write their own sentences about what habitat is, drawing pictures to go along with their words.

AQUATIC EXTENSION

Ask the students to think of an aquatic animal—any aquatic animal. Ask the students to draw a picture of their animal in a place where it lives. Ask the students to make sure they include: food, water, shelter and space in an arrangement that they think would make it possible for the animal to survive. Ask the students to talk about their drawings, pointing out the habitat components they have included.

EVALUATION

1. Choose which things wildlife need to survive: food, water, shelter, space, arrangement. Explain.

2. Choose which things people need to survive: food, water, shelter, space, arrangement. Explain. Write a sentence about what people and wildlife need to survive.

3. Tell a story. In the story, tell how a habitat meets the needs of different kinds of animals.

HABITAT RUMMY

OBJECTIVES

Students will: l) identify components of habitat as food, water, shelter and space in a suitable arrangement; and 2) apply knowledge of these components to habitat requirements of various species of animals.

The major purpose of this activity is for students to acquire a working understanding of the components of habitat.

METHOD

Students make cards and play a card game.

MATERIALS

writing paper and pencils; drawing paper; construction paper; scissors; glue; chalkboard or copies of included card masters for those who want to eliminate the research phase

BACKGROUND

NOTE: See "The Beautiful Basics," "Everybody Needs A Home," "What's That, Habitat?" or "Habitracks." Any one of these activities would be a good introduction to "Habitat Rummy," even though all except "Habitracks" are written for younger students.

PROCEDURE

PREPARATION OF CARDS FOR GAME (Skip this if you use card masters.)

1. Assign students to groups of two or three. Ask each group to pick one animal they will research. Encourage a wide range of animals, including both wild and domesticated.

Age: Grades 4-7 (and older)
Subjects: Science
Skills: analysis, application, classification, comparing similarities and differences, media construction, reading, small group work, writing
Duration: two 40-minute periods
Group Size: groups of two to three students
Setting: indoors or outdoors
Conceptual Framework Reference: I.C.2.
Key Vocabulary: habitat, survival needs, food, water, shelter, space, arrangement
Appendices: Local Resources

---

2. Ask each group of students to use reference materials to research their animal. (You may need to instruct students in the use of the library. If library skills or references are a problem, students might be asked to choose from a list of animals for which you have classroom references.) Included in their findings should be a list of what each animal uses to meet the following needs: food, water, shelter and space. They should also find out where the animal lives. For example, if a group of students picks a lizard, they might determine that most lizards eat insects for food; use insects as a water source because of their high mois-

ture content; rest in rock crevices or trees for shelter; and use a hillside or sandy wash as a space in which to find food. The lizard might live in a desert environment. Check the students' findings for accuracy. Note that some similar kinds of animals can live in a variety of kinds of habitat. Technical details can depend on the age of the students.

3. Either you or the students make a large, master "Habitat Information Chart" which includes the major categories of information found by the students as follows:

HABITAT INFORMATION CHART

ANIMALS

	LIZARD	SEAGULL	BEAR	CHIPMUNK
FOOD	INSECTS	FISH	INSECTS, FISH, BERRIES, BIRDS, EGGS, MAMMALS	SEEDS BERRIES
WATER	FRESHWATER (as available)	WATER (as available)	RIVERS LAKES STREAMS	FRESHWATER (streams, ponds, dew)
SHELTER	ROCK CREVICES	CLIFFS SAND DUNES	CAVES	BURROWS
SPACE	HILLSIDES	OCEAN COASTS	HILLS VALLEYS	HILLSIDES
ARRANGEMENT	DESERTS	COASTS	WOODLAND	MEADOW WOODLOT

HABITAT COMPONENTS

4. Once this information is on the master chart, make a smaller version on mimeograph or ditto stencils. You can make six, equal-sized rectangles on each stencil, with each stencil including the habitat components needed for one animal. Once printed, these rectangles will serve as playing cards. Or, the students can transfer the information to 3x5 cards for use to play. For example, the stencil for one animal could look like this:

OPTIONAL: Sample cards are included and can be used to skip the prior preparation procedures.

5. Make a copy of each stencil for every two to three students. (If you want every student to have a complete deck of cards to keep, print a copy of each stencil for every student.)

6. Pass out a complete set of the card sheets to every group of students, along with heavy construction paper and glue. They can glue the printed sheets onto the five individual habitat cards per animal according to the printed stencil. Once cut, each set of five habitat cards makes a "book." For example:

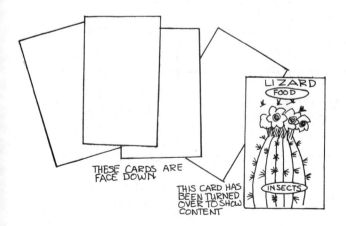

Blank on one side; kind of animal and habitat components on the other side.

With the deck of cards complete, it is time to play "HABITAT RUMMY!"

TO PLAY HABITAT RUMMY

1. The object of the game is for a player to get five cards from the one vertical column—or a complete set of habitat components for a kind of animal—as listed on the master "Habitat Information Chart." The game ends when all "books" or complete sets of habitat components have been made, with the student having the most complete sets the "winner" of the game. Every group of two to three students playing the game uses one complete set of habitat cards and each group has a "winner." The game is based on luck, but the students become familiar with the habitat components for the kinds of animals involved as the game is played. **The "Habitat Information Chart" must be in plain sight of the players.**

2. The game begins as one student deals five cards to each of the players in his or her group. This happens simultaneously around the room, as all groups begin play. The first player—after dealing is complete— may discard an unwanted card and select another from the remaining deck, situated in the center of the circle of play. Play progresses around the circle with discarded cards being added to the leftover cards in the center (either face-up or face-down) and new cards being drawn, until one player gets a book—a complete set of five habitat components for an animal. (The master "Habitat Information Chart" serves as a reference in this process.) When a player does get a book, he or she yells "HABITAT!" This process continues until all "habitats" are complete, and the student in each group with the most "books" or complete habitats is the "winner." "Winners" could play "winners" with class champion given the title, "Wildlife Biologist!"

3. Ask the students to summarize what they have learned.

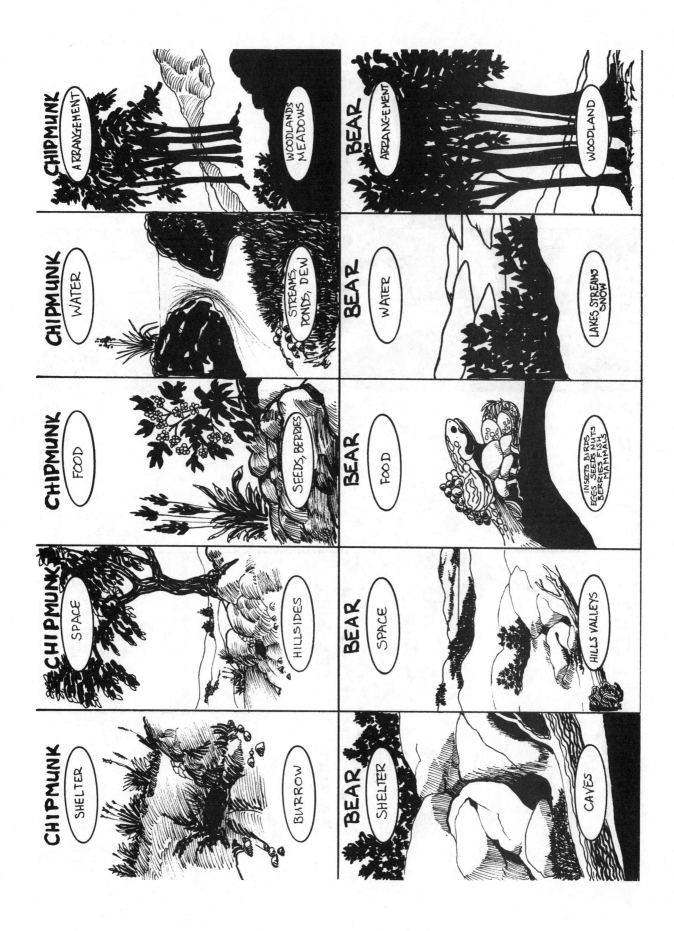

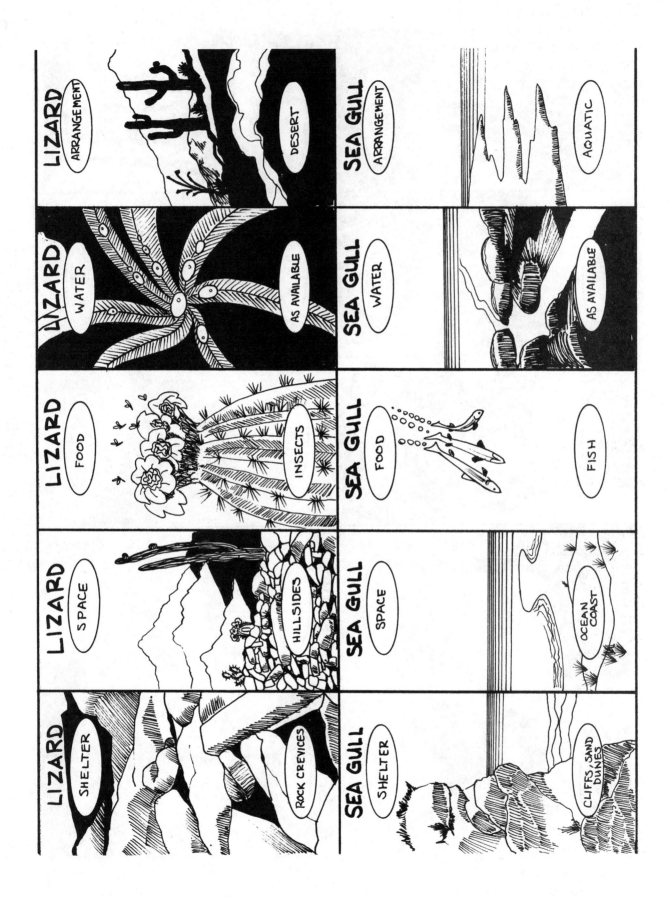

VARIATIONS OR EXTENSIONS

1. *Showdown Challenge:* Deal out all cards to players. Players showdown with the player to their left, starting at the dealer's left. Players challenge other players according to predator/prey relationships—with predators winning the challenge. The player with the most cards wins. Play for a specified time, using a time limit to end the game.

2. *Food Chain Rummy:* Play as in rummy. Players get a point for each component of every complete food chain. Cards may be added to either end of a food chain by any other player, acquiring points for every card involved each time. High score wins. Cards remaining in hand at the end of the game must be subtracted from the player's score.

3. *Add Additional Cards (for older students):* Instead of giving each group of 2-3 students a deck of cards with one complete habitat set for each animal, give them a deck with two or more habitat sets of each animal. This will encourage students to not just mechanically collect all the "lizard" cards, but actually make certain that they are collecting each component of habitat.

AQUATIC EXTENSION

Make new cards specifically for aquatic species in aquatic ecosystems.

EVALUATION

1. Identify habitat needs (what kinds of food, water, shelter and space, in what arrangement) for any five wild animals.

2. Tell a story that describes a day in the life of a wild animal as it meets its needs for survival. Identify and describe all the necessary components of habitat for that kind of animal.

MY KINGDOM FOR A SHELTER

OBJECTIVE

Students will identify and describe the materials and techniques used by at least one wild animal to construct its shelter.

METHOD

Students create replicas of wildlife shelters.

BACKGROUND

This activity emphasizes one habitat need of animals—shelter. The activity is most useful following an introductory activity which teaches all of the components of habitat. For example, see "The Beautiful Basics," "Everybody Needs A Home," "What's That, Habitat?," "Habitracks," "Habitat Rummy," "Ants On A Twig," "Habitat Lap Sit" and "Habitrekking."

Animals must use materials in their habitat to create shelters. Need for shelter is characteristic of animals—including people, farm animals, pets and wildlife.

The major purpose of this activity is for students to recognize the importance of suitable shelter to wildlife.

MATERIALS

natural materials

CAUTION: Do no damage to animals or their habitats while gathering materials.

Age: Grades 5-9
Subjects: Science, Art (emphasis is on shelter design and construction)
Skills: application, description, media construction, observation, research
Duration: minimum of two 45-minute periods (recommended 45 minutes to introduce activity and begin research; additional research and model construction as independent and at-home work; 45 minutes for reports and discussion)
Group Size: any
Setting: indoors, outdoors for observation
Conceptual Framework Reference: I.C.2.
Key Vocabulary: shelter, habitat, design
Appendices: Outdoors, Field Ethics

PROCEDURE

1. This can be an individual or small group project. Each student or group should choose a wild animal. Find out the characteristics of its shelter including what materials the animal uses to build it. Find out what techniques the animal uses and how long it takes to build the shelter. Pay attention to scale and form. Some animals with architecturally interesting shelters are: beavers, termites, muddaubers, caddis flies, spiders, cliff and barn swallows, chimney swifts, prairie dogs, siamese fighting fish, underwater bubble spiders, osprey.
2. Go outside if possible, as well as use reference materials, to learn what the animals use to construct their shelters (nests, dens, etc.)—paying attention to how the shelters are constructed. (If observing animal shelters, do not harm. Do not conduct this activity during mating and reproducing seasons.)
3. Ask the students to collect representative materials from the environment, similar or comparable to those the animals would use in constructing the shelters. Caution the students to be careful in collecting materials, doing no harm to the environment.
4. Build facsimiles or models of each animal's shelter. If possible, build these to scale. If not, indicate the difference.
5. Display the completed shelters, asking the students to describe the shelter and identify the animal that uses it. Contrast how much time it took to replicate the shelters with how much time it would take the animal. Contrast techniques the students use with those the animals would use. Compare similarities and differences in the shelters and kinds of habitats in which the animals live. Discuss consequences of habitat loss for each of the animals. Which animals are most vulnerable to loss of materials for creating shelter?

EXTENSIONS

1. Create a diorama, putting the shelter within a model of the habitat in which the animal lives.
2. Follow this activity with one on animal adaptation.

AQUATIC EXTENSION

If you have not already, create models of shelters used by a variety of kinds of aquatic wildlife.

EVALUATION

1. What would you look at in a library to discover the materials and techniques used by a yellow jacket hornet to construct its shelter?

2. Select an animal. Describe the materials and techniques it uses to build its shelter.

3. Write a poem that contrasts the characteristics of the shelter needed by at least two different kinds of animals.

WHAT'S FOR DINNER?

OBJECTIVE
Students will generalize that all animals, including people, depend on plants as a food source, either directly or indirectly.

METHOD
Students list and analyze the sources of foods.

BACKGROUND
Plants ultimately support all forms of animal life, including people, either directly or indirectly. Most people are omnivores, which means that they eat both plants and animals in some form. Some people include a lot of meat in their diets, others much less and some people none at all. It is easy to see that people who are vegetarians—who eat only plants and plant products—are supported directly by plants. It may not be as easy for children to see that even when they are eating animal products, they are indirectly relying on plant sources. For example, cows from which milk and other products are derived, and chickens which provide eggs and meat, are animals which depend upon plants for some or all of their food. Every animal, including people, either eats plants directly—or depends for food upon other species which in turn depend upon plants.

The major purpose of this activity is for students to trace human and other animals' dependence upon plants for food.

Age: Grades 3-7 (and older)
Subjects: Science, Language Arts, Health
Skills: analysis, classification, discussion, drawing, listing, media construction, writing
Duration: 20 minutes or longer
Group Size: any
Setting: indoors
Conceptual Framework Reference: I.A., I.A.1., I.A.3.
Key Vocabulary: food chain, plants, animals
Appendices: Local Resources

MATERIALS
writing materials; chalk board;
OPTIONAL: poster board and drawing materials

PROCEDURE
1. What's for dinner? Ask students to go home and make a list of everything that they have for dinner on a particular evening—perhaps with help from a parent, brother or sister—or, they can invent a dinner menu of their choice.
2. In the classroom, ask the students to work alone or in groups to analyze where their food comes from. Every food from their dinner menu should be traced back to a plant. As each item on a menu is examined, ask the students to create a flow diagram or chain which shows the major sources of each food—from the product they eat all the way back to the plant origin. For example: Me Milk Cow Grass. Some chains will be short; others will be long. Sometimes the students may not be sure what particular animals eat for food, so they will want to ask or do some library research to find out.

3. Have a general discussion with the students: "What are some of the things you have learned from this activity?" After the students have described things they have learned, encourage them to make two generalizations about plants and animals: 1) all animals, including people and wildlife, need food; and 2) all animals, including people and wildlife, depend upon plants

for food. (Watch for the insight that ultimately plants need animals, too! The decay of animal life after death into nutrients in the soil provides sustenance to plants as well!)

EXTENSIONS

1. Create posters of the menus showing the food chains involved in each. Add soil, water, sun and air—since these are necessary to plants, people and all animals too!

2. Create a master list of all the plants that were identified. Look to see which plants we seem to depend upon more than others. Some students might be interested to know that other groups of people—like people in other parts of the world who live in different environments—could come up with a very different list of plants upon which they depend.

3. Adopt a rock! Did you know that everything you ate for breakfast (lunch, dinner, or a snack!) started somewhere with a rock! Trace plants to soil and soil to its parent matter—including rocks!

AQUATIC EXTENSIONS

1. See the Aquatic WILD activity, "Water We Eating?"

2. Create at least two food chains that involve people, aquatic wildlife and plants.

EVALUATION

1. Using the organisms listed below, construct at least three food chains; people, rabbits, grass, lettuce, mountain lions, robins, earthworms, hawks, mice, insects, wheat, cows, corn, pigs, deer, acorns.

2. Which of these animals do not need food? horse, snake, frog, person, robin.

3. All of the food eaten by animals must first come from _____? (Although the objective of this activity stressed that animals rely on plants, please accept any reasonable response—like soil, sunlight—if the students explain it reasonably.

LITTER WE KNOW

OBJECTIVES

Students will: 1) identify and evaluate ways that litter pollution can endanger wildlife; and 2) propose ways they can help eliminate these dangers.

METHOD

Students collect and evaluate litter, making collages.

BACKGROUND

Environmental pollution affects all forms of life. Litter is unsightly. It also exposes wildlife and other animals to illness, injury and death.

For example, monofilament fish line may get tangled on legs and beaks of water birds like geese and herons. Some of these birds need to run short distances to take off when they fly. The fish line prevents this. It also interferes with their swimming. Birds with long bills often get line wrapped around their bills and cannot open them to eat. They starve to death. The line also gets tangled in their wings, preventing the birds from flying.

Sometimes fish or birds get into the loop portions of plastic six-pack can holders. The animal continues to grow, but the loop won't stretch. A slow death results. These loops can also get tangled around the feet of waterfowl.

Half-open cans are a problem for some animals. These are examples of the reasons that states are outlawing the use of plastic six-pack holders. Animals, like deer, can cut their tongues on the cans. Sometimes smaller animals get their heads stuck inside such cans and they can't eat. Starvation is the result. Mice and chipmunks crawl into opened bottles and get trapped inside, unable to get a footing on the slippery glass to push themselves out through the small opening.

Shiny bottle caps or pop-tops may be eaten by wildlife, including fish, injuring or killing them. Cigarette butts, cellophane wrappers and styrofoam cups, eaten by deer and other wildlife, can cause internal problems.

Broken glass from bottles and other glass objects can injure people, pets and wildlife.

You can contact your state wildlife agency, or other state agencies, for additional information about problems resulting from litter, including local examples. Such personnel and others—including representatives of private environmental, conservation and animal welfare organizations—may also be available to assist you in considering alternatives for reducing litter problems. They can talk about ways in which progress is being made and where improvements need to be made.

The major purpose of this activity is to alert students to the dangers of litter pollution and to consider responsible actions people can take to minimize consequences of litter pollution.

Age: Grades 4-6
Subjects: Social Studies, Language Arts, Science, Art, Math
Skills: analysis, classification, computation, discussion, evaluation, media construction, observation, problem solving, small group work, synthesis
Duration: minimum of 45 minutes
Group Size: small teams of three to five students
Setting: indoors and outdoors
Conceptual Framework Reference: I.B., I.B.2., I.B.3., I.C., I.C.3., I.C.4., I.D., V.A., V.A.5., V.B.1., VI.A.5., VII.A., VII.A.1., VII.A.2., VII.A.3., VII.A.4., VII.B., VII.B.1., VII.B.2., VII.B.3., VII.B.7.
Key Vocabulary: litter, pollution
Appendices: Outdoors, Local Resources

MATERIALS

large sheets of butcher paper for mounting collages; glue; different types of litter; work gloves; trash sacks

PROCEDURE

1. Divide the class into three or four teams.
2. Ask each team to bring a collection of litter to class in a paper bag. Suggest the students look in parks, camping areas, or school grounds. Advise students to wear work gloves. Caution them about hazards such as broken glass and medical wastes. NOTE: They should not take things out of garbage cans.
3. Have the teams make and display collages of these items.
4. Discuss the effects of litter. OPTIONAL: Ask a wildlife expert to join the class for the discussion. If available, show a film or read brochures on the subject.
5. Ask the students to assign a numerical value to each kind of litter. The item potentially most harmful to wildlife has the highest score, least harmful has the lowest score.
6. Have each team figure a total score for the collage based on the numerical values of each piece of litter.
7. Propose and evaluate ways that people can eliminate litter pollution. For example, can manufacturers make cans with openings other than pop-tops? Could they devise another method of packaging six-packs? How could people fishing have more control over losing their fishing line? How can individuals be instructed about the dangers as well as the unsightliness of littering? What progress has been made in recent years? What actions are still needed? What can students do personally—as individuals, as groups and as family units—to eliminate or reduce their own litter?

EXTENSIONS

1. Research local and state laws regarding recycling. Determine how those laws impact wildlife.
2. Is there a litter clean-up program in your community? If yes, learn more about it. If not, find out why not.

AQUATIC EXTENSIONS

1. See the Aquatic WILD activity, "Plastic Jellyfish."
2. Focus specifically on litter that can be potentially harmful to aquatic wildlife.
3. Consider what happens to garbage that is dumped into the ocean. Where off the coast of the United States is this done? What towns and cities contribute to this ocean dumping? Where does the garbage go? How are coastal towns affected by this? How is wildlife affected by this? When considering the impact on wildlife, think about any possible effects on the wildlife's food, water, shelter and space. Are there regulations affecting the dumping of garbage into the seas? If yes, are they enforced?
4. Plan a "Volunteers for Wildlife" clean-up program. Get it started in your community.

EVALUATION

1. Name four ways that litter can harm wildlife.
2. List three things you can do to eliminate these dangers.
3. Propose what you consider to be one of the most effective ways to eliminate or reduce litter. Explain why you think this proposal would be effective.
4. Invent a "Stop Litter for Wildlife" advertising campaign. Include a list of reasons for the campaign.

TRACKS!

OBJECTIVES
Students will identify common animal tracks.

METHOD
Students make plaster casts of animal tracks.

BACKGROUND
Looking for evidence of wildlife is one method of determining what types of animals are around. Signs such as burrows, nests, droppings or food litter can be identified—but some of the easiest signs to interpret are animal tracks.

Animal tracks can be the basis for several types of investigations. Identifying the tracks that you and your students find will help fill in a species list of those animals found in your area. Wildlife population estimates can be made from observing the number of tracks found during a specified length of time. Habitat requirements of individuals can be determined by finding their tracks in certain areas and not finding them in others.

Track hunting is really very easy. Just find a spot of level ground with fairly soft, fine, textured soil. Smooth it over and come back later to see what has been there! Obvious places for your smooth spot would be near water or on well worn trails. Larger animals will use the more open areas, while a small spot the size of your hand cleared under some bushes may reward you with many different little tracks of mice, shrews and reptiles.

Tracks can be preserved and collected by making plaster casts of them. This simple procedure will allow you to "collect" track and add them to other evidence like bones, nests or scats that you already may have collected.

Once these tracks have been observed or preserved, information about the animal that made them can be discovered. For example, all mammals have basically the same foot structure. They just use the parts in different ways. If we look at an animal's foot in relation to the human hand, we find that some animals walk on their hands—like raccoons and bears. Others walk or run on their toes, like cats and coyotes, while some walk on their "toenails" or hooves like deer and elk.

By looking at a track, we can make some determinations about how that animal lives. We can notice what part of the foot it walks on, whether claws are present and how many steps are taken in a measured distance.

The major purpose of this activity is for students to become sufficiently familiar with evidence of wildlife to be able to identify a few animal tracks common to their area.

MATERIALS
plaster of Paris; containers for mixing; spray shellac or plastic; vaseline; cardboard; knives; sandpaper; black ink or paint
OPTIONAL: loops of wire

PROCEDURE
1. Take your class on a field trip to a nearby lake, stream, or wildlife refuge area—somewhere where there will be lots of tracks!
2. Divide into small groups to find tracks. You may want to divide the students into groups according to areas in which they will look for tracks; e.g., one group under bushes, one group at a meadow's edge, one group near a pond's edge. Prepare the students in advance to assist them in looking carefully and responsibly.

Age: Grades 4-7
Subjects: Science, Art
Skills: analysis, application, comparing similarities and differences, psychomotor development, synthesis
Duration: two 45-minute periods or longer
Group Size: small groups of two to five
Setting: outdoors
Conceptual Framework Reference: I.B., I.B.1., I.B.3., I.B.4.
Key Vocabulary: tracks, evidence
Appendices: Outdoors, Field Ethics

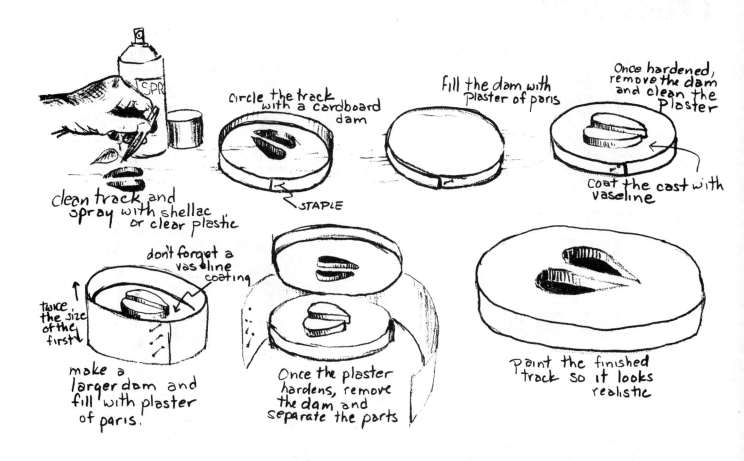

clean track and spray with shellac or clear plastic

circle the track with a cardboard dam

STAPLE

fill the dam with plaster of paris

Once hardened, remove the dam and clean the plaster

coat the cast with vaseline

twice the size of the first

don't forget a vaseline coating

make a larger dam and fill with plaster of paris.

Once the plaster hardens, remove the dam and separate the parts

paint the finished track so it looks realistic

3. Once a track is found, clean it of loose particles of soil, twigs, leaves and other litter.

4. Spray the track with shellac or plastic from a pressurized can if available.

5. Form a two-inch wide strip of cardboard or tin into a ring surrounding the track. Press firmly into the ground to give support, but allow at least one inch to form the edge of the mold for the plaster. Square forms can be made by cutting milk cartons horizontally—one of the easiest ways to make the forms! Simple round forms can be made by cutting both the top and bottom from a tuna or catfood type of can or a plastic margarine tub. Stapled strips of cardboard in the shape of a circle can also be used.

6. Mix about two cups of plaster of Paris in a tin can or plastic bowl, adding water slowly until it is about as thick as heavy cream. Pour carefully into the mold until the plaster is about to the top. Allow plaster to harden at least 15 minutes before lifting it out of the track. If the soil is damp, hardening may take longer.

7. When the cast is hardened, lift the cast out, remove the ring and clean the cast by scraping it with a knife blade and washing.

8. Back in class, apply a thin coating of vaseline to the track and surface of the cast. Place it on a flat surface and surround the casting with a two-inch strip of cardboard or tin as before.

9. Mix plaster of Paris and pour it into the mold, making certain that the top surface of the casting is smooth and level with the mold. If you plan to use the casting as a wall plaque, place a loop of wire in back of the casting while the plaster is still soft. Allow two hours for plaster to harden.

10. Carefully remove the mold when the plaster is dry. Separate the two layers and wipe the excess vaseline from the face of the cast and track. Scrape any rough places with a knife blade, or use fine sandpaper to smooth the surface. Wash the completed cast in running water.

11. When the cast is thoroughly dry, paint the inside of the track with India ink or black poster paint. Label each cast with the name of the track and the student's name. A coat of clear shellac or clear plastic may be applied to protect and preserve the casting.

Whitetail Deer

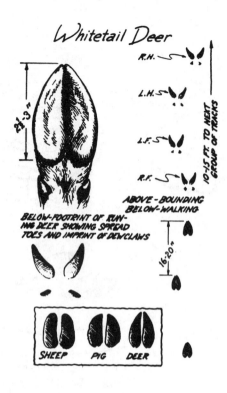

R.H. ⟍

L.H. ⟍

L.F. ⟍

R.F. ⟍

10-15 FT. TO NEXT GROUP OF TRACKS

2'-3"

ABOVE - BOUNDING
BELOW - WALKING

BELOW - FOOTPRINT OF RUNNING DEER SHOWING SPREAD TOES AND IMPRINT OF DEWCLAWS

16-20"

| SHEEP | PIG | DEER |

Gray Squirrel

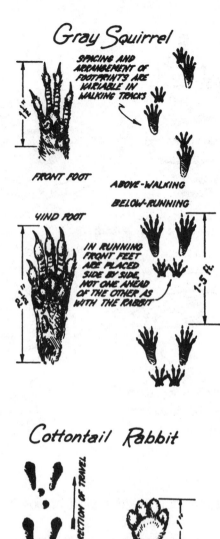

SPACING AND ARRANGEMENT OF FOOTPRINTS ARE VARIABLE IN WALKING TRACKS

4½"

FRONT FOOT

ABOVE - WALKING

BELOW - RUNNING

HIND FOOT

2⅜"

IN RUNNING FRONT FEET ARE PLACED SIDE BY SIDE, NOT ONE AHEAD OF THE OTHER AS WITH THE RABBIT

1-5 Ft.

Black Bear

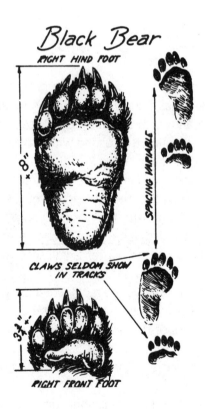

RIGHT HIND FOOT

8"

SPACING VARIABLE

CLAWS SELDOM SHOW IN TRACKS

3½"

RIGHT FRONT FOOT

Cottontail Rabbit

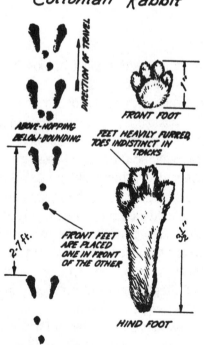

DIRECTION OF TRAVEL

FRONT FOOT

1"

ABOVE - HOPPING
BELOW - BOUNDING

FEET HEAVILY FURRED, TOES INDISTINCT IN TRACKS

2-7 Ft.

FRONT FEET ARE PLACED ONE IN FRONT OF THE OTHER

3½"

HIND FOOT

J. J. Shomon
Reprinted from December 1953 *Virginia Wildlife Magazine*

EXTENSIONS

1. In a sandy area, move in different ways. For example, you can walk, run and jump. Compare the differences between sets of tracks made by the same person. Evaluate how speed, directional changes and other variations in travel alter the tracks.

2. You may be able to obtain various animal feet or rubber replicas of feet from your local wildlife agency, nature center or scientific supply company. The feet or replicas can then be used to make tracks and plaster casts. Once you have made tracks with real or rubber feet, make up a wildlife story and express it by making the appropriate tracks. As a variation, make up a "track story" and have others guess what happened.

AQUATIC EXTENSION

Display all the tracks according to the habitats in which you found them. How many of the tracks, if any, were found near water? If any were found near water, identify the kind of aquatic environments in which the tracks were found—for example, pond, stream, lake, marsh, beach.

EVALUATION

1. Draw and label tracks of animals common to your area.

2. How would knowing about animal tracks and tracking help the following people? Consider: a biologist studying lions; a wildlife photographer interested in elk; a shepherd with a flock of sheep. What kinds of things would they need to know about animal tracks to do their jobs?

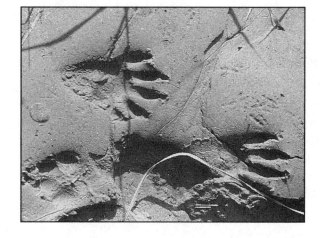

HABITREKKING

OBJECTIVES

Students will: 1) summarize evidence about the nature of habitats; and 2) generalize from evidence that people and wildlife have similar basic needs, share environments and are subject to the same or similar environmental problems.

METHOD

Students go outside to conduct an investigation requiring observation, interpretation and data-gathering skills, and then prepare and present their findings.

BACKGROUND

NOTE: Use this activity after one that introduces components of habitat. See "Ants On A Twig," "Habitat Lap Sit" and "Habitat Rummy."

All animals—including people, pets and wildlife—share similar basic needs. We have more in common than we may think.

All animals need some place to live. The term for an area in which an animal lives is "habitat." Habitat includes food, water, shelter and space in a suitable arrangement. People, domesticated animals and wildlife all have these needs.

Once we recognize the diversity of wildlife, we should realize that wildlife exists all around us. Wildlife is present in areas all over the earth's surface. We share our environment with wildlife. And, since people and wildlife share similar basic needs, it is likely that if people are without elements of their basic needs, wildlife will be as well. More often the case, wildlife

habitat is destroyed without people being aware that this has happened. The health and well-being of people, domesticated animals and wildlife is dependent upon environmental quality.

The major purpose of this activity is for students to recognize that people and wildlife share environments, have similar basic needs, and are subject to the same or similar environmental problems. Students are encouraged to generalize from their findings in investigating microhabitats to come to these conclusions.

MATERIALS

copies of "Habitrekking Evidence Lists" (see below); mixed media available for students to create visual and verbal reports

PROCEDURE

1. Divide the students into three groups. Have the students in each group pair off into two-person teams.
2. Each team should be equipped with observation tools. Students could have one or more of these optional items: hand lens, trowel, camera and film, sketch pad, tape recorder, tape, string, meter stick, empty corked test tubes, microscope slides, paper sacks, small containers with lids, video or still camera equipment , etc. Given advance notice, students might bring in a variety of such "observation tools" from home.
3. Provide "Habitrekking Evidence Lists" for the teams in each group:

**GROUP #1—
HABITREKKING EVIDENCE LIST #1**

CAUTION: You may bring back evidence, but be careful to do no harm to the environment, or wildlife.

FIND EVIDENCE THAT:

1. Humans, domesticated animals and wildlife have similar needs for food, water, shelter and space in an arrangement suitable for survival.
2. All living things are affected by their environment.
3. Plants support all forms of animal life—including people—either directly or indirectly.

Age: Grades 7-12
Subjects: Science, Language Arts, Social Studies
Skills: analysis, application, comparing similarities and differences, description, discussion, generalization, invention, media construction, observation, reporting, research, small group work, synthesis, writing
Duration: two or three 45-minute periods
Group Size: three groups, with a minimum of two students each
Setting: outdoors and indoors
Conceptual Framework Reference: I.A., I.A.1., I.A.2., I.A.3., I.A.4., I.B., I.B.1., I.B.3., I.B.4., I.C., I.C.1., I.C.2., I.C.3., I.C.4.
Key Vocabulary: evidence, wildlife, habitat, environmental quality, pollution
Appendices: Outdoors, Field Ethics

GROUP #2—
HABITREKKING EVIDENCE LIST #2

CAUTION: You may bring back evidence, but be careful to do no harm to the environment, or wildlife.

FIND EVIDENCE THAT:
1. Humans and wildlife share environments.
2. Wildlife is all around us.
3. Wildlife ranges widely in forms, colors and adaptations.

GROUP #3—
HABITREKKING EVIDENCE LIST #3

CAUTION: You may bring back evidence, but be careful to do no harm to the environment, or wildlife.

FIND EVIDENCE THAT:
1. Humans and wildlife are subject to the same or similar environmental problems.
2. The health and well-being of both people and wildlife is dependent upon environmental quality.
3. Environmental pollution in its various forms affects people, domesticated animals and wildlife.

4. Ask each group to read their "Habitrekking Evidence Lists." Make sure the students have clear definitions of wildlife and habitat. Establish the areas in which the students will be looking for evidence. The schoolgrounds may be used, or urban city centers, forested parks, vacant lots, etc. Establish a length of time for the investigations. Thirty minutes is recommended if the students stay on the schoolgrounds and one hour if you and they go to an off-campus site. Tell them they should exercise their creativity because there are no real right and wrong answers. They simply have to have reasonable explanations for what they select as evidence. They may observe and they may infer. Both are sources of evidence.
5. Send the students "habitrekking." When they return, ask each group to prepare to present their evidence in a form that includes both pictures and words. The teams within each group can compare their findings as they prepare for their group's report.

6. Spend one class period seeing, hearing and discussing reports.
7. In the discussion, ask the students to summarize what they learned. Emphasize the generalizations that people and wildlife have similar basic needs, share environments, and are subject to the same or similar environmental problems.
OPTIONAL: Check the observations and generalizations against resource books or other valid sources to verify the results and correct false impressions.

AQUATIC EXTENSION
Adjust the "habitrekking" instructions to apply specifically to aquatic wildlife and aquatic habitats. That is, find evidence that humans and aquatic wildlife are subject to the same or similar environmental problems, etc.

EVALUATION
Using one of the "Habitrekking Evidence Lists," conduct a similar investigation in the environment around your home or neighborhood. Write a brief summary of your findings.

SPIDER WEB GEOMETRY

OBJECTIVES

Students will: 1) recognize spiders as wildlife; and 2) generalize that people and wildlife share environments.

METHOD

Students research the spider of their choice, and then construct a replica of the spider's web, applying principles of geometry.

BACKGROUND

Spiders are one form of wildlife. Although many people have an aversion to spiders, they actually are important contributors to ecological systems. This activity emphasizes spiders as one of the diverse range of animals included within a definition of wildlife. Wildlife includes all animals other than those domesticated by people. Wildlife ranges from microscopic forms, like amoebas, to those many tons in size, like the whales. Wildlife occurs in a variety of forms, colors and adaptations, from the muskox to the manatee, the mollusk to the myna. Wildlife includes spiders, insects, worms, reptiles, amphibians, fish, birds and mammals, if non-domesticated. (See "Animal Charades.")

The major purpose of this activity is for students to identify spiders as one form of wildlife, developing and applying mathematical and research skills in the process.

MATERIALS

writing materials for use in research; measuring instruments; thread; glue;
OPTIONAL: photographic materials

PROCEDURE

1. Talk with the students about spiders! Some may express horrified reactions, while others will point out the contributions made by spiders—for example, in reducing populations of other insects. Expand the discussion to wildlife in general, assisting the students in establishing working definitions of wildlife and domesticated animals, if they have not already done so.
2. Send the students on a ten-minute investigation of their classroom or schoolgrounds, looking for any evidence of spiders. (Caution the students to touch neither the webs nor spiders. In advance, determine whether there are any poisonous spiders in your area. If they are in your area, teach your students how to recognize and avoid them. Remind your students that they may not touch the spider or its web. That precaution can be as much for their sake as the spider's.) If evidence of spiders is found, suggest that since we're sharing the same environment, we might as well find out more about them!
3. Ask the students to research a spider of their choice, investigating the appearance and characteristics of the spider and its web. Find out the spider's habitat needs, its common prey, and assess the spider's role in

Age: Grades 10-12 (and younger)
Subjects: Mathematics (Geometry), Science, Language Arts (with emphasis on research and writing skills), Art (emphasis on model construction)
Skills: analysis, computation, measurement, application of geometric principles, description, drawing, invention, media construction, observation, reading, research, writing
Duration: two 45-minute class periods
Group Size: individual or small group project
Setting: indoors and outdoors
Conceptual Framework Reference: I.B., I.B.1., I.B.3., I.B.4., III.B., III.B.1.
Key Vocabulary: wildlife, spiders, arachnids, geometry
Appendices: Outdoors, Field Ethics, Animals in Classrooms, Metric Chart

its environment. If they don't know already, ask the students to find out what makes a spider different from an insect, and what makes an arachnid different from an insect. They should design a replica of the spider's web as accurately as they can, using recognizable geometric shapes.

4. Next the students should make the web. Thread and glue can be used. The webs should be constructed to scale, and made as realistic as possible.

5. Ask the students to present their findings. What have they learned about spiders? What contributions do spiders make to the environment? What theorems of geometry were most useful in their web construction? Encourage the generalization that people and wildlife share environments—and that spiders are wildlife.

EVALUATION

1. Name five spider species common in your area.

2. List three characteristics that make an arachnid different from an insect.

3. Write a proof to support the geometric theorems that you used in constructing your web.

WE'RE IN THIS TOGETHER!

OBJECTIVES

Students will: 1) identify environmental problems of concern to both people and wildlife; and 2) generalize that people, domesticated animals and wildlife are subject to similar environmental problems.

METHOD

Students interview people to identify environmental problems, and then analyze, interpret and summarize their findings.

BACKGROUND

Once we recognize the diversity of wildlife, we begin to realize that wildlife exists all around us. Once we recognize that we share basic needs with wildlife and other animals, we recognize that we share environmental problems as well. The health and well-being of people, domesticated animals like pets, and wildlife is dependent upon environmental quality.

The major purpose of this activity is for students to recognize that people, domesticated animals and wildlife are subject to the same or similar environmental problems.

MATERIALS

writing materials; chalkboard

Age: Grades 9-12
Subjects: Social Studies, Environmental Problems, English, Science
Skills: analysis, application, classification, description, generalization, interviewing, listing, research, synthesis, writing
Duration: 30 minutes in class; 30 minutes in interviews both on campus and at home; plus additional 45 minutes in class
Group Size: any
Setting: indoors; outdoors optional
Conceptual Framework Reference: I.C., I.C.1., I.C.2., I.C.3., I.C.4., I.D., V.A., V.A.5., V.B.1., VII.A., VII.B.
Key Vocabulary: environmental problem, interview, components of habitat
Appendices: Local Resources

PROCEDURE

1. Begin a discussion with your students about environmental problems or issues they are concerned about. List any problems they identify on the chalkboard.
2. Ask the students to develop a set of questions for use in interviewing people concerning environmental issues. Review their final questions for clarity and appropriateness before they begin their interviews.
3. Ask each student to interview five people at school, finding out from other students and teachers what environmental problems they are concerned about. Ask the students to interview family members with the same questions. Suggest to the students that they not share the concerns of people at school until their family members have had a chance to generate their own ideas.
4. Combine the concerns identified from all the interviews, including the students' original list. Rank the concerns from those most to least often mentioned. Items on a list might look like this:
    *   crowding
    *   difficulty in buying or finding housing
    *   worry about toxic wastes
    *   air quality
    *   crime
    *   concern about nuclear power
    *   depletion of natural resources

5. Ask the students to try to categorize the concerns according to whether they are problems for people, domesticated animals, and wildlife. How are people, pets and wildlife affected by these problems? How do they cope with them, if they do? Also analyze the problems according to components of habitat (food, water, shelter and space, in a suitable arrangement). For example:

People	Domestic Animals	Wildlife	
X	X	X	1. crowding (space)
X	X	X	2. housing (shelter)
X	X	X	3. toxic waste (food, water)
X	X	X	4. air quality (shelter, food, water)
X	X	X	5. crime (shelter, space)
X	X	X	6. nuclear power (shelter, food, water, space)
X	X	X	7. depletion of natural resources (food, water, shelter, space)

This categorization is useful as an indicator that people, domesticated animals and wildlife share the same needs, and are subject to similar problems in environmental quality.

6. Ask the students to write an essay, poem, or short story which summarizes what they learned in this investigation of environmental concerns, emphasizing that people and wildlife are "in this together."

EXTENSIONS

1. Have a class reading of the essays and short stories.
2. Publish a magazine or book, for distribution to other students and family members, which includes the results of the interviews as well as the essays and short stories.
3. Put together a "TV News Special," featuring the common environmental problems of people and wildlife.

EVALUATION

Write an imaginary interview between yourself and a citizen of another country in the world. Ask that person the same questions you asked in your interviews with school and family members. Interpret your findings, comparing them with the results of your classroom study.

LEARNING TO LOOK, LOOKING TO SEE

OBJECTIVES

Students will: 1) describe differences seen in an environment as the result of casual and detailed observation; and 2) give reasons for the importance of looking closely at any environment.

METHOD

Students list what they remember seeing in a familiar environment, check their accuracy and discuss the results, and then apply their experiences and new skills to an unfamiliar outdoor setting.

BACKGROUND

NOTE: Use this as an introductory activity, especially for activities requiring observation skills.

Looking and seeing can be entirely different things depending on who we are, where we are, what we are concerned about and our purposes for looking. We look at our classrooms every school day, but if questioned about simple details, we may find that we are totally unaware of the existence of certain objects, colors, sounds and textures. As we walk through our neighborhoods, we have probably learned to notice only those things which are necessary to aid us in getting to our destination. We may not see a soaring hawk although we may be looking at the sky. We may not see a community of ants even though we are looking at the sidewalk. During a walk in the woods, we

may leave the trail to see a tree better—and then not see the wildflower we trample even though we are looking at the forest floor as we walk to the tree.

Each of us can educate ourselves to see. It takes at least three elements: 1) to learn to be a careful observer, even if we do not have sight through our eyes; 2) to be aware of our surroundings; and 3) to recognize any part of our environment as being part of a larger whole. As we enter a forest community, for example, we are a part of that community as much as we are part of our school community or neighborhood community. At a level, we are members of any community we enter. As a result, we have an opportunity and an obligation to see our neighbors and to be responsible members of each community we enter.

The major purpose of this activity is for students to be given an opportunity to enhance their powers of "seeing."

MATERIALS

note pads

PROCEDURE

1.   Let's practice seeing things. Cover a desk, bulletin board, other wall display, or table with a large sheet before students come to class. Ask the students to write down all the things they thought they saw there before the area was covered. When their lists are completed, ask them to turn over their papers. Remove the sheet. On the backside of their first lists, have the students make a new list of what they see. What kinds of things did they remember? What kinds of things were most often missed? Let them come up with reasons why they think this happened.

2.   Have the students go outdoors and pick one spot near a tree, a fence, a brook, a field, etc. Each student should find a spot alone, at least 50 feet from the closest human neighbor. Allow 15 minutes for this

Age: Grades K-8
Subjects: Language Arts, Science, Social Studies, Art
Skills: description, discussion, listing, observation
Duration: 20 to 45 minutes
Group Size: any
Setting: outdoors and indoors
Conceptual Framework Reference: I., IV.D.2., IV.E.5., VI.B., VI.B.2.,
Key Vocabulary: observe, see, appreciate, sense
Appendices: Outdoors, Field Ethics, Observations and Inferences

solo, or approximately five minutes for younger students. **The students should look in a broad sense of the word—seeing, touching, listening and smelling.** They should record everything they "see." (See "Wild Words" for a journal-making activity to use in recording their observations.) Fifteen minutes will provide time for an initial spurt of observations, a plateau and then another spurt as they begin to realize how much they missed the first time around. (Younger children need only record in their minds; no need to write.) Use an agreed upon signal to indicate when it is time to return to the group.

3. Bring the students together for a discussion, centering on the process they went through as well as their list of sightings. Did they focus on any one area for a long time? Did they continue to shift their gaze? How did they focus their hearing and smelling? Cupping hands around their ears to simulate animal hearing has a dramatic effect on abilities to hear. Blindfolding seems to cause a compensation toward better hearing as well. Moistening the undersurface of the nose and the entire upper lip area increases smelling ability. NOTE: Our role as teachers is a difficult one in that we are most effective when we teach our students **how** to look and see without telling them **what** to see.

4. Talk with the students about the joy and importance of seeing as fully as we can—as a way of appreciating, respecting, and learning more about the world in which we live. Older students: Discuss the importance of careful observation of our environments beginning with the basis for our fundamental life support systems—air, water, soil, plants, animals.

5. OPTIONAL, with older students: Talk about the process of continuing to develop our senses as being a life-long process for each of us. We are always learning and can learn even more. Sensing more in our surroundings can help us detect changes in our environment, cause us to become curious and ask questions, and help us to become better, more aware and informed decision-makers.

EXTENSIONS

1. Blur your eyes. What patterns and shapes do you see?
2. What else did you see? Any living things? What were they? Were they plant or animal?
3. Categorize what was observed as living or nonliving—and/or as animal, plant, mineral.
4. Play the game "Animal, Vegetable, Mineral" or "What Am I?"
5. Distinguish between qualitative and quantitative observations. Describe the differences between inferences and observations.

AQUATIC EXTENSION

Pick the nearest water in the outdoors you can think of. It might be a drinking fountain, a sprinkler hose, a pond, a stream, or the beach. Try to imagine it clearly in your mind. Draw a picture showing as much detail as possible of the water and its immediate environment. Include any wildlife and vegetation you think may be in the environment near and in the water. Did you leave anything out? Now, or as soon as possible, take your drawing to the spot. Look around. Make a written list of anything you did not include in your drawing. Add to your drawing to make it complete.

EVALUATION

1. Think of three of your friends. Without looking at them, write down the color of their eyes, and a description of what they were wearing last time you were together. Check to see if you were right.
2. Find and observe an insect. Pretend that you are making a report about what you observed to an entomologist (insect biologist). Include detailed observations. Explain the potential value of such detailed observations for two audiences: scientists and the general public.

SECTION TWO
DIVERSITY OF WILDLIFE VALUES

WILD WORDS. . .
A JOURNAL-MAKING ACTIVITY

OBJECTIVE

Students will observe and describe their surroundings, particularly in out-of-door settings, in a variety of ways.

METHOD

Students go into an outdoor setting to make and write in journals they design.

BACKGROUND

This journal-making activity can be used effectively as a means to record data and personal observations in combination with many Project WILD activities. With some activities it may be important to differentiate between field notes and creative journal entries. Field notes are typically factual accounts of nature; journal entries allow for personal interpretation.

A naturalist is a person who studies nature, especially by direct observation of plants, animals and their environments. Naturalists often spend a lot of time in the out-of-doors, and they often record their observations in some form—from sketches, drawings, paintings and photos to poetry and prose. Each person's motivation will be unique and may include sheer joy in learning more about natural systems, interest in contributing to scientific research, love for the art of writing as literature and simple satisfaction in being outside.

Age: Grades 4-12
Subjects: Language Arts, Science
Skills: application, description, discussion, drawing, media construction, observation, visualization, writing
Duration: one 20 to 45-minute period; recommend using the journal produced through this activity as a place for recording data, observations, images, etc., in other activities
Group Size: any
Setting: outdoors
Conceptual Framework Reference: II.A., II.A.2., II.A.3., II.A.4., II.B., II.B.3., II.E., II.E.1., II.E.3., II.F., IV.D.2., IV.E.2., V.A., V.A.4., V.A.5., V.A.6.
Key Vocabulary: journal, observation, naturalist
Appendices: Outdoors, Field Ethics, Simulated Field Trips

People benefit today from the insights and observations of those who have delighted in, and been fascinated by, the wonders of the natural environment. Henry David Thoreau, Walt Whitman, Enos Mills, John Muir, Edward Abbey, today's Gary Nabhan and Annie Dillard are among those who have captured their insights in words and offered them to others.

Most of the naturalists who put their observations in poetry and prose carry with them a small journal as they wander the woods, streams, lakes, oceans, deserts and other natural environments.

The major purpose of this activity is for students to learn to express and record their observations of nature in a variety of ways.

MATERIALS

construction paper for journal covers; blank, unlined writing or computer paper; staples and stapler; marking pens; crayons; pencils

PROCEDURE

1. Go outside to some pleasant outdoor setting. It might be an open area on the school grounds with clear sky above, near a large and inviting tree in a park that shades the earth on a hot day, or any outdoor setting from the immediate school grounds to a remote, wilderness setting.
2. Ask the students to sit quietly, listening carefully for any sounds. Ask them to look with "soft eyes"— that is, eyes that do not focus specifically on any one thing, but broadly sense what is in the environment. The students may move their heads at first in a scanning motion until they are accustomed to seeing without focusing on one thing at a time. "Hard eyes" are good for looking closely at a squirrel running up a tree. "Soft eyes" are good for seeing all the trees, the sky, the ground in an area—noticing the squirrel moving out of the corner of one eye, a bird moving sky-

ward out of the corner of the other eye and feeling the warmth of the sun from above. Encourage the students to try both "hard" and "soft" eyes, noticing the differences in how they feel and what they see. Both ways of seeing are useful.

3. Talk with the students about what they see, feel and notice. A simulated field trip (where the students close their eyes sitting quietly and you ask them to picture what you describe) can be useful at this point. For example, *"You are a tall tree standing in the forest. Picture yourself as the tree. See your roots digging deep into the soil. See the water from a recent rainstorm seeping into the earth around you. See that large rock tangled in your roots. See your branches swaying in the breeze, warmed by the sunlight."* And, or, read an excerpt from the writings of a naturalist.

A children's book for young and old students, *Another Way To Listen*, by Byrd Baylor and Peter Parnall (Charles Scribners Sons, New York, 1978) is an excellent way to set a mood and encourage greater awareness of natural surroundings. It includes:

"I used to know an old man who could walk by any corn field and hear the corn singing. . .Were you surprised to hear it?" I always had to ask. He said, "Not a bit. It seemed like the most natural thing in the world.'

For older students, any excerpts from, *The Wilderness World of John Muir*, edited by Edwin Way Teale (Houghton Mifflin Company, Boston, 1954) are good. For example, the chapter, "Windstorm in the Forest," is Muir's accounting of climbing a tall tree during a windstorm:

"It occurred to me that it would be a fine thing to climb one of the trees to obtain a wider outlook. . .Under the circumstances, the choice of a tree was a serious matter. . .Being accustomed to climbing trees in making botanical studies, I experienced no difficulty in reaching the top of this one, and never before did I enjoy so noble an exhilaration of motion. The slender tops fairly flapped and swished in the passionate torrent, bending and swirling backward and forward, round and round, tracing indescribable combinations of vertical and horizontal curves, while I clung with muscles firm braced, like a bobolink on a reed." (page 186)

4. Get out construction paper and blank unlined writing or computer paper for the students to make their own journals. Simply fold the paper in half with the construction paper on the outside and the unlined paper inside. Staple along the seams so that the booklet stays together. Provide marking pens and crayons so the students can put their name, a title and a drawing on the cover of their book. Or, make or buy more durable journals before going outside to start using them.

5. Give the students some time—about 15 minutes is fine to begin—to start getting accustomed to using their journal. Structured activities can be inserted at this point, or, each can find a quiet place to make a drawing of something they see. The students could begin to write a few words of description or a poem about their feelings in being outside in that place at that time. The important thing to stress is that the journal is theirs—for them to fill with whatever they choose. It is not the same thing as a diary that might be written in every day. It is a special way to keep memories and ideas about things in the natural environment. Encourage them to take their journals with them sometimes when they are outside, and regularly if possible—perhaps tucked in a backpack or a purse. It is especially good for those times when they are alone outside—perhaps walking to and from school, at a park over a weekend, on a camping trip with family members, etc. One of them may be the next John Muir or Annie Dillard!

6. Discuss the value of journals. In addition to recording impressions, feelings and observations, a journal can become a log of important data to be referred to later. It can reflect changes in ecosystems, vegetative types, animal populations—as well as attitudes about things. It can hold images as well as words. It can even hold artifacts from leaves to grains of sand!

EXTENSIONS

1. See "Animal Poetry."

2. Select an animal habitat. Find a spot within that habitat. (The students should literally experience the habitat as closely as possible to the perspective of the animal they choose to be; e.g., lying down on their backs looking skyward. They should not damage the animal's habitat, and they should still be near enough to you to hear your instructions.) Write one word that describes the animal you have chosen to be. On the next line write two words that describe what you look like. On the next line write three words that describe how you move, or where you live. On the next line write two words about how you contribute to the ecosystem where you live, or how you live. On the last line, write another word that describes who you are. For example:

Bird

Large, Strong

Soaring, Diving, Twisting

Predator, Hunter

Red-Tail

AQUATIC EXTENSIONS

1. See the Aquatic WILD activity, "Aqua Words."

2. Early explorers in North America often traveled by waterways. Lewis and Clark, LaSalle, voyageurs, and others were often the first to write in journals about what they saw. Pick a time period of your choice. Become a brave explorer, venturing into unknown territory. Write an imaginary account of what you see—including the terrain, vegetation and wildlife. Describe the water itself—its quality and the plant and animal life directly associated with it—whether you are on a great river, a lake, or ocean waters. Describe your feelings. Include an account of the "most hair-raising adventure" to date, and complete the sentence, "I find I am most often thinking about…"

EVALUATION

1. Write a description of some place that you like but that you have not visited in a long time. Include details about what it looks like, how you feel when you're there and what you like about it.

2. Go outside. Find a very small living thing. Look at it as closely as possible without harming it. Write a short description or poem about this small living thing.

ANIMAL POETRY

OBJECTIVE
Each student or group of students will recognize and experience the inspirational value of wildlife.

METHOD
Students go outside to imagine themselves as animals and then write poems.

BACKGROUND
NOTE: This is an excellent companion to "Wild Words: A Journal-Making Activity."

Poetry is an art form that is accessible to every student in some way. A poem is an organized way of expressing insight through language. Meter and rhyme combine as one kind of poetry. Song and free verse are other forms of poetry.

The major purpose of this activity is for students to experience wildlife as the inspiration for a poem—and to successfully write the poem!

MATERIALS
writing materials

PROCEDURE
1. Everyone can be a poet, at least to some extent—and yet many people think any kind of poetic expression is beyond their capacities. This activity is designed for every student—or group of students—to create a poem.

Age: Grades 4-7 (and older)
Subjects: Language Arts, Science
Skills: description, invention, synthesis, visualization, writing
Duration: one class period
Group Size: any
Setting: outdoors
Conceptual Framework Reference: II.A., II.A.1., II.A.2., II.A.3., II.A.4., II.B.3., II.F.
Key Vocabulary: poetry, imagine
Appendices: Outdoors, Field Ethics

2. Go outside. Find a pleasant setting on the school grounds, in a park, wooded area, or other natural environment. Ask everyone to pick an animal to think about. Any animal is okay, although some should be wild animals. Ask everyone to close their eyes for a few minutes and imagine they are the animal, living in its natural environment. With their eyes closed, you can guide their imagining process with a few words—or simply leave this process to the students on their own.

3. Give everyone five minutes to go find a spot to "become" that animal. Imagine how long it lives, where it travels, how other plants and animals look from its perspective. When the students return, ask everyone to write a short poem about their animal. Poems can be free verse or rhyming. Cinquain and haiku are interesting forms. Or, do a group poem. Everyone thinks of one animal. Each person contributes one word. One or more students or the instructor can put all the words together to form the poem while the others discuss their experiences in "becoming" an animal.

NOTE: Students can imagine they "are" their animal without giving the animal characteristics of humans which are not applicable.

4. OPTIONAL: Here are a few examples of poetic forms which can be used. These have been excerpted and adapted with permission from Project Learning Tree (Washington, D.C.; American Forest Institute, 1977).

Haiku Haiku, originated by the Japanese, consists of three lines of five, seven and five syllables each. The emphasis is syllabic, not rhyming. For example:

> *The hawk soared over*
> *Spirit bird in my living*
> *Guide to harmony.*

Cinquain Cinquain is derived from the French and Spanish words for five. This form of poetry is also based on syllables—or may be based on number of words—but there are five lines. Each line has a mandatory purpose and number of syllables or words. These are: 1) the title in two syllables (or words);

2) a description of the title in four syllables (or words); 3) a description of action in six syllables (or words); 4) a description of a feeling in eight syllables (or words); and 5) another word for the title in two syllables (or words). Here are two examples, the first using syllables and the second using words:

Panther

Vital, quiet
Moving swiftly to live
Endangered by human patterns
Near lost

Sea Otter

Mammal of living waters
Swimming, sleeping, eating, diving, basking, playing,
Sensitive indicator of the quality of continuing life
Still here

Diamante Diamante is a poem shaped in the form of a diamond. It can be used to show that words are related through shades of meaning from one extreme to an opposite extreme, following a pattern of parts of speech like this:

noun
adjective adjective
participle participle participle
noun noun noun noun
participle participle participle
adjective adjective
noun

For example:

egg
light bright
living stretching growing
bird beak wing flight
soaring seeing seeking
feathered fluid
raven

5.   The completed poems can be typed or printed neatly—and then displayed with a photograph or black and white pen and ink drawing of the animal. For example:

The Goat, "Mazama"

Rhime ice coats my nostrils
The gale rages from peak to crag

Warm, white wool shaggily hugging my body...
Cautiously I move on rock
Barely noticing the fear
Of the valley below.
The eagle—the feel of snow—
This is my home.

Hal Neace, Teacher
Seldovia, Alaska

AQUATIC EXTENSIONS
1.   See the Aquatic WILD activity, "Aqua Words."
2.   Create a poem in the shape of any aquatic animal you find interesting. Simply put words in order in the shape of the outline of the animal you have in mind. The words do not need to rhyme. You can use any words that come to mind that help to describe the characteristics of this aquatic animal—for example, where it lives, what it eats, how it moves and what you find interesting about it.

EVALUATION
1.   Why do you think some people say that they would not want to live in a world without wildlife? Are you one of those people? Why or why not? Would you prefer to choose the types of wildlife you would like to live with? If so, which types would you want to live with and why?
2.   Find a photograph or painting that features wildlife in an inspiring fashion. How does the artist portray wildlife in a way that you find inspiring?

MUSEUM SEARCH FOR WILDLIFE

OBJECTIVES
Students will: 1) identify wildlife portrayed in an art form; and 2) generalize that wildlife has sufficient aesthetic and spiritual value to inspire art.

METHOD
Students visit a museum, nature center or other source of artifacts—or they use reference books—to find examples of how wildlife is presented in cultural art forms.

BACKGROUND
Human relationships to wildlife are often expressed through painting, sculpture, drama, dance, literature, photography and other means of creative expression. Wildlife has served as an inspiration for art throughout human history.

The major purpose of this activity is for students to recognize one aspect of the value of wildlife—its impact as a source of inspiration for varying art forms.

MATERIALS
copies of Museum Search For Wildlife Chart; if done as a field trip, no other materials are necessary; if done in the classroom, various art books or slides featuring wildlife are needed.

Age: Grades 3-6
Subjects: Social Studies, Language Arts, Art
Skills: analysis, application, discussion, comparing similarities and differences, drawing generalizations, observation
Duration: 30 minutes if in class using reference materials; 45 minutes or longer if at museum
Group Size: any size, up to 30
Setting: indoors
Conceptual Framework Reference: II.A., II.A.1., II.A.2., II.A.3., II.A.4., II.B.3., II.C.1., II.D.2., II.F.
Key Vocabulary: art, artists, inspiration, wildlife
Appendices: Local Resources

PROCEDURE
1. This is a real field trip to a cultural setting! It requires a trip to a local art, natural history, or anthropological museum. NOTE: This activity can be added to a field trip already planned as part of a social studies unit, for example. (If no museum is available, use reference materials.)

2. Check your local community to see which museum, if any, would be appropriate. Make arrangements for your students to visit.

3. Before the trip, discuss different kinds of art that people have created throughout human history—including cave drawings, pottery, baskets, costumes, paintings, sculpture, drawings, dances, photography, literature and music. Ask the students what might inspire art.

4. At the museum, ask each student to find examples of wildlife represented in art. What kinds of wildlife? What kinds of art? Encourage the students to look closely since sometimes the image can be so stylized that it is hard to recognize. Ask each student to identify the art form and the wildlife—and to make a small sketch as a reminder of what they saw. (See "Wild Words." The students can put their sketches in their personal journals.) Or, use a worksheet. For example: Select one animal you saw represented at least three times. How did the artist portray it?

5. As a follow-up, discuss the students' observations with them. Identify which kinds of art seem to include the most images of wildlife (painting, pottery, sculpture, etc.). Compare how one animal—like a deer—might look in different art works. Talk about the varying ways artists portrayed wildlife, and some of the students' favorites. Talk about ways wildlife was portrayed during different historical periods. Talk about the relationships between people and wildlife during different periods. What are the clues? What if there were no wildlife?

6. Encourage the students to generalize that wildlife can serve as an inspiration and has aesthetic value.

EXTENSIONS

1. Portray wildlife in an art form of your choice!
2. Make your own wildlife art museum in the classroom. Collect photos or copies of paintings, sculpture, pottery, petroglyphs, weaving, etc. Or, make your own!

AQUATIC EXTENSION

Search through magazines or books for pictures of aquatic wildlife in art. Also look to see how frequently art that includes any kind of wildlife includes water. Make a list of the kinds of aquatic habitats you find in art work—and tally how many times each is portrayed.

EVALUATION

A group of people were discussing endangered plants and animals—that is, those that are very close to becoming extinct. Some of the people felt that we should preserve and protect all kinds of plants and animals because we might learn that they could be very useful to us for chemicals, medicine, foods and clothing, and as intrinsically valuable parts of our environment. Other people said that we do not need all those animals and plants, and we shouldn't worry about them. Suppose you are an artist in the group and you want to express your opinion about the importance of plants and animals. As an artist, how would you present your case? Make that presentation.

Museum Search For Wildlife Chart

Put a check after the name of the animals you find.

Animal Family	DOMESTIC ANIMALS (TAME)	WILDLIFE (UNTAMED)

LET'S GO FLY A KITE

OBJECTIVE
Students will recognize that wildlife has value as an inspiration for art.

METHOD
Students design, make, and fly kites.

BACKGROUND
Wildlife is an inspiration for many forms of art—ranging from music to mime, dance to drama, poetry to pointing, gymnastics to gymkhana, and more. Designing kites can be an art form—and one particularly accessible to young people.

The major purpose of this activity is for students to recognize the value of wildlife as an inspiration for art.

MATERIALS
tissue paper of a variety of colors; bamboo strips; small tacking nails and hammers; sturdy kite string (Bamboo is available in window shades as found in import shops; purchase and cut apart.)

PROCEDURE
1. Talk with students about the importance of wildlife as an inspiration for art. Ask the students for examples of different kinds of art where wildlife has been an inspiration.
2. Suggest that there can be more kinds of art than we sometimes think. At least a small number of people would suggest that the design and successful flying of

a kite is a special form of art in itself. This is a kite-making activity!
3. Students can work alone, or with one or two other students. Their task? To design and build a kite, inspired by a wild animal.
4. Give the students some time to begin designing their kites. What animal? What colors? What shape? What size? The kites can be realistic; e.g., employing concepts of "structure," "function," and "adaptations" based on a flying squirrel; or stylized. Let them know that the primary media for their kite construction will be brightly-colored tissue paper and a framing material such as bamboo. After providing some class time for the design work, give the students about two days outside of class to keep talking and thinking about their designs and to work on their plans on their own.
5. About two days later, in class, it's time to build the kites. Get out the tissue paper, bamboo, and other equipment. Give the students a class period to build their kites. Once they are built, it is a matter of waiting for a good day to fly the kites. Until the weather is just right, the kites should be stored in a safe place. At least one day, let the kites form a festive display in the classroom. When conditions are right, head out to the best available place for one trial run of each kite!
CAUTION: Be sure to stay away from power lines and cables, and if a thunderstorm is approaching, kites and students stay inside!

AQUATIC EXTENSION
Many classic kites are made in the form of fish. Make a fish kite in brilliant colors, using a real fish for inspiration. If everyone made a fish kite, would you then have a "school of fish?"

EVALUATION
1. Describe the features of your wild animal that made it seem like a good choice for a kite.
2. Find something other than a kite that was inspired by wildlife. Explain how the item's creator might have been inspired by wildlife.

Age: Grades 4-6 (and older)
Subjects: Art, Science, Math (measurement, forms)
Skills: discussion, invention, media construction, psychomotor skills, problem solving
Duration: 20 minutes to start design; 30-45 minutes to build kites
Group Size: one or more students, alone or in small groups
Setting: indoors and outdoors
Conceptual Framework Reference: II., II.A., II.A.3., II.A.4., II.F.
Key Vocabulary: inspiration, art, design, wildlife
Appendices: Outdoors

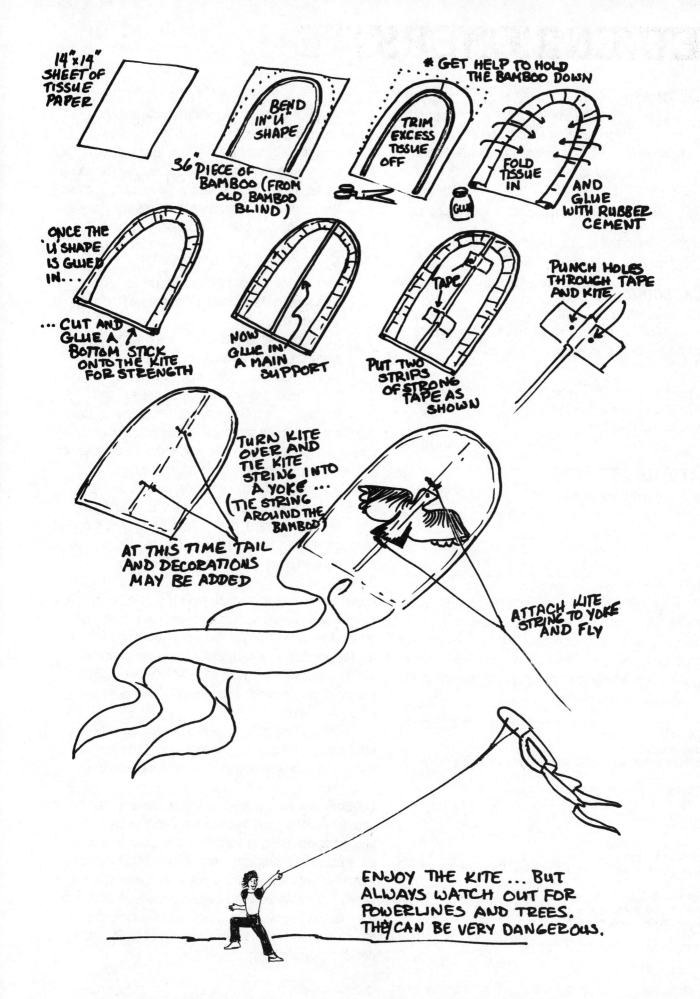

14"x14" SHEET OF TISSUE PAPER

36" PIECE OF BAMBOO (FROM OLD BAMBOO BLIND)

BEND IN A U SHAPE

GET HELP TO HOLD THE BAMBOO DOWN

TRIM EXCESS TISSUE OFF

FOLD TISSUE IN

AND GLUE WITH RUBBER CEMENT

ONCE THE U SHAPE IS GLUED IN...

... CUT AND GLUE A BOTTOM STICK ONTO THE KITE FOR STRENGTH

NOW GLUE IN A MAIN SUPPORT

TAPE

PUT TWO STRIPS OF STRONG TAPE AS SHOWN

PUNCH HOLES THROUGH TAPE AND KITE

TURN KITE OVER AND TIE KITE STRING INTO A YOKE ... (TIE STRING AROUND THE BAMBOO)

AT THIS TIME TAIL AND DECORATIONS MAY BE ADDED

ATTACH KITE STRING TO YOKE AND FLY

ENJOY THE KITE ... BUT ALWAYS WATCH OUT FOR POWERLINES AND TREES. THEY CAN BE VERY DANGEROUS.

ECO-ENRICHERS

OBJECTIVES
Students will: 1) evaluate the importance of plant and animal matter as contributors to soil; and 2) recognize that wildlife in many forms contributes to the diversity and balance of ecological systems.

METHOD
Students experiment with soil and earthworms.

BACKGROUND
Wildlife is an important contributor to healthy ecosystems. In this case, earthworms (not always recognized as wildlife) enrich a growing medium, soil.

The major purpose of this activity is for students to recognize one example of the kinds of significant contributions from wildlife.

MATERIALS
enough soil from the same source to fill three 1' x 1' x 1' containers; earthworms; composting material (like kitchen scraps and yard leaves)

PROCEDURE
1.   Select some soil that is not particularly rich—it might be heavily compacted; by a roadside; or in an area where there has been erosion. Note, however, that soil may look infertile but be rich with inorganic nutrients. Take a large enough sample of the soil to fill three 1' x 1' x 1' containers.

Age: Grades 6-12
Subjects: Science
Skills: analysis, application, classification, comparing similarities and differences, computation, description, discussion, generalization, kinesthetic concept development, observation, psychomotor development, reporting, research, writing
Duration: minimum of two 50-minute class periods, plus observation of soil boxes for six weeks
Group Size: whole class
Setting: indoors
Conceptual Framework Reference: II.B., II.B.1., II.F., II.B.1.
Key Vocabulary: ecosystem, soil, nutrients, fertility, acidity, alkalinity, porosity, organic, composting
Appendices: Outdoors, Field Ethics, Animals in the Classroom

---

2.   With your students, do some simple soil tests to determine the quality of the soil. For example:
*   Look for signs of plant and animal matter in the soil. Count the number of species you can identify, examine a sample under a microscope, count the number of organisms in the sample, and estimate the number of organisms in the entire quantity of soil in the container based on the number of the sample.
*   Test acidity and alkalinity with pH kits.
*   Check porosity by determining how fast water will run through.
*   Conduct a settling test to see what general proportions of soil components are present; i.e., sand, silt, clay, organic matter.

3.   After the soil tests have been completed and recorded, it is time to see what contributions at least one form of wildlife can make to the richness of soil. Divide the soil into the three containers. One container is the "control." The second is for soil and compost only. The third is for soil, compost and earthworms.

4.   Begin adding composting materials (plant matter)—like table scraps, grass clippings, leaves, etc.—to the second and third containers. Add earthworms to the third container. Occasionally water the soil **lightly**—to simulate a rainstorm. You can also lightly water the first box—but **do nothing else to the first box of soil.** Decaying organic materials usually have odors. Pick a location for the worm boxes where any unpleasant odors will not disrupt classroom activities. NOTE: You can begin with a larger number of earthworms if your soil box is large and if you want to speed up the process.

5.   Ask students to hypothesize the results expected after three weeks of experimentation. Have them write down their hypothesis to compare with their findings.

6.   Since the worms are in a limited environment, you and the students will need to keep adding the food and other composting materials. Compost may be added to the second container also. Plan on adding materials once a week for three weeks and watering lightly once a week. Encourage the students to watch for changes in any of the boxes. An observation sheet can be attached to the outside of each box for the students' reporting purposes.

7. At the end of the three-week period, conduct the same set of experiments you originally conducted with the soil. Conduct the tests with all three boxes. In testing the soil in the earthworm box, make sure the students take care not to harm the earthworms; many may die anyway. Be prepared for this possibility and add additional earthworms as necessary.

8. Discuss the findings. What differences are there in the three soil samples?

9. Now plant some seeds in all three of the soil boxes. Pick a fast-growing seed, like radishes. Seeds from plants native to the area might be available as well. Plant the same number of seeds in each of the soil boxes. Record the date of planting. Record all watering procedures and changes in the boxes as the plants begin to grow. After three weeks, compare and discuss the results. Describe the importance of plant and animal matter as contributors to soil. Talk about earthworms as one example of the role of wildlife as contributors to healthy environments!

VARIATION

Use two, two-liter soda bottles for the compost system. Cut the top off one and the bottom off the other. Invert one over the other such that the compost liquid would drain out. (The liquid can be used to water plants.) Use the cut bottom as a cover. Add vegetable scraps, water frequently and add soil occasionally.

EXTENSIONS

Many communities are encouraging citizens to compost their organic, non-animal wastes. Some trash collection services refuse to take lawn and other yard waste. The study of worms and soils is an excellent departure point for studying about composting. Investigate local regulations about organic wastes. A local gardener might provide information on composting.

EVALUATION

1. List three ways that earthworms have a positive effect on soil.

2. Explain how soil is important to plants and is a major factor in building wildlife habitat.

3. Write a story about what would happen to the soil, plants and some types of wildlife if there were no worms. Consider the impact on humans if there were no worms.

SEED NEED

OBJECTIVES

Students will: 1) explain how seeds are carried by animals; and 2) evaluate the importance of wildlife as contributors to ecological systems based on this example of seed dispersal.

METHOD

Students gather seeds by going outside and wearing socks over their shoes.

BACKGROUND

Wildlife contributes to the diversity and balance of ecological systems. One compelling example is in the process of seed dispersal. Many seeds are carried by animals—whether in the coats of fur-bearing animals or in seeds carried and dropped by some birds. Animals distribute seeds in other ways too. For example, some creatures, like pack rats and squirrels, gather seeds and store them. Some of those seeds are not eaten and the seed cache becomes a plant nursery. Many seeds are eaten but not fully digested. In those cases, animal droppings distribute and often fertilize seeds.

The major purpose of this activity is for students to understand one example of how wildlife contributes to healthy ecological systems.

Age: Grades 5-6 (and younger)
Subjects: Science, Math (Social Studies for older students with mapping)
Skills: analysis, classification, comparing similarities and differences, description, kinesthetic concept development, listing, observation, writing
Duration: 20-40 minutes or longer for gathering and analyzing data; minimal ongoing time in caring for planted seeds
Group Size: any
Setting: outdoors and indoors
Conceptual Framework Reference: II.B., II.B.1., III.B., III.B.1.
Key Vocabulary: ecosystem, dispersal, seeds, diversity
Appendices: Outdoors, Field Ethics

MATERIALS

one large fuzzy sock, or masking tape segment per student
OPTIONAL: one shoe box filled with planting medium per student; cookie sheets or trays in which to place shoe boxes used as planters

PROCEDURE

1. Ask each student to bring a large, old, fuzzy sock from home—or try to find an inexpensive or free source to obtain a sock for each student. Old socks with holes in them are fine for this activity. Ask each student to put on a sock over one shoe. Wearing the socks over the shoes, go on a walk through a grassy area or field—particularly one that is abundant in seed-bearing plants. (Masking tape over the foot or around the leg sometimes has more sticking power!) OPTIONAL FOR OLDER STUDENTS: Different students walk in different locations. Contrast seeds found in each location. Create an "environmental map." What ecosystem differences exist in the neighborhood, city, etc?

2. After walking through the area, look carefully at the socks. What has happened? Discuss briefly the seeds and other things that are attached to the socks. If the distance is not too great back to the classroom, the students should keep their socks on their feet until they return. If the distance is too great—they may lose too many of their seeds along the way! NOTE: Wildlife drops seeds too—that's one way they get dispersed!

3. The students should carefully remove their socks. They've gathered their "data"—seeds and other things attached to their socks. Removing the seeds and other particles from the socks—they should examine what they've brought back. Talk with the students about the major kinds of things they seem to have—like seeds, grass, small bits of twigs. Next, discuss the seeds in more detail, talking about the different kinds of seeds they have found: round, skinny, big, small, etc.

4. Each student should record—with words and small drawings—the kinds of things on the sock. Tally the **number** of each kind of thing on a sock as well.

5. Ask the students how different animals' fur might be similar to their socks. Has anyone ever brushed seeds, stickers, and things out of a dog's or cat's fur? Talk with the students about how, so often in nature, seeds are carried by animals almost like the way they carried seeds and things on their socks. Seeds may stick to an animal's fur in one location, and fall off in another. Discuss why such a process is an important one. Evaluate the consequences. How does wildlife contribute to environmental diversity.

6. OPTIONAL: Each student can plant his or her seeds in one of the shoe boxes filled with planting medium (soil or a commercial mix). Be sure the students put their names on their boxes. Water and care for the shoe-box gardens regularly—and see what grows! NOTE: Many wild plant seeds require freezing before they will germinate. If there is a question, put some seeds in ice cube trays and freeze them for several days. **Then** plant them. Even after freezing, some seeds may not sprout. Some seeds require scarring, scorching by fire, or digesting before they will grow. Also, some seeds are not viable and will not germinate or sprout.

EXTENSIONS

1. As the seeds in the boxes begin to sprout, measure the plants that grow. Take measurements every fifth day, and plot these measurements on a graph. (Primary students can use strips of paper for measurement and use those strips to make an individual bar graph. Intermediate students can measure their plants with a metric ruler and plot their measurements on a line graph.)

2. Try similar experiments at home, using seeds you find on your own or a neighborhood pet. If you actually get the plants to grow, you can try to match the plants you grow at home from the "pet-carried" seeds to the plants growing outside. Try to figure out how far the seeds might have traveled on the animal!

EVALUATION

1. Draw three different seeds that could be transported on the fur of an animal. Draw an arrow to show the part of the seed that makes this possible.

2. How are fur-bearing animals important to the types of plants that produce these seeds? Write a paragraph to explain.

3. Pick from a selection of sewing materials to demonstrate how seeds can attach to animal fur. (Buttons can represent the seeds. Attachment materials could include scraps of Velcro, string, rubber cement and safety pins. Describe the characteristics of the kinds of wildlife that might disperse seeds in this fashion.

ENVIRONMENTAL BAROMETER

OBJECTIVES
Students will: 1) observe and count wildlife in an area; 2) discuss why the wildlife is or is not present; and 3) consider ways in which the presence of wildlife can be seen as an indicator of environmental quality.

METHOD
Students go outside to observe and count or estimate wildlife in an area; do the same in another setting to compare findings; and—optionally—make a school "environmental barometer."

BACKGROUND
Some species of animals are more adapted to difficult conditions than others. Some, in contrast, are so specialized that it is quite difficult for them to find the food, water, shelter and other things they need.

Wildlife serves as an important indicator of the overall health of an area of the environment. If there are few wild animals—or little evidence of wildlife—present in an area, it is likely that there is little available food, water, or shelter in the area as well. There may not be enough space.

Even if these necessary components of habitat are available, they may not be suitably arranged to meet the needs of wildlife. The kinds of wildlife present are also important indicators. Birds of prey, for example, are high on the food chain. If they are present in an area, that is an indicator that there is some variety of

other animals and plants in the area.

The major purpose of this activity is for students to consider the importance of wildlife as an indicator of environmental quality.

MATERIALS
writing materials; poster board or construction paper; marking pens or crayons

PROCEDURE
1. Discuss the diversity of wildlife. Make sure students understand that the term wildlife includes insects, spiders and other invertebrates, as well as birds, fish, reptiles, mammals and amphibians.
2. Go outside with your students on the school grounds to do a wildlife count. Each student should work alone and have writing materials. Ask each student to find a spot, sit quietly for ten minutes, and observe. (Quiet is very important to increase the likelihood of seeing wildlife.) The students should record the kinds and numbers of any wildlife they see. They can include **evidence** of wildlife, in addition to actual sightings. Ask the students to total the number of each kind of wildlife they observe plus make a grand total. If they find evidence rather than sighting wildlife, they should estimate the numbers. Put all the students' information on one master chart.
3. Next, take the students to a setting where wildlife is more abundant. Repeat the process—with each student observing quietly for ten minutes and recording observations.
4. Make a master chart of the information from this second environment.
5. Compare the information from the two charts. Was there any difference in the two settings? Why or why not? Which environment seemed to have the most **different kinds** of wildlife? Where were there the most of any one kind of wildlife, like the most birds? What kinds of food, water, shelter and space were in each setting to support the survival needs of wildlife? If there were few animals, or many, in either setting—what might this tell us about the quality of

Age: Grades 3-5
Subjects: Science, Math, Social Studies
Skills: analysis, classification, comparing similarities and differences, computation, discussion, evaluation, observation, synthesis
Duration: two 30 to 45-minute periods
Group Size: any
Setting: outdoors and indoors
Conceptual Framework Reference: I.A., I.B., I.C., I.C.1., I.C.2., I.C.3., I.D., II.B., II.B.1., II.B.2., II.B.3., II.B.4., IV.C., IV.D.4., IV.D.5.
Key Vocabulary: evidence, wildlife, environmental quality, habitat, barometer
Appendices: Outdoors, Field Ethics, Taking Action

the environment? What is environmental quality? Can wildlife be an indicator of environmental quality? Talk about whether it is realistic for every environment to be a good habitat for varieties of wildlife. Discuss the possibility and appropriateness of making efforts to improve environments as habitats for wildlife and homes for people too.

NOTE TO TEACHER: Several possibilities may arise when doing this activity with your students. Your school may be in an area where there are few, if any, wild animals present—with little access to any other area with much wildlife. If there is no significant difference between your observations in the two settings, you can still talk with the students about what this means. It is also possible that your school is in a wildlife-rich setting—virtually as rich as any other setting in the area. Again, it is all right if there is no significant difference in the number and variety of wildlife observed in each area. **You may also choose to make the observations and create the information charts only for one setting, simply analyzing and discussing the quality of the one environment—without using another for comparison.**

EXTENSION

Make an environmental barometer to indicate the quality of your school environment as a habitat for wildlife. Share your barometer with other classes. OPTIONAL: Show seasonal changes in the barometer's readings.

AQUATIC EXTENSIONS

1. Make observations concerning the availability, apparent quality and suitability for wildlife needs of the water you find in each of the habitats you investigate. Is there more wildlife apparent in those areas where there is more water? If yes, what seem to be the contributing factors? If no, what seem to be the contributing factors?

2. Make an "environmental barometer" comparing the quality of two different aquatic habitats as places in which a diversity of wildlife can successfully live. Explain the reasons for the differences in the two areas.

EVALUATION

1. Each year, thousands of birdwatchers participate in a National Audubon Society bird count all over the United States. The information is kept and compared from year to year to see if changes occur in the total number of birds or in how many different kinds of birds are sighted. If a steady and long decrease in the bird populations occurred over a period of five years, should **everyone** be concerned—and not just the birdwatchers? Explain your response.

2. Make a list of things we do in cities and towns that tend to **decrease** the amount and kinds of wildlife that lives there. Make a list of things we sometimes do in cities and towns that tend to **increase** the amounts of some kinds of wildlife.

3. Identify and describe three things that people could do to increase the numbers and kinds of wildlife living in an area that has little evidence of wildlife.

MAKE A COAT!

OBJECTIVES
Students will: 1) identify that some historical and present-day sources of clothing are plants and animals; 2) collect and analyze data to infer the sources of most materials used in clothing today; and 3) distinguish between some examples of renewable and nonrenewable natural resources. (All three objectives are appropriate for upper elementary grades; kindergarteners and 1st grade students may only accomplish the first objective.)

METHOD
Students make replicas of coats using different materials and representing varying historical periods.

BACKGROUND
NOTE: "What You Wear Is What They Were" is a similar activity for older students.

In all but the most tropical of climates, people need an outside covering to keep warm. When ice floes receded after the last Ice Age about 10,000 years ago on the North American continent, people used fire for part of their warmth. Skins from wild animals were also used. Saber tooth tigers, bears, woolly mammoths and wolves were among the animals hunted for meat and clothing.

Age: Grades K-6 (Grades 2-4 recommended)
Subjects: Social Studies (History, Geography, Anthropology), Science, Art, Language Arts, Home Economics, Math (if measuring is involved)
Skills: analysis, classification, description, discussion, evaluation, invention, media construction, observation, psychomotor skills (cutting, sewing), synthesis
Duration: 45 minutes; 60 minutes possible (two 30-minute periods) for older students
Group Size: small groups; up to total of 20-30 students
Setting: indoors
Conceptual Framework Reference: II.A., II.B., II.C., II.D., II.D.2., II.D.4., II.E., II.F., IV.B., IV.B.1., IV.B.2., IV.D., V.A.1., V.A.2., V.A.3., V.A.5., V.B.1., VI.B., VI.B.1., VI.B.2., VI.C., VI.C.2., VI.C.12., VI.C.16., VI.D., VI.D.2., VI.D.3., VII.A., VII.A.1., VII.A.4., VII.B., VII.B.2., VII.B.3., VII.B.4., VII.B.5., VII.B.7.
Key Vocabulary: clothing, renewable resource, nonrenewable resource
Appendices: None

American Indian tribes have used animals for food and covering, and some still do as a part of their present lifestyle. Elk, deer, bear, buffalo, seal and almost all animals killed for food also provided valuable skins for clothing.

When European settlers came to the North American continent, they brought with them a tradition of making clothing out of spun fibers such as linen and wool.

Today we have coats and other clothing made from many materials. We can divide the sources of these materials into two categories: **renewable and nonrenewable natural resources.** Definitions of renewable and nonrenewable natural resources are commonly used within the natural sciences. Use of these terms is intended to describe inherent biological attributes, not to imply value judgments.

Renewable natural resources are living things, with the capacity for regeneration. Trees and wildlife are examples of renewable natural resources. However, even renewable resources have limits. For example, although animals have the capacity for regeneration by mating and bearing offspring, they cannot do this if their habitat is destroyed, or if environmental or human-caused pressures are too great to permit successful reproduction.

Nonrenewable natural resources are non-living things. Minerals and fossils are examples of nonrenewable natural resources. Although such resources may be replenished over time by natural processes, the time span is enormously long. It is, for example, in the case of accumulations of fossils from which to derive products such as petroleum.

Cotton (from the cotton plant) and linen (from the flax plant) are two major clothing products derived from renewable natural resources—in this case, both from plants. Some clothing products come from animals. Wool, for example, comes from shearing the fleece off sheep and does not require killing the animal. Other domesticated animals, like cattle, provide clothing products, such as leather and also provide food products. Geese and ducks provide feathers for down jackets.

In scientific terms, animals can be considered a renewable resource. In some cases, however, animal populations are endangered or threatened. In such cases, killing of these animals is forbidden by law. It is also illegal to hunt many animals that are not threatened. Of those animals that are hunted, they are hunted only under laws and regulations. Some people raise ethical questions as to the appropriateness of the use of animals, particularly wild ones, for products such as clothing, food, tools, medicines, cosmetics, jewelry and other ornaments.

Most synthetic clothing materials are derived from nonrenewable natural resources, such as fossil-based petroleum products. Some people raise ethical questions as to the appropriateness of the use of nonrenewable resources such as fossil fuels, in consideration of questions such as their essentially finite availability as well as costs to humans, wildlife, and the environment often derived from their mining and processing.

There are many aspects, aside from whether or not a resource is renewable, which are considerations in evaluating whether or not to use a particular material for clothing. For example, some materials (e.g., cowhide, petroleum-based synthetics) are derived as byproducts from the development of resources for other, primary purposes (e.g., food, energy). Other sources (e.g., furs) tend to be developed primarily or solely for manufacture of clothing. In addition, nonrenewable resources, such as fossil fuels, are used in obtaining, manufacturing and distributing clothes made from renewable as well as nonrenewable natural resources.

The pros and cons of appropriate uses of renewable and nonrenewable natural resources are difficult and complex—and may raise social, economic, ethical and political as well as biological questions. Even the con-

cept that wildlife and other animals is a renewable resource raises ethical objections from some people who feel it encourages the treatment of wildlife as a commodity to be used like food crops such as corn, without regard for the animals themselves.

The major purpose of this activity is simply for students to be able to identify principal sources of clothing. An additional major purpose for elementary age students in the upper grades is for them to be able to distinguish, in scientific terms, between clothing produced from renewable and nonrenewable natural resources.

MATERIALS

butcher paper or large shopping bags; scissors; paint; crayons; yarn; wool scraps; heavy thread and needle

PROCEDURE

1. Tell your students they are going to be making coats for themselves, but first, explore what coats are made of and why we need them. Have students answer this question: "On cold days, we wear coats. Where do we get them?" Most students will say, "At a store." Some will say that someone at home made it for them, or it was a gift. If made at home, it will usually be from purchased materials. Children from families who hunt or raise sheep for wool may have coats made from animal materials. "How would you keep warm in a cold climate if you couldn't buy a coat at a store—or if someone in your family or neighborhoods couldn't buy the materials to make a coat? NOTE: If your students are from families who make their own clothes directly from plant and animal materials, change the question to: "...If we couldn't make our clothes, . . .?"

2. Divide the students into groups of three or four. Assign, or have them choose, different historical periods and places in which to live.

3. Have each group make a coat. Cut a pattern out of butcher paper. Color and paint it to resemble a fur coat, a down parka, or some other kind of coat typical to their historical period. Use a simple pattern for all the coats. For example:

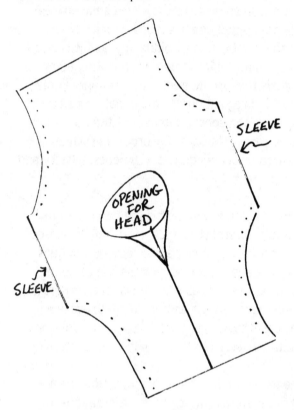

OR, use a shopping bag. Cut neck and sleeve holes. If time and materials permit, each student could make a coat. Students can sew the seams with carpet or quilting thread and a crewel embroidery needle.

4. Have a fashion show, or display the coats in the classroom. Ask the students to identify their coats, indicating the time period and place represented, and the materials used. Older students should be able to distinguish whether the materials are from renewable or nonrenewable natural resources.

EXTENSIONS AND VARIATIONS FOR OLDER STUDENTS

1. Divide the renewable resources into plants and animals. Then divide the animal-derived resources into those that require the killing of animals versus those that do not. Talk about under what conditions, if any, **it seems appropriate** to kill animals to get products for human use, like clothing. Talk about under what conditions, if any, **it does not seem appropriate** to kill animals to get products for human use, like clothing.

2. Talk about your reasons for designing your coats as you did, and out of the particular materials you chose. For warmth? Because of the availability of the materials? For convenience? For practicality? Because of the expense of the materials? For fashion? Because you like the looks or feel? For moral or ethical reasons? Because it seemed a wise choice, etc.?

3. Discuss the costs to wildlife of each of the following materials used for clothing: cotton, orlon, vinyl, wool, fur, silk, leather, nylon, rubber, polyester, paper, plastic, acrylic. Under what conditions? Costs to individual animals? Costs to populations of animals? Costs to habitats? Costs to ecosystems? Other costs?

4. Establish your own personal standards for choices in clothing. Identify the basis for your criteria.

5. Determine what natural resources were used to make the clothing that you are wearing. Consider the environmental consequences of each step in the production and transportation of your clothing. What impacts do different coat materials make on wildlife and the environment?

EVALUATION

Grades K-3 Where did the American Indians and early pioneers get the materials to make their clothing? Draw pictures to show how they made clothing.

Grades 2-6 Identify which of these materials are from renewable resources and which are from nonrenewable resources: plastic, wool, silk, polyester, paper, linen, cotton, leather, acrylic, rubber, fur, nylon?

Grades 4-6 List four renewable and four nonrenewable materials that are used to make clothing today. Describe three ways we make clothing differently today than during pioneer days. What do you think are likely some of the reasons American Indians have used furs in the past and some Alaskan Indians do today? What do you think are some of the reasons that most other people do not use furs in their clothing today?

DRAWING ON NATURE

OBJECTIVES
Students will generalize that wildlife and other animals are important inspiration for art and science.

METHOD
Students use techniques of observation and visualization to record wildlife by drawing.

BACKGROUND
Some significant breakthroughs have been made in recent years with respect to teaching drawing to young people and adults. Betty Edward's *Drawing on the Right Side of the Brain* and Robert McKim's *Experiences in Visual Thinking* are classics in this area, filled with actual instructional activities for use by oneself or with others.

Much of our understanding of science comes from interpreting visual images. The language of science is precise. The images that accompany scientific writing can enhance our knowledge of a subject and add more precision to our perception. Drawings that accompany field notes offer researchers several paths through which to interpret their experiences. The subject is the same, but the information is different. Incorporating drawing into research improves one's observation skills. Good science requires keen observation skills.

Wildlife has been an inspiration for artwork of varying kinds throughout human history. Skills for observation of wildlife are also important to the poet and scientist.

Age: Grades 7-12
Subjects: Science, Art, Social Studies, Language Arts
Skills: application, observation, drawing (visual-spatial skills, motor development), discussion, generalization, invention, kinesthetic concept development, media construction, synthesis, visualization
Duration: one 45-minute period
Group Size: any; individual student project
Setting: outdoors
Conceptual Framework Reference: II.A., II.A.1., II.A.2., II.A.3., II.A.4., II.B., II.B.3., II.B.4., II.E., II.E.3., II.F., IV.D.2., IV.E., V.A.4.
Key Vocabulary: observation, visualization, inspiration, art, science
Appendices: Outdoors, Field Ethics

The major purpose of this activity is for students to recognize the value of wildlife as an inspiration for art and science as well as to develop personal skills.

MATERIALS
drawing materials

PROCEDURE
1. This activity is best done in an outdoor setting and requires students to be able to observe an animal, preferably wildlife.
2. Tell students that they are going to be able to try their drawing skills. After the groans which may follow—since so many people are sure they can't draw at all—insist that you're serious. Encourage them not to worry about drawing but simply to enjoy this activity as a process of observing and recording wildlife.
3. Provide each student with drawing materials. See "Wild Words" to use personal journals for this activity.
4. Take the students to a park, wooded area, natural desert or even an area of the school grounds—if there is some chance they can each see an animal at the site. More than one student may see the same animal. If sites are limited, the wildlife may be a line of ants, a cricket or grasshopper. If you can't find animals outside in a natural setting, then do the best you can—perhaps by going to a zoo or using an aquarium at school. You're looking for the animals in some kind of habitat. (Once the students are familiar with the technique, animals at home can provide opportunities to practice.)
5. Give the students their instructions:
    * Find an animal. Watch the animal as closely as you can. Look at its color, form and body shape as if it were an outline against the sky.
    * Close your eyes and try to reconstruct the animal in your mind. See its color, body shape, etc., again in your mind. Remember—this time your eyes are closed.
    * If, when you open your eyes, that animal is gone—find another animal and start over. Find an animal. Watch the animal as closely as you can, etc.

- After you've watched it very closely, paying particular attention to the shape of its body as if it were against the sky in an outline, close your eyes again and see the animal in your mind as clearly as you can.
- Now, try to draw just the body shape of the animal. Draw the outline of the animal as you would see it if it were surrounded by sky. Draw that outline of the animal's body on your sketching paper. Sometimes it helps to look at the animal—and not at the paper—when you are drawing the animal's outline.
- Now that you've got the body outlined, that's the hardest part! Now fill in some of the body parts, still working more on outlining shapes than in filling in any details.
- Now fill in some of the details of the animal's surroundings—still first closing your eyes to see the shape clearly before you outline it on your paper. You might outline the limb of a tree for a bird or the horizon line for an ant!
- Now fill in as many details as you like. Your drawings may remain a pencil sketch, or you may use a felt-tip black pen for a pencil-and-ink impression, or you could use chalks or crayons to add color.

NOTE TO TEACHER: Try to be supportive and encouraging of each of the students in this process, without being too evaluative and judgmental. A number of the students who have never been able to draw anything with any feeling of success will experience some real delight with this activity. All of the students should be able to come up with something on paper they can be proud of. Encourage the students to keep using this technique—keeping a journal of words and images, for example.

6. Once their work is completed, talk with the students about what happened while they were working on their projects—what they saw, how they felt, etc. Talk with them also about the importance of wildlife and all of nature as a source of inspiration for varying forms of art and science.

AQUATIC EXTENSIONS

1. Use these techniques for enhancing observations of aquatic wildlife and habitat. Include drawings of aquatic organisms in your own "Field Guide to Our School's Aquatic Wildlife" or "Field Guide to Our Community's Aquatic Wildlife."

2. If you have an aquarium, or can visit one, use these techniques to record your observations visually!

3. At an aquarium, pick one feature of aquatic organisms to investigate. Make drawings of this feature in several different organisms. For example, try features used for locomotion in underwater animals!

EVALUATION

A group of people were discussing endangered plants and animals—that is, those that are very close to becoming extinct. Some of the people felt that we should preserve and protect all kinds of plants and animals because we might learn that they could be very useful to us for chemicals, medicine, food and clothing, or that they are a necessary part of our ecosystem. Other people said that we did not need all those plants and animals and we should not worry about losing them. Suppose you are an artist in the group and you want to express your opinion about preserving plants and animals. What will you say?

PHOTOS KEEP IT HAPPENING!

OBJECTIVES
Students will interpret the importance of wildlife as an inspiration for art.

METHOD
Students create photo or other visual studies of wild or domesticated animals, symbolic of their historical and contemporary influence on human cultures.

BACKGROUND
Human relationships to wildlife are often expressed through painting, sculpture, music, drama, dance, literature, photography and other means of creative expression. Wild, as well as domesticated animals, have served as an inspiration for art throughout human history. The importance of wild and domesticated animals to the development of human cultures is also portrayed through art.

The major purpose of this activity is for students to recognize the value of wildlife as inspiration for art, and to gain insight into the historical and contemporary influence of wildlife on human culture.

> **Age:** Grades 7-12
> **Subjects:** Social Studies, Art (Photography), Science
> **Skills:** inference, observation, media construction (camera work, lab work, artistic display), invention, problem-solving, synthesis
> **Duration:** minimum of three 45-minute periods; less if lab work is not involved
> **Group Size:** individual assignment
> **Setting:** outdoors for photography, indoors for lab work and display
> **Conceptual Framework Reference:** II.A., II.A.1., II.A.3., II.A.4., II.E., II.E.1., II.E.3., II.F., V., V.A.1., V.A.2., V.A.3., V.A.4.
> **Key Vocabulary:** art, inspiration, influence, culture
> **Appendices:** Field Ethics, Animals in the Classroom, Local Resources

MATERIALS
camera equipment; 35mm cameras are desirable, if possible, because of their professional quality; 400 ASA black and white film is recommended, because of its speed and flexibility; telephoto and macro lens would be useful; other visual media, e.g., drawing materials, magazine photos, may be substituted; video equipment can be substituted for still camera equipment

PROCEDURE
1. This is a "Wildlife's Influence on Human Culture" photography assignment. Encourage your students to select a wild animal for study. Some students may want to consider constructing a "photographer's blind" of some kind for use in observing wild animals outside without disturbing them. Others may find their wildlife in zoos. Remember that wildlife ranges from small to large—houseflies and caterpillars included! Be sure in any case that the students do not disturb the animals they are observing and photographing.
2. The live animal does not actually have to be photographed. For example, students studying lions might photograph a motel that has lion in its name, a sign that tells community members of the existence of a local chapter of the service club of that name, as well as a statue of a lion. The photographs can also be images taken by others and found in magazines and other sources.
3. Recommend that the students aim for a series—five photos, for example—of images of the wildlife, representing various aspects of the animal and its historical or contemporary influence on human culture.
4. If possible, have the students develop and print their images. Ask the photographers to describe their techniques and experiences, including their feelings of the importance of wildlife as an inspiration for art as well as insights they gained into the influence of wildlife on human culture.

5. The mounted photo series can be made an exhibit for others to enjoy!
Note: The photos can be mounted on poster board and "floated" away from the background to give an interesting display.

EXTENSION
Contact your local state wildlife agency, bird watching organization, or similar group to see if they provide talks on wildlife photography. Better yet, participate in an outdoor photography class specializing in wildlife.

EVALUATION
Identify and explain at least three major influences of wildlife on the development of human culture.

WILD EDIBLE PLANTS

OBJECTIVES

Students will: 1) identify at least one native edible plant; and 2) describe the relationship between wild plants and contemporary cultivated plants; that is, that all cultivated plants originally developed from a wild plant source.

METHOD

Students create a local seasonal calendar identifying native edible plants and their uses.

BACKGROUND

People are regaining an interest in and appreciation for native plants. Edible wild plants are gaining increased attention with growing human concern about unhealthy ingredients in many commercially prepared foods—additives, preservatives, artificial ingredients, pesticide residue, etc.

Edible wild plants can grow without the application of commercial fertilizers, pesticides and human labor. They comprise part of the original human foods. Some researchers suggest that some wild edible plants offer benefits not found in many contemporary, cultivated foods. Wild plants are still used today as a food source for some traditional peoples, including some Native American Indians. Present-day botanists and other plant researchers use wild plants as a source of important genetic attributes in order to improve plant strains already developed originally from wild plant sources. Wild plants are still used as a means for developing new food and medicine sources. In fact, with the rapid disappearance of plant and animal species from the planet, many researchers are concerned that those species remaining will be increasingly limited in their capacities to adapt. The genetic pool gets smaller with each species lost. Of course, wild plants are not just used as sources of food and medicine—but as important sources of many other natural materials used by people and animals.

This activity focuses on use of native edible plants as a food source for people. Caution should be taken with this activity. DO NOT PICK ANY WILD EDIBLE PLANTS without a resource person, knowledgeable both about the plant and its characteristics, and knowledgeable about the abundance and reproductive capabilities of the plant in the region. It is essential to know precisely which plants in the area are poisonous. It is also important that any wild plants are used sparingly, taking care not to use the plants so heavily that they cannot successfully reproduce and remain available over time. Make sure the plants are abundant, and not rare, endangered, or threatened. Find out what wild animals may depend either directly or indirectly on any plants you find and consider using; an example of an indirect use is when one species of animal depends for food on the availability of another species of animal which in turn depends on the plant source you have identified as a food source for people. People can pick wild plants and unknowingly impact threatened, rare, or endangered animal species. People and animals can use the same plants. We stress checking the abundance and range of the plants involved, and **emphasize conducting this activity without picking any plants unless proper precautions are taken.**

Local wildlife-related agencies can help with the necessary information about what animals depend on the

---

Age: Grades 7-12
Subjects: Social Studies (History, Geography, Anthropology), Science (Botany, Life Science), Environmental Problems, Language Arts, Art, Home Economics
Skills: analysis, application, classification, comparing similarities and differences, description, discussion, drawing, evaluation, media construction, research, synthesis, visualization, writing
Duration: minimum of two 45-minute periods
Group Size: any
Setting: indoors, outdoors if possible for field research
Conceptual Framework Reference: I.A.3., III.A.2., III.B., III.B.1., III.B.2., III.B.4., V.A., V.A.1., V.A.2., V.A.3., VI.A., VI.A.2., VI.A.3., VI.A.4., VI.A.5., VI.B., VI.D., VI.D.1., VII.A., VII.A.1., VII.A.2., VII.A.3., VII.A.4., VII.B., VII.B.1., VII.B.2., VII.B.3., VII.B.4., VII.B.7.
Key Vocabulary: wild, native, edible
Appendices: Local Resources, Field Ethics, Outdoors

plants you identify as potential human food sources; native plant societies are an important and useful source of information about which plants are edible for humans. Both agencies should be contacted for information about range and quantity of plants involved.

The major purpose of this activity is to introduce students to edible wild plants as a food source, making the connection that all cultivated plants originally derived from wild plants.

MATERIALS

poster-making materials; reference materials on wild edible plants
OPTIONAL: access to area with wild and edible plants

PROCEDURE

1. Ask students, alone or in small groups, to make a poster-sized seasonal calendar depicting: Winter, Spring, Summer, Fall.
2. Ask the students to prepare a list of some of the local wild plant species that can be used for food purposes by people, according to the season in which the plant is available. Local resource people and/or materials will be essential in this process.
3. The students next sketch (or include photos) and label the plants on the calendar according to the season in which it is or can be harvested for human use. Some plants may be used in more than one season. Additional information to be included with the identification of the plant on the calendar: its approximate location; which portion of the plant is used and for what purposes (CAUTION if any portion of the plant is poisonous); what animals—if any—also use the plant, and for what purposes (Note if any animals are threatened, rare, or endangered); what contemporary cultivated plants derived from this or a similar source, if any; and for what contemporary purposes the plant or its cultivated counterpart is used, e.g. food, medicine, fiber.
4. Discuss the findings. Talk about the usefulness and importance of wild and edible plants, to both people and wildlife. NOTE: Although the activity does not require it, its effectiveness is enhanced if the students are able to take a field trip to identify those plants in the wild!

EXTENSIONS

1. Prepare a Wild Edible Plants Book for your area—including hints as to where the plants usually may be found, necessary cautions in order to protect the available supply for future generations of people and animals, characteristics of the plants, information about what animals use them and for what purposes, and even recipes for people's use of the plants as a food source!
2. Identify traditional uses, e.g., by Native American Indian people in your area, of native plants and animals. Are plants and animals still available for historic uses? Why or why not?
3. Trace contemporary foods that have been derived from wild plants and animals.
4. Cultural conflicts may take place today as people with differing cultural traditions value plants and animals for different purposes. Investigate contemporary differences of opinion about appropriate uses of plants and animals, e.g., for food.
5. Study practices of traditional hunting and gathering societies. Contrast those practices with those of early farmers, with present day family farmers, with contemporary agribusiness. In each case, how was or is the continued availability of the food source provided for?
6. Check local stores to see what, if any, products make use of wild and native plants in their ingredients. If you find some, try to find out what regulations protect the commercial harvest of these plants, if any. How are regulations affecting these plants enforced?

EVALUATION

1. Identify three kinds of cultivated plants we can buy in a store that were originally wild plants, and identify the wild plants from which they were developed.
2. Name one native wild plant in your area, and describe its characteristics, history, and uses over time.
3. Other than food, describe two important uses of wild plants.
4. How could the loss of plant species through extinction be a loss for humans?
5. Describe three precautions that should be taken if selecting and collecting wild plants for any purpose.

WILDLIFE AS SEEN ON COINS AND STAMPS

OBJECTIVE

Students will describe coins and stamps as examples of ways that people have used symbols to represent values of wildlife.

METHOD

Students use reference materials to study portrayal of wildlife in coins and stamps.

BACKGROUND

People of various cultures have used images of wildlife on their coins, other currency, and stamps. The images may represent real or imagined species. In any case, use of wildlife symbols represents recognition of some human values.

Coins and stamp with animal images have been issued by many countries. Ancient Rome issued coins with wolves. China has issued coins with dragons (an interpretation of wildlife). Canada, Australia, and the Bahamas all have offered extensive issues of wildlife coins that can be obtained at face value.

The major purpose of this activity is for students to recognize that wildlife has value for people in a range of ways, reflected symbolically in the use of wildlife images on coins and stamps.

Age: Grades 7-12
Subjects: Social Studies (Geography, Anthropology, World History)
Skills: analysis, classification, comparing similarities and differences, discussion, generalization, inference, observation, reading, research, writing
Duration: 45 minutes or longer
Group Size: any
Setting: indoors
Conceptual Framework Reference: II.A., II.A.1., II.A.2., II.A.3., II.A.4., II.C., V., V.A.4., V.B.1., V.B.2., V.B.3.
Key Vocabulary: symbol, value, culture
Appendices: Local Resources

MATERIALS

reference materials

PROCEDURE

1. Students can either visit a library and conduct their own research, or the teacher can provide resource materials and establish a classroom learning center. The students can search reference materials for examples of coins and stamps with wildlife images. Encyclopedias often show pictures of coins, other currency, and stamps used in nations. Coin collectors' catalogs and journals are also good sources of images.

2. Students can make copies of images they find by reproducing or sketching them, making sure to identify the country of origin and value of the coin or stamp.

3. Next, students organize the coin and stamp images according to some characteristics. For example:
   - according to the kinds of animals pictured
   - according to whether the animal is real or imagined, abundant or threatened/endangered/extinct
   - animals pictured once, two to five times, many times
   - animals found in the U.S., contrasted with those not found in the U.S.
   - animals shown on coins or stamps from two or more countries
   - animals shown in their habitat
   - unusual animals
   - animals used to represent power or military strength
   - animals shown realistically

4. Discuss with the students why wildlife has been used so often as a part of currency and stamps. Wildlife has historical and present-day value for people in many ways (as sources of food, clothing, other products, inspiration, recreation; as contributors to healthy ecosystems; as representation of virtues, fears, etc.). Many of these values are represented in symbolic form on stamps and currency.

EXTENSIONS

1. Make a world map, showing the countries that use wildlife in their coins and stamps. Look for regional similarities and differences. Analyze the wildlife images. Are there regional trends?

2. Compare the public attitude toward wildlife in different countries and parts of the world. What nations are active in world-wide conservation efforts? Why might these nations be involved and others not?

EVALUATION

1. For each of the following emotions and values, list as many animals as you can which have been used on coins to express that emotion or value; love, power or strength, beauty or grace, fear, pride, freedom.

2. List the range of purposes for which it appears wildlife has been portrayed in coins and stamps.

WILDLIFE BIBLIOGRAPHY

OBJECTIVES

Students will: 1) give examples of ways in which wildlife has influenced the development of human societies; and 2) describe wildlife as having important social and political value for people.

METHOD

Students research and construct annotated bibliographies.

BACKGROUND

The development of human societies has been affected by wildlife. Throughout history, human populations in varying degrees have been dependent upon wild animals as a source of food, clothing, shelter and utensils.

Since the days of earliest humans, it might be argued that human society has affected the development, movement and size of wildlife populations, rather than the reverse; however, there are examples throughout human history and through the present where human populations have followed, been influenced by, and were or are dependent upon wildlife populations.

People have, and continue at times to, come into conflict over wildlife. Explorers and immigrants to North America came into conflict with native peoples over hunting grounds and fishing waters. Treaties and alliances between Native American Indian nations and between representatives of European nations, for example, sometimes were formed and shifted in struggles over wildlife resources. Some disputes continue today.

The major purpose of this activity is for students to recognize that wildlife has social, historical and political value in the lives of human beings.

MATERIALS

writing materials; access to library resources

PROCEDURE

1. Begin a discussion with students about ways in which wildlife has influenced the development of human societies. For example, the abundance of wildlife as a source of food and other products influenced the selection of sites for early human communities. Encourage the students to think specifically about the early development of the North American continent, with other areas of the world addressed optionally. Brainstorm ideas.

2. After discussion, refine the list of brainstormed topics into a smaller list of general topics which could be researched. Include these, as well as other topics you find useful:
   - historical influence of the availability of wildlife on the size and location of human communities
   - examples of issues and conflicts related to wildlife, historically and in the present
   - treaties and alliances within and between people and nations involving wildlife
   - creative portrayal of wildlife through art, literature, dance, music and drama as historic as well as contemporary means of expressing human relationships with wildlife

Age: Grades 7-12
Subjects: Social Studies (American History, World History, Geography), Language Arts
Skills: analysis, classification, comparing similarities and differences, discussion, listing, reading, research, small group work, synthesis, writing
Duration: two class periods, two homework periods
Group Size: any
Setting: indoors
Conceptual Framework Reference: II.A., II.B., II.C., II.C.1., II.C.2., II.C.3., II.D., II.D.2., II.D.3., II.D.4., II.E., II.F., V.A., V.A.1., V.A.2., V.A.3., V.A.4., V.A.5., V.A.6., V.B., V.B.1., V.B.2., V.B.3., VI.B., VI.B.1., VI.B.6., VI.C., VI.C.3., VI.C.4., VI.C.6., VII.B.3., VII.B.5., VII.B.6.
Key Vocabulary: society, historical, development, value
Appendices: Local Resources

3. Ask each student to select one of the research areas. After selecting an area to learn more about, each student will need access to a library or other source of resource and reference materials. Ask each student to identify from three to six resources for the research topic, to briefly describe the contents of each resource, and to include one interesting quotation from each resource. Using a bibliographic format you establish, ask each student to submit an annotated bibliography of resources for his or her research topic, including the author, title, publisher, copyright date, identification of kind of document (book, article, film, etc.), the brief description and the quotation.

4. Conclude with a class discussion of the students' findings. Ask the students to summarize key relationships between the development of human societies and wildlife, as well as to describe major social and political values to humans from wildlife resources. If possible, compile a master bibliography for each of the students to have, based on the total of their individual contributions.

EVALUATION

1. Write an essay describing the historical and present importance of wildlife.

2. Create an annotated bibliography of at least two sources that explore a problem related to wildlife, your state and a neighboring state.

SECTION THREE
ECOLOGICAL PRINCIPLES

WHAT BEAR GOES WHERE?

OBJECTIVES

Students will: 1) identify three species of bears and their habitats; and 2) generalize that animals are adapted in order to live where they do.

METHOD

Students construct posters of three different bear habitats.

BACKGROUND

Polar bears have long necks, slender heads and white fur. They live along the arctic coasts, mostly on the polar ice. They feed mainly on fish and seals. Their thick fur keeps them warm and the webbing between their toes makes them good swimmers. Grizzly bears dig up most of their food so they have long claws. They also have a distinctive hump between their shoulders. They eat roots, tubers, gophers, marmots and smaller rodents as well as carrion. They occasionally kill a larger animal for food. Grizzlies tend to live in the edges of forests but feed mostly in mountain meadows. They have wide heads and a "dished" face. Black bears are quiet, shy animals that live in a variety of habitats from forests to brush or chaparral. They eat mostly nuts, berries and fruit. They also eat rodents, insects and occasionally kill larger animals for food. The black bear may be black, auburn or cinnamon. Black bears are smaller than grizzlies or polar bears and have more pointed heads.

Age: Grades K-3
Subjects: Science, Art
Skills: analysis, application, classification, comparing similarities and differences, description, discussion, generalization, listing, media construction, observation, psychomotor development, synthesis
Duration: 30 minutes
Group Size: three groups of three to six students each; increase groups as necessary for class size
Setting: indoors
Conceptual Framework Reference: I.C.1., I.C.2., III.A., III.A.1., III.A.3., III.D., III.D.1., III.D.2.
Key Vocabulary: alike, different, adapt, survive, habitat
Appendices: None

The major purpose of this activity is for students to recognize that animals are adapted to live in different environments, based on the example of three different kinds of bears.

MATERIALS

pictures of the three bear species; three sheets of butcher paper with the outline of one bear species on each, labeled; construction paper; pencils; scissors; glue

PROCEDURE

1. Show the students pictures of the three different kinds (species) of bears. Ask them to talk about the things that are alike and are different about the bears.
2. Ask the students to imagine the place where each bear lives. Talk about what is alike and what is different about where the bears live. Think about how each bear looks and whether that helps it to live where it lives. Talk about "adaptation." Animals are "adapted" to survive.
3. Take out three large sheets of paper on which you have drawn the outline of one species of bear in the center of each sheet and labeled it accordingly. (A photo of each bear will serve just as well.)
NOTE: The outlines of each bear can be projected onto a chalkboard or a large piece of paper taped to a wall. Adjust the projected image until the bear's shoulder height is life size. The bear's outline can then be drawn to life size by tracing the projected image.
4. Divide the students into three groups. Give each group one of the sheets of paper with the outline of a bear species and a supply of construction paper, pencils and scissors.
5. Have each group draw and cut out elements of the habitat of their bear (trees, grassy meadows and rocks for the grizzly; blocks of ice, snow, fish and seals for the polar bear; forest trees, bushes, nuts, fruits and berries for the black bear) and glue these elements around the picture of their bear. (Make sure that examples of all major habitat needs are included: food,

water, shelter and space in which to live.)

6. Display the finished posters and ask the students what they have learned about bears and where they live. Discuss how each environment has characteristic life forms, adapted to its climate, kinds of available food, etc. Emphasize that all animals are adapted to survive.

AQUATIC EXTENSIONS

1. Look at pictures of three different kinds (species) of fish. Talk about the things that are alike and are different about the fish. Imagine the place where each fish lives. Draw a picture of each fish in a place where you think it could live. Find out if you are right!

2. Find out more about the adaptations of different kinds of fish that make it possible for them to live where and how they do. See the Aquatic WILD activity, "Fashion a Fish."

3. Help make a classroom bulletin board that shows, "What Fish Goes Where?" Show fish that live in ponds, fish that live in lakes, fish that live in streams, fish that live in rivers and fish that live in oceans. Include a picture of the appropriate habitat along with a picture of the fish. See the Aquatic WILD activity, "Fishy Who's Who."

EVALUATION

1. Describe three kinds of bears, what they need for food, where they live and how they look.

2. If someone took polar bears to Yellowstone National Park in Wyoming, and took grizzly bears to the Arctic coast—do you think the bears would be able to live in their new homes if everyone left them alone? Why?

© Pat Oldham '93

GRAPHANANIMAL

OBJECTIVE
Students will identify characteristic life forms in two different environments.

METHOD
Students create picture collections of animals in two different habitats and then "visit" the habitats by going on a "nature walk" in their classroom where they tally the number of animals they see and then graph and compare the results.

BACKGROUND
Different kinds of animals are found in different environments. Each environment is suitable for animals that are adapted to its climate, soils, water, vegetation and other ecological factors. Just as people need food, water, shelter and space in which to live, so does wildlife.

The major purpose of this activity is for students to recognize that each environment has characteristic life forms.

MATERIALS
photos or pictures of animals (from magazines); cardboard for mounting photos; notebook paper; graph paper; pencils.

PROCEDURE
1. Pick two environments in your state, such as the plains and the forest. Ask students to make a collection of animals for each place. They can draw pictures or cut out magazine photos. Each student should find two animals. Glue the pictures onto heavy paper or cardboard.

2. Ask the students to tell where their animals live. Make a pile for each place such as plains and forest and ask the students to put their pictures in the place where their animals live.

3. List the animals in each pile to show the students what kinds of animals live in each place. Some animals will appear on both lists. Ask the students to copy the two lists.

4. When the students are out of the room, place the animal cards in an area of the classroom that can hypothetically serve as the appropriate habitat. Label one part of the classroom as forest and the other as plains. Put the animals where they live. Some animals may be in both environments. Put the animal pictures in all sorts of places—by a table leg, on a window ledge, etc.—to simulate where they might actually live. If possible, check with wildlife officials in your area to see what the actual proportions of animals are in each of the chosen environments and use the animal cards accordingly. These people may also have wildlife pictures for various habitats!

5. Bring the students to the "forest" and the "plains" for a "nature walk." Let the students use their lists to tally the animals they see in each place. At the end of the walk, students should total their counts and write that number on their lists. Have the students take turns walking along the "path." A sample list and tally might look like this:

FOREST		TOTAL	PLAINS		TOTAL
RABBIT	₥₥I	6	COYOTE	₥₥	5
COYOTE	III	3	RATTLESNAKE	III	3
DEER	I	1	PRAIRIE DOG	₥₥ II	7
JAY	III	3	ANTELOPE	II	2

Age: Grades 2-6
Subjects: Science, Math (tally, addition, graph-making and use), Language Arts (word recognition and spelling)
Skills: analysis, classification, computation, kinesthetic concept development, listing, media construction (making and using simple bar graphs), observation, psychomotor development, reading, writing
Duration: two 30-minute periods; one 40-minute period if teacher prepares wildlife pictures
Group Size: 15 to 30 students
Setting: indoors or outdoors
Conceptual Framework Reference: III.A., III.A.1., III.A.3.
Key Vocabulary: environment, habitat, graph (as well as many different animal names)
Appendices: Local Resources

6. Show the students how to make a bar graph for each of the environments:

RABBIT									
COYOTE									
DEER									
JAY									

Give the students graph paper and show them how they can fill in each square for the number of each animal they saw or have them use a computer to compile and portray the data.

7. Using the graphs, compare the two environments. Which animals were seen the most? Which animals were seen the least? How could some animals live in both places? Why can't all the animals live in both places?

VARIATIONS

1. Skip having the students collect the animal pictures. If the teacher collects the photos, the activity may begin with the nature walk.

2. Use the strategies for the nature walk when taking any field trip to areas where real animals can be observed.

AQUATIC EXTENSION

Pick two aquatic habitats, such as lake and river; or pond and stream; or freshwater (lake) and saltwater (ocean). Make a collection of animals for each place. Make or cutout drawings or pictures of aquatic animals for each habitat, putting each animal on a separate card or piece of paper. Mix them all together. See if a friend can sort them out—correctly identifying which animals live in which aquatic habitats. Do any seem to live in both? If yes, which ones? Create a poster display to show the variety of animals that live in each of these two aquatic environments.

EVALUATION

1. Name five animals that might be found in each of the following areas: forest, desert, plains, stream, pond, ocean, seashore, park. (NOTE: Please select two areas common to your state.)

2. Two scientists went to separate parts of the world and studied the animals in each place. They made these graphs showing the kinds and numbers of animals they found. Why did the scientists see different animals? Do you think if the animals in one place were moved to the other place they would survive? Why or why not?

Scientist 1	Number of Animals
Seals	
Whales	
Polar Bears	

Scientist 2	Number of Animals
Lions	
Zebras	
Antelope	
Rhinoceros	
Hippopotamus	

URBAN NATURE SEARCH

OBJECTIVE
Students will generalize that each environment has characteristic life forms.

METHOD
Students go outside to observe an environment and use a questionnaire to assist in gathering data.

BACKGROUND
Every environment has its characteristic life forms—including animals—and the urban setting is no exception.

Many of these life forms have adjusted as their habitat has changed from undeveloped to urban. Not only have people altered the environment, the human environment has been shaped by the characteristics of the ecologies within which people live.

The major purpose of this activity is for students to recognize that all environments have characteristic life forms.

See "Wild Words" for a journal-making activity. Students can use their journals for this "Urban Nature Search."

MATERIALS
questionnaires (designed by the teacher); pencils; notebooks or journals (See "Wild Words"); an outdoor setting to conduct this investigation

Age: Grades 4-9 (and older)
Subjects: Science, Language Arts, Social Studies
Skills: analysis, application, classification, comparing similarities and differences, description, discussion, generalization, kinesthetic concept development, listing, observation, writing
Duration: 45 minutes to one-and-one-half hours
Group Size: any
Setting: outdoors and indoors
Conceptual Framework Reference: I.A.4, I.B., I.B.1., I.B.3., I.C., I.C.1., I.C.2., III.A., III.A.2., III.A.3., III.B., III.B.1., III.B.2., III.D., III.D.1., III.D.2., III.D.3., III.D.4., III.D.5., III.E.2., IV.C., IV.C.1., IV.C.2., IV.C.3., IV.E.5.
Key Vocabulary: investigation, observation, environment
Appendices: Outdoors, Field Ethics

PROCEDURE
1. Preview and select the route of the nature search. Note stopping places where students can observe and record information.
2. Discuss the diversity of wildlife. Make sure students understand that wildlife includes insects, spiders and other invertebrates as well as birds, fish, reptiles, mammals and amphibians. Also establish that students can identify wildlife species without knowing the animal's formal name. For instance, they can differentiate a black bird with a short tail from one with a long tail. As they conduct their urban nature search, students can invent their own names for the plants and animals they see.
3. Design a questionnaire to be distributed to the students for use on the "search." The questions and tasks should encourage increased student observation. For example, many of the following phenomena can be designed into this activity:
   - Tally, describe and sketch different kinds of plants growing on the north and south sides of buildings. (The differences may be due to temperature variations, sun and shade-loving species of plants and less evaporation on the north side of building.)
   - Look for birds. Tally the numbers of different kinds of birds. If they are migratory, sketch the pattern of their flying formation!
   - Look for animals establishing "territory." Try to map the animals' territory. (During the mating season, birds can sometimes be seen choosing mates; males fighting, strutting and dancing around the female species; and nest building.)
   - Look for evidence of predator/prey relationships. If any mammal, bird or insect is seen—attempt to determine what animal is its predator or prey.
   - Record evidence of plant disease and insect damage. It is always interesting to see insect galls or bag worms in their natural setting.
   - Look for evidence of food chains. For example, if insects are observed, look for partially eaten, damaged or mutilated leaves. Then look for who eats the insects. Draw a food chain and identify the parts.

- Try to observe a bee cross-pollinating flowers while gathering nectar for the production of honey. If you're fast, you can observe the specialized organs of the bee, and study them further (from diagrams and photos) back in the classroom.
- Sketch trees and list their contributions to the community. (For example, trees can be observed breaking the velocity or speed of the wind. This can reduce wind erosion and might save energy by reducing the winter heat loss from homes in the surrounding area. Trees also serve as part of the wildlife habitat, increase the oxygen content of the air and have aesthetic value.)
- Who likes lichen? Predict what plants and animals have a direct or indirect relationship with lichens. (Lichens will be found growing on rocks, tree trunks and even on soil. Lichens are really algae and fungi functioning as a partnership in a symbiotic association.)
- Trace water's path in an area—like on one street, around one tree, down a hillside. (For example, draw the route of any visible erosion.) Look for results of freezing and thawing on sidewalks and buildings.
- Find mulches around trees and shrubs. Record any evidence or observation of life forms. (These mulches allow the soil to absorb and retain large amounts of moisture and reduce evaporation. Mulches also reduce temperature extremes and contain earthworms as well as microscopic and other life forms.)
- Look for evidence of components of habitat. Students can observe first-hand the basic wildlife needs. Match animals with their habitat needs (food, water, shelter and space in appropriate arrangement). It can be a real challenge for students to determine if all basic needs can be met in the available habitat. Predict what animals should be able to live in the habitats identified.

4. On the field trip, each student should bring a copy of the questionnaire and a pencil and notebook or journal. Remind students not to disturb or destroy any plants or animals they may see.

5. What characteristic life forms did the students find that were most surprising? Involve the students in a discussion of their observations, their techniques and their conclusions. Encourage the generalization, warranted by the results of their investigation, that each environment has characteristic life forms.

EXTENSION

Chart the characteristic life forms found on the search, according to the environments in which they were found. For each animal listed, identify how its basic needs are met. Describe any animal adaptations that seem well-suited to survival in the urban environment. Note any interdependencies between plants and animals. Discuss ways in which people have altered the natural environment and ways in which natural forces have shaped the human environment.

AQUATIC EXTENSIONS

1. Make a map to show all the public water areas in your community, if any. Streams, ponds, a lake, or river are all possibilities. If there are no such public areas of water in a natural or near-natural environment within your community, look next for water that people have introduced, but which is still accessible to the public. For example, count and map the location of the public water fountains in the community! Next list and tally all the different kinds of wildlife that seem to depend on any single water source you identify. Remember—food, water, shelter and space in a suitable arrangement are the essential components of habitat for any wildlife.

2. Look at urban ponds and lakes in parks. Compare those species living in concrete-bottomed ponds with those living in mud-bottomed ponds. What lives where? Where and how do they get their food?

EVALUATION

1. List and describe ten types of plants you might see around the school.

2. List and describe ten types of animals you might see around the school.

3. Select any four animals you might see around the school—and describe how these animals find food, shelter and water in order to survive in the school community. If these animals were not living around people, how might the ways they meet their needs be changed?

GOOD BUDDIES

OBJECTIVES

Students will: 1) define symbiosis, commensalism, mutualism and parasitism; 2) identify animals that live in each type of symbiotic relationship; and 3) explain that symbiotic relationships are examples of the intricate web of interdependence within which all plants and animals live.

METHOD

Students research pairs of animals, play a card game, and classify the pairs of animals according to three major forms of symbiotic relationship.

BACKGROUND

Elements of any ecological system live in an intricate web of interdependence. When two species of organisms live in close physical contact with each other, their relationship is called "symbiotic." In a symbiotic relationship at least one of the organisms directly benefits from its close association with the other organism. There are three major forms of symbiotic relationships:

Commensalism A relationship in which one species derives food or shelter from another species without seriously harming that organism or providing any benefits in return.

Mutualism A reciprocal relationship in which two different species live in a symbiotic way where both species benefit and are dependent upon the relationship.

Parasitism A relationship between two species in which one species (the parasite) nourishes itself to the detriment of the other species (the host).

Age: Grades 4-7
Subjects: Science, Language Arts
Skills: application, matching pairs, reporting, research
Duration: two 30-minute periods; one 45-minute period if background is provided eliminating student research
Group Size: small groups of five or six each
Setting: indoors
Conceptual Framework Reference: III.B., III.B.1.
Key Vocabulary: symbiosis, commensalism, mutualism, parasitism
Appendices: Ecosystem

The major purpose of this activity is for students to become familiar with the concept of symbiosis as one example of interdependence in ecological systems.

MATERIALS

copies of cards; chalkboard; research materials

PROCEDURE

1. Reproduce several decks of cards. Each deck should contain 15 card pairs showing symbiotic relationships and one "no buddy" card for a total of 31 cards per deck. You may use the card masters provided. Here is additional information.

Animals	Relationship	Comments
barnacle/whale	commensalism	Barnacles create home sites by attaching themselves to whales. This neither harms nor benefits the whales.
remora/shark	commensalism	Remoras attach themselves to a shark's body. They then travel with the shark and feed on the left over food scraps from the shark's meals. This neither harms nor benefits the shark.
bee/maribou stork	commensalism	The stork uses its saw-like bill to cut up the dead animals it eats. As a result, the dead animal carcass is accessible to some bees for food and egg laying.
silverfish/ army ants	commensalism	Silverfish live and hunt with army ants. They share the prey. They neither help nor harm the ants.
hermit crab/ snail shell	commensalism	Hermit crabs live in shells made and then abandoned by snails. This neither harms nor benefits the snails.
cowbird/buffalo	commensalism	As buffalos walk through grass, insects become active and are seen and eaten by cowbirds. This neither harms nor benefits the buffalos.
yucca plant/ yucca moth	mutualism	Yucca flowers are pollinated by yucca moths. The moths lay their eggs in the flowers where the larvae hatch and eat some of the developing seeds. Both species benefit.

2. Pass out a card to each student (do not include the "no buddy" card), and, by means of looking at a posted list on the chalkboard, have each student find his or her "buddy."

3. These pairs of buddies should then research to find out why they are buddies, answering the following questions: Why do we live together? What advantages and disadvantages do we provide one another? What would happen if one of us weren't here?

4. Pairs of buddies then give short reports to the class, telling about their relationship.

5. Divide the class into groups of five to six students each, and give each group a deck of cards. Instruct the students as to how to play the game.

6. Deal out all the cards. Play starts to the left of the dealer and rotates in a clockwise manner. Each player draws one card from the player to his or her left. After the player has drawn a card, that player may lay down all cards in his or her hand which form symbiotic pairs. When a player does not have any cards left in his or her hand, the game is over. The player with the largest number of pairs at the end of the game is the winner. One player is left holding the "no buddy" card at the end of the game.

7. To culminate the activity, discuss the definitions given in the background information for **commensalism, mutualism,** and **parasitism**. Go through the list of symbiotic pairs and, as a group, decide to which classification each pair belongs. "Good buddy" pair members may be called upon to help decide the classification. Stress that symbiotic relationships are just one example of the interdependence of all elements of ecological systems. In a way, as the Northwest Native American Indian Chief Seattle is reported to have said, "We all share the same breath."

EVALUATION

1. Define: symbiosis, commensalism, mutualism, parasitism.

2. Give two examples of pairs of organisms which have these symbiotic relationships: commensalism, mutualism, parasitism.

3. With a buddy, pantomime each of these three concepts: commensalism, mutualism, parasitism.

4. Explain how cooperation and competition both exist in nature.

Animals	Relationship	Comments
honey guide bird/ badger	mutualism	Honey guide birds alert and direct badgers to bee hives. The badgers then expose the hives and feed on the honey first. Then the honey guide birds eat. Both species benefit.
ostrich/gazelle	mutualism	Ostriches and gazelles feed next to each other. They both watch for predators and alert each other to danger. Since the visual abilities of the two species are different, they each can identify threats the other animal would not as readily see. Both species benefit.
oxpecker/ rhinoceros	mutualism	Oxpeckers feed on the ticks found on a rhinocerous. Both species benefit.
wrasse fish/ black sea bass	mutualism	Wrasse fish feed on the parasites found on the black sea bass's body. Both species benefit.
mistletoe/ spruce tree	parasitism	Mistletoe extracts water and nutrients from the spruce tree to the tree's detriment.
cuckoo/warbler	parasitism	A cuckoo may lay its eggs in a warbler's nest. The cuckoo's young will displace the warbler's young and will be raised by the warbler.
mouse/flea	parasitism	A flea feeds on a mouse's blood to the mouse's detriment.
deer/tick	parasitism	Ticks feed on deer blood to the deer's detriment.

GAZELLE		OSTRICH
CUCKOO		WARBLER
YUCCA		YUCCA MOTH
BARNACLE		WHALE
MISTLETOE		SPRUCE
OXPECKER		RHINO
REMORA		SHARK

MASTER CARDS
FOR GOODBUDDY
ACTIVITY

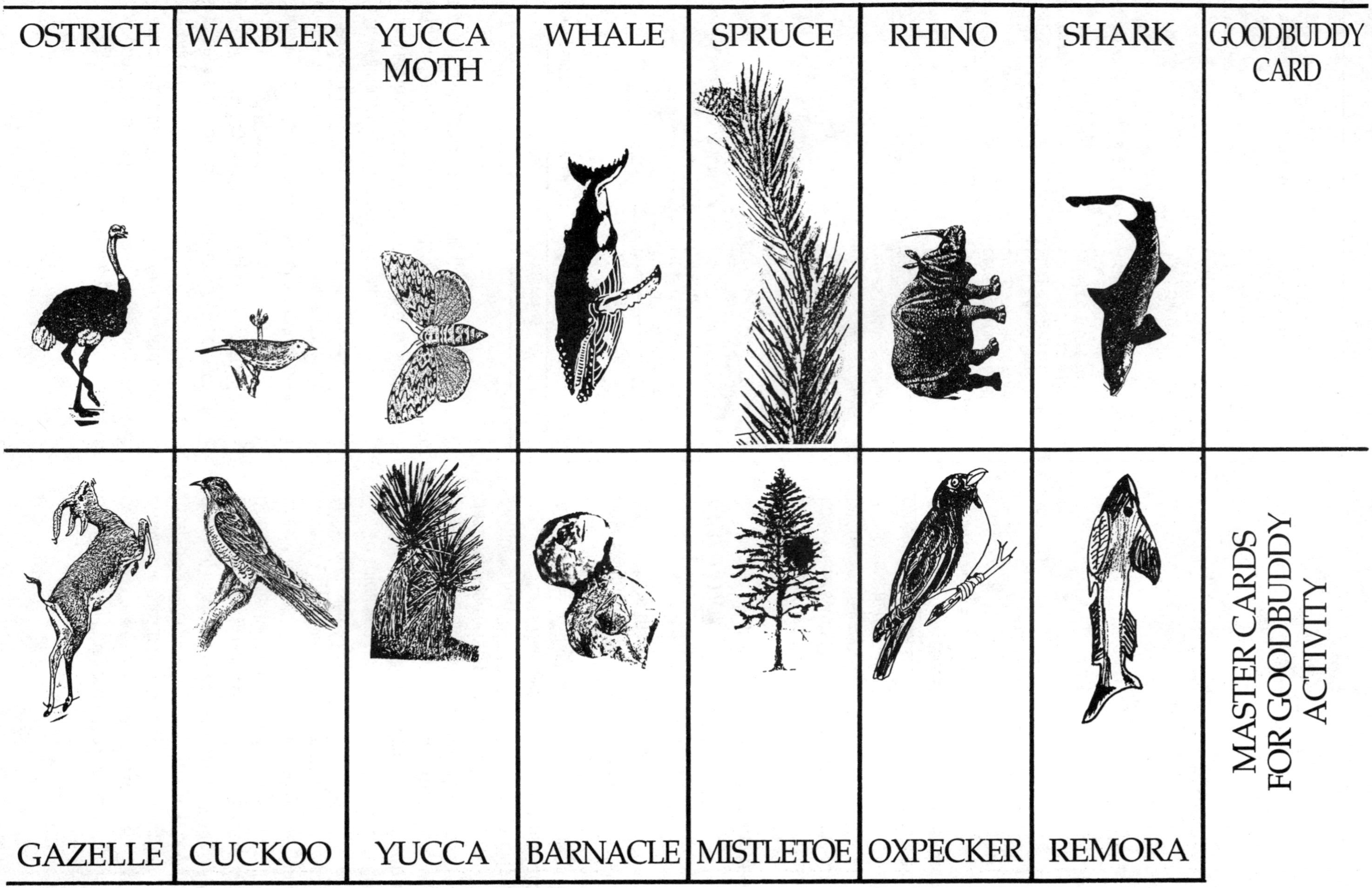

GOODBUDDY
CARD

ANTS		SILVERFISH
BASS		WRASSE FISH
COWBIRD		BISON
FLEA		MOUSE
DEER		TICK
HERMIT CRAB		SHELL
MARIBOU STORK		BEE
HONEY GUIDE BIRD		BADGER

FOREST IN A JAR

OBJECTIVES

Students will: 1) observe and describe succession; and 2) summarize what they have learned about how environments can change.

METHODS

Students conduct an experiment using soil, water, seeds, a plant and a jar; and then draw a poster to represent their observations and findings.

BACKGROUND

Succession is a term used to describe changes in an environment over time. Such changes affect the kinds of wildlife that live in the environment. Most forests, grasslands, deserts and other lands are actively changing in character. Many of these changes happen slowly, giving the human observer an impression of a stable environment. Some of these changes literally happen overnight, as in the case of a fire.

Succession is generally thought of as an orderly process. Theoretically, succession begins with bare ground and is completed when a climax forest, grassland or other environment becomes established. Seral or early successional plants are generally short-lived, thrive in sunlight, colonize rapidly and spread their seeds far and wide. Roadsides, recent burns, clear cuts and other areas of recent disturbance are good places to find examples of early succession.

The first plants change the environment by adding nutrients to the soil from fallen leaves and other plant parts and providing shade to the soil. This change allows different plants to grow. The presence of these newer plants changes the environment to allow even

later stage successional plants to develop. **Climax** or late successional plants usually thrive in shade, live a long time and reproduce more slowly. A plant community has reached a climax state when the plants present generally maintain the same population size over time. Old growth forests are good examples of a climax stage of succession.

Succession influences what kinds of animals live in an area. As succession proceeds from a young system to an older one or vice versa, the habitat available to animals changes character. Therefore, the kinds of animals that live in the area are associated with the area's stage of succession.

Ponds provide another example of succession. As a shallow pond fills with sediments, marshy plants often are established. As the soil dries even more, land plants move onto the old pond shore. Eventually, what was a pond can become a forest many years later!

In this activity, students will be able to see in miniature how a wetland area can be succeeded by a forest habitat. The major purpose of this activity is for students to recognize the process of succession.

MATERIALS

pint or quart jars or clear two-liter plastic soda bottles (one per student or small groups of students, or one for the entire class); water; soil; aquatic plants (one per jar); two cups bird seed

PROCEDURE

1. Place two inches of soil and three inches of water in a jar. Place the jar at a window, **without a lid,** and allow it to settle overnight.
2. Plant an aquatic plant in the jar. It should grow well in this environment. If your classroom has no windows, substitute a grow-light.
3. Do not replace the water that evaporates from the jar.
4. Once or twice a week, have students add three or four bird seeds to the jar. While there is water in the jar, the seeds should germinate and then rot. Continue adding seeds even after the water evaporates.

Age: Grades K-6
Subjects: Science
Skills: analysis, application, comparing similarities and differences, description, discussion, drawing, generalization, invention, media construction, psychomotor development, research
Duration: five to ten minutes for one or two days a week for several weeks; 20 to 30 minutes for summary activity
Group Size: any
Setting: indoors; outdoors optional
Conceptual Framework Reference: III.A., III.A.1., III.A.3., III.B., III.C., III.C.1., III.C.3., III.C.4.
Key Vocabulary: evaporation, change, succession
Appendices: Outdoors, Field Ethics

5. As the water evaporates down to the soil, the aquatic plant will die. The bird seeds will now typically find the environment suitable for successful growth. Sunflower seeds, which grow large, can be added to represent forest trees. You will now need to add water, as a substitute for rainfall, to keep the soil damp to keep things growing.

would be likely to be last.

Draw lines from each of these animals to the places where they would be most likely to live.

fish   turtle   raccoon   squirrel   deer

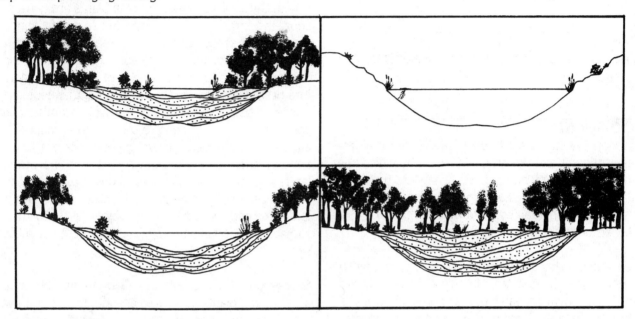

6. Have each student make a poster, drawing, or other visual representation of what they saw happen to their "pond." Ask them to talk about what they have learned about how environments can change. Introduce the term, "succession," to older students.

7. OPTIONAL: Take a field trip to a pond. What plants are growing in the water? What plants are growing on the shore? What parallels are there between this real pond and the "pond" in the jar? Make a second drawing of this real pond. Compare the similarities and differences between the two.

NOTE: See "Pond Succession," and use it as an extension to this activity.

EVALUATION

1. Describe three changes you saw occur inside the jar.

2. Above are some illustrations of succession in a pond. Number these drawings to show their order from what would be most likely to be first to what

3. What would happen if the lid were left on the jar? Explain how this closed system would or would not represent pond succession as well as when the lid is left off.

EXTENSIONS

1. Establish several jars and vary the amount of water you add to each. One jar may be the "desert" jar that does not get much additional water. The other extreme may be the jar that maintains its "pond" status. Several other jars would contain amounts of water somewhere in between. Identify and describe what the differences in "rainfall" mean to the plant communities that develop in each jar.

2. Experiment with different kinds of soils. For example, you could try three different kinds of soils and water each as if it were a "desert" environment. See what differences, if any, emerge.

POND SUCCESSION

OBJECTIVES

Students will: 1) recognize that natural environments are involved in a process of continual change; 2) discuss the concept of succession; 3) describe succession as an example of the process of change in natural environments; and 4) apply understanding of the concept of succession by drawing a series of pictures showing stages in pond succession.

METHOD

Students create murals showing three major stages of pond succession.

BACKGROUND

Succession is a term used to describe the ever changing environment and the gradual process by which one habitat is replaced by another. Many habitats that appear to be stable are changing before us—perhaps at a slow rate in human eyes but evolving rather quickly according to the earth's clock.

For example, a shallow pond may be transformed into a marshy, then forested, area in only a thousand years or so. Wind-blown or water-borne spores of algae are the first inhabitants. Eggs of flying insects are deposited. Small fish and amphibians arrive through the inlet. Surrounding sediments begin to fill the pond, some borne on wash-out from rainfall, some entering through the pond's inlet. Marshy plants growing along the shoreline spread inward as sediments fill the pond. Land plants also spread inward and replace the marsh plants as the ground is consolidated. As more plants and animals enter the system, more opportunities for habitat become available to others. Changes from

ponds to forest are only one example of succession.

Succession is generally thought of as an orderly process in which plant communities change over time in an environment. Theoretically, succession begins with bare ground and is completed when a climax forest, grassland, or other environment becomes established. **Seral** or early successional plants are generally short-lived, thrive in sunlight, colonize rapidly and spread their seeds far and wide. Roadsides, recent burns, clear cuts and other areas of recent disturbance are good places to find examples of early succession. The first plants change the environment by adding nutrients to the soil from fallen leaves and other plant parts and providing shade to the soil. This change allows other plants to grow. The presence of these newer plants changes the environment to allow even later stage successional plants to develop. **Climax** or late successional plants usually thrive in shade, live a long time and reproduce more slowly. Old growth forests are good examples of a climax stage of succession.

Succession influences what kinds of animals live in an area. As the plants in an area change, the habitat available to animals changes character. Therefore, the kinds of animals that live in the area are associated with the area's stage of succession.

The major purpose of this activity is for students to discover that environments are not static, but changing, and to see an example of how these changes progress over time through experience with the concept of succession.

MATERIALS

long pieces of drawing paper for murals; tape for securing paper to walls; crayons

PROCEDURE

1. Review with students the idea of succession, a process that is generally an orderly, gradual and continual replacement of one community of organisms in an environment with another.
2. Start by talking about a pond. How many people have seen a pond? What did it look like? After a

---

Age: Grades 4-9
Subjects: Science, Social Studies
Skills: analysis, application, comparing similarities and differences, description, discussion, drawing, media construction, observation, small group work, synthesis, visualization
Duration: one or two 30-minute periods or longer
Group Size: any
Setting: indoors (outdoors optional)
Conceptual Framework Reference: III.A., III.A.1., III.A.3., III.B., III.B.1., III.C., III.C.1., III.C.2., III.C.3., III.C.4., III.D., III.D.1., III.D.2., III.D.3., III.D.4., III.D.5.
Key Vocabulary: succession, sediment, change, pond
Appendices: Ecosystem

---

scription of ponds, ask the students to imagine what a pond would look like from a side view if you could see under the water and show the nearby environment. For example:

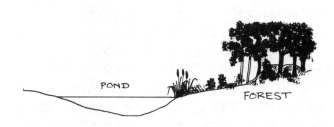

3. Explain to the students that they will be drawing a series of three views of a pond over time period of about 800 years. The first (left-hand) section will show the pond as it is today, the middle section how it might look 500 years later, after natural changes, and the third (right-hand) how the pond could look in 800 years. (These time periods are approximate and can vary greatly.)

4. Discuss with them the possibilities of plant and animal life in the first section. What kinds of plants and animals live:
   • in the water;
   • along the shoreline;
   • in the surrounding area?

5. Then give each group their piece of paper which they will divide into three equal sections (by folding or drawing). Instruct them to fill in the first section with their drawing of the pond and the surrounding area. Set a specific time frame for the students to draw (about ten minutes).

6. Bring the class together again for a discussion of the second section—to be labeled "500 Years Later." Consider the following items:
   • What changes in the environment have taken place?
   • How will the pond look now?
   • What lives and grows in the water now that it is much shallower and smaller?
   • What lives and grows around the shoreline which is now marshier? (marsh animals and plants, perhaps some willow bushes)
   • What lives and grows in the surrounding area? (larger trees, same types of animals) Have each group complete the second section of their mural, labeling it "500 Years Later."

7. Repeat the process for the third section, labeling it

"800 Years Later" and discussing the following topics:
   • By this time the pond is almost totally filled with sediment, leaving only a small marshy area with perhaps a stream running through. What changes have taken place?
   • What lives and grows in the environment?
   • What lives and grows where the shoreline used to be? (bushes, small trees)
   • What effects does the pond succession have on the surrounding area? (different animals, trees requiring less water)

8. After the murals are completed, students should sign them. Then they may be displayed in the classroom for all students to see and discuss differences and similarities between the various murals. Ask the students to summarize what they have learned, including how succession is one example of the ongoing process of change in natural environments.

Variation Use a stream table filled with standard soil to illustrate in three-dimensional, dynamic ways the processes of succession! Fill the table with soil, make an indentation in the center to represent the pond; run water into the table to represent rainfall, streams feeding the pond, etc.; and watch the pond fill as sedimentation takes place. This can show the geologic life cycle of the pond. Add replicas of plants and animals during successional stages for even more interest! OPTIONAL: Visit the real thing if you can!

EXTENSION

What might happen to your model of succession if an intense hot forest fire burned the trees surrounding the pond? Would the pond silt in faster? Would there be a source for tree seeds to colonize the pond site? Would there be differences if the fire were not as hot? How might fires affect the species that live there? Describe some possible differences in environments where fire affects succession and where it does not.

EVALUATION

1. Draw a picture, with explanations, to show stages in pond succession.

2. Select a field, vacant lot, park, or other area in your community. Make a sketch and write a paragraph to describe the area as it appears today. Make a sketch and write a paragraph to describe what the area might look like in 100 or 500 years from now if a gradual process of succession took place.

THE THICKET GAME

OBJECTIVES

Students will: 1) define adaptation in animals; and 2) generalize that all animals are adapted to survive.

METHOD

Students become "predator" and "prey" in a version of "hide and seek."

BACKGROUND

NOTE: See "Seeing is Believing" and "Surprise Terrarium" for other elementary-age adaptation activities.

Animals are adapted to their environment in order to survive. Animals may be adapted to changes in their habitats. For example, snowshoe rabbits have a white winter coat to blend with a snowy environment and a tan summer coat to blend with summer ground and vegetation colors. Chameleons change color to blend with their surroundings. The walking-stick insect can look like a twig or stick. Fawns have spotted hair that resembles dappled light on the forest floor.

The major purpose of this activity is for students to understand the importance of adaptation to animals.

MATERIALS

blindfolds; outdoor area like a thicket or other vegetated area free of poisonous plants and other hazards where students can safely hide

Age: Grades K-6
Subjects: Science, Physical Education, Language Arts
Skills: Analysis, application, description, discussion, generalization, kinesthetic concept development, observation, psychomotor development
Duration: 30 minutes
Group Size: minimum of five students
Setting: outdoors
Conceptual Framework Reference: III.D., III.D.1., III.D.2.
Key Vocabulary: adaptation, predator, prey
Appendices: Outdoors, Field Ethics, Simulations

PROCEDURE

1. Take the class to a "thicket."
2. Blindfold one student who will be the "predator." The predator slowly counts to 20 while the other students or "prey" hide. Hiding students must be able to see some part of the predator at all times.
3. After counting, the predator removes the blindfold and looks for prey. The predator can turn around, squat and stand on tip-toe but not walk or change location. The predator should see how many students he or she can find, identify them out loud and describe where they are. When identified, the prey come to the predator's location and wait until the next round to become predators but do not tell the original predator where anyone else is hiding.
4. When the original predator cannot see any more students, a new round starts. All of the predators put on blindfolds. Predators should be in close proximity to each other. Each predator has the same motion restrictions that the original predator had. The original predator again counts aloud to 20. All the remaining prey must move at least ten feet closer to the predators. Those remaining prey still try to remain hidden. All the predators remove their blindfolds and take turns naming students they can see.
5. Play as many rounds as necessary until only one or two students are left hidden. At that time, have the remaining students stand up and identify themselves. It may be surprising how close the prey got to the predators without being detected. Both the ability to remain undetected and to detect others are examples of successful adaptations. Introduce the term "adaptation."
6. Do the activity one or two more times.
7. Discuss what made predators and prey successful. Were they quiet, clever, camouflaged, or good listeners? Ask students to identify animals that are adapted with similar characteristics to survive.

8. Ask the students how they could change to be more successful predators and prey. Some ideas that may come out are: changing color (clothes); wearing clothing that doesn't stick to plants; being smaller; climbing a tree. Ask the students if animals can make any similar kinds of changes.

9. Talk about differences between physical and behavioral changes. Have the students identify which survival and adaptations related to predators and prey are behavioral, which are physical and which involve both. Explain that physical and behavioral adaptations take time.

10. Ask students to summarize what they have learned. See if students can think of other examples of animal adaptations. Generalize that all animals are adapted to survive.

AQUATIC EXTENSIONS

1. It is not just animals on land that are adapted for survival in a variety of ways! Imagine an underwater thicket. What would be the same, if anything, about predator and prey relationships in an underwater thicket? What would be different, if anything? Draw two different underwater thickets—one in a pond and one in an ocean. Include pictures of fish and other aquatic life that are hardly visible because of adaptations that make them hard to see and pictures of others that are easy to see.

2. Identify predators and prey in two or more aquatic environments.

EVALUATION

1. Describe the importance of adaptation to animals. Give at least two examples of animal adaptation.

2. Create a play or skit that shows how both predators and prey are adapted to survive.

ADAPTATION ARTISTRY

OBJECTIVES
Students will : 1) identify and describe the advantages of bird adaptations; and 2) evaluate the importance of adaptations to birds.

METHOD
Students design and create imaginary birds, and write reports including descriptions of the birds' adaptations.

BACKGROUND
Birds have a variety of adaptations—including characteristics of beaks, feet, legs, wings and coloration. These adaptations have evolved so that the bird is better suited to its environment and lifestyle. A variety of major adaptations are listed on the next page.

The major purpose of this activity is for students to realize that there are advantages for birds in looking how they do, recognizing some of the ways in which birds are physically adapted to their environments.

MATERIALS
drawing, painting, clay sculpture or papier maché materials; construction paper and glue; pencil and paper

PROCEDURE
1. Discuss with the students the various adaptations given in the background section of this activity, listing the charts on a chalkboard for reference by the students. Or, brainstorm a list of bird characteristics,

name the birds with such characteristics, and describe the advantage of the adaptation represented by the characteristic.

2. Tell the students they will each have a chance to design their own original bird—one well adapted to its habitat. Each student should decide:
   • where the bird will live
   • what it will eat
   • its type of mobility
   • its sex

3. Based on these choices, the students will decide the adaptations that are necessary for their bird, and write them down before proceeding further.

4. Using their list of adaptations, each student will create his or her own original bird; for example, by drawing or sculpting it.

5. In conjunction with each drawing or sculpture, each student should write a short report which includes the name of the bird and its food sources, habitat and lifestyle. Students should also include their lists of adaptations, the reasons for the adaptations, and the advantages provided by the adaptations.

6. Completed projects may either be submitted to the teacher, presented to the class, or displayed in the classroom.

7. OPTIONAL: Go outside and identify adaptations on real birds!

Age: Grades 4-9
Subjects: Science, Art, Language Arts
Skills: analysis, application of concepts, description, discussion, drawing, invention, media construction, observation, problem solving, reporting, synthesis, writing
Duration: one or two 45-minute periods
Group Size: any
Setting: indoors (outdoors optional)
Conceptual Framework Reference: III.D., III.D.1., III.D.2.
Key Vocabulary: adaptation
Appendices: None

Adaptation		Bird	Advantage
Beaks	pouch-like	pelican	can hold fish, a food source
	long, thin	avocet	can probe shallow water and mud for insects, a food source
	pointed	wood-pecker	can break and probe bark of trees, for insects, a food source
	curved	hawk	can tear solid tissue, like meat, a food source
	short, stout	finches	can crack seeds and nuts, a food source
	slender, long	humming-bird	can probe flowers for nectar, a food source
Feet	webbed	duck	aids in walking on mud, transportation
	long toes	crane, heron	aids in walking on mud, transportation
	clawed	hawk, eagle	can grasp food when hunting prey
	grasping	chicken	aids in sitting on branches, roosting, protection

Adaptation		Bird	Advantage
Legs	flexor tendons	chicken	aid in perching, grasping
	long, powerful	ostrich	aids running, transportation
	long, slender	heron, crane	aids wading, transportation
	powerful muscles	eagle, hawk	aids lifting, carrying prey, transportation
Wings	large	eagle	aids flying with prey, soaring while hunting
Color-ation	bright plumage	male birds	attraction in courtship, mating rituals
		female birds	aids in camouflage while nesting, protection in shelter
	change of plumage with seasons	owl ptarmigan	provides camouflage protection (brown in summer, white in winter), protection in shelter

EXTENSIONS

1. Make mobiles of the completed birds.
2. Prepare a slide presentation on an overhead projector showing different types of bird adaptations.
3. The teacher could give the students examples of bird adaptations on the overhead projector or a ditto sheet and the student could explain the reasons for these adaptations.
4. Collect pictures of birds to develop a bulletin board showing some of the adaptations discussed. Look for pictures showing bird parts compatible with the "invented" birds. Display the invented birds. Use the bulletin board during parent conferences.

EVALUATION

Name two bird adaptations for each of the following body parts, listing their advantages: beaks, feet, leg, wings, color.

SEEING IS BELIEVING or THE EYES HAVE IT!

OBJECTIVE
Students will identify different kinds of vision as an example of adaptation in animals.

METHOD
Students use kaleidoscopes, binoculars or telescopes, and fish-eye mirrors; imagine what animals might have such vision; and make posters showing animals that do have such vision.

BACKGROUND
NOTE: See "Thicket Game" for information about animal adaptation. Also see "Surprise Terrarium."

Vision is one example of animal adaptation—with different kinds of vision well-suited to the needs of different kinds of animals.

The major purpose of this activity is for students to recognize different kinds of vision as examples of adaptation in animals.

MATERIALS
Set up three learning stations: one with a kaleidoscope; one with binoculars or telescope; and one with a fish-eye mirror or photos taken with such a lens;

Age: Grades K-6
Subjects: Science, Language Arts, Art
Skills: analysis, application, classification, comparing similarities and differences, description, discussion, generalization, inference, invention, kinesthetic concept development, media construction, observation, psychomotor development, small group work, synthesis
Duration: five-ten minutes or longer at each learning center; 30 minutes for discussion and posters
Group Size: one or two students at a time at learning centers; any size group in summary activity
Setting: indoors, at learning centers
Conceptual Framework Reference: III.D., III.D.1., III.D.2.
Key Vocabulary: adaptation, vision, kaleidoscope, binocular, fish-eye lens
Appendices: None

magazines with wildlife photos or wildlife stamps; glue; poster material

PROCEDURE
1. Set up three stations or learning centers in the classroom: one with kaleidoscopes (the kind you can see through); the second with either binoculars or telescopes; and the third with a fish-eye mirror (or photos of objects taken with a fish-eye lens on a camera).

2. Have the students visit each station, trying out the different kinds of vision. (Younger students may require assistance in using the equipment.)

3. Ask the students to guess what kinds of animals might have each of these three types of vision, emphasizing that the way an animal sees is a form of adaptation. Adaptation is something animals have in order to survive in an environment. For example:

Binoculars Predatory birds (eagles, hawks, owls) have acute distance and depth of vision similar to telescopic vision. They do not have tunnel vision, however, as a telescope might suggest; they have exceptional peripheral vision. This allows them to see their prey from great distances.

Kaleidoscopes Insects have compound eyes. Each facet of their eye functions like a separate eye and allows them extreme peripheral vision. This allows them to detect predators.

Fish-eye mirror or photos Fish have eyes with wide-angle perception. They can see predators, prey, and other food sources.

4. Divide the class into three groups and have each group cut out magazine pictures and make a poster for one of the three stations, showing the kinds of animals that have that particular kind of vision.

EXTENSIONS

1. Write a paragraph with the title, "I'd like to see like a _____," in which you could describe how you would see things and why you would like to be able to see that way. Describe what that animal's view of the world would be like.

2. Make eyeglasses, and—by drawing or cutting out magazine photos—show the colors, shapes or patterns of an animal's eye. Or, create a small collage showing what that animal's view of the world would be. The art work occupies the space on the eyeglasses where the lens would normally be. Unlined tagboard paper is thin enough to cut out eyeglass shapes without tearing easily.

AQUATIC EXTENSION

Compare the size of the eyes of a variety of different species of fish! Of aquatic mammals! Of aquatic insects! Of aquatic birds!

EVALUATION

1. Each of the following animals has either **kaleidoscope, binocular, or fish-eye mirror eyes:** trout, owl, fly, eagle, cricket. Identify which kind of vision each animal has.

2. How do the eyes of eagles help them to hunt better?

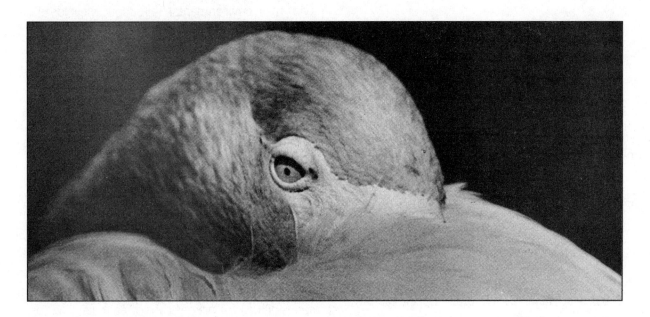

SURPRISE TERRARIUM

OBJECTIVES
Students will: 1) identify camouflage as an example of adaptation in an animal; and 2) describe the importance of adaptation to animals.

METHOD
Students observe a live animal that uses camouflage techniques.

BACKGROUND
NOTE: See "Thicket Game" and "Seeing is Believing."

One of the most important ways that living things survive is by their ability to adapt—to climate, soils, water, vegetation, other life forms and other ecological factors.

Animals that use camouflage techniques can be particularly interesting and visually compelling to young students as a means of illustrating the concept of adaptation.

The major purpose of this activity is for students to recognize that animals are adapted to survive.

MATERIALS
terrarium with vegetation and one animal suited to the kind of habitat components represented in the terrarium (the animal should be one that uses camouflage as a form of adaptation to survive; e.g., leaf hopper, tree frog, tree lizard, walking stick, grasshopper, earthworm); photos of animals using camouflage or magazines the students can use to find photos

Age: Grades K-3 (and older)
Subjects: Science, Language Arts
Skills: application, discussion, generalization, observation
Duration: 20-30 minutes
Group Size: any
Setting: indoors
Conceptual Framework Reference: III.D., III.D.1., III.D.2.
Key Vocabulary: adaptation, camouflage
Appendices: Animals in the Classroom, Field Ethics

NOTE: See the National Science Teachers Association's *Guidelines for Responsible Use of Animals in the Classroom* in the Appendices for suggestions concerning proper housing and care for animals in the classroom.

PROCEDURE
1. Make a "surprise terrarium" for your students, and bring it to class. The terrarium should contain an animal that is hard for the students to see at first because the animal uses camouflage as an adaptation technique.
2. Encourage the students to observe the terrarium and wonder if an animal might live there. Ask them to describe what they see.
3. Ask the students to think of animals that blend with their environments. Talk about their ideas. Show photos or bring in magazines and ask the students to look for pictures of animals that look so much like where they live they are hard to see. Are the animals camouflaged? Camouflage is one way animals are adapted in order to survive.
4. If they haven't found the animal that is living in their terrarium, encourage them to look very closely until they do.
5. Ask the students to summarize some of the things they have learned about "adaptation" and its importance to animals.
6. If the camouflaged animal was brought into the classroom from the wild, the students should participate in the process of returning the animal to its natural home. This is a good time to talk about human responsibilities for proper care of animals used for instructional purposes as well as a potential way to see the animal camouflaged in its natural setting.

EVALUATION
1. Name two animals that use camouflage, and talk about how camouflage is important to these animals.
2. Pick a photograph of one kind of habitat from a selection of images your teacher provides. Draw an animal that would be camouflaged in the habitat you pick.

POLAR BEARS IN PHOENIX?

OBJECTIVE
Students will identify problems for an animal moved from its natural environment to captivity.

METHOD
Students design and draw a zoo enclosure appropriate for the survival of a polar bear in a hot, arid climate.

BACKGROUND
Polar bears are arctic animals associated with regions of sea ice. They spend 90% of their time on floating ice. Much of that time is focused on hunting seals for food. The remaining 10% of their time is spent on land. When awake, polar bears are active. They spend considerable amounts of time foraging and hunting for food. They are able to get their food from the sea during both of the arctic seasons; the three-month summer of continuous daylight and the nine-month long, dark winter. They do, however, range on the tundra in summer, feeding on leaves and fruits of tundra plants and an occasional muskox or caribou, which a polar bear can outrun over short distances. These bears range over broad distances on the ice, traveling southward in winter to stay near open water and shifting ice floes, catching birds and seals as they come up for air and occasionally diving for fish. They eat seaweed in difficult times.

An increasing number of zoos are making an effort to display animals in a simulated version of their natural habitat. The local environment must be adapted to suit the animal's wants and needs in order for the animal to survive and thrive. In the case of polar bears, that represents quite a challenge!

In captivity, polar bears do not like being enclosed, making it very difficult to gain access for maintenance of their enclosure. On smooth surfaces, they have a habit of twisting around on their hindquarters in such a way that the hind claws get very little use, can grow too long, and—due to their curvature—can become imbedded in the bear's skin. Infant bears require warmth and the solitude of a den during their first several months of life. Male bears, if not kept separately, have been known to kill even partially grown cubs.

In the heat of summer, the bears spend most of their time in the cool recesses of their dens or in the cool, deep water in their pool. The Smithsonian Zoo in Washington, D.C. has air-conditioned their dens and installed windows in the side walls of their pool for sub-surface viewing of the animals. The keepers also change the bear's diet in summer in order to reduce the thickness of the bear's fat layer, thus keeping the bears cooler.

In designing a zoo enclosure for a polar bear, students should take this information into consideration:

Polar bears weigh 700 to 900 pounds at maturity, with a length of up to ten feet. They can jump ten to 12 feet into the air from a standing position.

The enclosure should contain everything the animal needs to survive: a sleeping place, hiding place or den for solitude, pool, source of drinking water, food, and space for exercise. The enclosure should look as unlike a cage as possible. The bear's enclosure does not need to be entirely refrigerated. Polar bears only need a cool place in which to retreat. Also consider:
- temperature (day, night)
- humidity
- floor covering
- slope of floor (for cleaning)
- color
- light intensity (day, night)
- length of day
- water
- food, diet
- plant life
- air pressure
- wind velocity and direction
- maintenance

Age: Grades 2-6 (and older)
Subjects: Science, Language Arts, Social Studies
Skills: analysis, application, comparing similarities and differences, discussion, drawing, evaluation, invention, observation, problem solving, synthesis, visualization
Duration: 45 minutes
Group Size: any
Setting: indoors
Conceptual Framework Reference: I.C.1., I.C.2., III.A., III.A.1., III.A.2., III.A.3., III.D., III.D.1., III.D.2., III.D.3., III.D.4., III.D.5.
Key Vocabulary: zoo, adaptation, survival
Appendices: Local Resources

The major purpose of this activity is for students to recognize that animals are adapted to the environments in which they have lived for a long time. If people move animals to environments different from those for which the animals are adapted, then special attention must be paid to creating conditions in which the animals can live.

MATERIALS
paper for drawing; crayons

PROCEDURE
1. Introduce polar bears to the students with a brief description of their habitat and habits. Try to include some pictures of both young and mature animals. (See "What Bear Goes Where.")
2. Tell the students they will each have the opportunity to design their own zoo enclosure for a polar bear that is being moved from its natural habitat in northern Alaska to the desert environment of Phoenix, Arizona. They are to create an environment that replicates to the extent possible the characteristics of the environment for which the bear is naturally adapted. What do they need to consider? Compare and contrast the two environments. Identify and describe the bear's habitat needs. What can be done to meet those needs in Phoenix? Students may want to work individually or in teams.
3. Give each student a large piece of paper and crayons. If possible, have them list some of the major features they would like their enclosure to include on a separate piece of paper before beginning to draw.
4. Display the drawings on a bulletin board. Allow the class time to view the drawings and discuss merits and drawbacks of the various enclosures.
5. As a summary, discuss some of the problems these bears would have in captivity. Talk about the responsibilities people have to meet animals' needs if we put them in captivity.

EXTENSIONS
1. Visit a polar bear at a local zoo, if one is available.
2. Visit any animals in captivity. Compare the animals' natural habitat to that provided in the captive conditions.
3. Discus the purposes of placing animals in captivity, and discuss arguments for and against such captivity.

AQUATIC EXTENSION
See the Aquatic WILD activity, "Designing a Habitat."

EVALUATION
Describe five problems a polar bear would face in captivity. Suggest possible solutions for each of these problems, explaining your reasoning.

QUICK FROZEN CRITTERS

OBJECTIVES

Students will: 1) discuss predator/prey relationships, including adaptations; 2) describe the importance of adaptations in predator/prey relationships; and 3) recognize that limiting factors—including predator/prey relationships—affect wildlife populations.

METHOD

Students play an active version of "freeze tag."

BACKGROUND

NOTE: This activity is best done after one or more that introduces the concepts of "adaptation" and "limiting factors." See the cross references for suggestions.

Predator An animal that kills and eats other animals for food.

Prey An animal that is killed and eaten by other animals for food.

Limiting Factors There are many influences in the life history of any animal. When one of these (e.g., disease, climate, pollution, accidents, shortages of food) exceeds the limits of tolerance of that animal, it becomes a limiting factor. It then drastically affects the well-being of that animal. Predators are limiting factors for prey. Prey are limiting factors for predators.

Animals display a variety of behaviors in predator/prey relationships. These are adaptations to survive.

Some prey behaviors are: signalling to others, flight, posturing in a fighting position, scrambling for cover and even "freezing" on the spot to escape detection or capture by predators. The kind of behavior exhibited partly depends on how close the predator is when detected by the prey. Each animal has a threshold for threat levels. If a predator is far enough away for the prey to feel some safety, the prey may signal to others that a predator is near. If the predator comes closer, the prey may try to run away. If the predator is too close to make running away feasible, the prey may attempt to scurry to a hiding place. If the predator is so close that none of these alternatives is available, the prey may freeze in place. The closer the predator comes to the prey animal, the more likely it is that the prey will "freeze" in place. This "freezing" occurs as a kind of physiological shock in the animal. (Shelter or camouflage may also make them invisible to the predator when they freeze.) Too often people who come upon animals quickly and see them immobile infer that the animals are unafraid when, in reality, the animals are "frozen", or, as the adage goes, "frozen stiff."

The major purpose of this activity is for students to recognize the importance of adaptations to both predators and prey and to gain insight into limiting factors affecting wildlife populations.

Age: Grades 4-6 (can be modified for younger and older students; simplify the discussion for younger students)
Subjects: Science, Physical Education (Language Arts optional: See Variations and Extensions)
Skills: analysis, description, discussion, evaluation, generalization, kinesthetic concept development, observation, psychomotor development
Duration: 20 to 45 minutes
Group Size: best with at least ten students; one "predator" per every four to six "prey"
Setting: indoors or outdoors
Conceptual Framework Reference: III.D., III.D.1., III.D.2., III.E., III.E.1., III.E.2.
Key Vocabulary: predator, prey, adaptation
Appendices: Outdoors, Simulations

MATERIALS

food tokens (pieces of cardboard), enough for three per student; gym vests or other labeling devices to mark predators; four or five hula hoops to serve as "cover" markers; pencil and paper to record number of captures, if desired

PROCEDURE

1. Select any of the following pairs of animals:

Prey	Predators
cottontails	coyotes
ground squirrels	hawks
deer	cougar
quail	foxes

Identify students as either "predators" or "prey" for a version of "freeze tag"—with approximately one predator per every four to six prey.

2. Using a gymnasium or playing field, identify one end of the field as the "food source" and the other end as the "shelter."

3. Four to five hula hoops are placed on the open area between the "shelter" and the "food." These represent additional shelter or "cover" for the prey and can be randomly distributed on the field. (If hula hoops are not available, string might be used, or chalk on asphalt.)

4. Food tokens are placed in the "food source" zone on the ground. Allow three food tokens for each prey animal. For example:

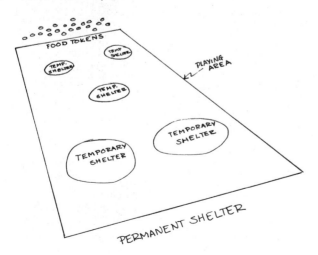

5. Predators should be clearly identified. Gym vests or safety patrol vests might be available.

6. Use a whistle or some other pre-arranged signal to start each round. When a round begins, prey start from their "shelter." The task of the prey animals is to move from the primary shelter to the food source, collecting one food token each trip, and returning to the primary shelter. To survive, prey have to obtain three food tokens. Their travel is hazardous, however. They need to be alert to possible predators. If they spot a predator, they can use various appropriate prey behaviors—including warning other prey that a predator is near. Prey have two ways to prevent themselves from being caught by predators: they may "freeze" any time a predator is within five feet of them; or they may run to cover (with at least one foot within one of the hula hoops.) Frozen prey may blink, but otherwise should be basically still without talking.

7. Predators start the activity anywhere in the open area between ends of the field and thus are randomly distributed between the prey's food and primary shelter. Predators attempt to capture prey to survive, tagging only moving (not "frozen") prey. (OPTIONAL: Prey can have bandannas in their pockets that the predators have to capture to represent the successful predation.) Predators must each capture two prey in order to survive. Captured prey are taken to the sidelines by the predator who captured them.

NOTE: Establish a ground rule for student behavior: Behave in ways that are not harmful to other students, even when simulating predator behavior; e.g., no full tackles!

8. A time limit of five to seven minutes is suggested for each round of the game. (Captured prey on the sidelines will get restless if rounds are much longer.) Remind prey that they can remain frozen for as long as they like, but if they do not have enough food at the end of the activity they will starve to death. In nature, an animal must balance the need to find food with the sometimes conflicting need for safety.

9. Play four rounds, allowing each student to be both prey and predator.

10. Discuss with the students the ways they escaped capture when they were prey. Which ways were easiest? Which were most effective? What means did they use as predators to capture prey? Which ways were best? What did the predators do in response to a prey animal who "froze?" In what ways are adaptations important to both predator and prey? Ask the students to summarize what they have learned about predator/prey relationships. How do predator/prey relationships serve as natural limiting factors affecting wildlife?

VARIATIONS AND EXTENSIONS

1. Conduct the activity for three or four rounds, recording the number of captures each playing period. Have students who are captured become predators, and each predator not getting enough food become a prey animal in the succeeding round. This quickly leads to the concept of dynamic balance as prey and predator populations fluctuate in response to each other.
2. Have the students walk only, or assign different locomotive forms to each animal.

3. Select an animal and research its behavior patterns for avoiding detection and capture. Reports or demonstrations of the behavior could be presented to the class.

AQUATIC EXTENSIONS

1. Do this activity again, using aquatic predator and prey species.
2. "Swim" toward your food while portraying trumpet fish, flounder, stonefish or other marine organisms that "freeze" as a defense mechanism.
3. If possible, conduct the activity in the shallow end of a real swimming pool. Hula hoops will float!

EVALUATION

1. Pick any predator and prey. Describe each animal's adaptations.
2. Identify an adaptation used by a prey species to stay alive. Create or tell a story about an imaginary person who might have used a similar adaptation to survive a difficult situation.

CLASSROOM CARRYING CAPACITY

OBJECTIVES

Students will: 1) define carrying capacity; and 2) give examples of factors which can influence the carrying capacity of an area.

METHOD

Students sit unusually close to each other and describe the results.

BACKGROUND

Carrying capacity affects all living things, including humans. Carrying capacity may be seen as a type of dynamic equilibrium. It is typically expressed as the number of animals of a given type which can be supported in a given area.

Carrying capacity is also interpreted more broadly as the number of living things—plants as well as animals—any area of land or water can support at any one time. Different life forms will have a different carrying capacity within the same area.

Carrying capacity is usually limited by some aspect of a species' habitat requirements. These requirements include the quantity and quality of available food, water, shelter, space and the suitability of their arrangement. Different factors will be important in each case. Natural and human causes both affect carrying capacity. Effects may be short or long term.

Carrying capacity for many species is in a constant state of change, both seasonally and from year to year. For example, it is typically most limited for terrestrial animals in the winter season when food supplies are reduced. Year to year variations may result from factors such as natural disasters, changes in rainfall and temperature patterns, or human interventions. Factors affecting plant growth will affect animals since they are either directly (as herbivores or omnivores) or indirectly (as carnivores) dependent on plants.

Populations of living things tend to fluctuate naturally around some level. Carrying capacity is that level. A population may be below carrying capacity such as in the spring following a hard winter, or temporarily above it. The latter situation inevitably results in a decline of the population due to a variety of natural limiting factors, e.g., mortality, disease, emigration, and lowered reproduction rate, and usually lasts for a short period. The carrying capacity of any area can be affected and adjusted by such natural factors as well as by human intervention.

A population will therefore tend to naturally fluctuate with carrying capacity, with or without human intervention. Humans may not always be willing to accept the consequences of natural events, however. Examples of intentional human intervention are reintroducing predators, feeding in winter, constructing nesting boxes, planting additional vegetation suitable for food, relocating animals and hunting. Human intervention can reduce a population or prevent its expansion to meet an expected natural reduction in carrying capacity. Such an intervention may result in a higher survival rate.

Alteration of habitat quality or quantity may increase or decrease carrying capacity. Environmental degradation may reduce it for affected species. Activities such as development or pollution tend not to be aimed at intentionally reducing carrying capacity but often have this impact.

Age: Grades K-6
Subjects: Science, Social Studies, Language Arts
Skills: analysis, application, comparing similarities and differences, description, discussion, evaluation, inference, kinesthetic concept development, listing, observation
Duration: Grades K-3, 20 minutes; Grades 4-6, 45 minutes
Group Size: any (does require at least a small group)
Setting: indoors or outdoors (designed for classroom)
Conceptual Framework Reference: III.B.6., III.F., III.F.1., III.F.2., III.F.3., III.F.4., III.F.5.
Key Vocabulary: carrying capacity, crowded
Appendices: Ecosystem

Intentional intervention may be based on a particular management philosophy or practice. Management of an area of land or water in relation to its carrying capacity for certain species can be subject to question and controversy. Whether and/or how it is appropriate for humans to intervene in natural systems is sometimes a part of such questions and controversy. Management may be defined as intentional choice based on human goals and objectives. Such goals and objectives are open to question by other groups and individuals.

The major purpose of this activity is to provide students with a general introduction to the topic of carrying capacity.

MATERIALS

chalkboard; any area with room to sit closely, in crowded conditions, and then move comfortably into a larger area

PROCEDURE

1. Ask your students to sit close together in a group on the floor. They should be fairly tightly packed together. Tell them to pay attention as you give a short lesson in spelling, language, or math. Conduct the lesson for five to ten minutes. Then ask the students to describe what happened during the lesson. Did they feel crowded? How did they act? Is this the way they usually act when they are sitting at their desks, not so close together? OPTIONAL: Try this a second time, with the available "habitat" even smaller!

For Grades K-3 Students

2. What if you were animals and you were this crowded? You might be domesticated animals, like cats or dogs or pet rabbits—or you might be wild animals, like deer or elephants. Would you be able to live? Is there enough room for you? What would you need in order to survive? (You would need food, water, shelter and enough space in which to live, arranged according to your needs.) The number of plants and animals that an environment can support is called its "carrying capacity." If the classroom were the

environment, were there too many, too few, or just the right number of people for the classroom carrying capacity when everyone sat together and crowded? (If the only area available were the small space with people crowded, there were probably too many people.) What are examples of things that can happen to affect how many plants and animals an environment can support ("carry")?

3. Ask the students to define carrying capacity, and say why it is important.

For Grades 4-6 Students

2. After students have returned to their seats, work with them in discussion to develop a basic definition of carrying capacity. How was the "carrying capacity" of their classroom instructional area affected when they were sitting so crowded and close together? Ask the students how the behavior of a population of animals might change if the population suddenly exceeded the carrying capacity of a habitat, or if the size of a habitat was suddenly decreased. Why might an animal population exceed the carrying capacity of a habitat? How might a habitat or its carrying capacity be suddenly decreased in size? What are some of the ways that the carrying capacity of a habitat might be increased? (For example, by providing some of the basic survival needs of animals. Some could be from natural causes, like increased rainfall and mild winters. Some can be from human actions like putting out nesting boxes, planting food crops, artificial feeding and revegetation programs.) Some people may have felt uncomfortable when they were squeezed together. Others may not have been bothered at all. It is important to recognize that even within a species, there is a range of tolerance for physical closeness. This is true for humans as well as other animals.

3. Introduce the students to the idea that the earth we live on may have a set carrying capacity. In what ways, if any, are people, domesticated animals and wildlife affecting the carrying capacity of the planet earth? Are there positive effects? Negative effects?

4. Ask your students to summarize what they have learned by listing, "Some Important Things to Remember About Carrying Capacity." Ask them to share their lists.

NOTE: Especially when discussing the carrying capacity of the planet, avoid frightening or depressing the students. Instead, emphasize the importance of learning about some difficult ideas in order to be able to contribute to effective, constructive and informed actions. We may face even the most difficult problems with optimism—as we do our work to study and learn along the way.

AQUATIC EXTENSION

Carrying capacity doesn't just apply to land. Water can only "carry" so many plants and animals as well. Ask the students to give examples of how the concept of carrying capacity might apply to aquatic environments—for example, to a pond or a stream.

EVALUATION

1. List four things that influence carrying capacity.

2. Choose a wildlife species in your area. Create a plan for a farm, city park or school grounds that will increase the area's carrying capacity for the wildlife species you choose. Describe some of the possible effects on other wild species and the habitat as a result of your plan. Describe some possible effects on people.

MUSKOX MANEUVERS

OBJECTIVES

Students will: 1) evaluate the effectiveness of some adaptations in predator/prey relationships; and 2) describe the importance of predator/prey relationships as limiting factors in wildlife populations.

METHOD

Students simulate muskoxen and wolves in a highly involving game of physical activity.

BACKGROUND

NOTE: This activity was inspired by a "New Game," and adapted to teach concepts related to wildlife. Although this activity does not illustrate all the complexities of predator/prey relationships, it does illustrate broad concepts.

The muskox is a large, shaggy herbivore called "omingmak" or "the bearded one" by the Eskimos, or Inuit (ee-new-eet), as they prefer to be called. A male muskox may weigh over 600 pounds at maturity, and mature females about 350 pounds. A young muskox may weigh only about 19 pounds at birth. These animals are inhabitants of the arctic regions of Alaska, Greenland and Canada.

Muskoxen often are found in herds of 20 to 30. Both sexes will vigorously defend the young, usually forming a line or circle around them, facing the threatening predator. Such a circle renders the animals relatively safe against natural predators, particularly wolves.

In this activity, the roles of bulls and cows are differentiated in ways not typical of actual muskoxen. Again, both sexes vigorously defend the young.

The major purpose of this activity is for students to recognize adaptation and limiting factors in a predator/prey relationship.

MATERIALS

two different colors of rag flags to use as tails (like what is used to play flag football); there will need to be as many flags as there are wolves and calves

PROCEDURE

NOTE: When dividing your group, use the following chart as your initial guide. You can vary the proportions in later rounds to respond to what happens in the simulations:

Total Players	Wolves	Bulls	Cows	Calves
15-18	2	3	Equal number or one more cow than calf	
19-28	2	4	Equal number or one more cow than calf	
29-35	3	6	Equal number or one more cow than calf	
36-45	4	8	Equal number or one more cow than calf	
46-50	5	10	Equal number or one more cow than calf	

1. This is a highly involving activity! It is best done outdoors, in an open, grassy area; however, it is possible to do the activity indoors—even in a classroom—if tables, chairs, and desks can be moved in order to create a large space in which students can do some moving, including "tag-like" running.

2. Once you have established an appropriate physical area for this activity, divide your students into four groups. (For example, a group of 33 students would break down into three wolves, six bulls, 12 cows and 12 calves.) Each will have a distinctive role.

Age: Grades 4-9
Subjects: Science, Physical Education
Skills: analysis, description, discussion, evaluation, generalization, kinesthetic concept development, observation, psychomotor development, small group work
Duration: 20-45 minutes
Group Size: 15-50; procedures above based on 33
Setting: outdoors
Conceptual Framework Reference: III.D., III.D.1., III.D.2., III.E., III.E.1., III.E.2.
Key Vocabulary: adaptation, predator, prey, defense, limiting factors
Appendices: Outdoors, Simulations

---

3. This activity provides students with an opportunity to experience adaptation behavior of both muskoxen and wolves. Muskoxen are herbivores and often graze peacefully in meadowed areas. While grazing, they spread out. Calves typically do not stray too far from their mothers, but the animals do not always stay clustered—except when predators appear! Begin the activity with the students grazing peacefully as muskoxen and the wolves out of sight of the herd.

4. These are the behaviors each animal should exhibit:

Cows: As soon as grazing begins, the cows should choose a lead cow to watch for predators. The cows should pick a signal the lead cow will use to communicate to the rest of the herd that predators are approaching. When the lead cow signals that predators are near, all the cows move to form a circle around the calves to protect the calves from the wolves. With the calves in the center of a circle, the cows stand with their backs to the calves, facing outward to watch the wolves. The cows can move very little. Mostly, they stay firmly in one place, moving their upper bodies to block the wolves from reaching the calves. The cows cannot touch the wolves with their hands or feet.

Calves: The calves depend totally upon the cows for protection. Each calf is to hold onto a cow with both hands, around the cow's waist, and only follow the cow's lead. Calves cannot influence the cows' movement.

Bulls: The bulls are the active defenders of the cows and the calves. As the predators near, the bulls form a circle around the cows, who in turn are forming a circle around the calves. The bulls form as tight a circle as they can around the cows and calves, never any farther than one step in front of the circle of cows. The bulls can move, however—but only in a clockwise direction around the circle of cows! The bulls do have use of their hands. As the wolves attack the herd, the bulls try to "kill" them by pulling the flag out of their back pocket, or wherever the flag is attached to the wolf. When a bull kills a wolf, the wolf moves off to the side, "dead," but able to watch the remainder of the activity.

Wolves: Wolves begin the activity out of sight of the herd. They try to get as close as possible to the herd without being detected. Wolves typically work as a unit so they can attempt a strategy for surprising the herd in order to kill the calves for food. The wolves are mobile, able to move at any time in any direction. They can use any maneuver (except pushing and shoving) to break the herd's defenses. Once a wolf kills a calf—by pulling the calf's flag out of its pocket—temporarily stop the game and move the calf's carcass to the side, where it too can watch the remainder of the activity!

A Note About Sound Effects: This is not a quiet activity much of the time. Wolves should be howling, communicating with each other in predetermined ways with signals, and as part of their tactics to startle and confuse the muskoxen. The muskoxen moo loudly.

5. **Muskox Maneuvers in Review:**
Muskox herd grazes quietly. Wolves are out of sight of herd. Wolves move in to attack herd. When lead cow spots wolves, the herd begins defense. A circle is formed, with calves in the center, cows facing out in a circle around the calves, and bulls in an outer circle, also facing the wolves. Each should behave appropriately, as described above.

6. The activity can conclude in several ways. For example:
a. All the wolves could be killed.
b. All the calves could be killed.
c. The wolves could give up in frustration after a period of time with no success in killing a calf.
d. The wolves could kill one or more calves, and the activity conclude at this time, based on the notion that the wolves are going to eat the calf (or calves) and the herd move on.

7. Once the excitement and enthusiasm have peaked—sit down with the students to discuss what happened, and what the activity represents in terms of animal adaptation, predator/prey relationships, and limiting factors. Ask the students to describe and evaluate the predatory behavior of the wolves and the various defense behaviors of the muskoxen. What would happen if the wolves could not get into the herd? What would happen if the wolves always got into the herd? Ask the students to distinguish between what would be actual, typical behaviors of muskoxen contrasted with their behaviors in this activity.

VARIATION

As mentioned earlier, this activity differentiates the roles of bulls and cows in ways not typical of actual muskoxen. To more naturally model muskox behavior, alter the activity in the following way:

Widely scatter food tokens (poker chips, drinking straws, etc.) across the playing field. Instruct the muskoxen to walk around the playing area and pick up food tokens. This will simulate dispersed feeding patterns. The muskoxen may not group together in a defensive posture until receiving the signal from the lead cow that a wolf is near. Allow both cows and bulls to reach for a wolf's flag. Cows still cannot use their hands or feet to block wolves. Permit bulls to move in either direction. In real life, both cows and bulls aggressively defend their young.

EXTENSIONS

1. A few students can research and report back to the class with more details about the life and times of muskoxen and wolves—acquiring additional information about their survival needs, habitat and behaviors.
2. Investigate predatory and defense behaviors of different species in different habitats. For example, selected species of plains, forest, desert, and ocean animals can be compared.
3. Plan a class and parent picnic. Let it be a potluck—with an after dinner activity, "Muskox Maneuvers." It could be good exercise, good fun, and a worthwhile sharing of teaching and learning!

AQUATIC EXTENSION

By no means just like muskox, many fish species also have effective adaptations that serve to protect them from predator species. Have one student be a predator and all the rest of the students be prey. This time, the predator is a tuna, and the prey are herring in a school of fish. (You can pick your own example of predator/prey. Just pick a prey species that forms a school of fish.) Pantomime the school of fish moving through waters with the predator trying to catch at least one for food to survive. In a large open area, have the students move as the school of fish. Have three or four students inside the school of fish wear a bright-colored cloth or tie that the predator will try to remove in order to have successfully caught its prey. The school of fish must keep moving. See if the school of fish can successfully move the length of the open area at least once without any fish being caught by the predator. The predator may move in any direction and may stop and start moving at any time. The prey must move generally together and may not stop. For the sake of safety, no running allowed!

EVALUATION

Name a prey species and its predator species. Describe how each is adapted to the other. How does the prey protect itself? How does the predator overcome this protection? Describe the overall effectiveness of each animal's adaptations.

HOW MANY BEARS CAN LIVE IN THIS FOREST?

OBJECTIVES
Students will: 1) define a major component of habitat; and 2) identify a limiting factor.

METHOD
Students become "bears" to look for one or more components of habitat during this physically-involving activity.

BACKGROUND
It is recommended that this activity be preceded by one or more activities on adaptation; basic survival needs; components of habitat; crowding; carrying capacity; habitat loss; habitat improvement; herbivores, carnivores, and omnivores; and limiting factors. See the cross references for suggestions. For additional information about black bears, see "Bearly Born."

In this activity, the black bears are the focus in order to illustrate the importance of suitable habitat for wildlife. One or more components of habitat—food, water, shelter and space in a suitable arrangement—are emphasized as one way to convey the concept of "limiting factors."

Black bear habitat limits black bear populations, especially through the influences of shelter, food supply and the social tolerances or territoriality of the animal. Shelter or cover is a prime factor. Black bears need cover—for feeding, hiding, bedding, traveling, raising cubs and for denning. With limits of space, adult bears will kill young bears or run them out of the area. These young bears must keep moving around either until they die or find an area vacated by the death of an adult.

When food supplies are reduced by factors such as climatic fluctuations, competition becomes more intense. Some adult bears might temporarily move to seldom-used areas of their home range, sometimes many miles away. They must live on what food is available in the area. These individuals may become thin and in poor condition for winter hibernation or, in the case of young bears, be forced from the area by more aggressive adults.

All components of habitat are important. Food, water, shelter and space must not only be available—but must be available in an arrangement suitable to meet the animals' needs. For black bears, shelter is especially important.

All possible conditions are not covered by the design of the activity. However, by this simple illustration, it is possible for students quickly to grasp the essential nature of the concept of limiting factors.

The major purpose of this activity is for students to recognize the importance of suitable habitat. Inadequate food and/or shelter are two examples of what is called a limiting factor—something which affects the survival of an animal or a population of animals.

Age: Grades 3-9 (and older)
Subjects: Science, Social Studies, Mathematics, Physical Education
Skills: analysis, computation, discussion, evaluation, generalization, kinesthetic concept development, listing, observation, psychomotor development
Duration: 20-45 minutes or longer
Group Size: 10-45
Conceptual Framework Reference: III.A.1., III.B., III.B.1., III.B.2., III.B.3., III.D., III.D.1., III.D.2., III.D.3., III.D.4., III.E., III.E.1., III.E.2., III.F., III.F.1., III.F.2., III.F.3., III.F.4., III.F.5.
Key Vocabulary: limiting factors, habitat, shelter, cover
Appendices: Simulations, Ecosystem, Outdoors

MATERIALS
five colors of construction paper (a couple of sheets each of red, yellow, green, blue, and orange) or an equal amount of light poster board; one black felt pen; envelopes (one per student); pencils; one blindfold; five sheets green construction paper (for extension).

NUMBER OF CARDS TO MAKE

Paper Color	Label	Represents	Number of Students in Group						
			10-15	16-20	21-25	26-30	31-35	36-40	41-45
Orange	N-20	Nuts, 20 lbs.	2	3	3	4	5	6	7
Orange	N-10	Nuts, 10 lbs.	8	13	17	21	25	29	33
Blue	B-20	Berries, 20 lbs.	2	3	3	4	5	6	7
Blue	B-10	Berries, 10 lbs.	8	13	17	21	25	29	33
Yellow	I-12	Insects, 12 lbs.	2	3	3	4	5	6	7
Yellow	I-6	Insects, 6 lbs.	8	13	17	21	25	29	33
Red	M-8	Meat, 8 lbs	2	3	3	4	5	6	7
Red	M-4	Meat, 4 lbs.	8	13	17	21	25	29	33
Green	P-20	Plants, 20 lbs.	2	3	3	4	5	6	7
Green	P-10	Plants, 10 lbs.	8	13	17	21	25	29	33

PROCEDURE

1. Make up a set of 2" x 2" cards from the colored construction paper. Use the table above to determine how many cards of each color to make and what to write on each one.

As shown in the table, the color of the card determines the type of food it represents:

orange—nuts (acorns, pecans, walnuts, hickory nuts)

blue—berries and fruit (blackberries, elderberries, raspberries, wild cherries)

yellow—insects (grub worms, larvae, ants, termites)

red—meat (mice, rodents, peccaries, beaver, muskrats, young deer)

green—plants (leaves, grasses, herbs)

The number on each card represents the number of pounds of food. For example, a card with the label M-4 represents four pounds of meat.

2. The following estimates of total pounds of food for one bear in ten days are used for this activity:

nuts	20 pounds	(25%)
berries and fruit	20 pounds	(25%)
insects	12 pounds	(15%)
meat	8 pounds	(10%)
plants	20 pounds	(25%)
	80 pounds	(100%)

NOTE: These figures represent a typical bear's food.

The components of an actual bear's diet will vary between areas, seasons and years. For example, a bear in the state of Alaska would likely eat more meat (fish) and fewer nuts than a bear in Arizona. One similarity among black bears everywhere is that the majority of their diet is normally made up of vegetative material.

If you follow the table when making the food cards, there should be less than 80 pounds of food per student, so that there is not actually enough food in the area for all the "bears" to survive.

3. If you want, you can also include "water" as a habitat component by making additional squares from light blue paper. To calculate how many water cards to make, multiply the number of students by 1.25 (round to the nearest whole number). For example, for a group of 20 students you would make 20 x 1.25 = 25 water cards. Divide the water squares into five equal piles (or roughly equal) and mark each group with the one of following letters: R, L, ST, SP, and M. These letters represent all the places where a bear could find water: rivers, lakes, streams, springs and marshes.

4. In a fairly large open area (e.g., 50' x 50'), scatter the colored pieces of paper.

5. Do not tell the students what the colors, initials, and numbers on the pieces of paper represent. Tell them only that the pieces of paper represent various kinds of bear food. Since bears are omnivores, they like a wide assortment of food, so they should gather different colored squares to represent a variety of food.

6. Have each student write his or her name on an envelope. This will represent the student's "den site" and should be left on the ground (perhaps anchored with a rock) at the starting line on the perimeter of the field area.

7. Have the students line up on the starting line, leaving their envelopes between their feet on the ground. Give them the following instructions: *"You are now all black bears. All bears are not alike, just as you and I are not exactly alike. Among you is a young male bear who has not yet found his own territory. Last week he met up with a larger male bear in the big bear's territory, and before he could get away, he was hurt. He has a broken leg. (Assign one student as the injured bear. He must hunt by hopping on one leg.) Another bear is a young female who investigated a porcupine too closely and was blinded by the quills. (Assign one student as the blind bear. She must hunt blindfolded.) The third special bear is a mother bear with two fairly small cubs. She must gather twice as much food as the other bears. (Assign one student as the mother bear.)"*

8. Students must walk into the "forest." Bears do not run down their food; they gather it. When students find a colored square, they should pick it up (one at a time) and return it to their "den" before picking up another colored square. (Bears would not actually return to their den to eat; they would eat food as they find it.)

9. When all the colored squares have been picked up, the food gathering is over. Have students pick up their den envelopes containing the food they gathered and return to class.

10. Explain what the colors and numbers represent. Each color is a kind of food and the numbers represent pounds of food eaten. Ask each student to add up the total number of pounds of food he or she gathered—whether it is nuts, meat, insects, berries or plant materials. Each should write the total weight on the outside of his or her envelope.

11. Using a chalkboard, list "blind," "injured," and "mother." Ask the blind bear how much food she got. Write the amount after the word "blind." Ask the injured bear and the mother bear how much they got and record the information. Ask each of the other students to tell how much food they found; record each response on the chalkboard. Tell the students each bear needs 80 pounds to survive. Which bears survived? Is there enough to feed all the bears? How many pounds did the blind bear collect? Will she survive? What about the mother bear? Did she get twice the amount needed to survive? What will happen to

her cubs? Will she feed her cubs first or herself? Why? What would happen to her if she fed the cubs? What if she ate first? If the cubs die, can she have more cubs in the future, and perhaps richer, years? (The mother bear will eat first and the cubs will get whatever, if any, is left. The mother must survive; she is the hope for a continued bear population. She can have more cubs in her life; only one needs to survive in order for the population to remain static.)

12. If you included the water squares, each student should have picked up at least one square representing a water source, or he or she does not survive. Water can be a limiting factor and is an essential component of habitat.

13. Ask each student to record how many pounds of each of the five categories of food he or she gathered. Ask each student next to convert these numbers into percentages of the total poundage of food each gathered. Provide the students with the background information about black bears so that they can compare their percentages with what are typical percentages eaten by black bears in Arizona. Ask each student to attempt to guess how healthy their bear would be. How do the bears' requirements for a diet seem to compare with the needs of humans for a balanced and nutritious diet?

14. Ask the students to arrive at a class total for all the pounds of food they gathered as bears. Divide the total by the 80 pounds needed by an individual bear (approximately) in order to survive in a ten-day period. How many bears could the habitat support? Why then did only _____ bears survive when your class did this activity? Is that realistic? What percentage of the bears survived? What percentage would have survived had the food been evenly divided? In each case, what percentage would not survive? What limiting factors, cultural and natural, would be likely to actually influence the survival of individual bears and populations of bears in an area?

EXTENSIONS

1. Cut paper or poster board into 2" x 2" squares. Make 5 squares per student. For example, with a class of 30 students, you would make 150 squares. Divide all the squares into 5 equal piles and mark the cards in each pile with one of these letters: B, T, D, H and F. These represent B = bedding sites, T = travelways, D = dens, H = hiding cover and F = feeding sites. For purposes of this activity, these are defined as follows:

Bedding Sites Black bears are usually active in early morning and late evening, and bedded most of the rest of the day and night. Bedding sites are usually in areas of dense vegetation, steep topography, and/or large trees where the bears feel secure.

Travelways Bears require corridors of cover (made up of thick vegetation and/or steep topography) to enable them to travel between areas of food, water and shelter within their home range.

Dens Black bears use dens as shelter for hibernation from November to April in each year. Bears have been found denning in hollow logs, caves, holes dug into hillsides, under buildings and even in culvert pipes. Bears often prepare and may use more than one den, and may change dens during the winter because of disturbance or if the den leaks. Bears seldom re-use dens from one year to the next.

Hiding Cover Black bears evolved as animals that escape danger from predators and other bears by hiding in thick cover.

Feeding Sites Bears will often use areas with less cover than hiding areas or bedding sites for feeding. Feeding sites are, however, often found close to thick hiding cover to allow the bear to quickly escape danger if necessary.

NOTE: This information is based on actual research data from a study in Arizona. These components of shelter may vary slightly in different parts of North America.

2. In a fairly large open area (e.g., 50' x 50'), scatter the colored pieces of paper.

3. Have the students line up along one side of the area. Tell them that they are to become "bears" for the purposes of this activity. Review the concept of habitat—that a bear would need shelter, food, water and space in a suitable arrangement in order to survive. Do not tell the students what the letters on the squares of paper represent. Tell them only that they represent one element or component of bear habitat.

4. Direct the students to move as individual "bears" into the area. Each bear must pick up as many of the components of habitat as possible. Some competitive activity is acceptable as long as it is under control. Bears are territorial. Remember that if bears fight, which they seldom do, they can become injured and unable to successfully meet their needs for survival.

5. When the students have picked up all of the squares of paper in the area, have them return to the classroom or be seated in any comfortable area. Ask the students to separate their squares of paper into piles according to the letter on each. Using a chalkboard or large pad for a visual reference, ask the students to guess what the letters on the green cards represent—giving them the clue that each is an element of cover or shelter for a black bear. What kinds of shelter would a bear need? What do these initials represent? Record how many bears got at least one of each kind of shelter. How many got only four kinds? Three? Two? How many got only one kind of shelter? For the purposes of this activity, only those bears with at least one of each kind of necessary shelter can survive through one year. Ask students what would happen if a bear has all types of shelter except a den? (The bear could live from April through October, but would not have a secure place to hibernate and might not survive the winter.) Ask the students what would happen if a bear did not have travelways? (Without travelways, home ranges become fragmented and bears are not able to reach needed food, water or other shelter.) Suggesting that the students need one of each kind of shelter represents the importance of appropriate shelter as a necessary component of an animal's habitat. Shelter is a very important part of a bear's habitat. A bear needs shelter in which to search for food and water. Bears also need shelter for traveling through their home range; and shelter for bedding, hiding, and denning. In this activity, how many bears survived? What was a "limiting factor" for this population of bears? (Shelter.) What other things possibly could become limiting factors? (Water and space, or territory, are two examples.) Would food be a limiting factor for bears? (Yes, however bears are omnivores and can utilize many sources of food.)

6. Ask the students to summarize what they have learned about the importance of suitable habitat for bears' survival. How is this similar and different to the needs of other animals?

EVALUATION

1. Define "limiting factor." Describe some of the factors which may limit the survival of an animal that lives in your area.

2. Invent a board game to demonstrate some of the limiting factors associated with wildlife.

VISUAL VOCABULARY

OBJECTIVE
Students will interpret and identify ecological concepts.

METHOD
Students review vocabulary through use of pantomime.

BACKGROUND
NOTE: Use the Project WILD "Glossary" as a reference for this activity.

The major purpose of this activity is to increase students' familiarity with terms that are important in understanding wildlife and ecological systems.

MATERIALS
"Glossary" of small pieces of paper with words printed on them; container

PROCEDURE
OPTIONAL: Go outside for this activity. The environment is conducive, and noise level less a problem.
1. Give students handouts with words and their definitions on them. The words selected should encompass a broad variety of ecological concepts and also be easily portrayable by a small group of students. Some good selections would be: carnivore, herbivore, omnivore, extinction, predation, prey, commensalism, mutualism, parasitism, food chain, pollution, habitat, shelter, prescribed burn and ecosystem.
2. List all the words on small pieces of paper and put them in a container.
3. Divide the class into groups of four. Each group draws one word from the container, looks up the definition using the handout, and decides how to pantomime that word. Allow about five minutes for the groups to prepare their mimes.
4. Groups of students then take turns miming their word to the class. Set a time limit of one minute per group.
5. The rest of the class may use the handouts as a guideline for guessing the word being mimed.
6. If time permits, repeat the drawing and miming using different words, but keep the groups intact. Or, have "star mimers" assist students who muddled their mimes!
NOTE: This can be a good way to review vocabulary used in a unit of study.

VARIATION
1. Define words together in class orally. List words and definitions on a chalkboard. Good review! This encourages students to think and remember. It can save paper, too. Leave the room or erase the board to do pantomiming. This provides a challenge and encourages good memory retention.
2. Groups gain one point for a successful miming (having their word guessed within the one-minute time limit) and one point for guessing another group's mime correctly.

AQUATIC EXTENSIONS
Pick concepts that apply to understanding aquatic ecosystems. For example: eutrophication, marsh, wetland, river, watershed, acid precipitation, anadromous.

EVALUATION
1. Pick any 15 words important to understanding wildlife. Write definitions for each.
2. Using magazines as a source of photos find images that portray the wildlife related concepts you studied in this activity. Explain your choices.

Age: Grades 4-7 (and older)
Subjects: Science, Language Arts, Drama
Skills: application, invention, kinesthetic concept development, observation, problem solving, psychomotor development, reading, small group work, synthesis, visualization
Duration: 30 minutes or longer if students research definitions first
Group Size: requires two students; best with at least two teams of four students each
Setting: indoors or outdoors
Conceptual Framework Reference: III.
Key Vocabulary: wildlife concepts
Appendices: Simulations

RAINFALL AND THE FOREST

OBJECTIVES

Students will: 1) correlate rainfall data with vegetative communities; 2) correlate vegetative communities with animal life; 3) recognize interrelationships among living and non-living elements of the environment; and 4) understand that populations and the fluctuations of those populations are influenced by ever-changing climatic conditions.

METHOD

Students work with state highway and vegetative maps to determine relationships between rainfall, vegetation and animal habitats.

BACKGROUND

NOTE: This activity is useful for understanding distributions of plant and animal communities in some but not all states.

Many natural systems affect wildlife survival and population fluctuations. An inch or two more rain per year may allow forest instead of grassland, thus creating habitat for forest wildlife; it may encourage or interfere with animal reproduction, depending on species and time and amounts of rainfall.

Rainfall is just one form of precipitation. The types and distributions of annual precipitation can influence which plants will survive in an area. Many plants would benefit more from a series of small rain showers than from a single thunder shower that drops five inches of rain in less than an hour. Although precipitation has

significant impact on an area's vegetative composition, other factors also influence what grows where. Those factors include elevation, latitude, soil condition and type and the average number of frost-free days.

Food, water, shelter and space in the appropriate arrangement are all fundamental to wildlife populations; all of these relate to plants in some way. Among other influences, plants are the product of rainfall amounts and temperatures. Rainfall is controlled by such factors as wind direction, elevation, proximity to bodies of water, etc. Essentially, specific rainfall amounts create specific types of plant communities; e.g., grasslands, chaparral, or tropical rain forest. Each of these plant communities supports specific types of animals.

For example, 25 or more inches of rain in northern Arizona commonly produce a fir forest which is not habitat for antelope or buffalo, but is habitat for squirrels, blue grouse and perhaps elk.

Comparable amounts of rain, in other parts of the world, will usually produce communities of similar but different plants and animals.

This activity is designed for students to learn that specific habitats are the key to specific wildlife; populations of those wildlife species will fluctuate within those habitats; conditions within habitats continually change; and specific conditions, e.g., ten inches of rainfall, will create specific vegetative types and those specific plants allow for special animal types. Open grasslands, for example, created by approximately ten inches of rain, tend to be suited to grazing animals like buffalo, antelope and prairie dogs. Forests, created by more rainfall, may be more suited to Stellar's jays, fox squirrels and porcupines.

The major purpose of this activity is for students to recognize some of the relationships between climate, vegetation and wildlife species.

Age: Grades 6-9
Subjects: Science, Social Studies
Skills: analysis, application, comparing similarities and differences, discussion, generalization, synthesis
Duration: minimum of one hour; preferably two to three hours
Group Size: groups of two or three
Setting: indoors
Conceptual Framework Reference: III.A., III.B., III.C., III.D., III.F.
Key Vocabulary: vegetation, rainfall, rain shadow, elevation, community, habitat
Appendices: Local Resources, Ecosystem

MATERIALS

highway map of state (one per each group of two or three students); one sheet of tracing paper the same size as the map (usually about 19" x 24" or 17" x 22"); four crayons of different colors per group; information including elevation and rainfall annually for 25 to 30 communities within the state; vegetative map of state (one per each group of two or three students) OPTIONAL: range maps of selected wildlife species in state

PROCEDURE

1.   Discuss the concept of interrelatedness with your students—the idea that all things, living and non-living, are connected.

2.   Divide your students into teams of two or three. Give each group a highway map of your state, one sheet of tracing paper the same size as the map and four crayons of different colors. Also supply each team with information listing 25 to 30 communities around the state, including their elevation and annual rainfall. (Students could have developed this in the form of a data sheet beforehand.)

3.   Ask the student groups to outline the state on the tracing paper. Have students separate the list of communities into four rainfall-level groups, such as: 0" - 5", 5.1" - 10", 10.1" - 15", 15" plus. (You may need to adjust these categories depending on the typical rainfall amounts within your state.)

4.   Assign a color for each level of rainfall. Ask the students to make a large dot of the appropriate color for each community at its location on the tracing paper over the map. Community names are not necessary on the tracing paper.

5.   Consolidate each color into rainfall patterns. Lines between areas should run between dots of different colors, not from dot to dot. Color maps.

6.   Have students fold the highway maps and put them aside. Issue a vegetative map of your state to each group. These maps usually may be obtained through university agricultural extension services or botany departments. Highway and vegetative maps should be the same size, as nearly as possible.

7.   Find similarities in shapes created on student maps and those on vegetative maps. What rainfall level fits what vegetative type? Your correlations will not be exact but should be graphic. Most of the time, more than one vegetative type will be covered by one rainfall amount. How much rainfall is needed for grassland, chaparral, pine forest, for example? Determine and list

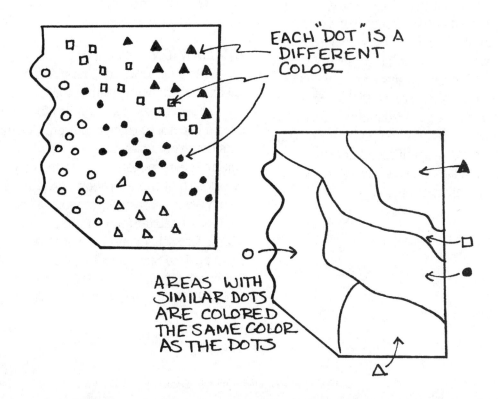

EACH "DOT" IS A DIFFERENT COLOR

AREAS WITH SIMILAR DOTS ARE COLORED THE SAME COLOR AS THE DOTS rainfall amounts for each vegetative community. Keep in mind that the student map has only 25 to 30 points of reference; there are thousands of data points used to develop the vegetative map so they will not be identical, but should be visibly similar.

8. Discuss rainfall in your area: Where does your rain come from? What influences rainfall patterns in your state? Does elevation influence rainfall? Why? What is rain shadow? Can you see where the typography influences rainfall in your state? Can you find two cities or towns that are at almost the same elevation, yet receive very different amounts of rain? Why is this? Would these rainfall/vegetative patterns be similar in other parts of the world? Would similar influences function all over the world?

9. Obtain information about the habitat needs of various animals in your state. If possible, obtain range maps of those species. Include animals such as crows, English sparrows and starlings that thrive in most locations as well as animals that are restricted to particular habitat types such as spotted owls and flying squirrels. Identify suitable habitat for your selected species on the vegetation map. Create a plastic overlay that shows those habitat areas. This can also be done by drawing symbols directly onto the vegetation map to represent the various animals. This creates a vegetation/habitat map without use of an overlay.

10. If available, correlate official range maps with the students maps. Ask if anyone has discovered locations where an animal's required habitat is present but the animal itself is not. Ask for explanations for why this might exist. Possible reasons include: disruptive human activity in the area; competition from other species; or circumstances in which a critical component of habitat such as water sources or a specific kind of plant is missing from the area although the vegetative map does not convey this information.

EXTENSION OR VARIATION
Obtain habitat maps of several mammals in your state. Translate these data to another transparent overlay. Identify correlations between parent overlay. Identify correlations between these data and the vegetative map. (Start with animals which are herbivores or omnivores. Save carnivores for last.) Habitats for reptiles and birds will also give good correlations. Have students make graphic representations, or write reports, about the interrelationships between rainfall, plant communities and various species of animals.

AQUATIC EXTENSIONS
1. See the Aquatic WILD activities, "Watershed" and "Where Does Water Go After School?"
2. Add major bodies of water, if any, to the map. Also add some way to identify watersheds. Identify and discuss possible influences of these areas of water and watersheds on the vegetation and wildlife in the associated areas.
3. Looking at the interrelationships among all the kinds of data and information you have gathered, generate a set of hypotheses about the factors that seem to most directly affect the availability of suitable habitat for wildlife in your state. Support your hypotheses with one or more paragraphs of writing based on your findings from this study.

EVALUATION
1. Write an essay describing the importance of rainfall and vegetative types to wildlife habitat.
2. Choose three wildlife species found in your state. Drop a handful of change, buttons or other small objects onto your state map. Notice where each of the objects comes to rest. Evaluate the habitat characteristics of each of those locations. Determine how well each of your chosen species would survive based on the type of habitat found at those various spots.
NOTE: This activity has been adapted from the Project Learning Tree Supplementary Activity Guide for Grades K through 6 (Washington D.C.: American Forest Institute, 1977.) Adapted with permission.

OWL PELLETS

OBJECTIVE
Students will be able to construct a simple food chain.

METHOD
Students examine owl pellets, reconstruct prey skeletons and identify prey.

BACKGROUND
On the floor of abandoned buildings, beneath a grove of tall trees, or under other structures that offer shelter from inclement weather, you may find the tangible signs left by some birds that most people see infrequently. These objects are uniformly dark grey and measure from one and one-half to three inches long and three quarters to one inch in diameter. You might think of them as mouse kits, sparrow kits, or prey kits. They typically include bones, fur and feathers. For those who read them, they contain a wealth of information about wildlife. They are owl pellets.

Owls are not picky eaters like certain other raptors. They swallow their prey as nearly whole as possible. Fur, feathers and bones, however, cannot be digested nor will they pass through the digestive system. About 12 hours after consuming a meal, an owl casts, or regurgitates, a "pellet."

Owls are not the only birds that cast pellets. Over 300 species of birds cast pellets. They include eagles and hawks as well as smaller birds like robins and tree sparrows.

Owl pellets are clean of all flesh and virtually odorless. After a short drying period they can be handled easily by all age groups. Because they are found under the perch they may occasionally be "whitewashed" by the bird. Pellets will keep almost indefinitely if dry and protected in a plastic bag or closed jar. Those collected on a field trip or during the summer can be saved for later examination. Pellets may also be purchased through scientific supply catalogs.

Owl pellets have been used for scientific study of small mammals and their distribution. With owls doing the collecting, the scientist must only locate the owl roost to obtain the skulls and bones of the small prey living in the area. From these parts, the species can be identified. This has helped map the areas occupied by certain small creatures that might otherwise have escaped detection.

Once the bones are separated from the mass of fur in the pellet, a number of anatomy lessons are possible. Hip bones and the upper leg bone with its large ball joint are readily identified. The scapula or shoulder blade, ribs, other leg bones, vertebrae and foot bones along with the skull are all recognizable when sorted out.

The major purpose of this activity is for students to construct a simple food chain, recognizing interdependence in ecological systems through study of owl pellets.

MATERIALS
owl pellets; dissecting tools (toothpicks work fine); posterboard; glue; small animal skeleton diagrams and skull guide
OPTIONAL: hand lenses or magnifying glasses; gloves

PROCEDURE
1.   Locate some owl pellets under trees or in abandoned buildings where owls may roost. Local wildlife organizations may be able to help you identify possible roosting sites. Bird watchers and people who rehabili-

Age: Grades 3-7
Subjects: Science
Skills: analysis, comparing similarities and differences, generalization
Duration: 20-45 minutes
Group Size: two or three students working in groups
Setting: indoors
Conceptual Framework Reference: III.B., III.B.1., III.B.2.
Key Vocabulary: owl, pellets, food chain, cast, raptors, skeletons of songbirds, skulls of small animals
Appendices: Ecosystem, Field Ethics, Local Resources

tate injured birds of prey may be of particular help. Collected pellets should be dried in a traditional oven at 325 degrees F for forty minutes or 20 seconds on high in a microwave oven. Pellets can also be purchased from scientific supply distributors. Identify the species of owl that cast the pellets if this can be done without disturbing the animal.

2. Divide the students into small groups of two or three. Review safe lab procedures including the need to wash hands before and after doing the activity and the importance of not eating or drinking during the activity. Give each student group an owl pellet.

3. Have groups of students separate the bones from the fur and feathers. This can also be done in a shallow pan of water. Where possible, identify the skulls and jaws of the prey species. Use a hand lens or magnifying glass to look at the teeth. Consider how the teeth are arranged. Would they work best at tearing flesh, grinding seeds, or eating plants? Using the teeth as a guide, determine what kinds of food the prey species most likely ate.

4. Determine if there are bones from more than one animal in the pellet. If there are, determine how many different animals and species are represented in one pellet.

5. Lay out the bones to form as many complete skeletons as possible. Skeletons may be glued on to poster board for display and labeling.

6. Make a food chain that includes the owl, its prey and what the prey eats. Discuss!

EVALUATION

1. Draw a picture of a simple food chain that represents the eating habits of another bird of prey and its food sources.

2. Write a poem that describes the interrelationships between owls, small birds, rodents and the environments in which they live.

OH DEER!

OBJECTIVES

Students will: 1) identify and describe food, water, and shelter as three essential components of habitat; 2) describe the importance of good habitat for animals; 3) define "limiting factors" and give examples; and 4) recognize that some fluctuations in wildlife populations are natural as ecological systems undergo constant change.

METHOD

Students become "deer" and components of habitat in a highly involving physical activity.

BACKGROUND

A variety of factors affects the ability of wildlife to successfully reproduce and to maintain their populations over time. Disease, predator/prey relationships, varying impacts of weather conditions from season to season (e.g., early freezing, heavy snows, flooding, drought), accidents, environmental pollution and habitat destruction and degradation are among these factors.

Some naturally-caused as well as culturally-induced limiting factors serve to prevent wildlife populations from reproducing in numbers greater than their habitat can support. An excess of such limiting factors, however, leads to threatening, endangering, and eliminating whole species of animals.

The most fundamental of life's necessities for any animal are food, water, shelter and space in a suitable arrangement. Without these essential components, animals cannot survive.

Age: Grades 4-12
Subjects: Science, Math, Social Studies, Physical Education
Skills: application, comparing similarities and differences, description, discussion, generalization, graphing, kinesthetic concept development, observation, psychomotor development
Duration: 30 to 45 minutes
Group Size: 15 and larger recommended
Setting: indoors or outdoors; large area for running needed
Conceptual Framework Reference: I.C.2., III.B., III.B.2., III.B.3., III.B.5., III.C., III.C.1., III.C.2., III.E., III.E.1., III.E.2., III.F., III.F.1., III.F.2., III.F.3., III.F.4., III.F.5., IV.C., IV.C.1., IV.C.2.
Key Vocabulary: habitat, limiting factors, predator, prey, population, balance of nature, ecosystem
Appendices: Outdoors, Simulations, Ecosystem

This activity is designed for students to learn that:

- good habitat is the key to wildlife survival;
- a population will continue to increase in size until some limiting factors are imposed;
- limiting factors contribute to fluctuations in wildlife populations; and
- nature is never in "balance," but is constantly changing.

Wildlife populations are not static. They continuously fluctuate in response to a variety of stimulating and limiting factors. We tend to speak of limiting factors as applying to a single species, although one factor may affect many species. Natural limiting factors, or those modeled after factors in natural systems, tend to maintain populations of species at levels within predictable ranges. This kind of "balance in nature" is not static, but is more like a teeter-totter than a balance. Some species fluctuate or cycle annually. Quail, for example, may start with a population of 100 pairs in early spring; grow to a population of 1200 birds by late spring; and decline slowly to a winter population of 100 pairs again. This cycle appears to be almost totally controlled by the habitat components of food, water, shelter and space, which are also limiting factors. Habitat components are the most fundamental and thereby the most critical of limiting factors in most natural settings.

This activity is intended to be a simple but powerful way for students to grasp some basic concepts: that everything in natural systems is interrelated; that populations of organisms are continuously affected by elements of their environment; and that populations of animals do not stay at the same static number year after year in their environment, but rather are continually changing in a process of maintaining dynamic equilibria in natural systems.

The major purpose of this activity is for students to understand the importance of suitable habitat as well as factors that may affect wildlife populations in constantly changing ecosystems.

MATERIALS

area—either indoors or outdoors—large enough for students to run, e.g., playing field; chalkboard or flip chart; writing materials

PROCEDURE

1. Begin by telling students that they are about to participate in an activity that emphasizes the most essential things that animals need in order to survive. Review the essential components of habitat with the students: food, water, shelter, and space in a suitable arrangement. This activity emphasizes three of those habitat components—food, water and shelter—but the students should not forget the importance of the animals having sufficient space in which to live, and that all the components have to be in a suitable arrangement or the animals will die.

2. Ask your students to count off in fours. Have all the ones go to one area; all twos, threes and fours go together to another area. Mark two parallel lines on the ground or floor ten to 20 yards apart. Have the ones line up behind one line; the rest of the students line up behind the other line.

3. The ones become "deer." All deer need good habitat in order to survive. Ask the students what the essential components of habitat are again: **food, water, shelter** and **space in a suitable arrangement.** For the purposes of this activity, we will assume that the deer have enough space in which to live. We are emphasizing food, water and shelter. The deer (the ones) need to find food, water and shelter in order to survive. When a deer is looking for **food**, it should clamp its hands over its stomach. When it is looking for **water**, it puts its hands over its mouth. When it is looking for **shelter**, it holds its hands together over its head. A deer can choose to look for any one of its needs during each round or segment of the activity; **the deer cannot, however, change what it is looking for;** e.g., when it sees what is available, during that round. It can change what it is looking for in the next round, if it survives.

4. The twos, threes and fours are food, water and shelter—components of habitat. Each student gets to choose at the beginning of each round which component he or she will be during that round. The students depict which component they are in the same way the deer show what they are looking for; that is, hands on stomach for food, etc.

5. The activity starts with all players lined up on their respective lines (deer on one side; habitat components on the other side)—and **with their backs to the students at the other line.**

6. The facilitator or teacher begins the first round by asking all of the students to make their signs—each deer deciding what it is looking for, each habitat component deciding what it is. Give the students a few moments to get their hands in place—over stomachs,

mouths, or over their heads. (As you look at the two lines of students, you will normally see a lot of variety—with some students water, some food, some shelter. As the activity proceeds, sometimes the students confer with each other and all make the same sign. That's okay, although don't encourage it. For example, all the students in habitat might decide to be shelter. That could represent a drought year with no available food or water.)

NOTE: If students switching symbols in the middle of a round is a problem, you can avoid that by having stacks of three different tokens, or pieces of colored paper, to represent food, water and shelter at both the habitat and deer ends of the field. At the start of each round, players choose one of the symbols before turning around to face the other group.

7. When you can see that the students are ready, count: "One. . . two. . . three." At the count of three, each deer and each habitat component turn to face the opposite group, continuing to hold their signs clearly.

8. When deer see the habitat component they need, they are to run to it. Each deer must hold the sign of what it is looking for until getting to the habitat component person with the same sign. Each deer that reaches its necessary habitat component takes the "food," "water," or "shelter" back to the deer side of the line. This is to represent the deer's successfully meeting its needs, and successfully reproducing as a result. Any deer that fails to find its food, water, or shelter dies and becomes part of the habitat. That is, in the next round, the deer that died is a habitat component and so is available as food, water, or shelter to the deer who are still alive.

NOTE: When more than one deer reaches a habitat component, the student who gets there first survives. Habitat components stay in place on their line until a deer needs them. If no deer needs a particular habitat component during a round, the habitat component just stays where it is in the habitat. The habitat person can, however, change which component it is from round to round.

9. You as the facilitator or teacher keep track of how many deer there are at the beginning of the activity, and at the end of each round you record the number of deer also. Continue the activity for approximately 15 rounds. Keep the pace brisk and the students will thoroughly enjoy it.

10. At the end of the 15 rounds, gather the students together to discuss the activity. Encourage them to talk about what they experienced and saw. For example, they saw a small herd of deer (seven students in a class size of 28) begin by finding more than enough of

its habitat needs. The population of deer expanded over two to three rounds of the activity until the habitat was depleted and there was not sufficient food, water and shelter for all the members of the herd. At that point, deer starved or died of thirst or lack of shelter, and they returned as part of the habitat. Such things happen in nature also.

NOTE: In real life, large mammal populations might also experience higher infant mortality and lower reproductive rates.

11. Using a flip chart pad or an available chalkboard, post the data recorded during the activity. The number of deer at the beginning of the activity and at the end of each round represent the number of deer in a series of years. That is, the beginning of the activity is year one; each round is an additional year. Deer can be posted by fives for convenience. For example:

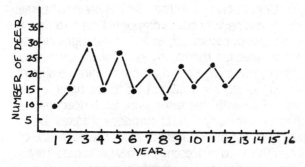

The students will see this visual reminder of what they experienced during the activity: the deer population fluctuated over a period of years. This is a natural process as long as the factors which limit the population do not become excessive, to the point where the animals cannot successfully reproduce. The wildlife populations will tend to peak, decline, and rebuild, peak, decline, and rebuild—as long as there is good habitat and sufficient numbers of animals to successfully reproduce.

12. In discussion, ask the students to summarize some of the things they have learned from this activity. What do animals need to survive? What are some of the "limiting factors" that affect their survival? Are wildlife populations static, or do they tend to fluctuate, as part of an overall "balance of nature?" Is nature ever really in "balance" or are ecological systems involved in a process of constant change?

VARIATIONS

1. After the students have played several rounds of "Oh Deer!," introduce a predator such as a mountain lion or wolf into the simulation. The predator starts in a designated "predator den" area off to the side. The predator has to skip or hop. This reduces the possibility of violent collisions between deer and predators. The predators can only tag deer when they are going towards the habitat and are between the habitat and deer lines. Once a deer is tagged, the predator escorts the deer back to the predator den. That simulates the time it takes to eat. The "eaten" deer is now a predator. Predators that fail to tag someone die and become habitat. That is, in the next round, the predators that died join the habitat line. They will become available to surviving deer as either food, water or shelter. During each round, the teacher should keep track of the numbers of predators as well as the number of deer. Incorporate these data into the graphs.

2. Instead of drawing the line graph for students as described in procedure 11, have the students create their own graphs. Provide them with the years and numbers of deer. Depending upon the age group, they can make picture, line or bar graphs.

EXTENSIONS

1. When you have finished tabulating and discussing the graph data, ask the students if they have ever heard of the Hudson Bay trappers in American history. Tell them, briefly, who they were.

There is a hundred years, or more, of records of the activities of these trappers. In those records are some interesting data. These data refer to pelts shipped from America to Europe, particularly the pelts of snowshoe hares and lynx. Researchers have found that snowshoe hare populations seem to peak about every seven to nine years and then crash, repeating the process over each comparable time period. So, a snowshoe hare population graph would look like this:

It has also been discovered that lynx populations do the same thing—except that they do it one year behind the hare populations. The combined graph would look like this:

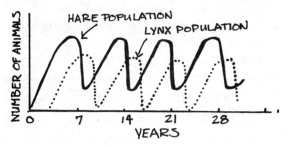

Graph this right over the deer graph that you made, adding first the hares, and then the lynx. Ask the students:

- Which animal is the predator? Which prey?
- Are predators controlling the prey, or are prey controlling the predators? (We have been brought up to "know" that predators control the prey—and are now discovering that this is not so. The number of prey animals available tells us how many predators can live in the area.)
- Is this like the deer habitat activity we just played? Who controls? (Sometimes the habitat—when the deer population is not too large; sometimes the habitat—when the deer population "gets on top of it" and destroys the vegetative food and cover.)

2. Some recent research has added a new dimension to the story of the snowshoe hares and the lynx.
It has been found that a major winter food of the hare is a small willow. As hare populations grow, the use of the willow plants grows too. But, when the willow plant has been "hedged" or eaten back so far, the plant generates a toxin (poison) which precludes use by the hare. That is when the hare population crashes, followed by the crash of the lynx population about a year later. Then the willow, relieved of pressure, begins to grow again. The hare population begins to grow in response, and last of all, within a year or so, the lynx population follows. And the cycle has begun again—over and over—every seven to nine years.

3. Discuss the "balance of nature." Is it ever in "balance?"

AQUATIC EXTENSION

Do the activity in exactly the same fashion, except substitute an aquatic species of wildlife. The essentials are still the same. In this case, rather than assuming all the necessary space is available, assume all the water is available but space is needed, as is food and shelter. Hands on stomach is food, hands together over head is shelter—and arms out to the side is space. Otherwise, conduct the activity in the same fashion. The objective remains the same, except that now you are identifying food, shelter and space as three essential components of habitat. Examples of possible aquatic species: manatee, salmon, frog.

EVALUATION

1. Name three essential components of habitat.
2. Define "limiting factors." Give three examples.
3. Examine the graph. What factors may have caused the following population changes.
   a) between years 1 and 2?
   b) between years 3 and 4?
   c) between years 5 and 6?
   d) between years 7 and 8?

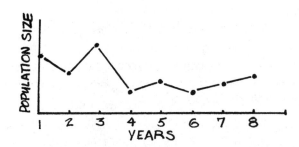

4. Which of the following graphs represents the more typically balanced population?

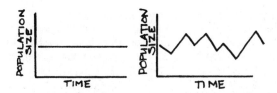

BIRDS OF PREY

OBJECTIVES

Students will: 1) interpret a graph of an animal population, noting changes over time; 2) hypothesize a relationship between temperature, ground squirrel behavior and falcon populations; 3) predict the foraging distribution of falcons following the aestivation of ground squirrels; and 4) generalize that ecosystems are comprised of interdependent parts.

METHOD

Students interpret data, and generate and test hypotheses.

BACKGROUND

In the Birds of Prey Natural Area in southwestern Idaho, a large number of prairie falcons nest in late spring and early summer each year. The falcon lives mainly off a large population of townsend ground squirrels which live in the surrounding flatlands. Throughout the breeding season, the population of falcons increases as more and more birds move into the area to nest, until available nesting sites are taken. Since the townsend ground squirrels serve as the food base for the falcons, continued activity and availability of this prey base is crucial for the support of the nesting falcons. As the summer progresses, the daytime temperatures in the area increase to a point (around July 4th) where it is too hot for the ground squirrels, and they immediately go underground and undergo a form of summer sleep called "aestivation" or summer hibernation. Without available prey, the falcons and their new offspring must either leave or die. Within a day of the ground squirrels' aestivation, nearly all falcons capable of flight move out of the area in search of other food (other ground squirrel species and rodents). Most move to higher, cooler elevations where other species of ground squirrels such as columbian ground squirrels remain active. This sudden seeming "loss" of falcons from the Birds of Prey area is directly tied to the important environmental factor of temperature.

The major purpose of this activity is for students to recognize the interdependence of elements of ecosystems, based on the example of prairie falcons and townsend ground squirrels in southwestern Idaho.

MATERIALS

graphs A-E (information below) enlarged for classroom use
OPTIONAL: photographs of predator and prey species

PROCEDURE

1. Set the stage by giving students the following background information:
The Birds of Prey Natural Area hosts the largest concentration of nesting prairie falcons in the world each spring and summer. The birds nest along the cliff above the Snake River and use the huge townsend

Age: Grades 10-12
Subjects: Mathematics, Science (Biology, Zoology)
Skills: analysis, comparing similarities and differences, computation (interpreting line graphs), description, drawing, evaluation, generalization, hypothesis formation and testing, observation, problem solving, reading
Duration: one or two 45-minute periods
Group Size: large group, with small groups working with data and discussing
Setting: indoors
Conceptual Framework Reference: I.A.2., III.A., III.A.1., III.A.2., III.A.3., III.B., III.B.1., III.B.2., III.B.3., III.B.5., III.C., III.C.1., III.C.2., III.D., III.D.1., III.D.2., III.D.3., III.D.4., III.E., III.E.1., III.E.2.
Key Vocabulary: aestivation, population, hypothesis, prediction, interdependence, ecological systems
Appendices: Observations and Inferences

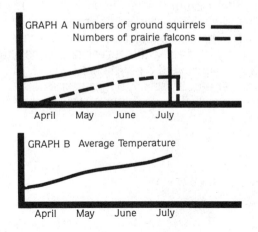

GRAPH A Numbers of ground squirrels
Numbers of prairie falcons

April May June July

GRAPH B Average Temperature

April May June July

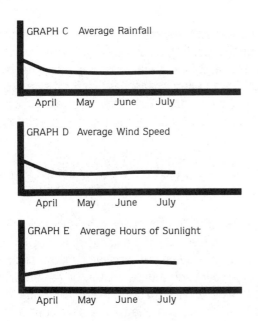

GRAPH C   Average Rainfall

April   May   June   July

GRAPH D   Average Wind Speed

April   May   June   July

GRAPH E   Average Hours of Sunlight

April   May   June   July

ground squirrel population for food. This prey species lives on the flat land above the canyon.

Each year, the populations of these two species change from April through July.

2. Show the students Graph A. Have them look at the graph to see what happens to the populations of predator and prey, and answer the following questions:
- What do you observe happening?
- What do you notice about the townsend ground squirrel population in April, May and June?
- What do you notice about the ground squirrel population in July?
- What do you think caused this? What might have happened to the squirrels?
- What do you notice about the falcon population in April and May?
- What do you notice happening to the falcon population in July? What do you think caused this?
- How do these populations seem to be related?
- What might have caused the change?

Ask the students to speculate, offer hypotheses and develop questions to assist with finding a solution to this dilemma.

3. Show the students Graphs B, C, D, and E. Using the information provided on these graphs, encourage the students to test their ideas and hypotheses.

4. Ask the students to share those ideas which seem to be most reasonable given the information presented in the graphs.

5. Summarize the activity by:
- Closed inquiry approach—Review the sequence of events and role of temperature in triggering "aestivation." Ask the students to predict where they might find the falcons after they leave the area. Where would they go to obtain food? What kind of prey species might they use? Have the students suggest other physical factors which influence or limit wildlife activity. Have the students also propose some ways these same factors influence or limit human activity.

OR

- Open inquiry approach—Do not provide the above information, but allow continued testing of ideas with data which the students could collect in teams.

6. Extend the discussion to the concept of interdependence in ecological systems. What was interdependent in this situation? Encourage the students to think of other examples of interdependence. Can they think of any ecosystems that are not composed of interdependent parts? Generalize that all ecosystems are made up of interdependent parts.

EXTENSIONS

1. The prey ordinarily used by the falcons at the Natural Area—the townsend ground squirrel—is distributed throughout much of the plains area above the river, which is also potentially good agricultural land. Given this information, the activity could be extended to an investigation into competitive uses for the land occupied by the prey base; the legislation behind the establishment of the Natural Area; and/or related controversies.

2. Investigate the process by which such natural areas are set aside, the agencies involved and related issues.

EVALUATION

Describe the usefulness of mathematical data in interpreting relationships between organisms in ecosystems, using the Birds of Prey Natural Area as your example.

CARRYING CAPACITY

OBJECTIVES

Students will: 1) formulate and test hypotheses related to wildlife populations and carrying capacity; and 2) describe the significance of carrying capacity.

METHOD

Students become herds of animals seeking food in a physically-involving activity.

BACKGROUND

Carrying capacity affects all living things, including humans. Carrying capacity may be seen as a type of dynamic equilibrium. It is typically expressed as the number of animals of a given type which can be supported in a given area.

Carrying capacity is also interpreted more broadly as the number of living things—plants as well as animals—any area of land or water can support at any one time. Different life forms will have a different carrying capacity within the same area.

Carrying capacity is usually limited by some aspect of a species' habitat requirements. These requirements include the quantity and quality of available food, water, shelter, space and the suitability of their arrangement. Different factors will be important in each case. Natural and human causes both affect carrying capacity. Effects may be short or long term.

Carrying capacity for many species is in a constant state of change, both seasonally and from year to year. For example, it is typically most limited for terrestrial animals in the winter season when food supplies are reduced. Year to year variations may result from factors such as natural disasters, changes in rainfall and temperature patterns, or human interventions. Factors affecting plant growth will affect animals since they are either directly (as herbivores or omnivores) or indirectly (as carnivores) dependent on plants.

Populations of living things tend to fluctuate naturally around some level. Carrying capacity is that level. A population may be below carrying capacity such as in the spring following a hard winter, or temporarily above it. The latter situation inevitably results in a decline of the population due to a variety of natural limiting factors, e.g., mortality, disease, emigration and lowered reproduction rate, and usually lasts for a short period. The carrying capacity of any area can be affected and adjusted by such natural factors as well as by human intervention.

A population will therefore tend to naturally fluctuate with carrying capacity, with or without human intervention. Humans may not always be willing to accept the consequences of natural events, however. Examples of intentional human intervention are reintroducing predators, winter feeding, constructing nesting boxes, planting additional vegetation suitable for food, relocating animals and hunting. Human intervention can reduce a population or prevent its expansion to meet an expected natural reduction in carrying capacity. Such an intervention may result in a higher survival rate.

Alteration of habitat quality or quantity may increase or decrease carrying capacity. Environmental degradation may reduce it for affected species. Activities such as development or pollution tend not to be aimed at intentionally reducing carrying capacity but often have this impact.

Intentional intervention may be based on a particular management philosophy or practice. Management of an area of land or water in relation to its carrying capacity for certain species can be subject to question

Age: Grades 7-12
Subjects: Mathematics, Science (Biology, Life Science), Social Studies
Skills: analysis, comparing similarities and differences, description, evaluation, generalization, hypothesis formation and testing, kinesthetic concept development, listing, observation, psychomotor development
Duration: 45 minutes or longer
Group Size: any; groups of five; six groups of five students each is 30 students with rounds of 12 minutes
Setting: indoors
Conceptual Framework Reference: III.B.6., III.F., III.F.1., III.F.2., III.F.3., III.F.4., III.F.5.
Key Vocabulary: carrying capacity, population, management, habitat
Appendices: Simulations, Ecosystem

and controversy. Whether and/or how it is appropriate for humans to intervene in natural systems is sometimes a part of such questions and controversy. Management may be defined as intentional choice based on human goals and objectives. Such goals and objectives are always open to question by other groups and individuals.

The major purpose of this activity is to provide students with a general introduction to the topic of carrying capacity.

MATERIALS
one bag of dried beans; kitchen timer

PROCEDURE
1. Count out enough beans so that there are five per student. Spread the beans out on a table in a cleared area of the classroom. This arrangement of the beans is to represent a food supply which has been fixed by the end of a growing season.
2. Divide the class into "herds" of five students each, and have them all gather on the periphery of the cleared area.
3. Act as a timekeeper and set the timer to ring at intervals of one minute or less.
4. Each "herd" is to come up to the table at each interval. Each student in each herd is to attempt to take one piece of food per turn, simulating the animal's need to eat reasonably regularly. When you start, all the first people from each herd will move at once to get food. Then they tag the next person in their herd who moves to get food, who then tags the next person, and so on. This continues long enough so that some students don't get to the food supply before the timer rings and the round ends. Any member of a herd going for three rounds without getting a bit of food dies. (The time interval you use per round depends on the size of the physical area you use for the activity as well as the size of your class of students. For the purposes of this activity, all students should not get enough food to survive.)
5. The food will run out before the next growing season begins and a significant percentage of the animals will die, depending upon the size of the "herd." Discuss with the students what could be done or might happen to allow more of the population to live

through the "winter" on the food available. Options may include reducing the population in various ways to match the carrying capacity—for example, by redistributing some of the population to another area, introducing or increasing natural predator populations, or opening the area to hunting before the winter begins. Options to increase the carrying capacity could include bringing in or planting more "food" for the "herds." Another option is no action in the form of human intervention. Each of these options involves costs as well as benefits, and each may be controversial. (See activities under the topics "Management of Habitat" and "Management Techniques" in the Cross References.)
6. Repeat the activity two more times, incorporating two different options the students have discussed. What happens to the number of survivors that live to reproduce the next year?
7. Repeat the activity one more time, incorporating one of the options used above, and also include five or six young animals born the previous spring. This can be done by designating one student in each "herd" to take food for themselves and an offspring. How does this annual increase affect the population? What must now happen to re-establish the herd size within carrying capacity?
8. Record the number of "survivors" that result from the various manipulations of carrying capacity on the chalkboard. What can be learned from this numerical representation? Which manipulation was the most successful? Using what criteria for success? What are examples of both cultural and natural influences on carrying capacity?
9. Ask for a summary of some of the most important things the students feel they have learned about the concept of carrying capacity.

EVALUATION
It is the early 1900s, and you are a scientist. You have just learned of the following situation: All the natural predators of deer in the Kiabab Plateau in Arizona were removed from the area. Within a few years, the deer population had increased tremendously and within another few years, the population had collapsed to a very small number. Formulate a hypothesis that might explain the increase and decrease of the deer population related to carrying capacity. Explain how you would test this hypothesis.

I'M THIRSTY

OBJECTIVE
Students will make inferences about the importance of adaptations in order for wildlife and other animals to survive.

METHOD
Students use data provided to perform mathematical calculations and make inferences.

BACKGROUND
NOTE: The effectiveness of this activity is enhanced when it is preceded by an introduction to the concept of adaptation. See "Adaptation Artistry," "Muskox Maneuvers" and "Who Fits Here?"

The major purpose of this activity is for students to manipulate simple data in order to heighten their awareness of the importance of adaptation to wildlife.

MATERIALS
paper and pencils

PROCEDURE
1. Provide the students with this background information about desert bighorn sheep:

Age: Grades 7-12
Subjects: Mathematics, Science (Biology, Life Science)
Skills: computation (use of data to calculate mathematical problems), discussion, evaluation, generalization, inference
Duration: 45 minutes
Group Size: any
Setting: indoors
Conceptual Framework Reference: III.A., III.A.1., III.A.2., III.A.3., III.B., III.B.1., III.B.3., III.C., III.D., III.D.1., III.D.2., III.D.3., III.D.4., III.D.5.
Key Vocabulary: adaptation, inflow
Appendices: Metric Chart

I'M THIRSTY

Animals make what sometimes seem to be incredible adaptations in order to survive in their environments. Use the following hypothetical example of the desert bighorn sheep: The desert bighorn live in dry, sparsely vegetated areas of the Southwest. Temperatures on summer days are frequently over 100 F. During the hottest months of summer, ewes (females) and lambs come to waterholes almost daily. The male sheep, however, called "rams," sometimes do not come to water for nearly a week at a time. These rams may range 20 miles away from the waterhole, and then travel the 20 miles back again for another drink. Add to this the approximate number of five miles traveled per day during the week away from water—and you arrive at a figure of almost 75 miles between drinks! The rams are believed to drink approximately four gallons of water when they do come to water, while an ewe drinks approximately one gallon and a lamb drinks two pints.

2. Given the above background information, ask the students to carry out these calculations:

Questions for Students

a) How many miles to the gallon does a ram get?

b) How many gallons of water would a ram drink in a month?

c) How many gallons of water would a ewe drink in a month?

d) How many gallons of water would a lamb drink in a month?

e) How much water must be available in a waterhole for 10 rams, 16 ewes, and 7 lambs in order for them to survive the months of June, July and August?

f) What rate in inflow would a waterfall have to have to sustain the population given above if water evaporated at a rate of ten gallons per day?

---

3. Predict various complications that could develop if there were only one-half the amount of water you calculated as being needed in step e).

4. Discuss the importance of adaptations to wildlife and other animals, based on the example of the bighorn sheep in the southwestern United States. NOTE: This activity can be used effectively as an extension or review for other activities about adaptation.

EXTENSIONS

1. Study topographical maps of typical desert bighorn sheep habitat. Predict the animals' food requirements based on available vegetation. Research caloric value of available foods. Estimate the animals' caloric intake per day, per week, per year.

2. Find out what the available seasonal water supply is in a desert bighorn sheep habitat area. Predict the seasonal maximum carrying capacity of the site based on water supply.

3. Adapt this activity for a social studies class. Compare daily bighorn sheep water usage to human daily water usage. Use as a point from which to discuss the importance of water conservation—to people, domesticated animals, wildlife, industry, natural resources, the planetary environment, etc.

EVALUATION

Discuss the importance of adaptation. Describe examples of adaptation and its importance to any species of animal, other than bighorn sheep.

Answer Key for Teachers

a) 75 miles/week ÷ 4 gallons/week = 18.75 miles/gallon

b) 52 weeks/year ÷ 12 months/year = 4.33 weeks/month
4 gallons/week × 4.33 weeks/month = 17.32 gallons/month

c) 1 gallon/day × 7 days/week = 7 gallons/week
7 gallons/week × 4.33 weeks/month = 30.31 gallons/month

d) 2 pints/day × 7 days/week = 14 pints/week
Convert to gallons. 8 pints = 1 gallon
14 pints/week ÷ 8 pints/gallon = 1.75 gallons/week
1.75 gallons/week × 4.33 weeks/month = 7.58 gallons/month

e) June = 30 days, July = 31 days, August = 31 days, 92 days total. This assumes there is no water evaporation and no rainfall—both of which are poor assumptions.
Rams: 4 gallons/week ÷ 7 days/week = 0.57 gallons/day
0.57 gallons/day × 92 days × 10 rams = 524 gallons of water for rams
Ewes: 1 gallon/day × 92 days × 16 ewes = 1472 gallons for ewes
Lambs: First convert daily water consumption to gallons.
8 pints = 1 gallon
2 pints/day ÷ by 8 pints/gallon = 0.25 gallons/day
0.25 gallons/day × 92 days × 7 lambs = 161 gallons of water for lambs
Total gallons for herd:
524 (rams) + 1472 (ewes) + 161 (lambs) = 2157 gallons of water for herd

f) 2157 gallons of water ÷ 92 days = 23.45 gallons/day for herd

23.45 gallons/day + 10 gallons to make up for evaporation = 33.45 gallons/day rate of inflow from waterfall

TIME LAPSE

OBJECTIVE
Students will describe and illustrate concepts of variation, change, or adaptation in ecosystems.

METHOD
Students prepare and present a visual interpretation of a concept.

BACKGROUND
Photographic and other visually oriented studies are not only ways to provide students with experience in developing a personal art form, but they also can be highly sophisticated and instructive means by which to portray concepts.

The major purpose of this activity is to provide students an opportunity to acquire and convey insight into concepts of variation, change and adaptation in ecosystems.

MATERIALS
photographic equipment and materials or any other visual medium of the student's choice

PROCEDURE
1. The assignment: to prepare a photo or other visual study of a concept important to understanding of natural systems. Recommended concepts: variation,

---

Age: Grades 7-12
Subjects: Science, Art, Photography, Drama, Language Arts
Skills: application, description, invention, media construction, synthesis, visualization, writing
Duration: one to three 45-minute periods from concept to presenting final product
Group Size: any; individual or small group activity
Setting: indoors and outdoors
Conceptual Framework Reference: I.B.4., I.C.4., II.A.3., II.B., II.B.1., II.B.3., II.B.4., II.E., II.E.3., II.F., III.A., III.A.1., III.A.3., III.B., III.C., III.C.1., III.C.2., III.D., III.D.1., III.D.2., III.D.5.
Key Vocabulary: environment, natural systems; additional vocabulary depends on student choices
Appendices: Ecosystem

---

change and adaptation. The time period may vary. In a science class, photos could be taken of an eroding hillside over a two-month period; or of seasonal change, winter to spring; or of rapid change, the shedding of a snake skin. In a social studies class, for example, students could use old photographs of natural areas to monitor change over time. The medium may vary; for example 8mm movie, video tape, slide show, or 35 mm black and white stills if students produce the images through photography. Or, magazine pictures, historical photos, natural artifacts (e.g., live and decaying pine boughs) could be used. Some students might want to present their interpretation of the concept through use of mime or other theater arts.

2. Students may work alone or in small groups. Each student or group should select a concept to portray, and then begin planning for the visual study. OPTIONAL: The students can develop a "treatment" or statement of the idea they wish to portray. This may include words and sketches. (Storyboard material is available at some art and photo shops, and can be useful in this process.)

3. When the students have developed and completed their products—with titles as appropriate—they may want to invite other students, faculty, parents, or community to see the results!

EXTENSION
Isolate five physical actions that could be used to demonstrate a concept. Demonstrate them for the class, and see if they can guess what the concept is. Or, several of you work together to present a group improvisation of a significant concept.

EVALUATION
Give three examples of the concept you chose to investigate. Describe its importance in natural systems.

WHICH NICHE?

OBJECTIVES
Students will: 1) define ecological niche; and 2) give at least one example of an animal and its ecological niche.

METHOD
Students compare ecological niches with careers in their community.

BACKGROUND
Each animal has a role in the community. This is called its ecological niche. The niche includes such things as where the animal lives, where and how it gathers food, its role in the food chain, what it gives to and does for the community, its habits, periods of activity, etc.

An animal's niche can be described as "what it does for a living." In a sense, this can be compared to what people do for a living—that is, what their jobs or professions are in the community in which they live.

The major purpose of this activity is for students to understand the concept of ecological niche, simultaneously learning more about potential careers in their own community.

MATERIALS
guest speaker; chalkboard; reference materials

Age: Grades 7-12
Subjects: Social Studies, (Community Studies, Economics), Career Education, Science (Biology, Life Science), Language Arts, Vocational Agriculture
Skills: analysis, application, classification, comparing similarities and differences, description, discussion, generalization, interview (guest speaker), listening, listing, public speaking, reading, reporting, research, small group work, synthesis, writing
Duration: one to four 45-minute periods
Group Size: any
Setting: indoors
Conceptual Framework Reference: III.A.2.
Key Vocabulary: ecological niche, career, community
Appendices: Local Resources

PROCEDURE
1. Explain to the students that in this activity they will be comparing human professions to the roles of animals in environments (animal "professions").
2. Begin with a discussion of jobs in your community. What jobs are there (those of parents, friends, their own, etc.)? (OPTIONAL: Invite a doctor, dentist, social worker, truck driver, cook, etc. to your class to talk about their work.) Select a few interesting jobs for discussion. (NOTE: If a speaker visits, ask these questions of them or provide them in advance. Work with the students to develop the questions. Have the students take notes and record the answers during or immediately after the presentation, asking additional questions for clarification as necessary.) Points to include:
    - what they do for the community (the service provided)
    - how they provide the service
    - what resources are used by them in providing the service
    - where they live and work
    - the times during which they work
    - what other professions they are dependent upon for the functioning of their profession (janitor, delivery person, secretary, repair person)
    - what special adaptations (skills, tools, behaviors) they use or they are required to have
    - what special habits they exhibit
    - what other professions they compete with, if any
    - what other professions they cooperate with, if any

Ask the students to produce a written summary of the information they acquire concerning each of the jobs they investigate.
3. Have the students brainstorm a variety of animals living in a particular community (forest, stream, desert, tundra). A photograph could serve as a stimulus. List representative members of this natural community on the blackboard. Make sure a variety of animals including predator, prey, scavengers, etc. are included.
4. Pick one of the animals listed and, as a group, begin discussing the same questions for it that were asked of the visiting professional. In this way the students can see how the "profession" concept applies as a metaphor. Identify the animal's profession as its "ecological niche."

OPTIONAL: As individual projects or in teams, students should select one animal, research the "niche" it fills, and answer the same questions used for human jobs. As a culmination, each team can make a visual and/or verbal presentation about its animal and its niche.

EXTENSIONS

1. Identify niches which are overlapping and where there is competition or cooperation for resources and services. Connections may also be made between niches to illustrate interdependency webs in the community.
2. Investigate a variety of human professions in different communities or cultures for an emphasis on career awareness. Illustrate overlapping professions, competition, cooperation and interdependency.
3. Develop commercials or ads for "recruiting" individuals into given ecological niches, using special contributions, advantages, etc., as points to highlight.
4. Select the animal you'd most like to be, from among those studied, basing your selection on the contribution of the ecological niche to the community's health, as well as other factors. Describe the reasons for your choices. You could do this for human professions, too!

AQUATIC EXTENSION

See the Aquatic WILD activity, "Blue Ribbon Niche."

EVALUATION

1. Define ecological niche.
2. Select any animal or person and describe its ecological niche. Include: What they do for the community, how they provide this service, the resources they use, where they live, when they do their work, what other organisms depend upon them, what other organisms they are dependent upon, what special adaptations they use or are required to have, what special habits they exhibit, what other organisms they compete with for the same niche and anything else you think is especially interesting about this niche and how it is filled.
3. Create a poster that shows all the facets of an animal's niche.

WHO FITS HERE?

OBJECTIVES
Students will: 1) identify characteristic life forms in ecosystems; 2) match appropriate life forms to ecosystems; and 3) generalize that each ecosystem has characteristic life forms, adapted to live there.

METHOD
Students play an identification game using posters and cards.

BACKGROUND
Each environment is suitable to those life forms that have adapted to its climate, soils, water, vegetation, other life forms and to other ecological factors over a number of years. Plants and animals tolerant of heat and little moisture are adapted to the desert; mountain goats to craggy hillsides and cold temperatures; and polar bears to ice fields and snowy vistas.

In this activity, students will research particular environments to discover characteristic live forms, and then match those animals' adaptations back to the appropriate environment.

The major purpose of this activity is for students to recognize that each environment has characteristic life forms, adapted to live there.

MATERIALS
posterboard for ten posters; crayons, paints, or magazine photos for posters; posterboard, index cards, or construction paper for 50 adaptation cards

Age: Grades 7-9
Subjects: Science (Life Science, Biology), Language Arts
Skills: analysis, classification, comparing similarities and differences, discussion, media construction, reading, research, small group work, writing
Duration: two 45-minute periods or longer
Group Size: ten to 30 students; fewer or more with adaptation of activity
Setting: indoors
Conceptual Framework Reference: I.A.1., I.A.2., I.A.3., I.B., I.C.1., I.C.2., I.C.3., III.A., III.A.1., III.A.3., III.B., III.B.1., III.B.2., III.B.3., III.B.4., III.D., III.D.1., III.D.2.
Key Vocabulary: adaptation, ecosystem, habitat
Appendices: Local Resources, Ecosystem

PROCEDURE
1. Divide the class into two equal groups. Explain that each group will make a game for the other. The object of the game will be to match animals to the environment in which they live.
2. Ask each half of the class to choose five ecosystems they would like to know more about; e.g., desert, hardwood forest, coniferous forest, alpine, marine. Divide each half of the class into the five groups, one per ecosystem. Have each group research their ecosystem, learning its characteristic life forms including adaptations of the animals that enable them to survive in that environment.
3. Ask each student group to make a poster showing the characteristic vegetation, terrain, etc., in the ecosystem they are studying. Posters of each ecosystem can be made with crayons and paints or magazine cut-outs.
4. For each ecosystem, students should make five cards, one per each of five species of animals characteristic of the ecosystem. Put a description of the animal's adaptations to its environment on one side of the card, and a coding number on the other side, so that the animal described can be identified later. Do not write the name of the animal on the card. The cards should describe adaptations that enable the animals to survive in the ecosystem. For example, for the desert environment, the five cards could read:

> Hunts at night for warm rodents and sleeping birds; can climb loose, sloping sand by throwing loops of its body up like coils."
> (sidewinder rattlesnake)

> "Relies on agility and speed to escape predators; needs little water; gets water from plants it eats." (cottontail rabbit)

"Hunts at night; lives in burrows of animals like gophers."
(burrowing owl)

"A bird which hibernates in winter to avoid desert cold."
(nightjar)

"Larvae feed on yucca flowers." (yucca moth)

5. When posters are made and cards completed, students in each half of the class should make a master list of the five ecosystems and animals their cards represent. Next, they shuffle all their cards for their five ecosystems together into one pile.
6. Each half of the class then exchanges posters and cards with the other half.
7. Each half of the class then tries as a group to decide to which ecosystem each card belongs.
8. Next give each half of the class the master list for their posters. One student per group can read off the animals that correspond with each card for each poster.
9. Has each animal been placed in its proper ecosystem? If not, why? Were there any animals found in more than one ecosystem? Are these ecosystems varied? How can some animals live in more than one ecosystem, and not others? What are similarities and differences among the ecosystems and characteristic life forms? What are some of the most interesting animal adaptations? What functions do these adaptations serve? How do they relate to the nature of the physical environment? Ask the students what characterizes animals and the environments in which they live. (Each environment has characteristic life forms. These animals and plants are adapted to live where they do.)

EXTENSIONS

1. Look for rare, threatened and endangered species in each ecosystem. Are there any? If not, why not? If yes, why? (usually habitat loss) See "Here Today, Gone Tomorrow."
2. Compare and contrast additional ecosystems and life forms from a variety of places on the planet.
3. Make an Ecosystem Quiz Show. Research the ecosystems, life forms, and adaptations—and then use a game show format to guess the animal and its environment.

AQUATIC EXTENSION

Do this activity again using only aquatic ecosystems—for example, pond, lake, stream, estuary, marsh, ocean, river.

EVALUATION

1. Pick any three animals. Describe the ecosystem in which each animal lives, including identification of the animal's habitat requirements.
2. Describe the importance of adaptation in animals.
3. Design an activity or simulation for younger students that teaches how wildlife is adapted for different ecosystems. This could be done in the form of a game. Have the younger people do the activity. Find out what the younger students learned.

SECTION FOUR
MANAGEMENT AND CONSERVATION

TURKEY TROUBLE

OBJECTIVES

Students will: 1) define and give examples of exponential and linear growth rates in wildlife populations; and 2) describe factors that affect and limit growth of wildlife populations.

METHOD

Students make computations and interpret results.

BACKGROUND

Growth rates can be characterized by two different growth curves: linear and exponential.

Linear growth occurs at a constant rate. Many increases or decreases occur at linear rates. An example of this would be having your salary increase by $1000.00 per year.

Exponential growth occurs at an increasing rate through time. An example would be having your salary increase (or decrease) at a rate of 5% per year.

Since all populations have the reproductive potential to increase at an exponential rate, it is difficult to comprehend the gravity of problems associated with population growth. Population is limited by many factors, including availability and quality of water, food, shelter and territory, as well as natural and human-made changes in habitat.

As an example, in 1935, Wyoming had no Merriam's turkeys within its borders. A decision was made to

plant 46 turkeys in a mountainous area of the state. This activity will provide students with the opportunity to compute the possible growth of the turkey population during its first five years after the planting. As background, students should recognize that, in reality, these turkeys will be affected by many natural and human-caused limiting factors. For example, growth of bird populations is affected by factors such as the availability of food, water, shelter and space; disease; predation; climatic conditions; as well as broken or infertile eggs.

The major purpose of this activity is for students to acquire a working knowledge of some factors affecting wildlife populations.

MATERIALS

paper; graph paper; pencils

PROCEDURE

TASK 1

Compute the size of the population of Merriam's turkeys in Wyoming for five years, using the following assumptions. Complete the data table (See Appendix A).

Assumptions:

1. None of the turkeys left the general area during the five years.

2. There was no disease or shortage of habitat that limited the population.

3. There were an equal number of males and females in each hatch.

4. All sexually mature females successfully hatched a clutch of ten eggs each year.

5. No turkeys reproduced until after they had completed more than one full year of life.

6. All turkeys died during the winter after their fifth year of life (after hatching their fourth clutch.)

7. All of the turkeys introduced were one year old and sexually mature.

8. There were an equal number of males and females in the original number of 46 turkeys which were planted.

Age: Grades 10-12
Subjects: Mathematics, Science, Social Studies, Environmental Problems
Skills: computation, discussion, interpretation, problem solving
Duration: two 45-minute periods, or one with homework
Group Size: any
Setting: indoors
Conceptual Framework Reference: III.E., III.E.1., III.E.2., IV.C., IV.C.1., IV.C.2.
Key Vocabulary: linear, exponential, limiting factors, population
Appendices: Local Resources

TASK 2

Plot the population against the five years on a graph as indicated by the diagram below. Use a full sheet of paper for the graph, making it as large as the paper will allow.

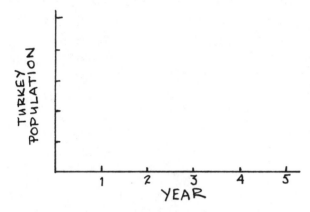

TASK 3

Compute the size of the population of Merriam's turkeys in Wyoming using a linear growth model for five years based on the following assumptions. Complete the data table (See Appendix B).

Assumptions:

1. 230 offspring were produced by the turkey population each year.

2. None of the turkeys left the area.

3. There was no disease or shortage of habitat that limited the population.

TASK 4

Plot the data from Task 3 on the same graph used in Task 2.

TASK 5

Assign or discuss the following questions as related to the previous tasks:

1. In the examples given, which growth patterns appear to be increasing at a faster rate? Why?

2. The estimate of the true population of the Merriman's turkey by the Wyoming Game and Fish Department at the end of five years was 2,500. How can we account for the difference? Were any of the original assumptions incorrect? Which ones?

3. All populations have the potential to increase at an exponential rate. What factors limit this potential?

EXTENSIONS

1. Transfer this to a similar situation in your state or province. Get background information and data from a local wildlife agency.

2. This activity does not address the consequences—potentially beneficial, harmful, or with no appreciable effect—of introducing or reintroducing species to an area. Introduction of non-native species in particular may have negative consequences for other wildlife and the environment. See related activities, "Planting Animals," "Who Lives Here?" and "Here Today, Gone Tomorrow."

EVALUATION

1. On an island, a rabbit population is doubling every year for six years. If you started with one pair (one male and one female), what would the population number after six years? This is an example of what kind of population growth?

2. A population of mountain lions is increasing by two members per year. If you started with two animals, what would the population size be after six years? This is an example of what kind of population growth?

3. List three natural limiting factors that could affect the growth of a rabbit population.

APPENDIX A (Teacher Copy) (Task 1) **EXPONENTIAL GROWTH DATA TABLE**

YEAR	1	2	3	4	5	6
1. Beginning population	46	276	506	1886	4416	13570
2. – five year olds	0	0	0	0	46	230
3. – last year's hatch (not yet breeding)	0	230	230	1380	2530	9200
4. = Breeding population	46	46	276	506	1840	4140
5. Breeding pairs (#4 ÷ 2)	23	23	138	253	920	2070
6. Offspring (#5 x 10 eggs/clutch)	230	230	1380	2530	9200	20700
+ breeding population (#4)	46	46	276	506	1840	4140
+ last year's hatch (#3)	0	230	230	1380	2530	9200
7. = Total population	276	506	1886	4416	13570	34040

APPENDIX A (Student Copy) (Task 1) **EXPONENTIAL GROWTH DATA TABLE**

YEAR	1	2	3	4	5	6
1. Beginning population	46	276	506			
2. – five year olds	0	0	0	0	46	230
3. – last year's hatch (not yet breeding)	0	230	230			
4. = Breeding population	46	46	276			
5. Breeding pairs (#4 ÷ 2)	23	23				
6. Offspring (#5 x 10 eggs/clutch)	230	230				
+ breeding population (#4)	46	46				
+ last year's hatch (#3)	0	230				
7. = Total population	276	506				

APPENDIX B (Teacher Copy) (Task 3) **LINEAR GROWTH DATA TABLE**

YEAR	1	2	3	4	5	6
Population	46	276	506	736	966	1196
+ increase	230	230	230	230	230	230
= total population	276	506	736	966	1196	1426

APPENDIX B (Student Copy) (Task 3) **LINEAR GROWTH DATA TABLE**

YEAR	1	2	3	4	5	6
Population	46	276				
+ increase	230	230				
= total population	276	506	736			

WILDWORK

OBJECTIVE

Students will name and describe three wildlife occupations.

METHOD

Students brainstorm a list of wildlife-related careers, prepare presentations and dramatize occupations for their classmates.

BACKGROUND

State and federal government agencies employ many specialists to help preserve and manage wildlife and wildlife habitats. These employees do field work, conduct laboratory research and oversee human interactions with wildlife. Universities and colleges, private and non-profit wildlife oriented agencies, zoos and museums, private industry and others all employ people trained in the wildlife field. Some individuals (artists, photographers, etc.) photograph, paint, draw or write about wildlife for magazines, books, films and television.

The major purpose of this activity is for students to become familiar with career possibilities available in wildlife-related fields.

MATERIALS

writing materials

PROCEDURE

1. Ask the students if they've thought about what careers they might be interested in pursuing when they grow up. What kinds of jobs sound interesting? What about working with wildlife?
2. In a class discussion, find out what kinds of jobs students imagine exist in animal-related fields. Do any of their parents have animal- or wildlife-related jobs? Make some suggestions about possible careers and compile a list of occupations that students have brainstormed.
3. From this list, have each student choose one job to portray to the class. Encourage them to bring props from home to help in their portrayal. Items such as realistic stuffed animals, toy cameras, research notebooks, outdoor dress and magazine pictures can be used.
4. Have each student, in turn, name, describe and portray his or her occupation to the class. (Or, portray first, and have the students guess the occupation!)
5. Wrap up with a discussion of the range of careers available in wildlife-related fields.

For Older Students

1. Ask the students what careers might be interesting after school. What about working with wildlife? Find out what kinds of jobs students imagine exist in animal-related fields. Do any of their family or friends have animal-related occupations, involving either wild or domesticated animals, or both?
2. Compile a list of possible wildlife-related occupations.
3. Ask each student or group of students to select one occupation to research. Find out what preparation (e.g., college) is needed for the job; what the responsibilities of the job entail; what special equipment, techniques, or skills are needed, if any; and whether there is growing, diminishing, or no change in the demand for people in this occupation.
4. Have each group report to the rest of the students. This reporting can take a variety of forms from skits about each job to a Wildlife Careers Resource Fair. The Resource Fair could have booths for each job, complete with visual aids; background information; and local contacts for additional information. Open the Fair to the whole school and invite people working at these jobs to attend and share their inputs in person.

Age: Grades K-12
Subjects: Career Education, Language Arts, Social Studies, Science
Skills: description, discussion, listing, synthesis
Duration: ten-minute introduction; 20 minutes for presentation or longer depending on size of group
Group Size: any
Setting: indoors
Conceptual Framework Reference: IV.F.10.
Key Vocabulary: occupation, vocation, career
Appendices: Local Resources

EXTENSIONS

1. Contact someone in a wildlife-oriented job and ask that person if he or she would be willing to contribute a class visit or letter describing the job and other wildlife-related jobs. Have the students prepare questions in advance for the visitor. (Government wildlife agencies usually have a descriptive leaflet about jobs. Write for a copy.) Compile a class letter to that individual, incorporating any questions that students might have. Some good questions to ask could be:

    • Why did you choose this career?
    • What education was necessary to prepare you for this job?
    • How hard is it to get a job after you are trained?
    • What do you do in a typical day's work?
    • How much do you actually work with wildlife? How much with people? How much with record keeping, reporting, etc.?
    • Do you work with people who have other wildlife-related careers?

Share the letter of reply with the class or have the professional visit the class to answer questions.

2. Investigate jobs related to a range of natural resources—from forestry to mining to litigation. Look at volunteer and private organizations as well as public and commercial, from attorneys for the National Wildlife Federation to public land coordinators for major oil companies.

3. Since most wildlife in the United States is managed as a legal responsibility of state wildlife agencies—and yet the wildlife habitat may be on public as well as private land—make a "wild web," showing the agencies, organizations and occupations that typically could be involved in a wildlife management issue.

AQUATIC EXTENSION

Focus specifically on the variety of aquatic-related careers that are available.

EVALUATION

1. Name and describe three jobs in which someone works with wildlife or other animals. Describe what kind of training and qualifications are required for each job?

2. Are there many jobs available in wildlife-related fields? Please explain your response.

3. Why, if at all, do you think careers in wildlife and other resource-related fields are important?

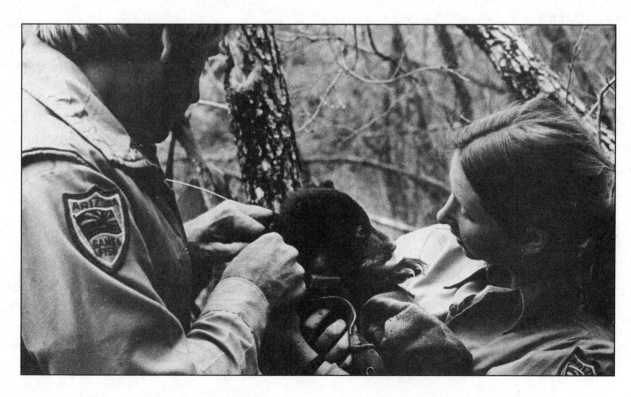

HERE TODAY, GONE TOMORROW

OBJECTIVES

Students will: 1) identify and describe some causes for extinction of animal species; 2) define "threatened," "rare," and "endangered" as applied to wildlife; and 3) name threatened and endangered animals living in their area.

METHOD

Students become familiar with classification of animals, conduct research, and make a master list of threatened and endangered animals locally and/or nationally, including factors affecting the animals' condition.

BACKGROUND

NOTE: This activity can be modified to include plant as well as animal species.

Pinpointing an exact number of species that become extinct each year is difficult. Many plants and animals are still unnamed and unknown. There is controversy surrounding estimates of species extinction rates. Some scientists estimate that human activity is responsible for 100 extinctions each day. Other scientists offer lower figures, but few experts disagree with the

belief that the rate of species extinction is being accelerated by human actions. In 1991, the U.S. Department of Interior listed 457 plants and animals in the United States as being endangered, with an additional 153 listed as threatened. Many other species are under review for classification as threatened or endangered.

Although extinction is a natural process, excessive and intensive human activities in the environment have caused a dramatic increase in its rate. Loss of habitat as a result of human activity is considered to be the most pervasive cause of species extermination. Other major causes of species extermination and endangerment include: habitat modification, unregulated or illegal commercial and personal use, disruption of migration routes and breeding behaviors, contamination by pollutants, human disturbance, predator control, competition or predation from introduced species and natural causes.

Generally accepted definitions of the terms to be used in this activity are:

Endangered Species in immediate danger of extinction.

Critically Endangered Species will not survive without direct human intervention.

Threatened Species present in its range, but threatened because of a decline in numbers.

Rare Species not presently in danger, but of concern because of low numbers. NOTE: Some species were always rare because of their position in the food chain or due to habitat preference.

Extinct Complete disappearance of a species.

Peripheral Scarce in area because it is fringe or marginal habitat.

Listings of animals currently in these categories may be obtained from state or province wildlife agencies.

A list of the U.S. "Endangered Species" is available from:

Age: Grades 5-12
Subjects: Science, Language Arts, Social Studies
Skills: analysis, classification, discussion, listing, synthesis
Duration: two 30 to 45-minute periods
Group Size: any
Setting: indoors
Conceptual Framework Reference: I.D., II.A., II.B., II.C., II.D., II.E., II.F., III.D.3., III.D.4., IV.A., IV.C., IV.C.1., IV.C.2., IV.C.3., IV.C.4., IV.D.5., IV.D.6., IV.D.7., IV.E., IV.E.3., IV.E.4., IV.E.5., IV.E.7., IV.E.10., IV.E.11., IV.F., IV.F.3., IV.F.4., IV.F.5., IV.F.6., IV.F.7., IV.E.10., IV.E.11., IV.F., IV.F.3., IV.F.4., IV.F.5., IV.F.6., IV.F.7., I.V.F.8., IV.F.9., IV.F.11., VI.A., VI.A.2., VI.A.3., VI.A.4., VI.A.5., VI.C.13., VI.C.16., VI.D., VI.D.1., VI.D.2., VI.D.3., VI.D.4., VII.A., VII.A.1, VII.A.2, VII.A.3, VII.A.4, VII.B., VII.B.1, VII.B.2., VII.B.3., VII.B.4., VII.B.5., VII.B.6., VII.B.7.
Key Vocabulary: endangered, critically endangered, threatened, rare, extinct, peripheral
Appendices: Local Resources, Agencies and Organizations

Director, Office of Endangered Species
U.S. Fish and Wildlife Service
U.S. Department of Interior
Washington, D.C. 20204

State, province, and federal listings of endangered, threatened and rare species may vary because areas encompass different habitat conditions within their boundaries. An animal or plant may have been lost within one state's boundaries, but may be abundant in another, and therefore not considered threatened. The U.S. Endangered Species Act of 1973 gives authority to protect endangered species to the U.S. Secretaries of the Departments of Interior and Commerce, with responsibilities further delegated to the U.S. Fish and Wildlife Service and the National Marine Fisheries Service respectively.

The major purpose of this activity is to provide students with a working knowledge of the terminology and factors affecting potential elimination of wildlife species.

MATERIALS
information from state and federal agencies about threatened and endangered animals; poster-making materials; writing materials

PROCEDURE
1. Contact your state or province wildlife agency. Ask for a list of animals in your state or province which are classified endangered, critically endangered, threatened, rare, extinct, and peripheral. Ask, too, for information regarding the reasons for these classifications. For older students and those wanting more depth: Write to the U.S. Department of Interior regarding any comparable information available at the national level. (See Background for address.) Also contact local chapters of conservation organizations (e.g., National Wildlife Federation, National Audubon Society, Defenders of Wildlife) for additional information they might

have about species and habitats for which there is concern in your area.

2. Review and discuss with the students the definitions of **threatened, endangered, rare, extinct** and **peripheral**—as used in wildlife conservation, as well as in a dictionary. Understand that words defined in a standard dictionary may have additional legal connotations. Ask each student or group of students to select an animal to learn more about.

3. Ask one or more students to take the information accumulated from the wildlife agencies and private conservation groups and come up with a master list of the animals according to the category in which they can be classified, the classification both locally and nationally, and the principal factors affecting the animals. For example:

Animal Name	State or Province						National						Factors Affecting Animal's Status
	Extinct	Endangered	Critically Endangered	Threatened	Rare	Peripheral	Extinct	Endangered	Critically Endangered	Threatened	Rare	Peripheral	

OR,

Divide the students into teams so they can all participate in constructing this chart; e.g., one team classifying mammals, another reptiles, birds, fish, insects, etc.

4. Make copies of this information for all the students. Discuss the findings. What seem to be the most prevalent factors affecting the animals; e.g., habitat loss, pollution, impact from introduced species?

NOTE: The U.S. Department of Interior listed the following numbers of endangered and threatened species in the U.S. in 1991: **Endangered**—54 mammals, 75 birds, 13 reptiles, 6 amphibians, 53 fish, 4 snails, 39 clams, 8 crustaceans, 16 insects, 189 plants = 457 endangered species; **Threatened**—6 mammals, 9 birds, 19 reptiles, 5 amphibians, 33 fish, 6 snails, 2 clams, 2 crustaceans, 9 insects, 62 plants = 153 threatened species.

EXTENSIONS

For Younger Students

1. Make a poster display showing the principal reasons for endangerment and the animals that are endangered in those ways. Poster displays could be made separately for both state and national endangered species.

2. Have a schoolwide contest in which students create posters honoring endangered species—from plants to wildlife.

3. Write a short essay, poem, or song about plants and animals facing extinction. What are these organisms "worth?" What are we humans losing?

For Older Students

1. Find out what is being done concerning the endangered plants and animals in your state or province; at the national level; at the international and worldwide levels. What can each of us as individuals do?

2. Each student can pick an endangered animal to find out more about. What will be the consequences of the disappearance of this species? What are the trade offs involved? What alternatives are available? What contributions does the animal make ecologically? Eco-

nomically? Medicinally? Aesthetically? Intrinsically? Pool and discuss all the students' findings.

3. What animals and plants are known to be extinct? In each instance, what seem to be the causes?

4. Explore the possibility that extinction can apply to human cultural forms; e.g., traditional languages, native peoples.

5. In ten minutes, name as many animals as you can that are not legally endangered or threatened. Find out what species have been taken off the endangered species list, how and why.

6. Research, analyze, summarize and interpret findings related to the following question: Why care about endangered species?

AQUATIC EXTENSIONS

1. Find out what kinds of habitats the aquatic species are dependent upon. Find out more about the conditions affecting each of these aquatic species, their current status and projections for their likelihood of survival as a species.

2. Are factors affecting threatened and endangered aquatic species significantly different from those affecting terrestrial species? If yes, why? If no, why?

EVALUATION

1. Arrange the following terms in a list so that they progress from the least amount of danger to a species to the greatest amount: endangered, rare, threatened, extinct, critically endangered.

2. Describe two reasons for possible concern when animal species become extinct.

3. Who decides what species are endangered or threatened and how do they decide?

4. Describe principal causes for extinction.

WHO LIVES HERE?

OBJECTIVES

Students will: 1) identify some native and non-native animal inhabitants of their area and of the United States; and 2) give some examples of effects of introducing animal species to an area where they were not originally found.

METHOD

Students research and write reports about native and introduced animal species and conduct a class "quiz" and discussion.

BACKGROUND

NOTE: This activity can be adapted to include native and non-native plants as well.

Fossil remains indicate that even in prehistoric times animal populations had migrated to different geographical regions in response to climatic and other conditions. These migrations took place over long periods of time. In some cases original inhabitants of an area would die out, having moved away or become extinct.

Natural land and water barriers have prevented some species spreading to certain areas. But people, with their sophisticated transport systems, have changed the wildlife populations of islands and continents. Many plants and animals that we take for granted as native residents of the United States actually were not on this continent when the first European settlers came; other original species have been destroyed.

Changes that once took place gradually have been accelerated by human manipulation of wildlife populations. (For example, pet dogs and cats brought to South Sea islands decimated native wildlife populations that had evolved unthreatened by predators.) Human beings sometimes move animals to their advantage, sometimes to their ultimate disadvantage, with mixed results for people and the environment. Some introduction of animals to new areas is accidental; some is intended, for example, as a management strategy. (See "Planting Animals.")

The major purpose of this activity is to acquaint students with the distinction between native and non-native species as well as with benefits and liabilities involved in introducing non-native species to areas.

MATERIALS

access to research materials; writing materials

Age: Grades 4-9
Subjects: Language Arts, Science, Social Studies
Skills: classification, description, discussion, evaluation, generalization, public speaking, reading, reporting, research
Duration: two to three 45-minute periods
Group Size: whole class, individual research
Setting: indoors
Conceptual Framework Reference: IV.E., IV.E.4., IV.E.5., IV.E.8, IV.E.9., IV.E.10., IV.E.11., VI.C.12., VI.C.13., VI.C.15., VI.C.16.
Key Vocabulary: native, non-native, indigenous, introduced species, migration
Appendices: Local Resources, Ecosystem

PROCEDURE

1. Explain the background information to your students. Then, go around the room asking each student to guess if the animal you name is a native (indigenous) or non-native (introduced) species to the area of the United States it now inhabits. OPTIONAL: get photos of each. For example:

Some introduced species

brown trout; pheasant; carp, Norway rat; nutria; Chukar partridge; starling; English sparrow; Barbary sheep; African onyx; Axis deer; Hungarian partridge

Some native species

Wood rat; elk; bald eagle; mule deer; marmot; woodchuck; wolverine; bluebird; coyote

NOTE: This list will vary greatly from place to place. Check for local and regional accuracy.

2. Ask each student to choose one of these animals to research, including:

- Is it native to the area it inhabits?
- What, if any, are the benefits of its presence?
- What, if any, are the detrimental effects of its presence?

- What is the history of its presence? (If introduced, include how and why it was introduced.)
- What wildlife regulations, if any, exist concerning this animal? (Your state or province wildlife agency will have this information.)

3. Ask students to write short research papers on their animals. Also, have each student write the name of his or her animal on a piece of paper. Collect these and use them for a native/non-native quiz. Have the students vote "native" or "non-native" as each animal name is pulled from a box. Then have the student who did research comment on that animal. Students can direct the voting, presentations and discussion. Were there some surprises; e.g., animals thought to be native that turned out to be introduced? Based on all the animals studied, do there seem to be more positive or negative effects from introducing non-native species to environments?

EXTENSION

Do the same activity with plants!

AQUATIC EXTENSION

See the Aquatic WILD activity, "Aquatic Roots."

EVALUATION

1. Name five species that are native (indigenous) to the United States.

2. Name five species that are non-native (introduced) to the United States.

3. When animals are introduced to new areas, they can either become extinct or be successful in their new home. What usually happens to other animals when an introduced species is successful? Why?

4. List and explain four reasons why animals may be introduced to an area.

5. Make a visual illustration to convey some of the possible effects of introducing non-native species into a habitat. Show "before" and "after." Provide examples to explain your portrayal.

PLANTING ANIMALS

OBJECTIVES
Students will: 1) describe reasons for "transplanting" animals; and 2) identify one animal that has been transplanted in their own state or province.

METHOD
Students write a letter to a state or provincial wildlife agency for information and make dioramas of transplanted animals in new habitats.

BACKGROUND
NOTE: This activity can be used independently or as an excellent extension for both "Who Lives Here?" and "Here Today, Gone Tomorrow."

Wild animals are sometimes introduced or reintroduced to suitable habitat. These animals may be called "transplants." Transplanting takes place for a variety of reasons, including: providing a new home to species which were crowded elsewhere; re-introducing animals to historic habitats; providing people with a new population of animals for consumptive and non-consumptive purposes; providing a natural check and balance in an ecosystem; restoring ecosystem diversity; and aesthetically enriching the local environment.

Introductions can have both positive and negative consequences. For example, re-introduction of predators can contribute to a healthy ecosystem as natural limits are thus placed on prey populations. Negative consequences can also occur. For example, some transplanted animals can go into shock and die; an animal population may be introduced for which there is no natural predator, with overpopulation of the introduced species and habitat degradation the result; and a new species can usurp food, water and shelter with harmful effects on native species.

The major purpose of this activity is to acquaint students with the concept of "transplanting" animals.

MATERIALS
writing materials; magazine photos; scissors; glue
OPTIONAL: boxes for dioramas

PROCEDURE
1. In a class discussion, review what wildlife species are found in your local area, state, or province; and what wildlife species may once have been found there, although they are no longer present. (See "Who Lives Here?" and "Here Today, Gone Tomorrow.") How would the class find out if there were a new wild animal living in the area? How would it have gotten there? On its own? Put there by people? Why?
2. Help the class to write a letter to the state or provincial wildlife agency as well as to other informed organizations or individuals, inquiring about newly introduced or re-introduced wildlife species in your region or local area. The following kinds of questions could be included:
    * What species of animal was transplanted?
    * Why was it introduced into that area? Did it once live there naturally?
    * Was another species displaced? Which niche did it fill? See "Which Niche?"
    * If the species were re-introduced, what previously had happened to the animals or habitat to cause their disappearance from the area?
    * If habitat changes influenced this disappearance, how have these changes been corrected?
    * When were the animals plentiful in the area and

Age: Grades 4-9
Subjects: Language Arts, Science, Art
Skills: analysis, discussion, media construction, psychomotor development, research, synthesis, visualization, writing
Duration: two 45-minute periods, longer if diorama is constructed
Group Size: any
Setting: indoors
Conceptual Framework Reference: IV.A., IV.A.1., IV.A.2., IV.A.3., IV.A.4., IV.C., IV.C.1., IV.C.2., IV.C.3., IV.C.4., IV.E., IV.E.4., IV.E.5., IV.E.8., IV.E.9., IV.E.10., IV.E.11., VI.A., VI.A.1., VI.A.2., VI.A.3., VI.A.4., VI.A.5., VI.B., VI.C., VI.C.12., VI.C.13., VI.C.15., VI.C.16.
Key Vocabulary: habitat, transplant, introduced, niche (for grades 7 or older), diorama, wildlife agency, management
Appendices: Local Resources

when did they disappear? How did this take
place?

- What indications, if any, are there that the transplant has been successful?
- What positive and/or negative effects, if any,
have taken place for the transplanted animals,
for other animals in the area, for the habitat?

3. Based on the information they have acquired, ask
the students to summarize what they have learned.

EXTENSIONS

1. Make a diorama of the animal in its new, "transplanted" habitat. These dioramas can be made by the
class as a group in a large cardboard box, or by small
groups of students working as a team, or by individual
students using shoe boxes. Cut out magazine pictures
of the animal and its habitat elements, back them with
cardboard, and prop them up to create a diorama.
Natural materials may also be used to create the background landscape.
2. Write a poem from the perspective of the animal.
See "Animal Poetry."

AQUATIC EXTENSIONS

1. See the Aquatic WILD activity, "Aquatic Roots."
2. Focus this activity specifically on aquatic species.
See what you discover—if not in your state, in your
region.

EVALUATION

1. List and explain four reasons for transplanting animals. Explain any major reasons for not transplanting
animals.
2. Write a short story to illustrate potential pros and
cons associated with transplanting animals.

SMOKEY BEAR SAID WHAT?

OBJECTIVES

Students will: 1) identify positive and negative consequences of forest and grassland fires; and
2) describe some of the changes fire can make in ecosystems.

METHOD

Students brainstorm positive and negative effects of forest and grassland fires; conduct research; and create murals showing changes from fire in forest and grassland ecosystems.

BACKGROUND

NOTE: See "Fire Ecologies" for a similar activity for older students.

In managing public lands, government agencies for many years have been making a slow movement to change their attitudes toward forest and grassland fires. Whereas once all fires were suppressed or vigorously fought, today many fires are allowed to burn as part of a natural cycle within forest and grassland ecosystems. In remote areas, some agencies monitor lightning-ignited wildfires and allow them to burn as long as they stay within "prescribed" limits of fire behavior and location. However, wildfires are still aggressively fought near populated areas. In fact, there has been a movement to "prescribe" fires under some

conditions and in some places in an effort to replicate natural cycles that contribute to maintaining healthy ecosystems.

Such "prescribed burns" are planned and tended by qualified resource managers. Prescribed burns are frequently designed to reduce the fuel load in a given area. Reducing the fuel load in a forested area, for example, can prevent fires from getting so hot that they eliminate virtually all life forms and even scorch the soil. That is, fires every five to ten years in some forest types can clear the heavy underbrush without harming the larger trees in the forest. A major fire after a 50-year accumulation of brush and maturing timber, however, can cause intensely hot and destructive fires.

Objectives for use of fire as a management tool are variable. Objectives may include restoring fire's role in the natural cycle within a particular ecosystem; eradicating some plant species; and promoting the stimulation of plant species that are preferred food by some wildlife. In some areas, fire is the most cost-effective tool to manage habitats.

Prescribed "burns" are planned and initiated by qualified professionals who are trained in using fire for resource management objectives. Prescribed fires are only employed after burn plans are approved. Those plans must specify objectives for the fire, location, size, type, how the fire will be started and controlled and how the smoke from the fire will be managed. Fire plans set limits for weather parameters which control how hot a fire burns and in which direction smoke dissipates. Fires outside of those limits will not be started. If the fire is started and the weather conditions change to go beyond these limits, plans call for putting out the fire.

Students may ask why—if some fires are helpful—the national symbol of firefighting agencies, Smokey Bear says, *"Only **you** can prevent forest fires."*

Age: Grades 4-6
Subjects: Science, Social Studies, Art, Language Arts (research)
Skills: analysis, classification, comparing similarities and differences, description, discussion, evaluation, listing, media construction, research, small group work, synthesis, visualization
Duration: one class period, 45 minutes
Group Size: two groups, from two to 15 students each
Setting: indoors
Conceptual Framework Reference: I.B., I.C., I.C.1., I.C.2., I.C.3., I.C.4., I.D., III.A., III.A.1., III.A.3., III.B., III.B.1., III.B.3., III.B.4., III.C., III.C.1., III.C.2., III.C.3., III.C.4., III.D., III.D.1., III.D.2., III.D.4., III.E., III.E.1., III.E.2., III.F., IV.A., IV.A.1., IV.A.2., IV.A.3., IV.A.4., IV.B.2., IV.C., IV.C.1., IV.D., IV.D.2., IV.D.4., IV.D.5., IV.E., IV.E.4., IV.E.5., IV.E.10., IV.E.11., V.A., V.B., VI.B., VI.B.4., VI.B.5., VII.A., VII.B.
Key Vocabulary: prescribed burn, management
Appendices: Local Resources

This message is aimed at humans causing fires by error and accidents, such as carelessness in camping situations. The message also warns us about the terrible destructiveness of arson—intentional fires set by people for malicious and mischievous purposes. Accidental and arson fires are often started near developed areas. They often occur during times of severe drought or high winds. This kind of wildfire can be terribly destructive. On the other hand, prescribed fires are lit under ideal weather conditions. They generally burn much cooler than wildfires that most often occur during extremely hot and dry times. Again, the only people who may be authorized to set prescribed forest and grassland fires are those who are fully qualified professionals, trained in the study of ecological systems to reinstate fire as a natural management tool. It is still correct, of course, the fires can have negative as well as positive effects. Forest products companies, for example, in most cases would rather harvest trees than see them burn.

If a fire is too large, too fast and too hot wildlife can't easily move to safety. Individual animals may die or be displaced from their habitat. Short-term and long-term loss of vegetation can have a variety of effects, including loss of food and shelter for wildlife, and increase in silting and sedimentation in the waters.

There are, however, possible benefits as well—particularly in the case of those smaller burns that do not get exceedingly hot. For example, fires can:
- maintain and enhance fire-dependent habitats such as prairies, savannas, chaparral, jackpine forests, southern pine forests, boreal forests;
- provide habitats for species primarily dependent on fire-driven ecosystems such as jackpine warbler;
- increase soil productivity by releasing and recycling nutrients in litter and undergrowth;
- prepare soil for germination of some seeds;
- activate heat-dependent seed varieties, such as lodgepole pines, jackpine, black spruce;
- contribute to an "edge effect," providing a greater variety of food and shelter sources for some species of wildlife; and

- open up habitat, generating new growth, diversity and abundance of food plants, such as for large herbivores.

The major purpose of this activity is for students to become familiar with positive and negative effects of fire (forest and grasslands) on wildlife species and their habitat.

MATERIALS
art supplies; butcher paper or other paper for mural display

PROCEDURE
1. Begin this activity with a discussion about forest and grassland fires. Students' reactions may be negative at first. Point out that while the effects of fire may be detrimental to some wildlife species, the fire may benefit other species of wildlife.

2. Brainstorm possible positive and negative effects of forest and grassland fires. Keep the list of brainstormed ideas posted for the students' reference.

3. Divide the class into two groups—one to find out more about forest fires and one to find out more about grassland fires. Using the brainstormed list as a beginning point, students in each group can volunteer to find out more about some of the topics. A few students might do this research or all of the students may be involved. Possible topics for further investigation include:

- terminology related to fires such as prescribed burn, ground fire, crownfire and wildfire;
- positive and negative effects of wildland fires in various vegetation types under various weather conditions;
- U.S. Forest Service, National Park Service, Bureau of Land Management, Bureau of Indian Affairs, local state forester's office and other state and federal agency policies toward forest and grassland fires;
- fire ecology information available from the agencies and organizations listed above;
- information about the number of different kinds of fires typical in specified areas during a year, such as caused from human activity (e.g., fireworks, campfires, smoking, arson and railroad-related ignitions); prescribed burns; and natural activity such as lightning;
- examples of historical and present-day cultural groups who use fire to improve wildlife habitat; and
- plant species dependent on fire for regeneration.

4. Once any necessary research has been done, ask the students to divide into groups to make two murals—one of a forested area and one of grasslands. Each mural should portray changes from before to during and after a fire. Analyze and discuss positive and negative consequences of forest and grassland fires. Compare similarities and differences in the two areas.

VARIATION

Do the murals first, then have the students research to find out if their murals are accurate. Correct and make additions to the murals after the research is completed.

EXTENSIONS

1. Design and make Smokey Bear Coloring Books for primary-age students in the school. Have a local forester or wildlife manager check it for accuracy before it is distributed. Show how fires can be both positive and negative. Also show that only trained foresters can set fires for forest management; the rest of us—when camping, hiking, wood gathering, etc., need to remember what Smokey still says, *"Only you can prevent forest fires!"*

2. Study a forested or grassland area that has burned.

AQUATIC EXTENSIONS

If not already included, investigate the potential impacts on watersheds from forest and grassland fires.

EVALUATION

1. Describe two differences between grassland that is burned frequently and grassland that is never burned.

2. Describe two differences between forested land that is burned frequently and forested land that is never burned.

3. Name ten species of plants and animals that are helped by fire under some conditions, and ten species that usually do better when fire is absent in forest or grasslands.

4. Summarize conditions in which fire can be helpful to some wildlife species and conditions when it is usually not helpful.

FIRE ECOLOGIES

OBJECTIVE

Students will identify, describe and evaluate some possible positive and negative effects on wildlife that result from forest and grassland fires.

METHOD

Students conduct a field investigation.

BACKGROUND

NOTE: See "Smokey Bear Said What?" for a similar activity for younger students.

In managing public lands, government agencies for many years have been making a slow movement to change their attitudes toward forest and grassland fires. Whereas once all fires were suppressed or vigorously fought, today many fires are allowed to burn as part of a natural cycle within forest and grassland ecosystems. In remote areas, some agencies monitor lightning-ignited wildfires and allow them to burn as long as they stay within "prescribed" limits of fire behavior and location. However, wildfires are still aggressively fought near populated areas. In fact, there has been a movement to "prescribe" fires under some conditions and in some places in an effort to replicate natural cycles that contribute to maintaining healthy ecosystems.

Age: Grades 7-12
Subjects: Science (Biology, Chemistry, Earth Science), Social Studies (in extension)
Skills: analysis, discussion, evaluation, generalization, observation, reporting, research, synthesis, writing
Duration: three or four 45-minute periods or longer, not including transportation to and from field sites
Group Size: any
Setting: indoors, outdoors if field research is possible
Conceptual Framework Reference: I.C., I.C.1., I.C.2., I.C.3., I.C.4., I.D., II.B.2., II.B.3., III.A., III.A.1., III.A.2., III.A.3., III.B., III.B.1., III.B.2., III.B.3., III.B.4., III.B.5., III.B.6., III.C., III.C.1., III.C.2., III.C.3., III.C.4., III.D., III.D.1., III.D.2., IV.A., IV.A.1., IV.A.2., IV.A.3., IV.A.4., IV.C., IV.C.1., IV.D., IV.D.2., IV.D.4., I.V.D.5., IV.D.6., IV.E., IV.E.4., IV.E.5., IV.E.10., IV.E.11., VI.C., VI.C.12., VI.C.15., VII.A., VII.B., VII.B.1., VII.B.3., VII.B.4., VII.B.5., VII.B.6., VII.B.7.
Key Vocabulary: wild, controlled, prescribed fire, ecology, management, species, organic, inorganic
Appendices: Ecosystem, Agencies and Organizations, Local Resources

---

Such "prescribed burns" are planned and tended by qualified resource managers. Prescribed burns are frequently designed to reduce the fuel load in a given area. Reducing the fuel load in a forested area, for example, can prevent fires from getting so hot that they eliminate virtually all life forms and even scorch the soil. That is, fires every five to ten years in some forest types can clear the heavy underbrush without harming the larger trees in the forest. A major fire after a 50-year accumulation of brush and maturing timber, however, can cause intensely hot and destructive fires.

Objectives for use of fire as a management tool are variable. Objectives may include restoring fire's role in the natural cycle within a particular ecosystem; eradicating some plant species; and promoting the stimulation of plant species that are preferred food by some wildlife. In some areas, fire is the most cost-effective tool to manage habitats.

Prescribed "burns" are planned and initiated by qualified professionals who are trained in using fire for resource management objectives. Prescribed fires are only employed after burn plans are approved. Those plans must specify objectives for the fire, location, size, type, how the fire will be started and controlled and how the smoke from the fire will be managed. Fire plans set limits for weather parameters which control how hot a fire burns and in which direction smoke dissipates. Fires outside of those limits will not be started. If the fire is started and the weather conditions change to go beyond these limits, plans call for putting out the fire.

Students may ask why—if some fires are helpful—the national symbol of firefighting agencies, Smokey Bear says, *"Only **you** can prevent forest fires."*

This message is aimed at humans causing fires by error and accidents, such as carelessness in camping situations. The message also warns us about the terrible destructiveness of arson—intentional fires set by people for malicious and mischievous purposes. Accidental and arson fires are often started near developed areas. They often occur during times of severe drought or high winds. This kind of wildfire can be terribly destructive. On the other hand, prescribed fires are lit under ideal weather conditions. They generally burn much cooler than wildfires that most often occur during extremely hot and dry times. Again, the only people who may be authorized to set prescribed forest and grassland fires are those who are fully qualified professionals, trained in the study of ecological systems to reinstate fire as a natural management tool. It is still correct, of course, that fires can have negative as well as positive effects. Forest products companies, for example, in most cases would rather harvest trees than see them burn.

If a fire is too large, too fast and too hot, wildlife can't easily move to safety. Individual animals may die or be displaced from their habitat. Short-term and long-term loss of vegetation can have a variety of effects, including loss of food and shelter for wildlife, and increase in silting and sedimentation in the waters. There are, however, possible benefits as well—particularly in the case of those smaller burns that do not get exceedingly hot. For example, fires can:

- maintain and enhance fire-dependent habitats such as prairies, savannas, chaparral, jackpine forests, southern pine forests, boreal forests;
- provide habitats for species primarily dependent on fire-driven ecosystems such as jackpine warbler;
- increase soil productivity by releasing and recycling nutrients in litter and undergrowth;
- prepare soil for germination of some seeds;
- activate heat-dependent seed varieties, such as lodgepole pines, jackpine, black spruce;
- contribute to an "edge effect," providing a greater variety of food and shelter sources for some species of wildlife; and
- open up habitat, generating new growth, diversity and abundance of food plants, such as for large herbivores.

The major purpose of this activity is for students to become familiar with positive and negative effects of fire (forest and grasslands) on wildlife species and their habitat.

MATERIALS

soil analysis equipment, e.g., pH testing paper; containers for soil samples; plant and animal identification guides for field work; OR classroom speaker; OR access to library and other reference materials

PROCEDURE

1. Begin this activity with a discussion of forest and grassland fires. Students' reactions may be negative at first. Point out that while one harmful effect of forest and grassland fires is the destruction of habitat and the killing of wildlife, in some cases fire improves habitat and contributes to the long-term well-being of wildlife.

2. Brainstorm possible positive and negative consequences of forest and grassland fires for wildlife. Specify kinds of wildlife and give examples.

3. Take a field trip to a forest or grassland where it is possible to see areas that have recently been burned, areas burned ten or more years ago, and areas not burned in recorded history. Try to arrange to go with an ecologist or wildlife biologist who can point out and explain some of the similarities and differences among the various areas. (NOTE: If such a trip is not possible, contact a regional forester, state wildlife agency, soil conservation district representative, or other resource person for information on the subject. It may be possible for a representative of the agency to come to the classroom and talk with the students about different circumstances under which fire can be helpful, and harmful, to wildlife—possibly bringing slides or a film on the subject. If neither the field trip nor the visit from a resource person is possible, the students will need to work from library and other reference materials on their own, or agencies may be able to provide you with before and after photographs of such sites.)

4. If the field trip is possible, prepare students to: a) make and record their observations, e.g., variety and quantity of vegetation, evidence of wildlife, actual sighting of wildlife; and b) with permission of the landholder, take small soil samples in the various areas for testing purposes. Back in class, these soil samples should be tested for structure, organic and inorganic parts, chemical composition, etc.

5. Ask the students to organize and present the findings of their research. For example, they could chart information including the following:

	SOIL DATA	PLANT SPECIES	ASSOCIATED WILDLIFE/ EVIDENCE OF WILDLIFE	WILDLIFE OBSERVED
RECENT FIRE AREA				
FIRE 10-15 YEARS AGO				
NO RECORDED FIRE				

6. Ask the students to summarize their findings, including short-term and long-term effects to wildlife in each area, both positive and negative. They should include in their summary an assessment of the importance of fire in natural systems, as well as of its effectiveness as a management tool. In the situations they studied, ask them to evaluate the role of fire, including its positive and negative consequences. Their findings should include a listing of those situations and forest types in which fire is generally most beneficial, those in which it is most harmful, and those where it has little effect. Ask them to address any limitations to their study; that is any aspects of their research which prevent them from generalizing their findings to all fires affecting wildlife.

EXTENSIONS

1. Also discuss other impacts from wild and controlled burns. What is the public attitude toward fires in forest and grassland areas? What are the broad range of consequences of fires, and lack of fires, on local economy, on aesthetic value, ecological value, agricultural value? What are trade-offs in allowing and preventing fires? For example:

CONSEQUENCES TO SPECIES				
	SHORT-TERM BENEFIT	**LONG-TERM BENEFIT**	**SHORT-TERM HARM**	**LONG-TERM HARM**
PLANTS				
ANIMALS				

Come up with a set of recommendations for conditions under which fires should be allowed, and when not. Check your recommendations against present guidelines used by the U.S. Forest Service, U.S. Fish and Wildlife Service, National Park Service, Bureau of Land Management, Bureau of Indian Affairs, local state foresters' office and other state and federal agencies involved in wildlands fire management. (See the appendix "List of Agencies and Organizations.")

2. Find out the history of fire management in the U.S. Contrast policies of native American Indian people and federal agencies. Compare public attitude toward forest and grassland fires today with attitudes during the 1930s and 1940s.

3. Add a study of succession to this activity.

EVALUATION

1. Describe two differences between forest land and grassland that is burned frequently and forest land and grassland that is never burned.

2. Name ten species of plants and animals that are frequently helped by fire, and ten which tend to do better when fire is absent in grassland or forest—and describe the circumstances or reasons involved in each case.

3. You have been hired by the U.S. Forest Service to work as an information specialist in one of their regional offices. It is evident that the general public in your region has little understanding of the role of fire in natural systems. How can you effectively communicate with the public, in order to give them a balanced and informed view of the subject? Design a radio, television or magazine advertisement that conveys that point of view.

CHECKS AND BALANCES

OBJECTIVES

Students will: 1) evaluate hypothetical wildlife management decisions; and 2) identify at least four factors that can affect the size of a wildlife population.

METHOD

Students become managers of a herd of animals in a paper-and-pencil and discussion-based activity.

BACKGROUND

Wildlife managers attempt to maintain healthy populations of wild animals, while factors—both avoidable and unavoidable—affect the populations. Some of these factors are loss of habitat, weather conditions, pollution of food and water sources, development of other natural resources, poaching and recreation pressures. Many people are unaware of how such pressures can affect wildlife.

In the United States, it is the legal responsibility of state wildlife agencies to manage the wildlife populations within their respective states. It is the legal responsibility of the U.S. Fish and Wildlife Service, under the U.S. Department of the Interior, to govern some policies and programs affecting migratory species of animals (principally birds) and threatened or endangered species, as well as illegal importation and exportation of animals and animal products, illegal interstate transportation of all species, with additional responsibilities related to the overall well-being of U.S. wildlife.

Wildlife management is based on the best scientific and technical knowledge available. Such knowledge is growing; however, it is still limited, and is continually affected by changes in the complex relationships between wildlife, human beings and their shared environments.

In a sense, everyone shares responsibility for wildlife management. Although there are legally responsible agencies, their work requires the thoughtful and informed cooperation of citizens. There are frequently differences of opinion about the most appropriate policies and programs affecting wildlife. Individual citizens, private conservation groups, private industry, community groups, and others all make important contributions to the overall conservation and protection of wildlife and its habitat.

The major purpose of this activity is for students hypothetically to assume the role of wildlife managers and thus gain insight into some of the complex variables that influence stewardship of wildlife. This activity is not designed to provide a comprehensive understanding of all possible factors which can affect wildlife.

MATERIALS

paper and pencils; paper to make condition cards; dice, one per student

PROCEDURE

1. Each student is asked to be the manager of a moose (or other animal) population. The carrying capacity of the habitat is 100 animals. The point of the activity is to end up with a viable population after nine rounds, simulating nine years. If at any time the student's population reaches less than 10 or more than 200 individual animals, that student no longer has a viable "herd" and watches the other students until the conclusion of the activity.

2. Each student has a beginning population of 100 animals. The cards are separated into three decks of a total of 36 cards: a condition deck (18 cards), a repro-

---

Age: Grades 6-12
Subjects: Mathematics, Science, Vocational Agriculture
Skills: analysis, computation (calculating percentages), evaluation
Duration: one to two 45-minute periods
Group Size: any
Setting: classroom
Conceptual Framework Reference: I.C.3., I.C.4., I.D., III.A.1., III.C., III.C.1., III.C.2., III.E., III.E.1., III.E.2., III.F., IV.A, IV.A.1., IV.A.2., IV.A.3., IV.C., IV.C.1., IV.C.2., IV.C.3., IV.D., IV.D.1., IV.D.2., IV.D.3., IV.D.5., IV.E., IV.E.1., IV.E.4., IV.E.5., IV.E.6., IV.E.7., IV.E.10., IV.E.11., VI.A., VI.A.2., VI.A.3., VI.A.4., VI.B., VI.C., VI.C.12., VI.C.15., VI.C.16., VII.A., VII.B., VII.B.2., VII.B.4., VII.B.7.
Key Vocabulary: management, population, herd
Appendices: Simulations

duction deck (9 cards) and a management deck (9 cards). Shuffle the cards within each deck. Explain that cards will be drawn in the following sequence: condition card, reproduction card, condition card, management card. This sequence of draw will be repeated, each repetition representing an annual cycle (the students may think of each draw as representing a different season, e.g., autumn, winter, spring, summer). As each card is drawn, it is read aloud to the entire class. Each student then rolls his or her die and follows the instructions on the card to determine his or her herd population's new size. Some computations will result in fractions; numbers may be rounded to the nearest whole. NOTE: Students may object to the use of dice to determine the impact of decisions made for wildlife management purposes. Their concerns are appropriate; wildlife management is based on more than the chance elements reflected in the use of dice. However, chance has its impacts as well, as in the case of weather conditions in a given year. Encourage the students to discuss and consider what is realistic, and what is

unrealistic, about the impact of dice in this activity—encouraging the recognition that wildlife management is far more complex than can be represented through this activity.

3. Wrap up the activity with a class discussion. Include topics such as: Identify and describe what appeared to be the impacts of the condition, reproduction and management cards. Given one of the objectives of this activity—to evaluate hypothetical management decisions—what seemed to be the benefits and/or liabilities, if any, of management decisions made? Did populations "managed" under different strategies by different students show different trends? How do these compare? Would students "manage" differently if given a second chance? What aspects of this activity seemed realistic? Which didn't? What are examples of ways that habitat can be improved? Short term? Long term? Is human management of wildlife populations necessary? Beneficial? Why or why not? For people? For the animals?

EXTENSION OR VARIATION

Add a monetary aspect to the activity. Students allowing hunting might have more available revenue for projects like habitat enhancement based on income from sale of hunting licenses. Other expenses might include salaries of wildlife managers, funds for research, feeding animals in severe conditions, relocation, etc.

EVALUATION

1. Name four factors that can affect the size of a wildlife population.
2. Some wildlife managers have said that wildlife management involves more management of people than of wildlife. Explain what they might mean by the comment.

INSTRUCTIONS FOR MAKING CARDS

Make the following cards, according to three categories: **Reproduction Cards, Condition Cards, Management Cards.** There are 36 cards in total. The number in parentheses indicates how many of each card are to be made. NOTE: The numbers of cards and the suggestions for numerical manipulations, e.g., three times the roll, are relatively arbitrary. They are designed for students to recognize that a number of diverse factors can affect wildlife; the numerical weights should not be interpreted literally.

As the cards are read aloud, be certain to note differences in decreasing or increasing herd size by percentage or by number.

(After using these cards once, students may want to experiment with making additional cards, or changing these cards. Students may also want to make additional complete sets of cards for use by small groups or individual students.)

NOTE CONCERNING REPRODUCTION CARDS: The rate of reproduction is designed to vary with population density. The method for determining your population's rate of reproduction at a particular population

size is derived from a number of assumptions. One of them is that carrying capacity is 100 individuals. As your population drops below 100, the potential rate of reproduction increases reaching a peak at just above 50 individuals. This effect mimics the potential for rapid population growth many herbivore populations can exhibit when population levels are well below carrying capacity; in other words, food resources are readily available for reproductive effort, given that other environmental factors prove favorable. Below 10 individuals, reproduction is not allowed, reflecting severe reduction in reproductive activity observed at very low population levels because of, for example, imbalanced sex ratios, the inability to find suitable mates, or the disruption of social and mating systems. As the population grows above 100 individuals, the reproduction rate steadily decreases, reflecting the increasing activity of limiting factors as the population exceeds carrying capacity.

Reproduction	**Reproduction Card—Average Year (6)** This has been an average reproduction year. Increase your herd by (100/your current population size) times three times your roll, if your current population is over 50 individuals. If your population is between 50 and 10, increase your population by three times your roll. If your population is under 10, don't reproduce.
Condition	**Weather Card (2)** _____Students need to specify what) has had a serious negative impact on the survival of the herd. Decrease your herd by the percentage equal to five times your roll.
Condition	**Weather Card (2)** _____(Students need to specify what) has had a dramatic positive impact on the survival of the herd. Increase your herd by the percentage equal to five times your roll.
Condition	**Habitat Destruction Card (2)** _____(Students need to specify what) has occurred, destroying critical habitat. Decrease herd size by the number five times your roll.
Condition	**Predator Card (1)** Predation has occurred, affecting the herd size. Decrease herd size by the percentage equal to your roll.
Condition	**Habitat Degradation Card (4)** _____(Students need to specify what) has occurred, damaging critical habitat. Decrease herd by the number equal to three times your roll.
Condition	**Disease Card (1)** Disease has struck the herd. Decrease herd by the percentage equal to your roll.
Condition	**Habitat Loss Card (5)** _____(Students need to specify what) has resulted in a loss of critical habitat for the herd. Decrease herd by the number equal to five times your roll.
Condition	**Poaching Card (1)** Poaching—illegal killing of animals—has reduced the size of the herd. Decrease herd by the number equal to two times your roll.
Management	**Habitat Restoration Card (1)** _____(Students need to specify what) has occurred, restoring critical habitat. Increase herd by the percentage equal to five times your roll.

Reproduction	**Reproduction Card—Excellent Year (3)** This has been an excellent reproduction year. Increase your herd by (100/your current population size) times five times your roll, if your current population is over 50 individuals. If your population is between 50 and 10, increase your population by the number equal to five times your roll. If your population is under ten, you may not reproduce.
Management	**Habitat Alteration Card (2)** _____(Students need to specify what) has occurred, altering critical habitat. Increase or decrease (students choose which before rolling die) herd by the percentage equal to three times your roll.
Management	**Habitat Improvement Card (1)** _____(Students need to specify what) has occurred, improving critical habitat. Increase herd by five times your roll.
Management	**Research Card (1)** _____(Students need to specify what) research has been successfully accomplished. Increase or decrease (students choose which before rolling the die) herd by two times your roll.
Management	**Law Enforcement Card (1)** _____(Students need to specify what) law enforcement activities have protected the herd against illegal actions like poaching. Increase herd by the percentage equal to two times your roll.
Management	**Education Card (1)** _____(Students need to specify what) education activities have led to increased understanding of wildlife and habitat. Increase or decrease (students choose which before rolling the die) herd by the percentage equal to two times your roll, or by two times your roll.
Management	**Habitat Acquisition Card (1)** Habitat acquisition has increased the area of available and suitable habitat. Increase herd by five times your roll.
Management	**Hunting Card (1)** A request for a hunting season has been made. Do you wish to allow hunting in your area? If yes, decrease your herd by the percentage equal to five times your roll. If no, record no change in the size of your herd.

THE HUNTER

OBJECTIVES

Students will: 1) describe their feelings about hunting;
2) compare their attitudes to those of other people;
and 3) make personal judgments about the appropriateness of hunting.

METHOD

Students read and discuss a story.

BACKGROUND

People have hunted animals since earliest times.
Products of the hunt have been used for a wide variety
of purposes including for food, clothing, tools, bedding, medicines and religious objects.

Centuries of time and modern technologies have tended to urbanize human populations, removing many
from the necessity of as much daily contact with natural systems.

By percent of population, fewer people hunt today.
For many, the opportunity, interest and necessity is
not available. Many people have lost the knowledge
and skills, as well as the need, to hunt. The grocery
and butcher shop serve many instead. There are still
those who hunt. Some seek wild meats for nutrition
and purity. Some utilize horns, antlers and hides for

tools, clothing and decoration. Today in the United
States, hunters pay fees to hunt, and hunt under strin-
gent and restrictive conditions, their hunting controlled by management practices and concern for perpetuation of species and habitat.

In recent times, hunting has been used by wildlife management agencies as a tool for managing some species
of wildlife. Human activities in much of North America
have greatly reduced the natural predators of many
animal populations. Wildlife management policies often
attempt to substitute human hunting as a check on the
population growth of prey species. The effects of mortality factors such as predation and human hunting are
subjects of debate and in need of further study.

Hunters pay fees in order to hunt, and simultaneously
must follow all regulations of the agency responsible
for wildlife management in their state or province. The
hunters' fees as well as a portion of taxes on certain
hunting-related equipment go directly to continuing
management of wildlife resources, purchase and
restoration of wildlife habitat, and enforcement of
wildlife-related laws.

Why do some people hunt? Most hunters in the United
States today find it difficult to express their feelings
about why they hunt and kill wildlife. Most hunters say
they hunt because they like to get outside. Most would
call their hunting recreation and some would call it
sport. Most hunters feel they are making a significant
contribution to the perpetuation of wildlife species and
habitat since the proceeds from the license fees they
pay as well as taxes on some hunting and fishing related equipment are used for wildlife management,
including major revenue support for most state fish
and wildlife programs. Most hunters use some of the
products of the hunt for food. Almost no one today
uses nearly all products of the hunt as our ancestors
typically did from necessity.

Some people are opposed to hunting. They may
believe it to be unethical, or that it is biologically
unnecessary and even detrimental to the long-range
health and genetic vitality of wildlife populations.
Another concern is for the suffering of individual animals. The ethical right of humans to take the life of
other animals is also questioned. Some object to management practices they perceive to be aimed solely at
producing wildlife for the benefit of hunters.

Age: Grades 5-9
Subjects: Social Studies, Language Arts, Science, Math
Skills: analysis, comparing similarities and differences,
description, discussion, evaluation
Duration: 45 minutes or longer class periods
Group Size: any
Setting: indoors or outdoors
Conceptual Framework Reference: II.A., II.B., II.C., II.D.,
II.D.1., II.E., II.E.1., II.E.2., II.E.3., II.F., III.C., III.C.1.,
III.C.2., III.E., III.E.1., III.E.2., III.F., III.F.1., III.F.2., III.F.3.,
III.F.4., III.F.5., IV.A., IV.B., IV.C., IV.C.1., IV.C.2., IV.D.,
IV.D.1., IV.D.2., IV.D.3., IV.D.4., IV.D.7., IV.E, IV.E.1.,
IV.E.2., IV.E.4., IV.E.5., IV.E.6., IV.E.7., IV.E.9., IV.E.11.,
IV.F., IV.F.1., IV.F.2., IV.F.3., IV.F.4., IV.F.5., IV.F.6.,
IV.F.7., IV.F.8., IV.F.9., V.A., V.A.3., V.A.5., V.A.6., V.B.,
V.B.1., V.B.2., V.B.3., VI.B., VI.B.1., VI.B.2., VI.B.3., VI.B.4.,
VI.B.5., VI.B.6., VI.C., VI.C.1., VI.C.2., VI.C.3., VI.C.4.,
VI.C.7., VI.C.9., VI.C.12., VI.C.15., VI.C.16., VII.A., VII.B.,
VII.B.2.
Key Vocabulary: browse, habitat, edgeeffect, carrying
capacity, adaptation, predator, prey, range, ecological niche,
consumer, hunter, hunting, management, responsibility
Appendices: Local Resources

Some who do not believe it appropriate to kill for sport or recreation may accept hunting as a tool in managing certain kinds of wildlife and under certain conditions. For example, they may accept hunting when the meat is utilized for food; or hunting to control a species which is harming important habitat.

Others choose not to hunt, but may not take an active stand either for or against hunting.

Within any community, there will be a range of views on the subject.

The major purpose of this activity is for students to examine their own attitudes about hunting.

MATERIALS
student copies of story

PROCEDURE
1. Ask each student to think about his or her personal feelings about hunting animals. The students may or may not choose to share their feelings in discussion. OPTIONAL: Ask each student to write a brief description of his or her personal feelings about hunting before proceeding with this activity.
2. Provide each of the students with a copy of the following story to read, or read it aloud to the students.
3. After having read or heard the story, ask each student to write their own ending to it. What does Jamie do? Why? How does he feel?
4. Next ask the students to discuss the story and their endings to it. How do they think Jamie feels about hunting? How do they think Jamie feels about the animal he is hunting? How do each of them feel about animals and about hunting? Additional questions for discussion could include: Why is legal hunting allowed? What is the difference between hunting and poaching? Do you think hunting should be allowed? What reasons do people have for hunting? What reasons do people have who believe that hunting should not be allowed? In your judgment, what, if any, are appropriate reasons for hunting to be allowed? In your judgment what, if any, are appropriate reasons hunting should not be allowed? What responsibilities do you think people have if they choose to hunt? What responsibilities do you think people have if they choose

not to hunt? NOTE: Set a tone for discussion where each student's personal judgments are acknowledged and respected.

EXTENSIONS
1. Find out the following: Who sets the rules and enforces the legal regulations for hunting? (Regulations for legal hunting are established by the state agency responsible for wildlife. All wildlife in the United States, even on private property, is considered to belong to the public. It is managed on the public's behalf by state and federal wildlife agencies. Private organizations and individuals influence management, but legal responsibility belongs to state agencies, with some species and practices involving the federal government through the U.S. Fish and Wildlife Service and other federal agencies.)
2. Check with your state wildlife agency to find out what kinds of hunting, if any, are allowed in your area—as well as when, why, by what methods, with what equipment, at what age, and under what regulations. Also find out what kind of hunter preparation or education is required, if any, for people who want to be allowed to hunt.
3. Check with a diverse and representative range of interested groups for their positions concerning hunting. Some groups may be for hunting, some against, and some may not take an official position. Investigate their reasons for their positions. Check each point of view for accuracy of information provided. For example, groups which could be contacted include: American Humane Association, Defenders of Wildlife, The Fund for Animals, Humane Society of the United States, International Association of Fish and Wildlife Agencies, National Audubon Society, National Rifle Association, National Wildlife Federation, The Wildlife Society and Wildlife Management Institute, as well as state and federal wildlife agencies. Examples of position statements from a variety of organizations are included in this activity as optional background information.
4. Hold a series of debates. Argue and support positions for and against hunting.

EVALUATION
Write an essay describing reasons for and against hunting. Include your personal feelings and recommendations about the appropriateness of hunting.

The Twins
By Dr. Clifford Knapp
and Suzanne Iudicello

The twin fawns were born on a May day when the sun dabbled the edge of the forest through the newly budding leaves, and apple blossom petals fell in the abandoned orchard like fragrant snow. They were not the only twins that year; food had been plentiful in the valley, and white-tailed deer were sleek and round-bellied.

Even as the doe licked her offspring clean, strength flowed into the young bodies. It hadn't hurt that she had been able, through the fall and winter, to slip into a nearby farm at night for corn, alfalfa and clover to add to the leaves, twigs, juicy weeds, acorns and mushrooms the forests and fields offered to the white-tails.

The valley was a generous place for the herd of 60 animals. Where the hillsides dipped down to meet the farm fields, the shady forest ended. This edge meant that food was varied and abundant. It hadn't always been that way.

In the early 1700s, when the valley was first settled, the forests were widespread. Since white-tailed deer require a mixture of forest, openings and edge, they were present but not plentiful then. By 1900, however, the deer population had been almost eliminated by a human appetite for venison. Too much hunting had reduced the size of the herds. Much of the once abundant forest had been cleared for wood products and use as agricultural lands. This limited suitable habitat for the deer. Later, laws controlled hunting and changes in land use practices led to a return of some of the forest. The mixture of agriculture and young forests provided the deer herds an excellent environment and, with the regulated hunting, the deer thrived. The young plants that grew in the open areas of the cut-over forest yielded an abundance of food, and by the 1930s there were more deer in the valley than when the settlers first came.

That soft, May afternoon saw another birthday celebrated in the valley. The boy ran out to greet his father who was climbing down off the tractor after a day of making furrows for the spring planting. He looked up into the lined face of his father and barely contained his impatience while the farmer removed his hat and wiped the sweat from his forehead with a big, blue kerchief.

"Is it time?" the boy asked breathlessly.

The man smiled down at his son—a strong, wiry boy, made tough by summers of throwing hay bales and winters of chopping wood.

"Yes, Jamie," he grinned. "It's time." He put his arm across the boy's shoulders and they walked up onto the wide porch, where a table stood decked with early daisies and tiger lilies in a Mason jar, bright orange and yellow paper napkins, and a three-decker chocolate cake with 12 yellow candles. The boy's mother was already sitting at the table, pouring tall glasses of foamy, fresh milk.

"Do you want us to sing first?" She laughed, as Jamie scraped the chair legs across the porch floor in his haste to get to the table.

"Nope. Where's my present?"

"Now, Jamie," his father scolded good-naturedly, "birthdays aren't just for presents. This is a special year for you, and it brings with it not just a gift but some responsibility. You're no longer a little boy. You're a young man. This is not a birthday for toys."

Jamie looked down at his hands on his lap. "I know, Dad; I'm sorry."

But when he looked up again at his father, the excitement and expectation shining in his eyes were not those of a serious young man, but of a boy about to burst with anticipation.

As his mother cut the cake, Jamie's father took from behind the door a long, narrow box, tied with a gold ribbon. "Okay, son, this is what you've been waiting for, and we won't keep you from it."

Jamie tore the ribbon from the box and lifted the cover. There, gleaming from the soft yellow cloth, lay the rifle. It wasn't new, but the gloss on the stock showed a new coat of oil and betrayed hours of careful rubbing, and the barrel shone with new blueing. The scratches he remembered on the dull grey were done, but the initials his grandfather had carved on the stock were still there.

He drew the rifle from the box, taking care to point it away from anyone as his grandfather and father had taught him. It was much heavier than the .22 he'd lugged through the woods to stalk squirrels.

"It's yours now, Jamie, just as we promised," his father said. "You're 12 now, and old enough to go deer hunting this fall."

Although Jamie thought the fall would never arrive, the summer passed quickly, filled with days of helping his father in the fields, fishing and swimming, and lots of practice with the rifle.

In the hills above the farm valley, the twin fawns gained strength quickly. By June, they followed the doe along the well-worn trails. As summer ripened, they roamed with the herd over the length of the valley and high on the hillsides. They were just two of 50 fawns that had been born that spring, swelling the herd from 60 to more than 100.

They fed on leaves, twigs, fruits and nuts of the trees and shrubs in the forest, and on the grasses and weeds along its edges. The summer habitat provided abundant food. The doe and her fawns grew strong and healthy on the bounty. This was fortunate, for the stark winter ahead would not offer such abundance.

November blew in rainy and cold, and Jamie was restless after the crisp, bright days of October. The harvest was complete, the fields lay in a stubble under the grey sky, and the few brown apples remaining on the trees were torn down by the wind. He sat in the warm kitchen and looked out at the glistening black branches scratching at the sky.

"Can I go out, Mom?" he asked. She looked up from the lunch dishes at her son, his dungaree cuffs well above the tops of the worn boots, and the elbows frayed out of his plaid flannel shirt. The restlessness was about to burst his skin as his growing body had burst the seams of most of his clothes that summer.

"All right, but wear your father's poncho," she called as he was already halfway out the door, the rifle over his shoulder.

Jamie knew, from his summer forays and from past autumns when he'd been too young to hunt, that the deer often came down to the abandoned orchard to nip at the withered apples that grew on the overhanging trees. That part of the farm wasn't used now, and the orchard had long since overgrown, producing only tiny, bitter fruits, but the deer seemed to like them. He had watched, enthralled, many an evening, as the slender, tawny forms moved delicately and then froze like shadows in the dusk.

As he trotted away from the yellow light in the kitchen window, dusk gathered and the rain turned to sleet. The grey afternoon was threatening to turn bleaker yet. He scrambled over the crumbling remains of a stone wall, and entered the orchard in a blast of wind that nearly took his breath away. "At least it's blowing toward me," he thought, settling in under a tree to wait. Just before nightfall, his patience was wearing thin, his foot was tingling where he had been sitting on it, the rain was trickling under his collar, and the sleet was stinging his face. He was about to stomp his foot to bring it back to life so he could walk home, when the doe entered the orchard; Jamie caught his breath.

The words of the wildlife license agent echoed in his ears as he raised the rifle to his shoulder. "We're going to open the season this year—bucks, does, fawns." The man had punched Jamie's slip of yellow paper for fishing and hunting—the first time he'd been the age to have a license for deer. "This is your first hunting season, son?" he'd asked. "Good luck."

Jamie watched the doe down the barrel of the rifle. She was stretching up, her front feet off the ground, trying to reach a last, wrinkled apple clinging stubbornly to a high branch. The slender neck glistened from drops of rain caught in the soft hair. His heart was pounding and he wasn't sure if he was still breathing. He reached around with his thumb and gently pushed the safety off the rifle.

Just then the twin fawns stepped delicately into the orchard, melting from the darkened tree trunks like slightly smaller shadows of the doe. Jamie lifted his eyes from the barrel to the fawns. They, too, were stretching to try to reach the last brown leaves and few apples high in the branches, but they were too short. They moved close to the doe, where her efforts at pulling on the branches had jostled a few apples to the ground.

Jamie refocused on the doe, sighted down the barrel, and let out a deep breath to steady his hand. Just then, a blast of wind ripped through the orchard, carrying sleet and snow before it, ripping a tree branch in its fury. The branch tumbled down and the three deer bolted back into the thicket.

The boy reset the safety on the rifle, and gingerly got to his feet. He looked into the darkening sky and the tossing branches and thought, "I'm glad. Maybe those three will make it through the winter."

Winter hit that night, lashing the valley with wind and snow that piled into high snowdrifts, froze into hard crusts, and remained. The herd, trapped on the hillside, didn't move more than a quarter of a mile the whole winter. They competed for the dwindling food supply that remained poking above the snow, and many fawns and does died.

Jamie thought often about the trio, as he looked out over the white landscape.

The grip of the season finally loosened one moist, February day. Rain pelted the snow, turning it to slush and pitted mounds where the mud showed through. Spring and summer returned to the valley, and with them the activity that kept life for a farm boy busy and full.

For the herd, the winter had taken its toll. Most of the fawns had died of starvation and cold, as did many older bucks and does, weakened by age. The herd was reduced from the summer high of more than 100 to fewer than 50. Those remaining ventured down out of the hills to the greening valley where their favored plants sprouted anew. Throughout the spring and summer, they found plenty of food to go around among their reduced numbers, particularly since few fawns had been born after the harsh winter.

Summer's hazy, golden days burned into fall, and as harvest time ended, Jamie's thoughts drifted again to the abandoned orchard and his rifle. One evening he took it out of its wrappings, and cleaned and polished it, wondering if the twin fawns were among this autumn's yearlings.

The frosty straw stubble crunched under his feet as he made his way across the fields to the orchard. The passing of a year had seen more stones fall from the top of the wall, and Jamie noted that the tree that had been his resting place last season was uprooted and lying broken. He concealed himself among the twisted branches and settled to wait.

The evening was still, the sky a pale salmon color where the sun had just slipped below the hills. Jamie hoped the slight varying breeze would not carry his scent. He slid a round into the chamber of the rifle, wondering how many times his grandfather had sat like this, in this very orchard, with this very rifle. He checked to make sure the safety was on.

Dusk fell with the twittering of a few last thrushes, and Jamie started at the sound of a snapping twig. A yearling doe stepped into the orchard, the brush rustling back to fill the space where she had emerged from the forest. Jamie exhaled quietly, trying to relax again, because this year was bucks only, the season restricted because the herd had so dwindled over the harsh winter. He watched the doe nosing among the brown weeds for fallen apples, wondering if she were the fawn of last autumn. He watched, still, admiring the sleek brown sides and graceful curve of the neck. The doe raised her head and listened, so close he could see her nostrils flickering to catch a scent. The deer glanced at the forest edge, tensed, then bent her head to browse again as a yearling buck emerged from the same trail, disguised by the thick brush.

Jamie lifted the rifle to his shoulder, nestling it close against the rough wool of his jacket. He looked down the barrel at the young white-tail, wondering if these were the twins of that blustery evening a year ago. He questioned whether this time he would pull the trigger. "He made it through the winter—who am I to kill him now?" he asked himself.

The buck stepped away from the doe, and began pulling apples from the drooping branches. It would be a clean shot, Jamie knew, well away from the doe, certain to be a quick kill. He exhaled, steadied his arm, and concentrated on a patch of rusty brown hair on the animal's shoulder. "I can't look at his head," he thought. "I just have to keep thinking of him as meat for my family." As he thumbed off the safety, he allowed himself one last, stolen glance at the sculptured head, arching up to grasp an apple. Jamie swallowed and. . .

NOTE: *"The Twins" is adapted, with permission, from a story which originally appeared in* **Open Lands and Wildlife** *(Union, New Jersey: Pollution Control Education Center, 1975), a multimedia instructional unit including both teacher and student materials. Thanks to Dr. Clifford Knapp for his cooperation and encouragement in providing the original material for use in Project WILD.*

NOTE: These statements were requested from the following organizations specifically for use in the Project WILD Activity Guide. Each organization was asked to contribute a statement, including a brief description of the organization, its purpose or goals, and its position or policy concerning hunting. These statements have not been edited by Project WILD; they appear as they were submitted.

National Wildlife Federation

The Nation's largest conservation organization, with over four million members and supporters, the National Wildlife Federation (NWF) attracts concerned citizens on both sides of the hunting question.

While recognizing the concerns of those opposed on moral grounds, the Federation supports responsible, well-controlled hunting and fishing as appropriate uses of wildlife resources. Regulation of these activities should be based upon sound, scientifically-based wildlife management practices and designed to ensure the continued diversity and health of wild species.

The real danger to wildlife populations today is not hunting, but rampant habitat destruction and degradation. In response, the Federation uses education, litigation, and advocacy to foster habitat conservation and healthy environmental practices worldwide.

By promoting common-sense conservation to concerned citizens on both sides of the hunting question, NWF is protecting habitat and natural resources for the benefit of wildlife and people everywhere.

National Rifle Association of America

The National Rifle Association (NRA), chartered in 1871, is not only the oldest shooting and hunting organization in America, it is also an educational, recreational, and public service organization dedicated to the right of responsible citizens to own and use firearms for all legitimate purposes.

The NRA is a nonprofit organization supported entirely by its over 3 million members and 10,000 affiliated clubs. It is not affiliated with any arms or ammunition manufacturers. Although it receives no appropriations from Congress, the NRA cooperates with all branches of the U.S. armed forces, Federal agencies, States, and local governments interested in teaching firearms skills and safety to interested Americans. The NRA's Hunter Services Division has several departmental programs that seek to expand the hunter's knowledge and skills, promote habitat improvement, and foster the tradition of sharing the bounty of the hunt.

Well regulated hunting is a beneficial use of renewable wildlife resources that when left to nature, are lost to predation, disease, starvation, or old age. Proper hunting is in complete accord with the moral tenets and historical facts of human existence. The hunting heritage predates recorded history by many centuries. The hunter's participation in the chase today is a healthy exercise, both physically and spiritually.

The hunter's interest in wildlife has been the principal factor in fostering sound management and conservation practices. Provision for the hunter's harvest provides the incentive for the hunter's contribution, without which all else would be lost. The commitment of the hunter's contributions of voluntary taxing, licensing, and regulation assure propagation of all wildlife.

Hunting is dominant among American traditions and has contributed substantially to our strong national character. Its future is a primary concern of the NRA.

National Audubon Society

The National Audubon Society is an organization of more than 500,000 members working at the national, state, and local level for the conservation and restoration of natural ecosystems, focusing on birds, other wildlife, and their habitats for the benefit of humanity and the earth's biological diversity. For nearly a century National Audubon has provided leadership in scientific research, conservation education and environmental action. Our nationwide sanctuary system protects more than 250,000 acres of unique natural habitat for birds, wildlife and plants. We run education centers, workshops and camps, which are supported by more than 500 chapters and ten regional offices located throughout the United States. Our publications, most notably AUDUBON magazine, are known for their beauty and accuracy. By participating in a number of international organizations, including the International Union for the Conservation of Nature and the International Council on Bird Preservation, Audubon helps foster a better understanding and resolution of global environmental issues.

Audubon has never been opposed to the hunting of game species provided such hunting is done ethically and in accordance with the laws and regulations designed to prevent depletion of the resource. However, we will advocate restrictions on hunting—including the complete closure of a season—whenever we are convinced that the welfare of a species requires such action. We would be remiss in our responsibilities as a conservation organization if we failed to implement such convictions. At the same time, we insist on sound scientific information before deciding these issues.

The National Audubon Society does not advocate hunting. Our objective is wildlife and environmental conservation—not the promotion of hunting. We believe that many of the justifications for hunting are weak—and too often exaggerated for commercial purposes. We do not hesitate to say so when the occasion demands.

Defenders of Wildlife

The goal of Defenders of Wildlife is to preserve, enhance and protect the natural abundance and diversity of wildlife including the integrity of natural wildlife ecosystems. Defenders recognizes the intrinsic value of wildlife, the importance of its humane treatment and the many benefits of wildlife to society. Defenders seeks to achieve its goals through education and reasoned advocacy of appropriate public policies.

Incorporated in 1947 to reform trapping practices, including banning the leghold trap, Defenders has maintained its historic purposes while expanding its mission to match today's challenges to wildlife.

Defenders opposes utilitarian notions that wildlife is most important for human consumption, opposes claims that wildlife plants and animals are "renewable resources" to be managed or harvested like crops and opposes single species management plans where the primary goal is the production of more "game" for hunters.

The defense of predators including grizzly bears, wolves, coyotes and golden eagles has long been a priority commitment of Defenders. Defenders promotes concepts of animal damage prevention through the use of livestock guarding dogs and other nonlethal alternatives.

Defenders of Wildlife advocates policies which are in the best interest of all wildlife by analyzing wildlife management programs to determine the appropriate response. Hunting is evaluated by this standard on a case-by-case basis. Defenders has opposed hunting in instances where it has jeopardized sensitive species or their essential habitat.

Fund for Animals

The Fund for Animals is a national animal protection society that actively opposes all sport hunting of wildlife. Hunters kill more than 200 million animals each year in the U.S. — crippling, harassing, and orphaning millions more — all in the name of fun. These animals experience fear and pain, and there is no reason they should suffer for someone's hobby.

While some native cultures may still hunt for food, hunting in the U.S. is done primarily for sport. The average cost of deer meat — after calculating the costs of firearms, ammunition, hunting licenses, travel expenses, etc. — is about $20.00 per pound. No one who needs to feed their family would pay so much money for a recreational activity.

Hunters claim they hunt to control overpopulation. But they only make this argument for white-tailed deer. Deer represent only 2 percent of all the animals killed by hunters. The vast millions of victims are doves, squirrels, rabbits, and ducks — and no one claims they are overpopulated. Hunters even breed pheasants and quail in captivity and then release them to be shot. Surely, they are not controlling overpopulation by breeding more animals so they can have more moving targets.

When it comes to deer, wildlife agencies try to increase their deer herds so they can sell more hunting licenses and make more money. They burn down forests to make the habitat better for deer reproduction, and they manipulate the sex ratios of deer to make sure the females will have more babies.

This wildlife mismanagement based on the desires of sport hunters must end. Animals are not "resources" to be "harvested" like crops. They are living creatures and they deserve our respect.

Hunters' numbers are dwindling and they now represent fewer than 6 percent of the public. The new generation of young people has respect for wildlife and the environment, and has no interest in killing animals for sport. If people shoot animals in the future, they will use cameras instead of guns.

Humane Society of the United States
Organized in 1954, The Humane Society of the United States (H.S.U.S.) is a nonprofit organization dedicated to ensuring the protection and humane treatment of animals, both companion and wild. We conduct major programs oriented toward humane education and toward ensuring the welfare of companion animals, farm animals and laboratory animals, as well as wildlife.

The Humane Society of the United States is strongly opposed to the hunting of any living creature for fun, trophy, or for sport, because of the trauma, suffering and death to the animals which results. The H.S.U.S. also opposes such killing because of the negative effect upon the young who may learn to accept and live with needless suffering and killing. The H.S.U.S. believes that a civilized society should not condone the killing of any sentient creature as sport.

The H.S.U.S. believes that the characterization of wild animals as "game" denies their intrinsic value and belittles their ecological importance. The Society finds that a great deal of wildlife allegedly killed for management reasons actually is killed as "game" for "sporting" purposes. In such cases, we oppose both the killing and the duplicity. Rather than attempting to justify or romanticize the modern-day killing of wildlife as food gathering, society should, through educational and other means, encourage the values of compassion, kindness, and humane stewardship in our relations to wildlife and our natural world.

The H.S.U.S. recognizes that the welfare and responsible management of animals may, on occasion, necessitate the killing of wildlife. When such killing is permitted, it must be used as a last resort, be demonstrably necessary, be conducted by responsible officials, and methods utilized must result in an instantaneous and humane death.

The H.S.U.S. also recognizes that the legitimate needs for human subsistence may necessitate the killing of wildlife. In such cases, killing must be accomplished in a humane and non-wasteful manner and must not involve endangered or threatened animals.

WILDLIFE RESEARCH

OBJECTIVES

Students will: 1) identify reasons for research related to wildlife; 2) evaluate appropriate kinds of research related to wildlife; and 3) design and conduct a wildlife research project.

METHOD

Students evaluate types of research involving wildlife, apply their results to develop individual research proposals that meet criteria for appropriateness and conduct research.

BACKGROUND

Research, by definition, represents a quest for knowledge. It typically involves careful, systematic study and investigation. It does not necessarily involve intervention or experimentation; it may be entirely based on observation and other data-gathering techniques.

One area of scientific research involves study of wildlife. Such research may be conducted in field or in laboratory settings. Research may involve wildlife directly or indirectly, or both. For example, it may focus directly on wildlife species, or indirectly on habitats; or on societal factors such as human attitudes, beliefs, and values.

Age: Grades 7-12
Subjects: Science (Biology), English, Environmental Problems, Social Studies (Psychology, Current Issues)
Skills: analysis, application, classification, comparing similarities and differences, description, discussion, evaluation, generalization, invention, listing, problem solving, reading, reporting, research, writing
Duration: three to five 45-minute periods plus homework
Group Size: any, whole class working individually or in small groups
Setting: indoors
Conceptual Framework Reference: I.D., II.A., II.A.1., II.A.2., II.A.3., II.A.4., II.B., II.B.1., II.B.2., II.B.3., II.B.4., II.C., II.D., II.E., II.F., IV.A., IV.D., IV.D.2., IV.E., IV.E.4., IV.E.5., V.A., V.A.5., V.B., V.B.1., V.B.2., VI.B., VI.B.1., IV.B.2., VI.C., VI.C.1., VI.C.2., VI.C.6., VI.C.12., VI.C.13., VI.C.14., VI.C.15., VI.C.16., VI.D., VI.D.4., VII.A.4., VII.B., VII.B.3.
Key Vocabulary: research, ethics
Appendices: Field Ethics, Outdoors, Local Resources, Animals in the Classroom

Wildlife research involves more than studying about large mammals such as elk and deer. Wildlife is diverse and includes insects, spiders, other invertebrates, birds, amphibians, fish and reptiles. In fact, wildlife includes any animal that is not domesticated or tame.

Such research may have a variety of purposes, including examples such as these: 1) research to acquire knowledge specific to the animal under study, e.g., field research to identify food and cover needs, disease problems, and adaptability of transplanted bighorn sheep; and 2) research to acquire knowledge specific to human activities which influence wildlife, e.g., potential impacts of a proposed land development on species of wildlife in an area.

Study of conditions affecting wildlife can be important to people as well as to the animals, and for environments. However, there is controversy about what is ethical research involving animals. For example, questions of ethics may arise for some where any research involving animals is proposed, or if research procedures involve activities which may harm or cause discomfort to individual animals in the process of acquiring insights which may be helpful to populations of animals or to people.

The major purpose of this activity is for students to identify reasons for research related to wildlife, and, through designing a possible research proposal, to consider what seem appropriate and inappropriate kinds of research and research practices.

MATERIALS

writing materials; possible need for access to reference materials; observation tools such as video cameras, sketch books, hand lens, etc.

PROCEDURE

1. Brainstorm with your students a list of possible reasons to do research about or involving wildlife, directly or indirectly.

2. Discuss what seems to be reasonable, acceptable, and appropriate research, and what does not.

3. Ask each student to classify the kinds of research as acceptable or unacceptable, and their reasons for these classifications. Following this personal evaluation, ask them, as a group, to develop a set of criteria for acceptable and appropriate research.

4. OPTIONAL: Before categorizing and evaluating the various types of research, ask the students to do some library work to find additional information on the topic. A few students could be asked to place phone calls or write letters for additional information. For example, local agencies or organizations that might conduct research related to wildlife could be contacted to find out what kinds of research they conduct and what methods they use. Other agencies or organizations that oppose research involving wildlife could also be contacted for information. Please review the questions the students would ask, before the students place their calls or send their letters, to assure the clarity of the request and to coordinate the inquiries, avoiding duplication of effort. If such contacts are made, ask the students to report back to the rest of the class.

5. Ask each student team to design and write a "Proposal to Conduct Research." The plan must follow good scientific method, take place on the school grounds or other approved site and follow the class determined ethical guidelines developed in step 3. A proposal might be a behavioral study (e.g., students observe how house sparrows foraging for food respond to adjacent human activity). Their study might involve census work (e.g., how many ant colonies exist on the school site and the number of different species of ants represented). The research project does not need to involve wildlife directly, but, for example, could involve a survey of people's attitudes concerning wildlife. Such a research project could explore whether students think spiders serve any useful purpose on the school site. If the project directly involves wildlife, have the students become familiar with and incorporate the National Science Teachers Association's Code of Practice on Animals in Schools (see appendix) into their plan.

6. Evaluate each proposal to determine that it follows good scientific procedures and adheres to the class determined ethical guidelines and the National Science Teachers Association's *Guidelines for Responsible Use of Animals in the Classroom*. Ensure the plan is realistic. Students must be able to complete the research in the allotted time with the available resources. A field biologist, such as one described in step 4, might be available to review the plans and make suggestions. Students are often surprised at how narrow their research questions will have to be.

7. After project approval, students conduct their research. They should compile their results and, if possible, draw conclusions. Their data may not support any conclusions. It is important for students to learn not to extend their conclusions beyond what their data support. Students can identify areas for further study, and, if time permits, conduct some of those studies.

EVALUATION

Suppose you are the director of a wildlife research institute at a university and have been told by the university president that your program is under review for possible elimination from the budget. You have been requested to submit a justification for the continuation of your research program. What will you say?

BIRD SONG SURVEY

OBJECTIVE
Students will identify and describe the importance of bird counting as one means of inventorying wildlife populations.

METHOD
Students investigate an area and use bird-counting techniques.

BACKGROUND
People interested in wildlife and its habitat use a variety of techniques to learn about it and to assist in management for its conservation and protection. Some techniques are used to acquire information and some to apply knowledge. Inventory is a technique that is used to acquire information about the number and kinds of wildlife in a given area.

This activity is designed to give students some experience in the use of inventory. Birds are the subject of study. The variety of species and the number of individual birds in an area are good indicators of the quality of that particular environment. Their presence indicates food, water, shelter and space in an appropriate arrangement to suit their needs. "Bird watching" can be a valuable research tool, as well as an aesthetically pleasing activity that brings the student into touch with intangible values.

Age: Grades 9-12
Subjects: Mathematics, Science (Biology, Zoology), Language Arts
Skills: application, classification, comparing similarities and differences, description, discussion, mapping, media construction, observation
Duration: minimum of three 45-minutes periods, not including transportation to bird inventory site
Group Size: up to 30, with need to break into smaller groups for bird watching
Setting: indoors and outdoors
Conceptual Framework Reference: I.D., II.A., II.A.3., II.B., II.B.1., II.B.2., II.B.3., II.B.4., II.D., II.E., II.E.1., II.E.3., II.F., III.A., III.B., III.D., III.D.1., III.D.2., III.D.3., III.D.4., III.D.5., IV.A., IV.A.1., IV.C., IV.C.1., IV.C.2., IV.C.3., IV.C.4., IV.D.2., IV.D.4., IV.D.5., IV.E., IV.E.2., IV.E.3., IV.E.4., IV.E.5., IV.E.10., VI.A., VI.A.2., VI.A.3., VI.A.4., VI.A.5.
Key Vocabulary: inventory, population, management, habitat
Appendices: Outdoors, Field Ethics, Animals in the Classroom

One means of identifying a bird species is by sight, another by sound or song. Male birds of most species sing from conspicuous perches to mark territory, except during the nesting period. With practice, identification of many bird songs can be learned easily.

The major purpose of this activity is for students to recognize the importance of inventory as one technique by which to learn more about wildlife, people and our shared environments. The activity also enhances students' appreciation of wildlife's aesthetic values.

MATERIALS
paper and pencil for note-taking; bird books as reference materials; drawing paper or magazine photos to illustrate final written project
OPTIONAL: binoculars; tapes of bird call recordings and battery-operated player

PROCEDURE
1. This can be an annual project—or a one-time project during a single school year. Offered each year for several years, the students who participate can be contributing to a meaningful record of the natural history of their area.
2. Establish a suitable tract of land and an optimal season for conducting this activity. Check to find out which time of year in your area there would be the greatest variety and number of birds. (Local members of the National Audubon Society are often happy to assist.) Find an area that is most apt to offer a variety of habitats and thus more likely to offer variety in birds as well. Transition areas between differing ecosystems—like pond, woods and meadow areas—are apt to be good locations. Watering sites in desert areas, and city sites with vegetation and water, may serve. If the students are assisting in identifying the most suitable site, remind them of the basic habitat needs of animals, including birds—food, water, shelter and space in an appropriate arrangement. They can use these components as working criteria. (If there is no way to travel except by foot, however, find the best and closest available site.)
3. Invite a member or members of a local bird club (e.g., affiliate chapter of the National Audubon Society) to instruct the class on field study techniques for

bird watching. These people can help the class determine what bird species are common to the area, which most easily identified, which most difficult to spot, any precautions to take in order not to disturb the birds or other wildlife in the area to be studied, etc. As part of the students' preparation for their guests from the local bird club, ask them to bring in bird guides from home (if possible) or from school and local libraries or natural history museums.

4. Try to get recordings of bird songs of selected species. Practice identifying the birds by their songs.

5. Now it is time to visit the site to apply the knowledge and skills the students have been working to acquire. Select a trail, path or road to walk in the area that has an easily discernible starting and ending point. If possible, the students should walk the trail in the early morning, using techniques they were taught by the bird club members in making and recording their observations. Ideally, members of the bird club, parents or other community members can come along to assist as well. OPTIONAL: Take along the recorded tapes of bird songs with a battery-operated recorder. This reference "in the field" is a big help in identification.

6. Repeat the inventory one or more times that morning to try to account for all breeding pairs. The number of singing males identified on each walk should be consistent.

7. Once back in class, have the students compile the results of their observations. Map the site and mark the locations of bird sightings, e.g., using colored dots for birds with an explanatory key. Encourage the students to discuss their observations as well as the feelings they experienced in the process of watching the birds. Also talk about any difficulties they feel they might have experienced in getting an accurate count.

8. As an option—a small group of students might volunteer to compile all the findings in a written format, including magazine photos or sketches of the birds, etc. This booklet could serve as the beginning of a year-to-year record of the inventory of birds in that location at that time of year, and thus could be used by students conducting this project in subsequent years. As a new group of students repeats the inventory each year, the results could be graphed, showing year-to-year changes, if any. Trends could be analyzed, etc. Additional information can be included in this report format, including a map of the area selected for the inventory with the trail and other notable landmarks identified.

EXTENSIONS AND VARIATIONS

1. In one school year, conduct several counts throughout the migration period, checking to see what happens in the area selected. Take counts seasonally, noticing similarities and differences.

2. One or two singing male birds could be followed closely to determine the size of their respective territories. Be sure that students are following rather than chasing the bird. This could be a mapping and mathematics project, using geometry to calculate the area of the bird's territory. Map each location where the bird perches to sing his song and try to determine where he comes into conflict with a neighboring, singing male.

3. Compare the class results with those of statistical count experts, if such research data are available.

4. Send for inventory techniques, counts, trends and management implications for other species of animals from the state or province wildlife agency, etc. Make comparisons with class techniques and data.

CAUTION: Do not disturb the birds; make sure not to disrupt mating, nest-building and nesting activities. Check with local authorities (e.g., the bird club members, state wildlife personnel) for precautions.

EVALUATION

1. Summarize the findings from your study. Why is it important to be able to inventory wildlife populations?

2. Design a wildlife survey plan for conducting a butterfly census.

DEER CROSSING

OBJECTIVES

Students will: 1) identify various factors involved in a wildlife management issue; and 2) evaluate alternatives in a complex issue involving wildlife.

METHOD

Students are given background information and asked to make recommendations.

BACKGROUND

The major purpose of this activity is to provide students with an opportunity to analyze and evaluate complex factors that frequently arise in wildlife management issues. The situation used to illustrate this activity is based on actual occurrences involving a herd of deer in the state of Idaho.

MATERIALS

hand-out of information below

PROCEDURE

1. Provide groups of two to four students with the following background information, based on an actual situation in the state of Idaho. Ask the students, working in their groups, to read the information, discuss and evaluate options they think are available to resolve the situation in the best possible manner, and be prepared to offer and explain the recommendation of their group.

2. Ask the student groups to present and explain their recommendations. If students do not already have background, they may need to do research to prepare for their presentation. If additional research is not possible, the students can identify areas where they think additional information is needed—and why—before they feel they can make responsible recommendations. Where such points arise, ask for one or two students—if not more—to volunteer to get and verify this additional information. To formalize the reporting, each group could:

- describe the situation (or briefly review)
- provide background information
- identify and describe factors involved in the issue
- identify and describe alternative solutions, and
- state recommended action, with reasons

Age: Grades 7-12
Subjects: Social Studies (Government, History, Civics), Language Arts, Environmental Problems, Science
Skills: analysis, description, discussion, evaluation, public speaking
Duration: two 45-minute periods or longer
Group Size: large group
Setting: indoors
Conceptual Framework Reference: IV.A., IV.A.1., IV.A.2., IV.A.3., IV.A.4., IV.E., IV.E.5., IV.E.10., IV.E.11., IV.F., IV.F.1., IV.F.2., IV.F.3., IV.F.4., IV.F.5., IV.F.6., IV.F.8., IV.F.11., V.A., V.A.5., V.B., V.B.1., V.B.2., VI.A., VI.A.1., VI.A.2., VI.A.3., IV.A.4., VI.A.5., VI.B., VI.B.1., VI.B.3., VI.B.4., VI.B.5., VI.B.6., VI.C., VI.C.1., VI.C.2., VI.C.6., VI.C.12., VI.C.15., VI.C.16., VI.D.1.
Key Vocabulary: land use, condemnation, deed
Appendices: None

DEER CROSSING

A major highway was to be built in an area previously served by an old road. Building the new highway would make it possible for auto travelers to get to a nearby town approximately six minutes faster than they could by the old road. The new highway would pose a major problem for a herd of deer in the area. Whereas the old road skirted a migration route used by the deer in moving between summer and winter feeding ranges, the new highway would lie directly in the path of the deer's migration.

The new highway was built, and it did block the deer's migration. The deer tried to cross the highway, but many were killed in the process in collisions with autos and trucks. People were also injured and some were killed. A large fence was built along both sides of this highway, in hopes of preventing the animals from trying to cross. Even so, some deer were able to cross, with collisions and fatalities still the result.

Most of the deer, however, were not able to jump the fence that was built. Instead, the majority of the herd bunched up on one side of the fence, without being able to cross. The problem was particularly critical each winter. The deer were trying to move out of the high mountains, where they spent the summer months, to get to lower feeding areas for the winter. There was not enough food for the deer if they could not get to their winter feeding area. They bunched up by the fence, ate any food in the area quickly, and began damaging the remaining vegetation and soil structure as they looked for food.

Every year since the highway was built, the state wildlife agency has brought in food for the hungry deer. Even so, some deer die from starvation each winter, while more than 1,500 are fed a pellet food. Deer being fed under these crowded conditions in a central feeding area are more apt to contract and spread disease. They also become accustomed to being fed by humans. The wildlife agency has taken several approaches to relieve this situation. A seven and one-half mile long fence was constructed to the north and east of the highway. This has helped to hold the deer farther north and helps to disperse the animals to minimize damage to the watershed in the vicinity of the feeding area. The U.S. Bureau of Land Management initiated a project to plant saltbush and bitterbrush on several hundred acres of land adjacent to this fence. An additional 1,500 acres has been seeded aerially. These bushes are now three to four feet high and provide natural winter range for the deer herd. Plans call for seeding another 3,000 to 4,000 acres, the acreage calculated as necessary to support a herd of 2,000 deer.

Consider the following possibilities—including costs and benefits of each—and any others that you might come up with that you think would be effective and appropriate:

- Issue hunting permits to reduce the size of the herd in the area
- Live-capture and transplant deer to areas where there is sufficient room and food for them to live
- Persuade the highway department to build underpasses or overpasses the deer can use to move from one feeding area to the other
- Keep feeding the deer artificially
- Let the deer starve
- Other?

EVALUATION

1. What are the factors involved in this deer problem? What are the values that must be considered by the people trying to solve this problem? How might the problem have been avoided, or at least solved less expensively?

2. Consider this situation: A stream, dammed for flood control five years ago, has become an area for a number of wildlife and human problems. Because of the quantity of still and warm water available, the mosquito population is up and the number of fish species is being reduced. Nutrients running off local farms have increased the growth of aquatic plants. The fishing, boating, swimming and picnicking use of the area has been reduced from the early years. However, flooding concerns for the city downstream virtually have been eliminated. The residents in the town do not report being bothered too much by the mosquitos.

List at least four factors that should be considered in this resource management issue. Identify, describe and evaluate at least four possible actions that could be taken to resolve the resource problems which have developed, attending to the diverse values represented in the community as well as overall wildlife and human needs. Select what you think is the most reasonable and appropriate solution, and explain your reasons.

RIPARIAN ZONE

OBJECTIVES

Students will: 1) identify and describe factors frequently involved in land use planning; and 2) evaluate possible consequences for wildlife and other elements of the environment—including people—where land-use planning does not take place.

METHOD

Students simulate a Board of Commissioners hearing.

BACKGROUND

See "To Zone or Not To Zone" for another simulation activity about land-use planning. See also "Shrinking Habitat" and "Planning for People and Wildlife." This activity is most appropriate when students already have some background in land-use issues, or to dramatize need for good information in land-use decision making and planning.

Worldwide, loss of habitat is generally considered to be the single most serious threat to the future of wildlife. Development of land areas for varying purposes affects wildlife—whether for business and industry, housing, agriculture, and even recreation. This is not to say that all development need be considered "bad," nor all development ceased. However, in the spirit of protection, wise use, and conservation of natural resources and the environment—it is important for people to recognize the impacts of their actions, and learn to make decisions based on informed processes wherever possible.

The riparian zone is the area next to a waterway which is immediately affected by the presence of water. Typically, the vegetation in a riparian zone requires much more water than that of neighboring plants. Riparian zones are generally more lush and support a greater variety and number of wildlife species than surrounding uplands. Streams and rivers provide a natural seed dissemination route. Seeds may fall in a river upstream, be transported downstream, and eventually germinate and grow several miles from their origin. Riparian areas, due to their exposure to seeds from other areas and their ideal growing conditions, often provide homes for new or introduced species of plants. These introduced plants often occupy a niche held by a native species. Occasionally the newcomer is more competitive than the native species and replaces the native plant in the plant community. These introduced species are called exotics.

Age: Grades 7-12
Subjects: Social Studies (Government), Environmental Problems, Language Arts, Science
Skills: analysis, description, discussion, evaluation, generalization, public speaking, reporting, research, synthesis
Group Size: minimum of five students, with one serving as commissioner; easily serves large classroom of students
Setting: indoors
Conceptual Framework Reference: I.A., I.A.1., I.A.2., I.A.3., I.A.4., I.B., I.C., I.C.1., I.C.2., I.C.3., I.C.4., I.D., III.A., III.A.1., III.B., III.B.1., IV.A., IV.A.1., IV.A.2., IV.A.3., IV.A.4., IV.C., IV.C.1., IV.C.3., IV.D., IV.D.4., IV.E., IV.E.10., IV.E.11., IV.F., IV.F.1., IV.F.2., IV.F.3., IV.F.4., IV.F.5., IV.F.6., IV.F.8., IV.F.11., V.A., V.B., V.B.1., V.B.2., VI.A., VI.A.2., VI.A.3., VI.A.4., VI.A.5., IV.B., VI.B.1., VI.B.2., VI.B.3., VI.B.4., VI.B.5., VI.B.6., VI.C., VI.C.1., VI.C.2., VI.C.5., VI.C.6., VI.C.9., VI.C.10., VI.C.11., VI.C.12., VI.C.15., VI.C.16., VI.D., VI.D.1., VII.A., VII.A.1., VII.A.2., VII.A.3., VII.A.4., VII.B., VII.B.1., VII.B.2., VII.B.3., VII.B.5., VII.B.6., VII.B.7.
Key Vocabulary: planning, land use, interest groups, riparian
Appendices: Local Resources, Simulations

AT ISSUE: LAND USE PLANNING AND DECISION MAKING

Approximately 100 miles of what is called "riparian zone"—in this case riverbank property—is vegetated with mature trees and associated plants. The state (or province) division of forestry has recommended that selected trees be harvested commercially. Some of the property along the river is public, and some is private. Of the public lands, some are protected as wildlife refuge areas, and the trees would not be harvested on those lands. Some of the public lands, however, could be subject to such harvest. The private lands would also be available for such use, if each of the owners of the various parcels of private land involved were willing.

Wildlife-related groups—from the public agency responsible for management of wildlife in the area to active private groups dedicated to wildlife preservation—are adamantly opposed to the proposed plan to harvest the trees. They have argued that the impact on wildlife in the area will be extreme—from loss of food and shelter for many animals, to siltation and increase in water temperature in the river affecting the fish and other water-based organisms due to the removal of trees which do so much to hold the soil in the banks by their roots.

All of the land involved falls within the immediate jurisdiction of one governmental unit—in this case referred to as the county. The county Board of Commissioners is preparing to hold a hearing on the topic of this proposed use of land.

The major purpose of this activity is for students to increase their understanding of effects of various kinds of development on wildlife and the environment, as well as to recognize the usefulness of land-use planning as a means by which to minimize negative impacts of some kinds of development.

MATERIALS

butcher paper or poster-making materials; classroom available to be arranged as a "commission hearing room"

PROCEDURE

1. Provide students with the following background information:
OPTIONAL: Provide copies of site maps or photos that you find or develop and which seem appropriate.
2. Ask the students to divide into interest groups, representing groups such as these, and any others the students suggest:
   - State (or province) wildlife management agency, with responsibility for the animals involved
   - State (or province) division of forestry, responsible for the vegetation on the state-owned lands
   - U.S. (or Canadian) Forest Service, responsible for the vegetation on the federally owned lands
   - Private land owners in the area—including farmers, ranchers, people interested in developing their land as a subdivision, and people interested in no development but total preservation of the land they own
   - Private interest groups—including people interested in recreation on and near the river, preservationist groups who want all species of plants and animals in the area to be protected
3. Ask each group to appoint an illustrator, spokesperson and recorder.
4. Provide the groups with time to research and prepare a presentation for the "commission hearing" in which they would convey their point of view on the topic.
5. About half-way through the preparation time, ask the students to appoint one individual from each group

to serve on the "Board of Commissioners." Ask this group of students to prepare criteria against which they will evaluate the land use proposals and recommendations that will be given at the commission hearing by each of the interest groups.
6. Ask each of the interest groups to prepare an illustration of their land use proposals and recommendations on butcher paper for visual aid as a part of their presentation at the hearing.
7. When the groups are ready, ask the "Board of Commissioners" to convene the commission hearing. An impartial individual may be chosen to maintain order and keep time. Each group should, as called upon, present its position on the topic to the commissioners, making use of their visual aids, and speaking no more than five minutes. The commissioners may ask questions of the presenters.
8. After all of the presentations have been made, the "Board of Commissioners" should make a decision as to how the land will be used, defending their decision with a short explanation.

AT ISSUE: LAND USE PLANNING
AND DECISION MAKING

Approximately 100 miles of what is called riparian zone—in this case riverbank property—is vegetated in mature trees and associated plants. The property includes both publicly and privately-owned land. Many of the riparian zone's tree species are not native to the area. These non-native plants are called exotic species. For the past 90 years, exotics have been introduced into this ecosystem. The exotic trees were both intentionally and accidentally introduced. Native trees still survive in the area, but their numbers are declining. The exotic trees have crowded out some of the native trees creating a different type of habitat than the original one. Many native wildlife species are not as well adapted to the new exotic tree-filled habitat.

Some ecologists have recommended that the exotic trees be eliminated from the riparian zone. These ecologists recommend that all of the riparian zone's properties be treated to eliminate the exotic trees. Any exotic trees left in the riparian zone would be potential seed sources for re-establishing exotic trees in areas where they have been removed. The ecologists propose that the cut logs could be sold as firewood or left on the ground.

Because the land has many owners, there are several different philosophies about how the land should be managed. The riparian zone public lands include both a wildlife refuge which has a policy against cutting trees for any reason and a state forest land which permits tree removal, but lacks the funding to complete such a project. The tree removal could occur on private lands only if the property owners choose to let that happen.

County ordinances would be necessary to prohibit any new introductions of non-native species. The ordinances could allow for exceptions for things like fruit trees or prohibit all exotic trees. These ordinances would particularly affect homeowners along the river who want to landscape or plant windbreaks. Many of the existing non-native trees are in established windbreaks and visual screens surrounding homes in this area.

The public agency responsible for management of wildlife in the area and a group dedicated to wildlife preservation strongly oppose the proposed plan to harvest trees. They argue that the impact on wildlife in the area will be extreme. Local wildlife will lose food and shelter that is provided by many of the exotic trees. They further argue that the project would cause many fish and other aquatic organisms to die. Logging would remove shade that keeps the water cool. Since the roots of the exotic trees hold the soil in the bank their removal would lead to increased siltation in the river.

Other groups, including a local native plant association and a public agency responsible for endangered plants and animals, adamantly support the proposed plan to remove the exotic trees. They argue that native plants and animals are losing their position in the environment in favor of exotic plants and animals. Although they admit that short term effects of siltation and habitat loss may present some problems, they argue that the long term effects of re-establishing the native ecosystem will outweigh any short term side effects.

All of the involved land is found in one county. The county Board of Commissioners will hold a hearing on the topic of removing the exotic trees. The proposal is called The Vegetation Manipulation Plan for the Riparian Zone.

9. What were the major issues in this situation? What were the major points made? Describe, discuss, and evaluate possible consequences—positive and negative—for wildlife, people and the environment—in the situation. What seem to be major factors to consider in such land-use issues? Summarize the importance of land-use decision making and planning.

EXTENSION

1. Try this activity a second time with the following modifications. Begin with this background information.

Using this as background, conduct the procedures as before. Discuss similarities and differences.

OPTIONAL: Provide site maps or photos that you find or develop and which seem appropriate.

2. Find out what land-use planning procedures are used in your community. What group or groups have authority to make binding decisions to ensure planning, if any?

3. Contact local agencies for information on woody species and other plants in a local riparian area. Determine which, if any, of these species are not native to the area. Hypothesize how these plants were introduced to the riparian area. List positive and negative effects of these species on other plants and animals. What can be done to reduce the impact of introduced plants in riparian areas?

AQUATIC EXTENSION

Do this activity in conjunction with other riparian activities from the Aquatic WILD Guide. See "Blue Ribbon Niche," "Riparian Retreat" and "To Dam or Not To Dam."

EVALUATION

1. Identify three varying uses for which the same parcel of undeveloped land might be used.

2. Describe possible negative consequences for people and wildlife if development occurs with no planning.

3. List, describe and evaluate three different value positions that might be represented in a land-use controversy.

WHO PAYS FOR WHAT?

OBJECTIVES

Students will: 1) identify major sources of income historically used in support of wildlife and its habitat in the United States; 2) identify major present sources of funding; 3) describe any trends in funding; and 4) describe problems related to funding, if any.

METHOD

Students identify principal sources of wildlife-related funds; correspond with agencies and organizations to investigate sources, amounts, uses, trends and problems concerning such funding; and summarize their findings.

BACKGROUND

Through the purchase of licenses, tags, stamps, and permits, hunters and anglers historically have financed the greatest share of the cost of wildlife management programs in this country. It is still the case today that the bulk of monies used for wildlife management programs in this country are derived from fees paid by such consumptive users. This is especially true of the budgets of state wildlife agencies. For example, fees for hunting and fishing licenses are set in accordance with state laws; the revenues are collected and used for the wildlife management programs of the state agencies. The sources of funding for wildlife agencies determine to varying degrees their program priorities and objectives.

Taxes on sporting equipment such as fishing gear, ammunition, firearms, and archery equipment are collected by the federal government and returned to the state wildlife agencies. These funds, initially paid by sportsmen and women in purchase of their equipment, actually provide many millions of additional dollars to state fish and wildlife programs. In some states, general tax revenues and voluntary tax contributions supplement these user fees.

Fish and wildlife management programs conducted by federal resource agencies are financed primarily through federal income tax revenues, although these agencies also receive revenue from some types of user fees, like the U.S. Fish and Wildlife Service's Duck Stamps, all revenues from which go to purchase of waterfowl habitat. Private wildlife conservation and animal welfare organizations obtain most of their financial support through membership fees, donations, grants, and sales of wildlife-feature items. In the face of increasing interest in wildlife by a wide range of citizens, questions exist over who should pay for fish and wildlife programs and the level of payment appropriate to each interest group. New taxes on items such as binoculars, bird seed and camping gear have been proposed, for example, as a way of obtaining income from those who view, feed and photograph wildlife.

Many states have adopted income tax checkoff systems as a means of involving the general public more broadly in support for wildlife-related programs. Many of these funds are being used for nongame and other special programs involving nonusers, non-consumptive and consumptive users of wildlife.

Like private organizations, government agencies are also beginning to establish their own private not-for-profit foundations and donation campaigns to provide additional support for wildlife programs, including habitat acquisition and research.

As funds provided by traditional sources such as hunting and fishing licenses level off or begin to decline, and demands on fish and wildlife populations and habi-

---

Age: Grades 7-12
Subjects: Social Studies, Science, Language Arts
Skills: analysis, comparing similarities and differences, computation, discussion, evaluation, generalization, research, synthesis, writing
Duration: two 30 to 45-minute periods; two to three week wait for responses from groups
Group Size: any
Setting: indoors
Conceptual Framework Reference: II.A., II.B., II.C., II.D., II.E., II.F., IV.A., IV.A.4., IV.F., IV.F.1., IV.F.2., IV.F.3., IV.F.4., IV.F.5., IV.F.6., IV.F.7., V.B.2., VI.C., VI.C.1., IV.C.2., IV.C.5., IV.C.9., VI.C.10., VI.C.11., VI.C.12.
Key Vocabulary: income, revenue, license, fee, donation, tax
Appendices: Local Resources, Agencies and Organizations

tats continue to escalate, the scramble for new dollar sources must likewise intensify. There is a need for thoughtful analysis of traditional and potential sources of funds for wildlife programs. Emerging trends must be identified and plans made for the future.

The major purpose of this activity is for students to acquire a working knowledge of the major sources of funds used in support of wildlife and its habitat in the United States—historically, presently, and potentially in the future.

MATERIALS
research and letter writing materials

PROCEDURE
1.   Provide students with background information. Initiate discussion about "Who pays for what?" Ask the students to brainstorm a list of organizations, agencies and/or individuals who they think are or might be instrumental in paying costs of programs that contribute to the well-being of wildlife and its habitat. Suggestions might include: taxpayers, through "check-off" for wildlife (typically non-game and endangered species in those states where this is offered on state income tax return forms); revenue from hunting, fishing, trapping and related consumptive-use license fees; federal dollars derived from consumptive-use related taxes returned proportionally to states; private industry dollars from income derived from consumers, e.g., forest products and mining companies that support projects such as habitat improvement on some of their lands; private groups that derive funds from membership and donations, e.g, American Humane Association, Animal Protection Institute, Defenders of Wildlife, Ducks Unlimited, Friends of the Earth, Fund for Animals, Greenpeace, Humane Society of the United States, International Association of Fish and Wildlife Agencies, Izaak Walton League, National Audubon Society, National Rifle Association, National Wildlife Federation, Safari Club International, Sierra Club, The Cousteau Society, The Nature Conservancy, The Wilderness Society, The Wildlife Society, Wildlife Man-

agement Institute, and among these groups support programs ranging from habitat improvement through purchase and management of lands to lobbying for legislation to initiating court actions to conducting research and education programs.

2.   Ask each student or small groups of students to compose a letter to one of the groups. A set of letters should result to be mailed to what you believe represents the spectrum of major sources of income used in support of wildlife programs. Review each letter for accuracy of spelling, grammar and information requested. Each letter could ask: 1) what are the major sources of income (including approximate dollar amounts) that your organization uses in support of wildlife-related programs; 2) what are the major programs you support with these dollars; 3) what major funding problems, if any, do you have; 4) what have been the historical sources of funding for your wildlife programs; 5) what trends, if any, do you see in funding wildlife programs in this country; and 6) what major needs do you see—from your organization's perspective as well as overall—for wildlife today, in our area, in the United States, in the world? The students may have additional questions; however, do encourage them to be as concise as possible.

3. When the responses arrive, ask the students to compile, analyze, evaluate and summarize their findings into a report.

EXTENSIONS

1. Research the history, sources, and allowable uses of specific funds, such as:
- Pittman-Robertson
- Wallop-Breaux
- Dingell-Johnson
- Check-off for wildlife on tax forms, where offered
2. Discuss or debate, "Who should pay for what—and why? How? In what proportions?"
3. Check for accuracy—and graph sources of dollars and uses.

AQUATIC EXTENSION

Review the background information. Identify, describe and indicate the annual monetary amounts of the major sources of funding used to protect, conserve and manage aquatic species and aquatic habitats in the United States. Describe the major purposes for which these funds are used. Be sure to include licenses, stamps and permits; taxes on equipment and fuels; private donations; general tax revenues. Distinguish between private and public sources of funds.

EVALUATION

1. Which of these organizations is (are) most likely responsible for: a) purchasing and managing a marsh in North Dakota for duck propagation; b) managing an endangered species propagation program; c) delaying development along a stream in which an endangered fish species lives, and conducting extensive research on food and breeding requirements of the species; and d) creating a habitat improvement program on farmland, in cooperation with farmers, to create fence rows and pond borders for wildlife: National Audubon Society, Friends of the Earth, Defender of Wildlife, Ducks Unlimited, National Wildlife Federation, Nature Conservancy, Sierra Club, state fish and wildlife commissions, U.S. Fish and Wildlife Service, and Humane Society of the United States?
2. List five to ten major organizations or agencies which participate in, or are responsible for, wildlife-related activities, and indicate the primary sources of funds for each of these groups; e.g., membership fees and donations, general tax dollars, license fees, and taxes paid on equipment.
3. Based on the information you have acquired, what, if any, seem to be the most significant funding-related problems affecting wildlife, habitat and management of wildlife resources?

HISTORY OF WILDLIFE MANAGEMENT

OBJECTIVES

Students will: 1) define wildlife management; and 2) describe major trends in wildlife management philosophies and practices.

METHOD

Students generate questions and contact agencies and organizations involved in wildlife management for information.

BACKGROUND

NOTE: This activity can be used as an extension of "Wildwork."

In the United States, wildlife is considered to be a public resource. That means that even when lands or waters are privately owned, the wildlife is not. In some states, there are exceptions to this rule. This is notable with wild animal ranches where wildlife is raised by private individuals for hunting or fishing purposes. For the most part, however, wildlife is held in the public rather than private domain. Primary legal responsibility for managing and conserving most wildlife in the

United States is delegated to government agencies, to serve on behalf of the public. A state wildlife agency has legal responsibility for managing most of the wildlife in your area, whether that wildlife is on public or private lands and waters. Federal agencies, primarily the U.S. Fish and Wildlife Service, in cooperation with state agencies, are legally responsible for managing wildlife affecting national interests such as threatened and endangered species, marine mammals and migratory wildlife. The range of wildlife managed will vary widely by states, agencies and jurisdictions.

Wildlife management may be seen as part of the large field of resource and environmental management. We define a resource as "a portion of an environment upon which people have placed or assigned value, or see as being available for use." Uses may be consumptive or nonconsumptive. Assigning a value or recognizing a use does not necessarily connote judgments based on ethical considerations, nor does it imply that ethical judgments are not involved. Use of the terminology "resource" is intended as descriptive, not evaluative. Questions of ethics are uniquely personal and cultural.

We define wildlife management as "the application of scientific knowledge and technical skills to protect, preserve, conserve, limit, enhance, or extend the value of wildlife and its habitat." In wildlife terms, we define management as "the intentional manipulation or non-manipulation of habitat and the organisms within the habitat."

Management is, by definition, a set of practices that involve intention to accomplish determined goals. Specific management practices may look like no management, e.g., letting wildfires burn in national parks and wilderness areas. Other management practices may depend upon carefully calculated intervention, e.g., adjusting hunting permits with the objective of reducing, increasing, or maintaining a wildlife population in an area.

Age: Grades 7-12

Subjects: Social Studies (Government, History, Civics), Language Arts, Career Education, Vocational Agriculture, Science, Environmental Problems

Skills: analysis, description, discussion, interview (optional), research, synthesis, writing

Duration: three 45-minute periods

Group Size: any

Setting: indoors

Conceptual Framework Reference: IV.A., IV.A.1., IV.A.2., IV.A.3., IV.A.4., IV.D., IV.D.1., IV.D.2., IV.D.7., IV.E., IV.E.1., IV.E.2., IV.E.3., IV.E.4., IV.E.5., IV.E.6., IV.E.7., IV.E.10., IV.E.11., IV.F. IV.F.1., IV.F.2., IV.F.3., IV.F.4., IV.F.5., IV.F.6., IV.F.7., IV.F.8., IV.F.9., IV.F.10., IV.F.11., V.A.5, V.B., V.B.1., V.B.2., VI.B., VI.B.1., VI.B.2., VI.B.3., VI.B.4., VI.B.5., VI.C., VI.C.1., VI.C.2., VI.C.3., VI.C.4., VI.C.5., VI.C.6., VI.C.7., VI.C.8., VI.C.9., VI.C.10., VI.C.11., VI.C.12., VI.C.13., VI.C.14., VI.C.15., VI.C.16., VI.D.

Key Vocabulary: resource, management, agency, law, regulation, game, nongame

Appendices: Local Resources

Wildlife management philosophies and practices have undergone changes as new information becomes available and circumstances change. As in all resource management professions, there is much to learn in order to do the best possible job in accomplishing goals of preserving, conserving, enhancing and protecting environments, as well as the natural resources and interrelated life forms that live within them. There are also differences of opinion—even among "experts"—as to which management practices and philosophies are most appropriate and most effective. See the activity "Philosophical Differences."

The major purpose of this activity is to provide students with some background in understanding wildlife management, beginning by studying the development and present philosophy and practices of the public agency legally designated with responsibility for wildlife management in their own state and community. Also see the activity "Who Pays for What?" for a focus on the sources of funding, historically and to the present, of wildlife management in the United States.

MATERIALS
research, writing, and skit materials

PROCEDURE
1.   Ask the students to generate a list of questions to be directed to the agency responsible for wildlife management in their state and community. Their questions might include:
When was the agency organized? Why was it organized? How is it legally constituted, and with what responsibilities? What is the agency's philosophy of wildlife management, how does it define wildlife management and what are its objectives? What major programs does the agency have in order to accomplish its objectives and responsibilities? Are these the same kinds of programs for which the agency has been responsible since it was established? What major similarities and differences are there in the programs, practices and underlying philosophy of the agency since it was established? What major trends does the agency see in wildlife management philosophies and practices? What are the major sources of funding for the agency? What, if any, changes and trends in the major funding sources have there been over time? What regulations and laws affecting wildlife should we know and tell others about? What are the most difficult problems facing the agency at this time? What are the most important things we can know and do to be informed and responsible citizens concerning wildlife?

2. Once the major questions of interest have been identified, ask the students to send a letter to the agency asking for information in response to their questions. Before the letter is mailed, be sure to review it for clarity and appropriateness. One concise letter to the Director's office, with all the questions included, is recommended. Under the circumstances as a class project, the students should not each send individual letters.

3. Ask the students to develop similar questions and letters to send to other agencies and organizations interested in wildlife management, like: federal agencies (U.S. Fish and Wildlife Service, U.S. Forest Service, Bureau of Land Management, National Park Service, Soil Conservation Service, U.S. Department of Agriculture Extension Service, etc.); private organizations (American Fisheries Society, American Humane Association, Animal Protection Institute, Canadian Wildlife Federation, Cousteau Society, Defenders of Wildlife, Ducks Unlimited, Friends of the Earth, Fund for Animals, Humane Society of the United States, Izaak Walton League of America, National Audubon Society, National Rifle Association, National Wildlife Federation, Sierra Club, Sport Fishing Institute, The Wildlife Society, Wildlife Management Institute, etc.); private industry (forest products, utilities, mining, commercial fishing, etc.); and associations like the International Association of Fish and Wildlife Agencies. Encourage the students to make a real effort to contact a diverse and representative range of groups.

4. Once responses have been received from the students' letters of inquiry, ask the students to summarize and interpret their findings.

EXTENSIONS

1. Compare similarities and differences between the wildlife management philosophies and practices of the agencies and organizations researched in this activity with those of Native American Indian people of the region—today and in early historical periods.

2. Construct a matrix comparing similarities and differences of wildlife management philosophies and practices among all the agencies and organizations researched as a part of this activity.

3. Create a visual interpretation of apparent trends in wildlife management.

4. Contrast the development and current status of wildlife management in the United States with that in other countries of the world today.

5. Investigate the overlap between and within agencies and organizations interested in wildlife and other resource management.

6. Look for wildlife references in historic journals to get a feeling for what people saw in earlier times. Interview "old timers" in the community who can describe changes they have seen in numbers, kinds and range of wildlife in your area. How have attitudes changed, if at all?

AQUATIC EXTENSIONS

1. In some states, fish are not managed by the same state agency that manages other wildlife species. In some states, freshwater fish are managed by one agency and marine fish by another. Find out what state agency is responsible for managing fish species in your state. Find out if this agency also manages all other aquatic species. If not, find out which agency does. Identify the major responsibilities of the state agencies responsible for managing fish and other aquatic species of wildlife in your state.

2. Develop a summary of all major laws and regulations affecting fish and other aquatic species of wildlife in your state.

3. Pick an aquatic organism. Investigate the laws and management practices affecting that organism. Are the regulations local, state, national, global? Are they effective? Are there any areas in which improvements could be made? If yes, what?

EVALUATION

1. Define wildlife management.

2. Who owns the wildlife on public and private lands in your area, and how is it managed?

3. If you have a question involving laws and regulations affecting wildlife in your area, to whom could you go for assistance?

4. What seem to be major trends in management of wildlife?

5. What seem to be the most critical problems affecting wildlife populations in your area?

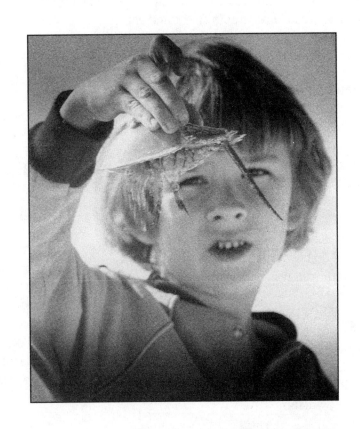

SECTION FIVE

PEOPLE, CULTURE AND WILDLIFE

LOBSTER IN YOUR LUNCH BOX

OBJECTIVES

Students will: 1) identify which foods are derived from plants and which from animals; and 2) recognize that all food sources derived originally from wild plants and animals.

METHOD

Students plan and calculate the costs of a family's meals for one day; create a classroom chart; and analyze, discuss, and summarize findings.

BACKGROUND

We all have to eat! All of our food comes directly or indirectly from the wild. Plants, wild and domestic, support animal life. Animal food sources, when not wild, were derived from wild animals. For example, most experts believe the chicken is descended from wild fowl which lived in the jungles of southeast Asia.

The major purpose of this activity is for students to recognize that all domesticated plants and animals have been derived from wild sources.

MATERIALS

supermarket advertising in newspapers; scissors; pencil and paper
OPTIONAL: cookbooks

Age: Grades 4-7
Subjects: Mathematics, Science, Language Arts, Health (nutrition)
Skills: analysis, classification, computation, discussion, listing, media construction, writing
Duration: three class sessions of approximately 30 minutes each: 1) plan menu (at home find ads for costs); 2) calculate costs; and 3) identify plants and animals, discuss
Group Size: two or three students working in groups
Setting: indoors
Conceptual Framework Reference: V.A.1., I.A.3., II.D.2.
Key Vocabulary: domesticated, nondomesticated
Appendices: Observations and Inferences

MEAL COST FOR FOUR PEOPLE

PRODUCT	COST	
EGGS	.80	.20 each
TOAST	.24	.06 each
BUTTER	.12	.03 each
MILK	.60	.15 each
JUICE	.60	.15 each
	2.36	.59 each

(MEAL 1)

PROCEDURE

1.   The following directions may be given to the students:

a.   You have been given the responsibility of planning meals for one day for a family of four people.

b.   Plan three meals for the day. Make a grocery list of all ingredients that you will need for those meals. Use newspaper advertisements to establish prices of the ingredients, cutting or clipping the ads and attaching them to a piece of paper with the parts of the meal listed alongside the ads. Calculate the cost of each meal. Add up the total cost of all three meals. What is the cost for all four people? What is the cost per person? Use a chart to record your data. For example:

2.   Using the preceding chart, discuss the following questions:

- What plants or plant products are on your menu? Place a P by these on your chart.
- What animals or animal products are on your menu? Place an A by these on your chart.
- Which prices are higher—plants or animals?

For Older students:

- What percentage of food on the menu derives directly from plants?
- What percentage derives from wild animals, if any? From domesticated animals, if any?

3. Create a classroom chart, listing all the plants and animals. Discuss questions such as the following, noting results of the discussion on the class chart.

- Identify what these plants and animals need in order to survive.
- Trace each animal back to dependence on plants.
- Identify which of these plants and animals were once wild, and are now domesticated as a food source. If possible, identify what the original wild plants and animals were from which the foods were developed. Place a D by any domesticated plants and animals.
- Why have plants and animals been domesticated as food sources (e.g., efficiency, convenience, cultural preference)? What are some of the consequences of domestication (e.g., on prices, energy, plants, animals, environment)?
- Summarize the discussion.

NOTE: Students may notice differences in eating habits and preferences; for example, some students may choose no meat or dairy products.

EXTENSIONS

1. Trace the life cycle of foods in the grocery store. Find out where the foods come from. Are they locally grown and raised? Imported from foreign countries?

2. Have an International Foods Day. Compare food preferences of different cultures. Look especially at whether food sources are primarily wild or domesticated.

3. Analyze foods for their nutritional value. For example, look at sources of protein. If possible, identify what you consider to be the most efficient producers of protein. For what reasons?

4. Explore the systems under which plants and animals are raised for food. Compare the various systems using a variety of criteria, including consequences to the plants and animals involved; impact on other plants, animals, and people; impact to the environment; efficiency; ethics; etc. Consider short- and long-term costs, as well as primary and secondary consequences.

5. Examine your own personal eating habits. Consider overall healthfulness, as well as criteria such as those in step 4 above.

AQUATIC EXTENSIONS

1. Be sure to include foods derived from aquatic environments in your study—for example, from rivers, streams, ponds, lakes or oceans. Aquatic foods might range from fish to the kelp that is used in many foods, including ice cream, as a stabilizer.

2. See Aquatic WILD activities, "Kelp Help" and "Water We Eating?"

EVALUATION

1. Examine a copy of your school cafeteria menu. Next to each menu item, mark "P" if the item came from a plant or plant product. Mark "A" next to items that came from animals or animal products.

2. Make a list of nondomesticated animals that are used regularly for food by people living in the United States or Canada.

3. For each of these animals—commonly domesticated and used as a food source for people—name a wild animal in North America which is similar: cow, chicken, pig, sheep, goat.

FIRST IMPRESSIONS

OBJECTIVES

Students will: 1) distinguish between reactions to an animal based on myth or stereotype and those based on accurate information; and 2) recognize the value of animals' contributions to ecosystems—even those that people sometimes respond to with fear.

METHOD

Students react to a variety of photos as a beginning to study of contributions of a range of animals.

BACKGROUND

Many people don't like spiders. Their first reaction may be to recoil if they see a spider; their second may be to kill the animal as quickly as possible. And yet most spiders are harmless to people. In fact, spiders are important contributors to healthy ecosystems.

Spiders are not the only wildlife that frequently raises a response of fright in people. Wolves, snakes and bats elicit fear among many people in a number of cultures. Bats, however, are viewed as signs of good luck among some people in China. Reactions may vary from species to species in different cultures.

This activity is designed for students to examine their spontaneous reactions to different animals—separating reactions based on information and experience from those based on misinformation and myth.

The major purpose of this activity is for students to

recognize that all animals are important contributors to ecosystems.

MATERIALS

large photos or drawings of a variety of animals, including some the students might think are "cute" and some they might think are "scary."

PROCEDURE

1. Prepare a series of large photos or drawings of a variety of different kinds of animals. As you show a photo to the entire group of students, ask them to take turns saying the first word that comes to their minds as they look at the picture.
2. With younger students, take the time yourself to write the name of the animal and the words the students suggest on the chalkboard. With older students, have at least two students serve as recorders, writing the words on the chalkboard for the whole group. Let the recorders share the words they think of too, if they like.
3. Ask the students to identify the animals on the list that seemed to generate a response of dislike or fear and those that seemed to generate a popular and generally favorable response.

Age: Grades K-6
Subjects: Science, Language Arts
Skills: analysis, comparing similarities and differences, generalization, listing; additional skills for older students: description, research, reporting, small group work, writing
Duration: two 20-minute periods; older students: three 30-minute periods
Group Size: any
Setting: indoors
Conceptual Framework Reference: II.A.1., II.A.2., II.B., III.B.1., V.A., V.A.5., V.A.6., V.B.1.
Key Vocabulary: fear, environment, feelings, information
Appendices: Field Ethics, Animals in the Classroom

For Older Students

4.　Divide the students into teams with each team asked to find out more about one of the animals. In their research, they should find out whether the reactions of the students to the animals were based on accurate information and experiences or were based on misinformation and inadequate information. Each team should prepare a report to present, including a description of the importance of the animal's contribution to the ecosystem.

5.　Ask the students to present their reports. Talk about the values and contributions animals make—from ecological to aesthetic. Identify animals, if any, where the students change their feelings based on having additional and more accurate information. Identify animals, if any, where the students don't change their views. Talk about "first impressions," contrasted with the importance of basing perceptions of animals, plants, people, ideas, etc., on the best information available.

For Younger Students

4.　Ask everyone to help choose an animal that seems especially scary. Tell the students that this animal makes a contribution to the environment in which it lives—and you'll find out what! On your own, or with the help of a local resource person, find out more about the contributions this animal makes—and report back to the students! If possible, and safe, bring in the animal for the students to get to know. See Extensions below. Talk about "first impressions" contrasted with reactions based on knowing more about the animal.

EXTENSIONS

1.　Bring in one or more live animals—harmless, but ones that students might not want to get close to. For example, such animals might include a large non-poisonous snake, large non-poisonous spider, toad, or caterpillars. (Make sure the students do not hurt the animal and that the animal cannot hurt the students. Care should be taken in advance of removing any animal from the wild to make sure that it can legally be moved. If the animal was taken from the wild for this activity, see that it is returned safely—exactly to the place where it was originally found if at all possible—at the conclusion of the activity. See the National Science Teachers Association's *Guidelines for Responsible Use of Animals in the Classroom* in the Appendices for additional guidance concerning care of the animal.)

2.　Draw a picture of a "favorite" animal and one of a "scary" animal. Write a short story about each—including the value of each.

3.　Classify animal groups; e.g., mammals, spiders, insects. Which groups seem to be most "loved," "feared," etc.

4.　Work in small groups to select an animal that has a negative image for some people. Write an advertisement or produce a simulated television commercial for that animal and include the positive things the animal does for the community. Share the results!

AQUATIC EXTENSIONS

Prepare a series of large photos or drawings of a variety of different kinds of aquatic animals. Select a range so that there are likely to be some that you or others may have a fearful or negative "first impression" of. Do the activity as described above. Here's one list of a variety of aquatic animals, just as an example: mosquito, pelican, trout, frog, dragonfly, shark, dolphin, sea otter, seal, sea gull, manatee, catfish. There are many different aquatic animals and they are diverse. Each animal has an important role to play in aquatic ecosystems.

EVALUATION

1.　What might someone say about a snake, a spider, a wolf, and a deer if they liked the animal? What might someone say about each of these animals if they did not like the animal?

2.　Invent a story. You can tell it or write it. Describe someone's first impression to one of these animals: brown bat, bullfrog, spider, garter snake, or northern harrier. Then tell how that person's impression changes as he or she learns more about the animal.

AND THE WOLF WORE SHOES

OBJECTIVES

Students will: 1) distinguish between animals based on "real life" and those based on "make believe;" and 2) give examples of real and make-believe animals and their characteristics.

METHOD

Students divide books into those about "real" and those about "make-believe" animals and then distinguish between real and fictitious animal characteristics.

BACKGROUND

Portrayal of animals in books, fairy tales, comics, cartoons, movies and other media may have an influence on the perceptions young people have of those animals.

The major purpose of this activity is to give students experience in actively distinguishing between realistic and fictionalized portrayal of animals in literature.

MATERIALS

children's books and comics about or including both real and "make-believe" animals

PROCEDURE

1. Put out a small stack of books for every group of two to four students. Each stack should have some books that portray animals realistically and some that give the animals unrealistic qualities such as human attributes.

2. Let the students look through the books in their stack and try to divide them into **books about real animals,** or animals that act in real ways; and **books that are about imaginary or make-believe animals,** or even real animals that act in make-believe ways. If necessary, help the students to make their distinctions.

3. Work quietly with each of the groups to check their classifications into "real" and "make-believe."

4. Ask any volunteer from any of the groups to give an example of a "make-believe" animal. Talk about what makes that animal "make-believe."

5. Ask any volunteer from any of the groups to give an example of a "real animal." Talk about what makes that animal real.

6. Using a chart like the one below, ask the students for examples from the books in their stack to fill in the blanks in the chart:

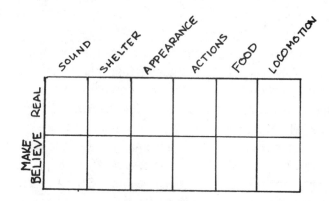

7. Talk with the students about their ideas concerning the importance of being able to tell when something is real and something is make-believe. Talk about why that is important to remember when learning about animals and how they live.

Age: Grades 2-5
Subjects: Language Arts, Reading, Science
Skills: analysis, application, classification, comparing similarities and differences, discussion, listing, observation, reading, small group work
Duration: two to three 20-minute periods
Group Size: small groups of two to four students
Setting: indoors (or outdoors)
Conceptual Framework Reference: V.A., V.A.4., V.A.5., V.A.6., V.B., V.B.1.
Key Vocabulary: real, imaginary
Appendices: Outdoors

EXTENSIONS

1. Pick animals in your favorite stories, like *Stuart Little, Charlotte's Web, Wind in the Willows* and *Winnie the Pooh*. Are these "real" or "make-believe?" In what ways?

2. Tally the animals in familiar stories. For example, how many mammals, birds, reptiles, amphibians, fish, insects, etc.? Are there more of some kinds of animals than others? If yes, why might this be?

AQUATIC EXTENSIONS

1. See the Aquatic WILD activities, "Mermaids and Manatees" and "Micro Odyssey."

2. Establish categories of aquatic habitats or environments—for example, pond, stream, river, lake, ocean. Do the activity as described above, except classify the aquatic animals according to what aquatic environments they are supposed to live in—and then indicate whether the portrayal you find in books is "real" or "make-believe."

EVALUATION

Name three things a make-believe animal often does that a real-life animal cannot do.

SATURDAY MORNING WILDLIFE WATCHING

OBJECTIVES

Students will: 1) discriminate between realistic and unrealistic portrayals of wildlife and other animals in cartoons; 2) identify possible influences on people from watching cartoons; and 3) make judgments about appropriate and inappropriate behaviors they think can result from cartoon watching.

METHOD

Students watch, report, discuss, and evaluate cartoons on television or in comics.

BACKGROUND

NOTE: This activity can be used as an extension for "First Impressions" and "And the Wolf Wore Shoes."

Donald Duck and Mickey Mouse are two prime examples of universally recognized cartoon characters who have come to us from the animal world. Many other animated wildlife and domesticated animal characters can be found in television and movie cartoons. Saturday morning television watching in the United States offers a wide range of "wildlife watching."

Television animals—including mammals, birds, insects, reptiles, spiders, one-celled organisms and fish—animated and not, both represent and misrepresent the real world. Sometimes the treatment of these animals models informed and responsible behaviors. At other times, it exaggerates the worst of ways to treat wildlife and other animals.

Age: Grades K-6
Subjects: Language Arts, Social Studies, Science
Skills: analysis, classification, comparing similarities and differences, discussion, evaluation, observation (older students: reporting, small group work, synthesis)
Duration: one or two 20 to 30-minute periods
Group Size: any
Setting: indoors
Conceptual Framework Reference: V.A., V.A.4., V.A.5., V.A.6., V.B., V.B.1.
Key Vocabulary: wild, tame, influence, real, make-believe
Appendices: Field Ethics, Animals in the Classroom

Cartoons regularly portray animals in anthropomorphic fashion; that is, giving them human qualities or attributes. These may include walking upright, talking, thinking, and building things in a human manner. This misimpression carries strong implications for inappropriate future actions toward wildlife and other animals.

The major purpose of this activity is for students to discriminate between realistic and unrealistic portrayals of animals in cartoons, and to make judgments about what they consider to be positive and negative influences of such portrayals in cartoons.

MATERIALS

access to television at home for cartoon watching; or comic books at school or at home

PROCEDURE

1. The required homework assignment is to watch cartoons! In homes where there is no television, students—with parent permission—might make arrangements to watch cartoons at a friend's house, or comic books may be substituted for cartoon watching on television. (The teacher might arrange to have a supply of comic books with animal characters available in the classroom. Daily newspapers, particularly the Sunday comics, have a range of animal characters. Cartoon videos might also be brought to class.)

2. Ask older students to take notes as they watch the cartoons, preparing themselves to respond to questions such as the following: (Younger students should be given these questions to think about while they are watching. They could draw a few pictures to help themselves remember things they want to be able to talk about in class.)

    • Give the names of three animal characters in cartoons.
    • Identify whether the real animals upon which these characters are based are wild or tame, or could be either (e.g., duck).
    • Describe each of the three cartoon animals: what

CARTOON ANIMAL	REAL ANIMAL	TAME	WILD	EITHER	CHARACTERISTICS SHOWN IN CARTOON
DONALD DUCK	DUCK			✓	TALKS, THINKS WEARS CLOTHES DRIVES A CAR
YOGI BEAR	BEAR		✓		TALKS THINKS, DRIVES CAR, STEALS PICNIC BASKETS

it looks like, where it lives, what it eats, how it behaves, how others treat it.

3.   Back in class, ask the students to report on what they noticed about the ways animals are portrayed in cartoons. Identify whether the animal characters they watched were based on real live animals. If so, were the animals wild, or tame, or could be either? (See "What's Wild?") Pick one animal and chart information like the following. (Older students can each pick one or more animals and construct such a chart.) For example:

OPTIONAL: Describe what an animal would look like, where it would live, what it would eat, how it would behave, and how others would treat it if it were real— contrasted with how it was portrayed in the cartoon.

4.   Ask students to discuss the ways they think cartoons might influence people. What kinds of information do they provide? Is the information accurate and real, not real, or sometimes both? In what ways might cartoons encourage people to treat animals? Ask the students to think of one appropriate way to treat an animal, and one inappropriate way to treat an animal, that they have seen in cartoons. (Older students: con-

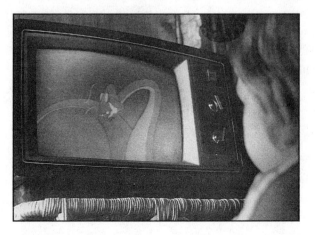

duct this discussion in small groups of two to four students. Ask each group to report.) After each of the groups has reported, make a master list for all the students to see and discuss that includes:
- real ways to treat real animals
- ways animals are treated in cartoons that they shouldn't be treated in real life.

After looking at the completed lists, make any additions the students think are too important to leave off.

EXTENSION OR VARIATION

1.   Watch a cartoon at school—like Donald Duck, Bugs Bunny, Scooby Doo, Sylvester the Cat, or Mickey Mouse. Bring in a tame real-life counterpart for the students to see, observe, and handle if possible, without harming the animal or the children. Discuss the similarities and differences between the "make-believe" and "real" animal.

2.   Discuss how make-believe animals can symbolize human values and attributes. Consider what they tell us about our relationships, values and behaviors.

AQUATIC EXTENSION

Be sure to look for any examples of aquatic wildlife portrayed in Saturday morning cartoons. Add these to the other examples of wildlife portrayed in cartoons, and do the activity as described above.

EVALUATION

1.   Describe five things that cartoon animals can do or that can happen to cartoon animals that are not true for wild animals or for pets.

2.   Describe three ways that cartoon-watching might affect how people act toward animals.

3.   Make a suggestion for how to help people distinguish between real and "make-believe" in cartoons and comics. Explain your reasoning.

4.   Create two stories that portray the same animal. The stories can be acted out or drawn. In one story show the animal realistically. In the second story show the animal unrealistically. Explain how each of these two stories might affect how people think about the animal.

CARTOONS AND BUMPER STICKERS

OBJECTIVES

Students will: 1) identify cartoons and bumper stickers that are designed to make a statement about some issue affecting natural resources and the environment; and 2) describe the influence of humor as a means for conveying information about such issues.

METHOD

Students find, analyze and discuss cartoons and/or bumper stickers.

BACKGROUND

Humor may be one of the most profound and subtle tools used in influencing people's attitudes. A good laugh can be worth a lot. The process can be an efficient and pleasant means by which to communicate information. It can diffuse differences of opinion, although—if the joke isn't appreciated—it can make the differences seem even greater.

Humorous media are diverse, including monologues by stand-up comics, movies, plays, books, articles, photographs, dance, paintings, commercials and more. Two of the most popular forms used in contemporary culture to make a political statement quickly are bumper stickers and cartoons.

Stereotypes are a rich resource for the humorist. Stereotypes of animals are frequently used to get a

laugh. These may be accurately founded, or sufficiently off-base to perpetuate misunderstanding. "The Big Bad Wolf" may be a classic case of the latter. Fine humor probably exploits realistic characteristics—based in the familiar—by comparison with what could be ridiculous or absurd.

Not all humor is actually meant to be funny. It may be poignant, angry, bitter, or sad. Political cartoonists, for example, frequently pull in a range of such emotions where, after the initial laugh, the response may be, "That's not so funny—it's true."

The major purpose of this activity is to examine two forms of humorous media in contemporary culture—the bumper sticker and the cartoon. Both may be seen to have some influence on people's attitudes. Some of this influence affects people's perceptions of issues affecting natural resources and the environment.

MATERIALS

marking pens and strips of construction paper for "bumper stickers;" drawing materials for cartoons

PROCEDURE

1. Ask the students to spend some time in the library or at home looking for examples of cartoons or bumper stickers dealing with an environment-related issue in some way. Each student should find and bring in at least one cartoon or bumper sticker. NOTE: Newspapers can be accumulated in the classroom for one month preceding this activity, providing an opportunity to track the conditions leading to some of the cartoons.
2. Ask the students to post their cartoons or bumper stickers in the classroom where everyone can look at them and read them. Given time for everyone to examine them, questions such as these could be addressed:

Age: Grades 6-12
Subjects: Language Arts (Communication, Composition), Social Studies
Skills: analysis, discussion, evaluation, observation, reading
Duration: one 45-minute period; time outside of class looking for cartoons or bumper stickers
Group Size: any
Setting: indoors (may be done outdoors)
Conceptual Framework Reference: II.A.2., II.A.4., II.C., II.C.3., IV.E.11., V.A.4., V.A.5., V.A.6., V.B., V.B.1., VI.B., VI.B.1., VI.B.6.
Key Vocabulary: stereotypes, media, attitudes
Appendices: Local Resources

- What major topics are the focus?
- What people, if any, are involved?
- What elements of the environment?
- What natural resources, if any?
- What purpose does the cartoonist or author of the bumper sticker seem to have in mind?
- What kinds of emotions seem to be elicited?
- What feelings?
- What actions, if any, do the cartoons or bumper stickers seem to be designed to promote?
- What influence, if any, do you think these will have?
- Who will they influence? In what ways?
- Do the cartoons or bumper stickers seem designed to mislead? Distort? Perpetuate negative stereotypes? If yes, in what ways?
- Do the cartoons or bumper stickers seem designed to inform? Serve accuracy? Encourage constructive, responsible attitudes?
- If yes, in what ways?

3. Ask the students to summarize their views of the effectiveness and appropriateness of use of media such as bumper stickers and cartoons to attempt to influence people's attitudes.

EXTENSIONS

1. Make your own cartoons and/or bumper stickers, inspired by some natural resource or environment-related issues. In fact, you can start this activity this way! (Put the cartoons in a mimeographed or book format—and/or print the bumper stickers—and use them as a source of income for some class project.)
2. Take existing magazine or newspaper photos and write captions for them.
3. Include analysis of elements of propaganda; e.g., band wagon, in order to demonstrate components of persuasion.
4. Look for humor in other communications media involving natural resources, the environment or other issues; e.g., editorials (newspaper, radio, television, magazines), situation comedies, music, etc.

AQUATIC EXTENSIONS

1. Create at least five bumper stickers or cartoons focused on important issues related to aquatic wildlife and aquatic habitats.
2. See the Aquatic WILD activities, "Aqua Words" and "Aquatic Times."

EVALUATION

Describe the significance and usefulness of humor as a way to convey information about environmental topics. Describe its effectiveness as a way to influence opinion about environmental topics.

DOES WILDLIFE SELL CIGARETTES?

OBJECTIVES

Students will: 1) identify use of wildlife and other natural images in advertising; 2) critically analyze and evaluate the purposes and impacts of use of such images in advertising; and 3) recommend appropriate uses of such nature-derived images in advertising.

METHOD

Students evaluate and categorize advertisements.

BACKGROUND

A cowboy boot manufacturer ran a series of advertisements for its boots showing boot and wearers in conflict with wildlife. In this particular case, the wearer of the boot is about to kill a rattlesnake and a scorpion. There is a sense of drama in the ads—with the boot raised in the air, ready to flatten the offenders. The advertisement portrays a person in battle with forces of nature, and plays on the stereotype that some sort of virtuous strengths might accompany such actions. It also plays on the stereotype that some animals are worthless and should be killed.

In contrast with the images chosen by this advertiser, the rattlesnake and the scorpion could be portrayed as integral components of natural ecosystems. The lustre and patterning of the snake's scales, and the grace in motion of both of the animals could be portrayed. Fewer boots would likely be sold—since the market-

place may still be steeped in too many stereotypes of such animals for the fears the first ad plays upon to be quieted. One could imagine, however, the kind of advertising campaign that an Edward Abbey, Annie Dillard, or Ansel Adams might design.

A substantial amount of contemporary advertising exploits people's biases and emotional responses to elements of nature. Advertising, by design, is intended to evoke a response—usually one that will lead to some action, as in buying the advertised product.

The major purpose of this activity is for students to evaluate the uses and impacts of nature-derived images in advertising.

MATERIALS

magazines or newspapers as a source of advertisements

PROCEDURE

1. Ask each student to find at least one advertisement that makes use of some aspect of the natural environment in order to sell its product. The advertisement might show crystal waters, an eagle soaring the skies, an elk standing majestically, a forested hillside, snow-capped peaks, etc. Bring the advertisement to class. If the advertisement is on a billboard, perhaps the student can bring in a photo; if it is from a television commercial, a sketch and/or description will work. NOTE: The teacher may want to establish a file of such advertisements, laminating and keeping them for future use.
2. Working in small groups of two to four, ask the students to examine their advertisements according to questions such as the following:
    - What is the advertiser's purpose?
    - What image from nature is used to sell the product?
    - Does the image have any direct relationship to the product?
    - If yes, what is that relationship?

Age: Grades 6-12
Subjects: Language Arts (Communication, Media, Semantics), Social Studies, Business Education
Skills: analysis, classification, discussion, evaluation, observation, reading
Duration: two 45-minute periods
Group Size: any
Setting: indoors
Conceptual Framework Reference: V.A., V.A.1., V.A.2., V.A.3., V.A.4., V.A.5., V.A.6., V.B., V.B.1., V.B.2., VI.B., VI.B.3., VII.A., VII.A.1., VII.A.2., VII.A.3., VII.A.4., VII.B., VII.B.3., VII.B.6., VII.B.7.
Key Vocabulary: stereotype, metaphor, advertising
Appendices: Local Resources

- If no, what purpose does the image serve for the advertiser in attempting to sell the product?
- What feelings, if any, does the ad elicit?
- What stereotypes, if any, does the ad encourage or build upon?
- If not a stereotype based on people's reactions to the image portrayed, does the ad portray a metaphor as a means to sell its product? If yes, describe its purpose. For example, a porcupine might be pictured alongside an electric shaver with, "Get rid of the bristles." The porcupine's quills serve as a metaphor for a stubbly beard.
- Does the advertisement seem to portray the natural image in a realistic way? Describe what seems realistic and what doesn't.
- Identify and describe any ways in which the ad might contribute to practices that could be wasteful, destructive, inappropriate, etc., in terms of wise use of natural resources and the environment.

3. According to criteria the students establish and explain, ask them to categorize the advertisements as appropriate or inappropriate means by which to attempt to sell products.

EXTENSIONS

1. For advertisements considered inappropriate; e.g., harmful or misleading, you could;
- redesign the advertisement to make it more appropriate in your judgment;
- write a letter to the advertising company explaining your concerns;
- write a letter to the managing editor of the magazine or newspaper in which the ad appeared;
- write an editorial about the ad for a city or school paper; and
- call other people's attention to the ad and your reasons for concern.

2. For advertisements considered appropriate; e.g., constructive or accurate, you could:
- write a letter to the advertising company in praise of the ad, explaining the basis for your opinions, etc.;
- call other people's attention to the ad and your reasons for praise.

3. Design advertisements to encourage wise use of natural resources, and responsible actions toward people, wildlife and the environment. Send these ideas to the advertising departments of companies that would seem most able to benefit from them with courteous letters of concern and explanation.

EVALUATION

1. Describe two examples of advertisements which portray animals in informative, accurate or positive ways. Describe two examples of advertisements which portray animals in inaccurate, misleading or negative ways.
2. How, if at all, does the use of wildlife help the image advertisers wish to portray?
3. How, if at all, do the ways wildlife are used in advertising help wildlife? Harm wildlife?
4. Describe a way that advertisers could use wildlife to the best advantage of both wildlife and the advertisers.
5. Describe what you believe would be the most responsible and appropriate ways to include wildlife in advertising, if at all.
6. Observe a TV commercial or series of commercials that use wildlife. Compare the treatment of wildlife in video advertisements and print advertisements.

THE POWER OF A SONG

OBJECTIVES

Students will: 1) analyze popular music for environmental messages; and 2) interpret some influences of popular music and other art forms on people's environmental attitudes.

METHOD

Students listen to songs and analyze lyrics.

BACKGROUND

Art reflects the artist. It may also influence one who sees, hears or feels the art. Social attitudes toward environmental issues are affected by the communications media, including the classical and popular arts.

Artists may influence different people in different ways. For example, Sting and U2 are recognized as talented artists both by people who strongly agree and those who strongly disagree with their political views on specific issues.

Historical and contemporary artists have expressed their views about issues, including environmental issues, and have influenced others in the process. The Transcendentalists of the 19th century United States—including Bronson Alcott, Ralph Waldo Emerson and Henry David Thoreau—influenced some of their generation through their teachings and writings. Their influence continues.

John Denver is a popular songwriter and performer who has consistently included what may be described as an environmental theme in much of his music, and has made a statement with his music to public officials as well as private citizens. For example, "Rocky Mountain High" has been identified by some as having had a role in the decision not to bring the Winter Olympics to Colorado in the early 1970s. These words in that popular song spoke to the issue:

> Now his life is full of wonder
> But his heart still knows some fear
> Of a simple thing we cannot comprehend
> Why they try to tear the mountains down
> To bring in a couple more,
> More people, more scars upon the land..."

From "Rocky Mountain High." Words by John Denver, music by John Denver and Mike Taylor. Copyright 1972, 1974 by Cherry Lane Music Company. All rights reserved.

John Denver spoke and sang to the U.S. Congress in Washington, D.C., on the Alaska Land Bill issue. Mr. Denver was in favor of protection of Alaska lands as wilderness areas. He sang from a series of songs he has written about Alaska, including "To the Wild Country." Mr. Denver has also spoken and sung before a meeting of the International Whaling Commission (IWC) in support of a cessation of world-wide commercial whaling. Mr. Denver sang, "I Want to Live." Mr. Denver sang his song, "It's About Time" to a congressional subcommittee as part of his testimony in

Age: Grades 6-12
Subjects: Language Arts, Music, Social Studies
Skills: analysis, discussion, evaluation, listening
Duration: one 30 to 45-minute period
Group Size: any
Setting: indoors or outdoors
Conceptual Framework Reference: I.D., II.A., II.A.1., II.A.2., II.A.3., II.A.4., V.A.4., V.A.5., V.A.6., V.B., V.B.1., V.B.2.
Key Vocabulary: music, song, lyrics, influence, attitudes
Appendices: Local Resources

support of what became law as the National Environmental Education Act.

These are a few examples of the strong environmental statements in one songwriter's lyrics and performances. Look also at the musical writings of: Dan Fogelberg, Jackson Browne, Joni Mitchell, Jimmy Buffett, Judy Collins, Stevie Wonder (The Secret Life of Plants), Paul Winter, U2, Alabama, Hammer, The Grateful Dead, Michael Jackson, Midnight Oil, Garth Brooks, Dolly Parton and Sting. Your students will be able to add other artists to this list. Traditional songs such as "Home On the Range," "Wild Mountain Thyme," "Woodsman Spare That Tree" and "April Showers" could also be used.

The major purpose of this activity is for students to examine the role of the arts and other communications media in influencing the attitudes of people. In this case, the influence is narrowed to people's attitudes about the environment and issues affecting it.

MATERIALS
radio; records, tapes or song books as sources of popular songs

PROCEDURE
1. Ask the students to listen to the lyrics of popular songwriters in contemporary music. Look for any artists who include lyrics with an environmental message.
2. Bring examples of music with an environmental message to class.
3. Listen to the lyrics. If possible, obtain written versions of the lyrics to at least one song. Identify the particular issues being written about in these songs. If necessary, find out more about the issues in order to attempt to better understand the perspective of the artist as conveyed in the lyrics.
4. The students may find that few contemporary artists include lyrics about environmental issues. Discuss why or why not. Talk about why some might and others don't. Discuss whether people are influenced by the work of popular artists, as in this case—by the lyrics of songwriters' songs.

EXTENSIONS

1. Invent your own environmental song! Songs could be about a specific issue, a favorite animal or general feelings about the environment. Share your song with family, friends, other students at school, your local politician or anyone else who might enjoy your musical expression!

2. Look for songs and lyrics with harmful environmental messages. Look for songs and lyrics with upbeat, hopeful messages. Look for those that seem to be calling for action.

3. Review music videos that have environmental themes.

AQUATIC EXTENSIONS

1. Dale and Linda Crider have written a whole book of songs about water, aquatic wildlife and aquatic habitats. It is called "The Watersong Book." Various tapes of Dale and Linda's have songs with water and aquatic themes. Information about the availability of any of these tapes for purchase may be obtained by writing Anhinga Roost Music Company, Route 2, Box 342T, Gainesville, FL 32601. Dale and Linda have been involved with Project WILD since some of its earliest days and wrote the song, "To Be Wild," that appears in this book.

2. Aquatic themes are abundant in traditional songs as well as some contemporary songs. Sea chanties, "Oh Shenandoah," and John Denver's song, "Calypso," are examples. Listen to a variety of songs with aquatic themes. Analyze their lyrics. Look for examples of ecological concepts, historical information, political messages, and examples of the many ways that people value water and aquatic environments.

EVALUATION

Describe the ways, if any, in which you believe music and other art forms influence people's attitudes. In what specific ways, if any, do such art forms affect people's attitudes toward the environment?

To be WILD

by Dale and Linda Crider

By DALE and LINDA CRIDER

CHORUS

Oh, to be ___ to be wild ___ and free like an ea-gle o-ver the land;

Oh, to sing, ___ to be wild and sing ___ all o-ver A-mer-i-ca ___ a-gain. ___ FINE

VERSE

1. O-ver the moun-tains, for-est, o-ver the plains; ___ O-ver the riv-ers, marsh-es
2. Wild is the wild-est word, why can't it be more? More than the moun-tains, more

(all) wild life do-main, Wild is the free-est word ___ we can ev-er sing; ___
than the o-cean shore; Wild-life of tun-dra, marsh-es, lakes and for-est floor;

Oh, to be, to be wild. Yes, wild ___ is the wild-est life, ___ im-ag-
Wild is this and more. *D.C. al Coda*

CODA

- ine, if ___ you can, ___ Un-tamed by zoos or cag-es; Wild is wild-er than ___ the

wild-est thing im-ag-ined by ___ do-mes-ti-cat-ed man. ___ Wild all o-ver A-

mer-i-ca ___ a-gain! ___ Oh, to sing ___ this song, ___ to be ___ wild is why. The

song, ___ "To Be Wild" ___ lets my own ea-gle fly ___ O-ver the prair-ies, des-erts,

D.C. al Fine

o-ver the plains, ___ Wild ___ all o-ver A-mer-i-ca ___ a-gain.

(Repeat Chorus)

WILDLIFE IN NATIONAL SYMBOLS

OBJECTIVES

Students will: 1) identify wildlife used in national symbols; and 2) hypothesize reasons wildlife are used in national symbols.

METHOD

Students research national symbols and make posters to depict their findings.

BACKGROUND

The lion is a good example of how wildlife has value as a symbol in many different cultures. It might be a national symbol, serve as a logo for an organization or cause, represent a youth or civic group, or be included in the symbols of a religious group. The lion, for example, is associated with regal qualities—courage, nobility, strength, and power. According to *The Cousteau Almanac* by Jacques-Yves Cousteau and the Staff of the Cousteau Society (Doubleday and Company, New York, 1980, 1981), "Lions appear on the United Nations coats of arms of more countries than any other animal—on those of India, Kenya, Malawi, Singapore, Burma, Burundi, Sengal, Sri Lanka, Swaziland, and several European nations." *The Almanac* continues to point out that lions no longer exist in the wild in most of these countries. (page 365)

Many other species of fauna that have been honored by being made the national symbol of a country are on endangered species lists. Some examples are:

Chile	Andean condor
Dominica	imperial Amazon parrot
Guatemala	quetzal bird
United States	bald eagle

The major purpose of this activity is for students to become acquainted with the diversity of countries and cultures that include wildlife in their symbols.

MATERIALS

access to library reference materials; poster-making materials

PROCEDURE

1. Generate hypotheses about national symbols. Where do they come from? What do they represent? Strength? Natural resources? Cultural heritage?
2. Ask each student or group of students to select one country to research—finding out its national symbol or symbols. The more countries, the more interesting the results will be. Sometimes the symbols will be stylized; sometimes they will be literal and based on actual plants and animals; and sometimes several symbols will be combined. Ask the students to include in their findings information about:
   - the plants or animals the symbols are based upon;
   - whether those plants or animals are native, exotic or non-existent to the environment of the country;
   - characteristics about those plants and/or animals;
   - whether the plants or animals are in abundance, threatened, or endangered in the environment where they exist;
   - what values they might represent that led to their use in the national symbol;

Age: Grades 4-9
Subjects: Social Studies, World Geography, World History, Anthropology, Government, Art, Science
Skills: analysis, comparing similarities and differences, evaluation (formulating and testing hypotheses), media construction, research, synthesis
Duration: two 45-minute periods
Group Size: any
Setting: indoors
Conceptual Framework Reference: II.A., II.A.1., II.A.2., II.A.3., II.A.4., II.C., II.F., V.A., V.A.2., V.A.4., V.A.6., V.B., V.B.1., V.B.2., V.B.3.
Key Vocabulary: symbol
Appendices: Local Resources

3. Ask each student or group of students to make a poster depicting their findings.

4. Given hypotheses the students generate about why wildlife are used in national symbols, ask the students whether the findings of their research supported these hypotheses. Discuss their findings and observations.

EXTENSIONS AND VARIATIONS

1. Examine state, province, or community symbols (e.g., state birds, animals, plants, seal) instead of national symbols.

2. Look at trademarks, logos, and product advertising campaigns.

3. Try coats-of-arms!

4. Many schools use wildlife or other animal symbols as mascots or in school emblems, team names, etc. Survey the local community to compile a list of plants and animals used as school symbols. Contact the schools to find out how the names were chosen.

5. Study lyrics of state or school songs for references to wildlife.

EVALUATION

1. Identify five animals or wildlife signs that are used as national symbols. What might each species have been chosen to symbolize?

2. Make a flag for a mythical country somewhere in the world. Use wildlife in that flag. Write a brief narrative explaining why the people of this mythical country chose the animal they did to represent themselves.

CHANGING ATTITUDES

OBJECTIVES

Students will: 1) give an example of a change in attitudes related to a wild animal and/or the environment; and 2) describe factors which may influence change in attitude.

METHOD

Students design and conduct community interviews, compiling and summarizing findings.

BACKGROUND

Attitudes toward wildlife, the environment and appropriate uses of natural resources have changed and continue to change over time. They also vary greatly from culture to culture, within subgroups of a culture, within communities and among individuals.

For example, 60 years ago in the United States, predator control was more or less taken for granted, especially in the western United States. There were efforts to control grizzly bears, cougars, coyotes, wolves, hawks and even eagles. There was even a bounty on many of these animals, as they were considered a threat to domesticated animals and human safety.

Today, there is still much controversy around predator control. However, it is now more generally recognized that these animals have a role in the overall health of ecosystems. Most predators are now protected by law.

Age: Grades 5-12
Subjects: Social Studies, Language Arts
Skills: analysis, comparing similarities and differences, evaluation, interviewing, public speaking, research, reporting, writing (questionnaire construction, compiling results)
Duration: minimum of three 45-minute periods; out-of-school time for interview
Group Size: any
Setting: indoors and outdoors
Conceptual Framework Reference: V.A., V.A.1., V.A.2., V.A.3., V.A.4., V.A.5., V.A.6., V.B., V.B.1., V.B.2., VI.B., VI.B.1., VI.B.2., VI.B.3., VI.B.4., VI.B.5., VI.B.6., VI.C., VI.C.1., VI.C.2., VI.C.3., VI.C.4., VI.C.5., VI.C.6., VI.C.7., VI.C.8., VI.C.9., VI.C.10., VI.C.11., VI.C.12., VI.C.13., VI.C.14., VI.C.15., VI.C.16., VIII.A.1., VII.A.2., VII.A.3., VII.A.4., VII.A.5.
Key Vocabulary: attitude, interview, community
Appendices: Outdoors, Local Resources, Field Ethics

In some circumstances, predator control is still being carried out, but the trend is toward limiting control to the individual predators causing damage.

The major purpose of this activity is for students to interview members of their community to gain information concerning changes in attitudes about wildlife and the environment.

MATERIALS

paper for taking notes and/or tape recorders and tape; information about local laws and regulations affecting wildlife

PROCEDURE

1. Initiate a discussion with students about whether or not they think people's attitudes about some subjects might change, for example, over a generation. Fashion in clothing, furnishings and food might serve as examples to begin. If not raised by the students, ask them if they can think of any examples of changes in attitudes about wildlife, the environment, uses of natural resources, lifestyles involving natural resources and the environment, etc. Discuss their suggestions and list the topics they suggest.

2. Ask the students, working in groups of two to four students, to generate a list of questions relating to wildlife and the environment that they might ask of adults in their community. For example:

- How do you feel about wildlife?
- Does wildlife live in your neighborhood? Did wildlife live in your neighborhood when you were a child growing up? What kind?
- What animals, if any, are no longer seen that once were?
- What animals, if any, are more common now than they once were? What happened?
- What were some attitudes you remember having about wildlife when you were a youngster? Which of these attitudes, if any, have you changed during the past 20 years? What has caused these changes, if any?
- What laws, if any, did you know about when you were young that affect wildlife and the environment? What laws do you know about now which

affect wildlife and the environment?

- What are the reasons for such laws? Do you think we need laws protecting wildlife, natural resources and the environment? Why or why not?
- What general changes, if any, do you think there are in our society's attitudes toward wildlife and the environment—perhaps some changes you think are good and some you do not?
- What problems, if any, involving wildlife are you concerned about?
- What recommendations, if any, do you have about solving those problems?

3. Review the questions generated by each student or group of students before they conduct their interviews. Younger students' questions may be shorter and fewer.

4. Ask the students—working alone or in groups—to interview at least one long-living person in their community. The students should be prepared to take notes or tape the interviews. You might instruct the students to be sure to take time to listen to any of the stories the people might tell that are slightly off the subject—out of courtesy, and also in recognition that the slightly divergent topics will also be interesting and pertinent in some ways.

5. Next, ask the students to "interview" each other or themselves. That is, record their own responses to these questions as a point of contrast for looking at some changes in attitudes. OPTIONAL: Add other people to interview, e.g., family members, wildlife managers, members of city council, farmers, ranchers, animal welfare group members, hunting club members, agricultural agents, private conservation group members, members of preservationist organizations, office workers, people at community gatherings, neighbors, or other community representatives. In choosing people to interview, encourage students to seek diversity and a range of perspectives.

6. Compile the results of the interviews. This might be done in a time-consuming way, where the interviews are transcribed, analyzed, summarized and discussed. Shorter approaches may also be taken where each group of students is responsible for summarizing the results of their interviews in a one-page format and then a small group of students volunteers to prepare a summary representing the findings of all of the students.

7. Discuss with the students their findings, including what changes in attitudes have taken place, if any, and what are some factors which might contribute to any changes in attitudes that they have identified.

EXTENSIONS AND VARIATIONS

1. Expand the questions to include any changes in the local community and its natural resources. Include vegetation (e.g., what plants are here that were not here previously; what plants are no longer here); water (e.g., more, less, or the same in available quantity, quality); human population; etc.

2. Identify a local controversial issue involving or affecting wildlife or other natural resources. Fact find. What is the issue? How did it develop? What attitudes and information are involved? What possible solutions are available?

3. Start this activity by pretending you were settlers living 100 or 200 years ago. What animals, if any, did you see? How did you live? Day to day, week to week, season to season? After imagining yourself at that time, discuss what your attitudes might have been toward natural resources and environment. Might they be different today? In what ways?

4. Look in literature for information about historic wildlife populations in your area, the U.S., Canada, or other parts of the world. Compare to present-day populations.

5. Explore Native American Indian attitudes toward wildlife and other natural resources—in historic times and today.

EVALUATION

1. Describe how you think most people form their attitudes—what they know and how they feel—about animals.

2. Give two examples of attitudes about animals that you have reason to believe are based on wrong information or not enough information.

3. Give an example of a change in attitude about an animal that has occurred in this country during the past 100 years. How did this change come about?

4. If you were going to try to change someone's attitude about snakes from negative (they do not like snakes) to positive (snakes are okay and contribute to ecosystems), how would you do it?

PHILOSOPHICAL DIFFERENCES

OBJECTIVES

Students will: 1) identify points of view of groups and organizations concerning wildlife, natural resources and environmental issues; and 2) describe possible effects of various groups and organizations having differing points of view about wildlife, natural resources and environmental issues.

METHOD

Students select a wildlife or other environment-related issue of concern to members of their community, and correspond with representatives of a range of interest groups about their philosophical positions concerning the issue.

BACKGROUND

One definition of the word "philosophy" describes it as a "system of principles for guidance in practical affairs." Private and public organizations and agencies frequently have an identifiable philosophy. Most organizations involved with natural resource and environmental issues support their actions and recommendations with statements of their philosophy. These may be made available in the form of speeches, newsletters, news releases, goal statements and position and policy papers. The organizations and agencies may not clearly identify their underlying philosophical perspectives, but they can be recognized after analysis of the groups' written and spoken statements and actions.

Age: Grades 7-12
Subjects: Language Arts, Social Studies, Environmental Problems, Journalism, Communication
Skills: analysis, classification, comparing similarities and differences, discussion, evaluation, synthesis, writing
Duration: two to three 45-minute periods, over a three-week period
Group Size: large group
Setting: indoors
Conceptual Framework Reference: IV.F., IV.F.1., IV.F.2., IV.F.3., IV.F.4., IV.F.5., IV.F.6., IV.F.7., IV.F.8., IV.F.9., IV.F.10., IV.F.11., V.A.5., V.B.1., V.B.2., V.B.3., VI.B., VI.B.1., VI.C., VI.C.1., VI.C.2., VI.C.6., VI.C.7., VI.C.9., VI.C.10., VI.C.11., VI.C.12., VI.C.13., VI.C.14., VI.C.15., VI.C.16.
Key Vocabulary: issue, interest groups, philosophy
Appendices: Local Resources, Agencies and Organizations

The major purpose of this activity is for students to recognize that organizations and groups may have differing perspectives with respect to wildlife, natural resources and environmental issues, and to describe possible effects of several different points of view.

MATERIALS

newspapers, magazines, or other sources of news; writing materials; chalkboard

PROCEDURE

1. Ask students to identify a wildlife or other environment-related issue in the news. They might read newspapers and magazines, or watch television newscasts, on a regular basis for one or two weeks to identify an issue and acquire some information about the issue. If the issue is related to wildlife, they could go directly to a range of interested organizations and groups like their state wildlife agency; federal agencies involved with wildlife; representatives of private environmental, conservation, or animal welfare organizations; industry with land holdings involving wildlife; farmers; and people working in recreational or commercial activities involving wildlife. A range of organizations interested in wildlife which could be contacted include: American Humane Association, Defenders of Wildlife, Humane Society of the United States, National Audubon Society, National Rifle Association, National Wildlife Federation, The Wildlife Society and the Wildlife Management Institute. Representatives of such organizations as well as other groups can be of assistance in identifying an issue, as well as for background information. Ask all the students to bring in information about any issues they have identified. After reporting and discussion by the students, ask them to select one issue that seems most interesting to them, and which involves various—if not clashing—philosophies on the parts of individuals, groups and organizations with respect to the issue that is identified.

2. List pertinent information about the issue on the chalkboard. Identify the individuals, organizations, agencies and other groups who seem most involved. Ask the students to select several of the groups, trying

to identify those groups that seem to have strongly different points of view on the issue. Ask the students to divide themselves into working groups, with each group of students selecting one of the interest groups to investigate further. Ask each student group to try to predict and describe the philosophical point of view of the interest group or organization they have selected to study.

3. Ask each group of students to draft a letter to be sent to their interest group. The letter should ask what the organization's point of view (policy or position statement) is with respect to the particular issue involved, the reasons the organization is taking that point of view, and a general statement of the goals of the organization, if available. Assist the students in making sure their letters are clear, grammatical, neat and correctly spelled.

4. Mail the letters.

5. While waiting for a response, ask the student groups to write a brief written statement that predicts the point of view they think they will receive from their group.

6. When the letters have been received, ask the students to compare the responses to their own predictions. Were there any differences between what the students predicted, and the responses they received from the various groups? Were there any differences between past actions and statements from the groups and their present statements? If so, what were these differences and do they represent actual philosophical and policy changes in the groups or organizations? Do all or most members of an organization necessarily agree with its philosophy?

7. In summary, ask the students to identify and describe points of view, if any, which some or all of the groups share in common, and points of view, if any, in which the groups strongly differ. In what ways, if any, is it healthy for there to be groups with differing points of view? In what ways, if any, might it be damaging? What possible effects are there from individuals, groups and organizations having differing points of view with respect to wildlife, natural resources and environmental issues?

EXTENSIONS AND VARIATIONS

1. Skip the letter writing phase and just get and use position statements from different groups on one issue.

2. Invite local members or representatives of the various groups to present their points of view in person!

3. Invite the students—as a group or as individuals—to decide (write, discuss, or present orally) their own position statement of the issue. How is it like and unlike others?

4. Emphasize the potential for communications skills, including analysis of points of view, in this activity. For example, analyze the stated positions of each group according to the following criteria:

- most of the scientific community accepts these as accurate
- there is some evidence, but it is inconclusive
- rejected by the scientific community

Establish other criteria, e.g., economic, social, ethical, historical, political, biological, ecological, philosophical. To what degree are groups with opposing views similar and different, when analyzed by these criteria? Are there areas where it is appropriate and feasible to work for compromise? Why or why not?

EVALUATION

Not enough is known about the whooping crane, an endangered bird species. Some people feel that additional research must be conducted to learn more about the species. Some worry that direct human contact will accelerate the birds' population decline. Some feel that habitat loss is the real problem. Some think propagation in captivity is the best means of achieving a viable population. Some say that the species is going to become extinct anyway, and therefore any available funds should be spent on those species with a better chance for survival. Others are heartened by recent successful efforts to reintroduce some of the cranes. Predict and describe the points of view that five diverse groups could have concerning this issue. Describe and evaluate at least three possible effects of five diverse organizations having differing views.

WILDLIFE ISSUES: COMMUNITY ATTITUDE SURVEY

OBJECTIVES

Students will: 1) assess the values held by various groups and individuals regarding some selected issue; and 2) distinguish between beliefs, values and attitudes.

METHOD

Students develop a questionnaire and conduct a community survey.

BACKGROUND

Individuals in a community may hold differing beliefs, attitudes and values toward wildlife and the environment. There are many different reasons for any beliefs, values and attitudes that people hold. Whatever the reasons or sources, the result may be strongly held differences of opinion related to the same issue in the same community.

Sometimes the best solution to a local issue may seem clear-cut. More frequently, there are no clear "right" or "wrong" answers, yet emotions may be aroused and different "solutions" may have dramatically differing impacts on all involved, including the environment.

For purposes of this activity, the following definitions are recommended:

Belief An information-based assumption. It may be right or wrong.
Example: Where there are more pheasants there are more foxes.
Example: A given habitat will only support so many animals.

Value A worth attached to some event, place, idea, etc.
Example: Foxes are beautiful and important creatures.
Example: It is important to protect animals.

Attitude Based on an implied belief system, an implied value system, with a predicted behavior.
Example: Foxes should not be controlled. This statement implies a belief that human intervention in the populations of foxes will reduce some value which is also implied. The predicted behavior is opposition to control.
Example: Foxes should be controlled. This statement implies a belief that human intervention in the populations of foxes will enhance some value which is also implied. The predicted behavior is support of control.

Interest Groups Those individuals or groups who have an interest in an issue, e.g., for personal, ecologi-

---

Age: Grades 7-12
Subjects: Language Arts, (English, Media, Communications, Speech), Environmental Problems, Social Studies, Science, Mathematics
Skills: analysis, application, classification, computation, discussion, evaluation, interview, invention, public speaking, reading, research, small group work, synthesis, writing
Duration: approximately one week of class time, 45-minutes to one hour per day, plus time out-of-class to interview people in the community
Group Size: any
Setting: classroom and in the community
Conceptual Framework Reference: V.A., V.A.5., V.A.6., V.B., V.B.1., VI.B., VI.B.1., VI.B.2., VI.B.3., VI.B.4., VI.B.5., VI.B.6., VI.C., VI.C.1., VI.C.2., VI.C.3., VI.C.4., VI.C.5., VI.C.6., VI.C.7., VI.C.8., VI.C.9., VI.C.10., VI.C.11., VI.C.12., VI.C.13., VI.C.14., VI.C.15., VI.C.16., VI.D., VI.D.1., VI.D.2., VI.D.3., VI.D.4.
Key Vocabulary: interview, survey, value, attitude, belief
Appendices: Outdoors, Observations and Inferences, Local Resources

cal, or economic reasons. They may or may not have much information, and may or may not have a strong opinion.

The major purpose of this activity is for students to acquire skills by which to analyze beliefs, values and attitudes related to environmental issues.

MATERIALS
writing materials to make questionnaires

PROCEDURE
1. Ask students to watch, read and/or listen to local media in order to identify environment-related issues of concern to people in their community. For example, a proposed dam construction project for purposes of generating hydroelectric power might serve, with people strongly "for" and "against," based on informed, uninformed, emotional, irrational, rational, economic, ecological, political, etc., grounds. An issue most people have heard something about would be best. List the possibilities.
2. Select one issue. Describe what you already know about the issue you have selected. Find out more about the issue, e.g., by contacting local spokespeople for involved interest groups, systematically clipping newspaper articles, taking notes on television and radio coverage, checking library for pertinent information on related topics. Conduct class discussion for students to share their findings about the issue—adding to the breadth.
3. Working in small groups, ask the students to prepare a questionnaire or questionnaire items that can be used to measure people's views about the issue. Questions should be constructed so that they can be analyzed according to people's beliefs, values and attitudes. Questions that can be responded to in brief, e.g., "yes" or "no," will contribute to the students' success in getting people to take the time to cooperate in the survey. "Yes" and "no" questions are also easily

quantified when the students are putting together the results. For example:
"Are you in favor of the proposed new hydroelectric project on the X River just north of town?"
47 Yes; 51 No; 67 Undecided
Questions can be designed to provide information about whomever is completing the questionnaire. For example:
"Do you use the river at present for recreational purposes? Yes or No?"
"If yes, do you: fish on the river? white-water raft? water-ski? hike on the shoreline trails? other?"
(They answer what it is they do. These responses, if any, can also be categorized and quantified, if useful.) Such questions can be used when analyzing the data in order to distinguish between users and non-users, consumptive users, non-consumptive users, etc.
4. Students should sort and compile the questionnaire items generated by each group and come up with a final version of the questionnaire. The teacher should review the final draft before it is printed and used. When the questionnaire is completed, copies should be made so that each student has at least one copy for his or her own use as part of the survey. Each student takes the questionnaire and after school, on weekends, etc., interviews five individuals in the community. Students may work in pairs to conduct the interviews. The students record the people's responses by tallies on the copy of the questionnaire they are carrying. NOTE: Students should of course be courteous, ask permission to interview whomever they contact and briefly explain their purpose.
5. When the interviews are completed, the students may tally, analyze and discuss the results. NOTE: Here's an excellent opportunity to incorporate a wide variety of exercises in mathematics. Depending on the level of your students, they could do everything from addition and division to finding the mean, median, mode and standard deviation of the sample.
A NOTE OF CAUTION: It is very difficult to conduct what may be considered a scientifically valid

community attitude survey. Such surveys require careful question construction, with the questions tested on a pilot basis and statistically analyzed in special ways to ensure that they are measuring what they are supposed to measure. **Who** responds to the questionnaire is critically important before any generalizations can be made. For example, if the students find the first five people they see, or interview their parents and their next-door neighbors, they are likely to be getting what may be called a "biased sample." The students may validly say,

"_____ % of the people we interviewed for our survey said...,"

but—unless more precise procedures were followed than those described in this activity—it would be unlikely that the students could say,

"Based on our research, _____ % of the people in our community believe..."

6.   Although "yes" and "no" style questions will provide the best basis for quantifying answers, students may also consider asking several open-ended questions. By asking open-ended questions, students may gather insight into aspects of their community's underlying belief system. The answers they receive to the open-ended questions might cause the students to conduct a follow-up survey in which they revise their closed-ended questions. Those questions may also prompt them to qualify their data interpretation.

EVALUATION

1.   Choose one of the following animal populations and describe one belief, one attitude and one value that might be held related to it: coyotes, deer, California condor, opossums, Norway rats, garter snakes, bald eagle, trout.

2.   Why is it important that people understand that their own attitudes about wildlife come from their values and beliefs?

3.   Mr. Smith is in favor of a dam which is being proposed to produce water for irrigation in the area. You inform him that the dam will have drastic environmental impact on the river. He understands that, considers it, and votes in favor of the dam anyway. How would you explain his vote in terms of values and beliefs?

SECTION SIX
TRENDS, ISSUES AND CONSEQUENCES

PRO AND CON: CONSUMPTIVE AND NONCONSUMPTIVE USES OF WILDLIFE

OBJECTIVES

Students will: 1) identify examples of consumptive and nonconsumptive uses of wildlife; 2) describe reasons given for both consumptive and nonconsumptive uses of wildlife; and 3) evaluate their personal views about consumptive and nonconsumptive uses of wildlife.

METHOD

Students research and debate the topic.

BACKGROUND

NOTE: This activity is enriched if offered after other wildlife-related activities. See, in particular, activities related to Section Two of the Conceptual Framework (Human Values and Wildlife); Section Three (Wildlife and Ecological Systems); and Section Four (Wildlife Conservation).

Age: Grades 7-12
Subjects: Language Arts, Social Studies, Science, Speech
Skills: analysis, comparing similarities and differences, debate, description, evaluation, public speaking, reporting, research, small group work, synthesis
Duration: minimum of two 45-minute periods
Group Size: from two students to two teams of students
Setting: indoors
Conceptual Framework Reference: II.A., II.B., II.C., II.D., II.E., II.E.1., II.E.2., II.E.3., II.F., III.E., III.E.1., III.E.2., III.F., III.F.1., III.F.4., IV.A., IV.A.1., IV.A.2., IV.A.3., IV.A.4., IV.D., IV.D.1., IV.D.2., IV.D.3., IV.D.7., IV.E., IV.E.4., IV.E.5., IV.E.6., IV.E.7., IV.E.8., IV.E.9., IV.E.10., IV.E.11., IV.F., IV.F.1., IV.F.2., IV.F.3., IV.F.4., IV.F.5., IV.F.6., IV.F.7., IV.F.8., IV.F.9., V.A., V.A.1., V.A.2., V.A.3., V.A.5., V.A.6., V.B., V.B.1., V.B.2., V.B.3., VI.B., VI.B.1., VI.B.2., VI.C., VI.C.1., VI.C.2., VI.C.3., VI.C.4., VI.C.5., VI.C.6., VI.C.7., VI.C.8., VI.C.9., VI.C.10., VI.C.11., VI.C.12., VI.C.15., VI.C.16., VI.D., VI.D.2., VI.D.3.
Key Vocabulary: consumptive, non-consumptive, fact, value
Appendices: Local Resources, Agencies and Organizations

Among many areas in which there are differences of opinion concerning wildlife and its habitat, one area which gives rise to particularly heated discussion at times has to do with questions of "consumptive" and "nonconsumptive" uses of wildlife.

Consumptive uses are generally considered to be those in which wildlife is killed, as in hunting, fishing and trapping. Such uses may include as a food source; for sport; for recreation; as a source of products for personal use; as a source of products for commercial use and sale; as a means to control damage to private land and crops; and as a population management tool.

Nonconsumptive uses are generally considered to be those in which any wildlife is watched, studied, or recorded without being killed, such as in hiking, bird-watching, sketching and photography. Such uses may be for purposes of recreation, education and research. Some nonconsumptive uses may actually be vicarious, such as movie, television and gallery viewing of wildlife.

Just as consumptive uses of wildlife have impacts on individuals and populations, so can nonconsumptive uses. There are times, for example, when nonconsumptive uses may actually be damaging to wildlife and its habitat, such as observation of wildlife at too close ranges during breeding seasons and high human use of areas where endangered species may be negatively impacted.

At first glance it seems like distinguishing a consumptive from a nonconsumptive use of wildlife should be easy. When people directly kill an animal, it is clearly a consumptive act. Yet, direct killing is just one factor that affects wildlife mortality. The issue of wildlife consumption has some gray areas. One gray area is habitat and how people affect its quality and availability for wildlife. That gray area is defined by human impact on wildlife's basic needs for food, water, shelter and space suitably arranged for survival.

Human impact takes many forms. For example, the piping plover is a little shore bird that in part of its range feeds along the ocean's edge. At low tide it runs behind receding waves and feeds on exposed marine worms and other invertebrates. When people approach a plover it stops feeding and becomes defensive. A beachful of swimmers or a regular stream of joggers or sea shell hunters can keep plovers from feeding. Because of nearby human activity, many plovers starve to death. The piping plover is now classified as a federally threatened species. Loss of habitat and human disturbance are two of the plover's primary problems. This is also true for inland piping plover populations.

Are the beach goers, sea shell hunters and joggers consuming wildlife when they disrupt the piping plover's feeding? Without a doubt, they are having an impact on wildlife. The question is, "Are they wildlife consumers?" Some could argue that wildlife consumption is a matter of degrees. The discussion is as much about indirect impacts as it is about obvious direct wildlife consumption and easily expands into exploring what roles humans should play in natural systems.

The major purpose of this activity is for students to acquire information about different uses of wildlife as well as reasons offered both for and against consumptive and nonconsumptive uses.

NOTE: There may be seen to be a difference between "use" and "value." All wildlife has value in some sense of the word—from ecological to intrinsic. Consumptive and nonconsumptive uses of wildlife do not include all values of wildlife since use requires, in this sense, intentional human activity.

MATERIALS
research and writing materials; debate arrangement in classroom

PROCEDURE
1. Ask students to brainstorm a list of ways in which wildlife is used. Note that "uses" of wildlife do not necessarily represent all ways in which wildlife has value. Provide students with definitions of "consumptive use" and "nonconsumptive use," or see if they can provide the definitions.
2. Ask the students to volunteer to represent one side or another on the following debate topic: "Wildlife should be used consumptively and nonconsumptively." One team of students should research and prepare arguments in favor of one position, and one team of students should research and prepare arguments against that position.
3. Provide the students with time to research and prepare for the debate.
4. On the day of the debate, arrange the classroom in a format where each team of students can face the others. Each team should appoint a captain to present the team's opening remarks, limited to three minutes. Each team captain should then call on one student from each team to face a person from the other team. First one person, then the other, is given one minute to present his or her point of view. Each person is

then given one minute for a rebuttal. The remaining students on each team may serve as judges of which argument was presented most effectively and accurately. A point is given the team represented by the person judged to be most effective and accurate. NOTE: The students should vote based on the effectiveness of the argument, irrespective of which team they personally represent. Such a process may prove difficult; if so, another classroom of students may be invited to serve as a team of judges, or a speech and debate teacher, impartial adult, etc., could be invited to judge. After all team members have debated a spokesperson from the other team, each team captain should give a three-minute closing statement. Five points should be awarded to the team judged to have given the most effective and accurate overall arguments.

5. Invite the students to summarize—personally, and as a group if they choose—their views about the uses of wildlife . . . consumptively, nonconsumptively, both, or neither.

EXTENSIONS AND VARIATIONS
See "Community Attitude Survey." Interview people about their views regarding consumptive and nonconsumptive uses of wildlife. Talk with a range of representatives of differing perspectives, including, for example, people from private conservation organizations; private environmental organizations; private preservation organizations; animal welfare organizations; hunting, fishing, or trapping organizations; state wildlife agencies; federal agencies; people who secure their livelihood directly or indirectly from consumptive activities involving wildlife; people who secure their livelihood directly or indirectly from nonconsumptive activities involving wildlife; artists; teachers; community planners; and others.

EVALUATION
1. Name five examples of consumptive uses of wildlife and five examples of nonconsumptive uses of wildlife.
2. What facts, if any, are given by consumptive users to defend their position, and what facts, if any, are given by nonconsumptive users to defend their position.
3. Describe differences, if any, in the ways and reasons that consumptive and nonconsumptive users may value wildlife. Describe similarities, if any.
4. Summarize your personal views about consumptive and nonconsumptive uses of wildlife and describe the reasoning behind your views.

TOO CLOSE FOR COMFORT

OBJECTIVES

Students will: 1) describe possible negative consequences for people and wildlife under conditions of crowding; and 2) identify ways people can behave in order to reduce negative consequences of crowding for wildlife.

METHOD

Students experiment with physical distance and levels of comfort in humans, estimate appropriate distances between humans and wildlife under various conditions, hypothesize about indicators of animal discomfort, and summarize reasons to avoid animal discomfort through crowding.

BACKGROUND

Sometimes wildlife seems to want to say, "Don't get too close!" From a tree branch a bird watches a person approaching; when he or she gets too close, the bird takes flight.

Animals are often threatened when crowded by humans, even though the humans may mean no harm and merely want to observe the animal. Animals may display their discomfort by fleeing, grinding teeth, coiling, hissing, stomping feet, snarling, coughing, or woofing. Flight is the usual way of showing stress. Noises may come when an animal is ready or threatening to attack.

Wildlife photographers have learned that when the wildlife they are photographing begins to act strangely, they have probably gotten too close. Animals may run away if you are outside a certain distance. At a closer distance, they may charge or in other ways respond to the threat of human presence by aggressive behavior.

One way of understanding the way wildlife acts is to recognize that many animals have certain distances that they keep from their own kind. Wolves may demand large areas of range which no other wolf outside of their own pack (family) may enter. Studies show that certain kinds of finches will always leave a certain distance between themselves when they perch on a telephone wire or fence line.

When crowding occurs, many animals react with bizarre, aggressive, disordered behavior, and may develop skin diseases like mange. They may adjust to the crowded conditions, over time, by ceasing reproduction.

In the United States, great blue heron rookeries have been disturbed by the mere presence of people. Rookeries are the birds' breeding grounds. Herons live most of the year as lone individuals; when they come together to breed—to go through courtship and nesting—they experience stress, if disturbed by humans. Under circumstances of stress, they may not breed, may lay few eggs, or may abandon the rookery, leaving eggs or young birds to perish. At a heron rookery in Colorado, wildlife managers have established a 1000 foot limit; no human disturbance is allowed close to the rookery. They are not sure this limit will save the rookery from development pressures, but they know any closer range would certainly disrupt the rookery.

The major purpose of this activity is for students to recognize the possible negative consequences for people and wildlife as a result of conditions of crowding.

Age: Grades K-7
Subjects: Science, Social Studies, Language Arts
Skills: hypothesis-formation, inference
Duration: ten to 30-minute class period, depending on age of students
Group Size: any
Setting: indoors or outdoors
Conceptual Framework Reference: I.D., VI.A., VI.A.2., VI.A.3., VI.A.4., VI.A.5., VI.B., VI.B.1., VI.B.2., VI.B.3., VI.B.4., VI.B.5., VI.C., VI.C.1., VI.C.2., VI.C.5., VI.C.16., VI.D., VI.D.1., VII.A., VII.A.1., VII.A.2., VII.A.3., VII.A.4., VII.B., VII.B.1., VII.B.2., VII.B.3., VII.B.7.
Key Vocabulary: crowding, disturbance, safety, behavior
Appendices: Simulations, Field Ethics

MATERIALS

none needed

PROCEDURE

1. Introduce the concept of discomfort from crowding by asking one student to stand in front of the class. Approach the student slowly, asking the student to tell you when your closeness makes him or her begin to feel uncomfortable. Ask the class whether they allow strangers to approach them as close as they do their friends or family. How do they feel in the middle of strangers on a crowded bus or elevator? Discuss what physical reactions they have in some kinds of crowded conditions, like avoidance of eye contact, nervousness, sweaty palms, etc.

2. Introduce the idea that animals in the wild might also be uncomfortable when approached by strangers. Talk about why they might be uncomfortable, e.g., fear of predation, need to protect young. Discuss what other conditions might increase or decrease wariness—such as ability to fly away, climb quickly, run fast, swim fast; animal size; whether the animal is alone or with a group, is on a nest, or has young.

3. Have the students make a list of animals they are likely to encounter in the environment and have them estimate what distance should be maintained from each animal species—both for reasons of personal safety and for the comfort and safety of the animal. Emphasize that these are just estimates. As a rule, it is better to stay farther away than you think might be necessary than to get too close.

4. Have the students hypothesize about animal behaviors which might indicate discomfort such as foot stomping, teeth grinding, raising up on hind feet, nervous looking around and eventually flight.

OPTIONAL: Students can mime or role play such situations and have their classmates guess what animal they are, in what situation.

5. Discuss ways in which wildlife harassment might occur unintentionally, such as flying too close in small airplanes, getting too close to photograph, calling or heckling for animals to react (especially at zoos), hiking near a nesting site, and using loud vehicles near baby animals or in places where animals are unaccustomed to seeing them. Explain the possibility that there are certain times of the year when some animals are more sensitive to intrusion such as at mating season and during severe climatic conditions such as heavy winters or drought. What ways can communities minimize disturbances? What can individual people do? Summarize reasons it is important to minimize such disturbance from people for wildlife.

EXTENSIONS

1. Draw life-sized outlines of some of the animals and mount them on an outside wall of the school building. Break into small groups; have each group establish a distance from each species which the group feels would be far enough for the animal not to be threatened by the pressure of a person. Using measuring tapes, each group should measure the established "comfort zone" for each species, under different conditions—and then present their suggested distances for the animal comfort zones. Verify the accuracy of these distances under these general conditions by contacting a wildlife resource person. Discuss whether a general rule is apparent about the relationship of the size of the comfort zone to conditions such as size of the animal, presence of young, ability to flee, single or group animal species, etc.

2. What are reasons it is important to minimize such disturbances for domesticated animals, like pets, dairy cows, etc?

3. What are reasons it is important to minimize such disturbances for people? What actions can we take to do so? With what consequences?

AQUATIC EXTENSION

Since water is one of the essential components of habitat, areas where water is available in the natural environment are frequently visited by many species of wildlife. Some live in or near the water. Others come to the water as needed. As a result, ponds, lakeshores, river banks, ocean beaches, streams, reservoirs, canals, irrigation ditches, and even city fountains can sometimes be places where people get "too close for comfort" when it comes to wildlife. Think of three examples of situations where people can get "too close for comfort" in aquatic habitats, with possible negative consequences for wildlife. Think of three examples of people and wildlife being able to successfully coexist near and in water.

EVALUATION

1. What behaviors might indicate a person speaking in front of a group is nervous?

2. How might a mother dog let you know that you are getting too close to her and her pups?

3. Rank order the following, from animals you could get closest to without harming to those you should stay the furthest away from: a heron rookery during breeding season, young raccoons seen in a forest, a large garter snake in the grass of your yard, honey bees around their hives, frogs in a freshwater pond in the summer.

4. Describe negative results of crowding for humans. Describe negative results of crowding for animals.

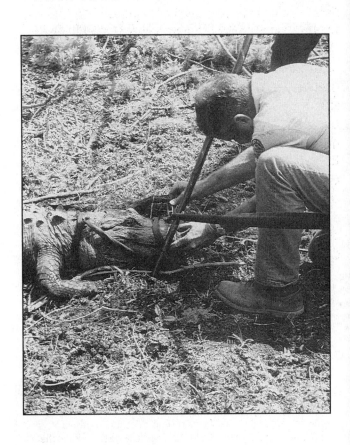

SHRINKING HABITAT

OBJECTIVES

Students will: 1) describe some effects of human development of land areas on plants and animals previously living in the area; 2) evaluate the importance of suitable habitat for wildlife; and 3) recognize that loss of habitat is generally considered to be the most critical problem facing wildlife today.

METHOD

Students simulate a process of land development in a physically involving activity.

BACKGROUND

All around us, and all over the planet, wildlife habitat is being lost. Whenever an area of land is paved for a shopping center, divided and excavated for homes for people, and sometimes when it is plowed to grow a crop—small animals lose their homes, and frequently their sources of food and water. As these small animals disappear, so too do the larger animals that previously depended upon the smaller animals in the food chain as a source of food. Animals that cannot tolerate human intervention may also disappear without any direct relationship to the food chain. (For example, see "Too Close For Comfort.")

Students can observe this phenomenon near their homes and schools or at least in their region. This process is happening in large ecosystems and small all over the earth.

For example, many wetlands on the planet have been filled in and drained to make land for farming and homes. When they are filled in, many kinds of water birds, reptiles, amphibians, crustaceans and other life forms—including a wide variety of vegetation—are lost. Sometimes the animal forms can move on; most often they cannot.

Some of the tropical forests of the planet have become extremely vulnerable in recent years. Scientists estimate that huge numbers of plant and animal forms exist in these forests that have not even been identified as yet. They are tremendously important sources of the earth's biological diversity. In fact, some scientists warn that as these genetic pools are reduced, the flexibility and thus capacity to survive of the remaining plants and animals on earth will ultimately be reduced.

The major purpose of this activity is for students to simulate some of the potential impacts of land development on wildlife and its habitat, to recognize that this process is one that is taking place in areas all over the planet, and to understand that loss of habitat is generally considered to be the most critical problem facing wildlife today.

MATERIALS

green and blue construction paper; classroom desks, tables or chairs; five or six large bedsheets or blankets for a student group of about 25

Age: Grades 4-7
Subjects: Social Studies, Science
Skills: application, comparing similarities and differences, description, discussion, evaluation, generalization, kinesthetic concept development, observation, synthesis
Duration: one 45-minute period or longer
Group Size: minimum of six students, with one developer, one carnivore, three herbivores, and one tree
Setting: indoors or outdoors, large area with room for people and props
Conceptual Framework Reference: I.A., I.B., I.C., I.C.1., I.C.2., I.C.3., I.C.4., I.D., II.B.2., III.C.1., III.D.2., III.D.3., III.D.4., IV.C., IV.C.1., IV.C.2., IV.C.3., IV.E.10., V.A., VI.A., VI.A.2., VI.A.3., VI.A.4., VI.A.5., VI.B., VI.B.1., VI.B.2., VI.B.3., VI.B.4., VI.B.5., VI.C., VI.C.2., VI.C.12., VI.C.16., VI.D., VI.D.1., VII.A., VII.A.1., VII.A.2., VII.A.3., VII.A.4., VII.B., VII.B.1., VII.B.2., VII.B.3., VII.B.4., VII.B.5., VII.B.6., VII.B.7.
Key Vocabulary: habitat, food chain, development, herbivores, carnivores, vegetation, consequences
Appendices: Simulations, Ecosystem

PROCEDURE

1. Review with the students the elements necessary for a habitat (food, water, shelter and space arranged suitably for the particular animal). (See Components of Habitat in the "Cross References.") After some discussion to make sure that the elements of habitat are clearly in mind, tell the students that in this activity they will be simulating wildlife in its habitat.

2. Divide the students into four groups: **herbivores, carnivores, vegetation** (trees, shrubs, grasses, etc.) and people who will be **land developers**. If the students are not familiar with the terms "herbivore" and "carnivore," provide them with working definitions of those terms (herbivore—a plant-eating animal; carnivore—a meat-eating animal; and although not needed for this activity, omnivore—an animal that eats both plants and animals.) Plan for three times as many herbivores as carnivores with a small number of developers in proportion to the other two groups. The numbers (amount) of vegetation may vary. For example, two developers, three carnivores, nine herbivores and six trees or bushes (vegetation).

3. Establish a large area—either in the classroom, with tables, chairs and desks moved to the sides of the room, or outside—that can be used to simulate the wildlife habitat area before development. The "land developers" are to stay on the sidelines at this time,

simply observing the undeveloped land and its wildlife inhabitants—or meeting on their own, nearby, to make plans for development. In fact, they can make their entrance rather suddenly once the wildlife habitat has been established—simulating the arrival of heavy construction equipment.

4. Provide each "herbivore" with:
    *   two desks or chairs to use as "shelter" (or string or hula hoops);
    *   three pieces of green construction paper to represent food;
    *   one piece of blue construction paper to represent water; and
    *   some of the vegetation portrayed by students.

Provide each "carnivore" with:
    *   one desk or chair to use as a "lair" (or string or hula hoop);
    *   space equivalent to that used by three herbivores;
    *   three herbivores as a potential food source;
    *   one piece of blue construction paper to represent water; and
    *   some of the vegetation portrayed by students.

5. Ask the "herbivores" to arrange the food, water and shelter—including the students who are "vegetation"—in a space to represent their habitat. Once the

herbivores have arranged their habitat, ask the "carnivores" to move into the area to establish their lairs
and water sources, keeping an eye on the herbivores
as possible food sources. For added interest, suggest
that the students identify what particular kind of animal they are and role-play its characteristics. (This
phase takes about ten minutes, with the developers
planning while the herbivores and carnivores arrange
their habitat.)

6. Once all the animals are established in their habitats, it is time for the developers to enter the picture.
These developers have been given the opportunity to
create a housing and shopping area. (They may use
three to seven minutes to construct their development,
explaining their actions as they take them.) They are
restricted in how much space they can use. They may
use the space equivalent to that used by three herbivores. The developers may use the sheets and blankets
to build their development. They may remove trees
(represented by students) without physically hurting
the students, shelter (represented by desks), food and
water.

7. Once they have constructed their development, en-
gage all of the students in a discussion of what happened. What action took place? With what consequences? Would or did any animals die? From what
causes? Could the developers have done anything differently to change the consequences? Could they have
developed several scattered small areas instead of one
large area, or vice versa, with what effects? Would it
have reduced negative consequences for wildlife if they
put the development in a different area of the habitat?

Rather than negative consequences, were there positive consequences? If so, what were they? How were they achieved? Ask the students to consider and discuss what seemed realistic about the activity and what did not. For example, sometimes development can take place that enhances the area for some kinds of wildlife. Often, however, it will not be the same kinds of wildlife that were in the area before development. Planners and developers can sometimes add to the vegetation in an area, creating additional shelter and food for some kinds of wildlife, and make water sources available under some conditions, if there is insufficient water in the area.

8. Ask the students to summarize some of the possible impacts on wildlife from human activities like development of land areas. Are there places in your community where wildlife habitat has been lost by human development? Are there places where wildlife habitat has been enhanced by human activity? What choices, if any, are there to development of previously undeveloped areas? What trade-offs are involved; for example, in developing vacant areas within communities rather than undeveloped areas outside of communities? If development does take place, what kinds of actions can people take to minimize the negative consequences for wildlife, vegetation and other elements of the environment? What about possible economic costs? Social costs? Ecological costs? Aesthetic costs, etc.? Discuss loss of habitat as something that is affecting wildlife all over the planet. Ask the students to summarize the importance of suitable habitat for wildlife. Discuss the students' concerns and recommendations.

EXTENSIONS

1. Conduct this activity twice, with the students trading roles the second time. When the former wildlife become land developers, they could see if they could produce a development plan that could benefit the area for people and wildlife in some ways. The activity can also be conducted to show differences between developing the entire area—with likely loss of all wildlife in the area—to developing only part of the area, with some wildlife likely to survive.

2. Ask students to complete the following sentence, and discuss their response: "If I were going to build a house for my family in a previously undeveloped area, I would. . . "

AQUATIC EXTENSIONS

1. Generate a list of possible human activities that can reduce or eliminate aquatic habitats (Examples: draining wetlands; building construction on shorelines; diversion of waters for agricultural, domestic, or business purposes.) For every example given, identify possible reasons both for and against taking such action.

2. Look at old and new maps of your area or state. Are there any areas where there used to be wetlands that are no longer there? If yes, what happened to these wetlands?

EVALUATION

1. Name and describe three animals or plants which used to live in your area but no longer do.

2. Describe the changes that seem most responsible for eliminating each of these plant or animals.

3. Suggest and evaluate the advantages and disadvantages, if any, of possible actions that could have been taken to prevent the elimination of these plants or animals from the area.

4. Name one kind of wildlife that would do better, and one kind of wildlife that would do worse, in areas in which humans cut down a forest and planted grass; dammed a creek to flood a valley; put in a housing development with large lawns and many shrubs; built a city on a lakeshore with crowded skyscrapers.

MIGRATION BARRIERS

OBJECTIVES

Students will: 1) define migration as it relates to wildlife; 2) describe possible impacts on wildlife migration patterns as a result of human activities; and 3) give an example of the importance of land-use planning as it affects people, wildlife, and the environment.

METHOD

Students draw murals showing deer migration routes and the consequences of development of a highway through the area.

BACKGROUND

The major purpose of this activity is for students to recognize some of the problems that can arise as a result of human actions affecting aspects of the environment. In this case, road building through a deer migration route is used as an example.

MATERIALS

drawings materials; large butcher or poster paper; background information about deer or other animals in your region that migrate seasonally on land; information about the animals' habitat needs. Check with local wildlife specialists for assistance.

PROCEDURE

1.   Divide the students into small working groups, with each group provided with drawing materials and a large piece of butcher or poster paper. Ask each group to draw a mural of a deer habitat (or habitat for another migrating land animal in your area) that includes a variety of environments from mountains to valleys. The deer herd in this habitat lives in the mountains in the summer and moves or migrates to the valleys in the winter. Ask the students to put in appropriate vegetation, water sources and pictures of other animals in addition to the deer that might live in this environment. The students may choose the time of the year to be represented in their mural. Ask them to put their herd of deer in the area they think the deer would most likely be living at that time of year. Also ask them to draw a set of arrows to show the path they think the deer would likely take each year during the time they move from one feeding area to another; for example, from the mountains to the valleys as winter nears, and from the valleys to the mountains in the summer. (NOTE: Get background on the animal habitat characteristics and migration patterns in your area or region, if possible.)

2.   Once the murals are complete, either ask the students to describe what they have included in their murals, pointing out the deer travelway—Or, simply move on to the next step in this activity. The next step is to tell the students that a major highway has been proposed for the area they have drawn. The highway is to be built somewhere in between the mountains and the valleys that the deer travel to and from in their annual migration. An Environmental Impact Statement has been done which indicates that it is possible to build the highway in ways that can minimize the negative consequences for wildlife and other elements of the natural environment. The Environmental Impact Statement is being contested in court, therefore it is not clear whether the highway will actually be built. Introduce the concept of land-use planning to the students. Each group is attempting to plan for the land use in their area, represented by their mural. Ask each group to discuss how they could draw a highway on their mural in a way that they think would have the least possible negative consequences. How could the highway be built in a way that would do the least harm to the environment and its wildlife? They could consider

Age: Grades 4-6
Subjects: Social Studies, Science
Skills: analysis, application, comparing similarities and differences, description, drawing, evaluation, generalization, media construction, observation, problem-solving, reporting, small group work, synthesis, visualization
Duration: one or two 30 to 45-minute periods
Group Size: any; small groups for mural-making
Setting: indoors or outdoors
Conceptual Framework Reference: VI.A., VI.A.2., VI.A.3., VI.A.4., VI.A.5., VI.B., VI.B.1., VI.B.2., VI.B.3., VI.B.4., VI.B.5., VI.B.6., VI.C., VI.D., VI.D.4., VIIA.1., VII.A.2., VII.A.3., VII.B., VII.B.1.
Key Vocabulary: migration, land-use planning, consequences
Appendices: Local Resources

impact to the environment during the actual road construction, ways to minimize runoff and erosion, replanting any areas where vegetation is destroyed in the building, and replanting with what kinds of plants. Ask them to pay particular attention to the herd of deer and its migration pattern, trying to figure out a way for the deer to move from their summer to their winter ranges and back again. NOTE: Sometimes this can be done by building underpasses or overpasses for the deer to use so that they don't actually have to try to cross the highway. Sometimes the highway can be built in such a way that the migration route is avoided entirely. Groups that achieve a consensus—making a land-use planning decision—can draw the highway on their murals.

3.   Ask each group to report. What land-use decisions did they make? With what consequences? To the deer? Other wildlife? Vegetation? Soil? People? Ask them to identify solutions they think would be acceptable, those that would be unacceptable, and for what reasons. What about convenience to people in transportation? Other possible questions include: What about costs to the builder of the highway? Who pays the builder? Is it actually taxpayer dollars? What are some of the factors to be considered in land-use decisions?

EXTENSIONS AND VARIATIONS

1.   Pick an actual situation in your region or anywhere on the planet—with similar concepts.
2.   Use a topographical map rather than a mural. Provide each person with copies of the map. Compare similarities and differences in solutions, all working from the same visual reference (the maps).
3.   Represent the area in question in three dimensions using clay, papier maché, or even mud!

AQUATIC EXTENSION

Many animals migrate. Many depend upon available water and aquatic habitats. For two examples, see the Aquatic WILD activities, "Hooks and Ladders" and "Migration Headache."

EVALUATION

1.   Define animal migration.
2.   Name three animals that migrate. For each, describe a human activity that might interfere with migration.
3.   Offer one or more suggestions for decreasing the negative impacts of human land use on animal migrations. Explain the reasoning behind your suggestions.

CABIN CONFLICT

OBJECTIVES

Students will: 1) describe possible circumstances in which public and private interests may conflict in land-use issues; and 2) evaluate points of view which may arise under such circumstances.

METHOD

Students participate in a role-playing activity.

BACKGROUND

Today, many conflicts arise concerning land use. It is recognized that large, continuous areas of land are necessary to provide some wildlife with suitable habitat. Sometimes individual, private land owners come into conflict with state or federal government mandates to provide adequate wildlife habitat.

The major purpose of this activity is to provide students with the opportunity to look at various points of view in a land-use issue involving both public and private interests.

MATERIALS

classroom set up as courtroom; copies of background information

Age: Grades 7-12
Subjects: Social Studies (Government, History, Civics), Language Arts, Environmental Problems, Science
Skills: analysis, description, discussion, evaluation, public speaking
Duration: two 45-minute periods or longer
Group Size: large group
Setting: indoors
Conceptual Framework Reference: IV.A., IV.A.1., IV.A.2., IV.A.3., IV.A.4., IV.E., IV.E.5., IV.E.10., IV.E.11., IV.F., IV.F.1., IV.F.2., IV.F.3., IV.F.4., IV.F.5., IV.F.6., IV.F.8., IV.F.11., V.A., V.A.5., V.B., V.B.1., V.B.2., VI.A., VI.A.1., VI.A.2., VI.A.3., VI.A.4., VI.A.5., VI.B., VI.B.1., VI.B.3., VI.B.4., VI.B.5., VI.B.6., VI.C., VI.C.1., VI.C.2., VI.C.6., VI.C.12., VI.C.15., VI.C.16., VI.D.1.
Key Vocabulary: land use, condemnation, deed
Appendices: Local Resources

PROCEDURE

1. Provide the students with the background information. Ask them to describe any similar situations they might know about. Provide a time period of a few days to a week to look for similar land use conflicts, examples of the use of condemnation for the public interest, or other conservation related conflicts between public and private land owners being reported in local media. Encourage the students to bring in newspaper or magazine articles, etc. Discuss their findings, and encourage the students to use some of the information as background.

2. Set up a role-playing situation in which students become:
    - cabin owners
    - state wildlife agency officials
    - jury (12 members)
    - judge
    - lawyers (two)
    - witnesses (as many as needed; identify characters and perspectives which would be useful)

3. Allow cabin owners and the wildlife agency people time to prepare testimony stating their arguments for either continuing private ownership or releasing that ownership. During this period, the judge and jury pre-

pare to hear the case, plan procedure, etc. Lawyers and witnesses also prepare.

4. After the testimony has been presented and opportunity for rebuttal provided, the jury members should meet briefly to reach a decision. They should then return and report their decision to the entire class, explaining the reasons for their decision.

5. Ask the students to discuss the results. What were the issues involved? What arguments support each side? Which arguments, if any, seem most persuasive? Which do not, and why? What additional information, if any, would have been helpful in reaching a decision in this situation? Where and how could we get that information, if we needed it?

EVALUATION

Pro or con: In some situations, it is appropriate for private land to be condemned for public use. Pick a position and support it.

CABIN CONFLICT

The following, imaginary conflict is based on one family's real experience and similar cases:

A dispute has arisen between owners of three cabins situated on deeded land which has been designated a state wildlife primitive, management, or refuge area by a legislative act and by the state wildlife agency. Under the act, all property owners would be required to sell to the state or their property would be condemned and taken by the state.

Two property owners use the property for weekend and summer homes, while the other property owner utilizes the property as an environmental learning base for her elementary school students as well as a summer cabin. This property owner would like to keep the property to enhance the educational program and for historical value.

Seventy-five years ago, the area was the site of a small mining community of about 500 people. Zinc and lead were mined. Part of the old smelter remains near the educational cabin. A black mountain of charcoal used in the smeltering process and several old mine shafts still exist. The existing three cabins are located on original deeded mining claims of about three acres each.

TO ZONE OR NOT TO ZONE

OBJECTIVES

Students will: 1) identify social and ecological considerations where human uses of land conflict with each other and with wildlife habitat needs; and 2) describe the importance of land-use planning.

METHOD

Students role-play a meeting of a county commission pertaining to a land-use issue.

BACKGROUND

This activity uses a role-play strategy for study of the importance of land-use planning. It emphasizes the complexities of decision-making where people of different points of view are involved.

Land use decisions affecting wildlife have become a familiar issue where housing developments are concerned. The following is an imaginary conflict that corresponds to some real life dilemmas. This information should be provided to students as background.

The major purpose of this activity is for students to understand the importance as well as some of the complexities of land-use planning and decision-making.

MATERIALS

copies of role descriptions; props optional for role-play; room set up for hearing

Age: Grades 6-9
Subjects: Social Studies, Science, Environmental Problems, Language Arts, Speech
Skills: analysis, application, comparing similarities and differences, description, discussion, evaluation, generalization, public speaking, reporting, research, synthesis, writing
Duration: three 45-minute periods
Group Size: large group; depends on students assuming roles
Setting: indoors
Conceptual Framework Reference: I.D., II.A., II.B., II.C., II.C.2., II.C.3., II.D., II.D.1., II.D.2., II.D.3., II.E., II.E.1., II.E.2., II.E.3., II.F., IV.F.11., V.A.5., V.B., V.B.1., V.B.2., VI.A., VI.A.1., VI.A.2., VI.A.3., VI.A.4., VI.A.5., VI.B., VI.B.1., VI.B.2., VI.B.3., VI.B.4., VI.B.5., VI.B.6., VI.C., VI.C.1., VI.C.2., VI.C.6., VI.C.7., VI.C.12., VI.C.16., VI.D., VI.D.1., VII.A., VII.A.1., VII.A.2., VII.A.3., VII.A.4., VII.B., VII.B.1., VII.B.5., VII.B.6., VII.B.7.
Key Vocabulary: land-use planning
Appendices: Local Resources, Simulations, Taking Action

PROCEDURE

1. Provide the students with copies of the background information concerning this hypothetical land-use dilemma.

2. Fifteen students will be assigned (or volunteer) for roles as county commissioners, local residents and business people—with each receiving a card describing his or her situation. The rest of the students will have roles as news reporters, outside experts, concerned citizens, etc. These students may ask questions of people testifying at the hearing. They can be required to write letters to the editor or one of the commissioners in support of a particular point of view; write news articles about the hearing or personal impact stories describing the potential consequences for local workers, residents, school children, etc; prepare technical reports as researchers, etc. Every student should have a role—either as one of the 15 people preparing testimony for the hearing, or as active observers who prepare written questions, reports, or news articles.

3. To set the stage for the simulation, have each of the 15 participants read their personal data cards. The other students should select their role; they do not need personal data cards, although they may write their own. Students should then be given homework time to prepare their presentations as members of the inquiry; or questions, letters to the editor and news stories as public observers. Students should be encouraged to improvise in developing their presentations and questions.

4. The day (or days) of the hearing, the chairperson of the commission is to run the meeting. It is up to him or her to maintain order. All participants must be recognized by the chairperson before they speak. After all those presenting prepared testimony have spoken and have been questioned—the reporters, researchers and concerned citizens will be asked to read their statements (articles, reports, letters to the editor, etc.). This is an excellent way to start the final day of the simulation. After all testimony, questions and statements, the commissioners vote and give the reasons for their decisions.

5. Suggested time line for this activity:
   - Day 1 Read background information and select roles (approximately 30-45 minutes)
   - Homework Prepare presentations

- Day 2   Conduct hearing (approximately 30-45 minutes)
- Day 3   Continue hearing, including reading of news items and letters to the editor; vote; discuss results

6. After the hearing and vote, discuss questions such as the following:
- What are some things we have learned about land-use decision making?
- What factors influence land-use decision making and planning?
- What differences and similarities were there between how decisions were made in this activity and how they happen in our community? Other areas? Other parts of the world?
- What responsibilities do we as citizens have in helping to make land-use decisions?
- Why are land-use decision making and land-use planning important for people, wildlife and the environment?

EXTENSIONS AND VARIATIONS

1. Have students identify a wildlife issue in their local area, gather data and develop their own simulation.
2. Alter the role descriptions and repeat the simulation.
3. Use copies of a topographical map as common references for everyone.

4. Bring in real expert witnesses; e.g., local people who can add their perspectives and expertise. If you do, make an effort to get a balanced range of points of view rather than hearing from only one perspective on the issues involved.
5. Adapt this activity to a debate format.
6. Attend a local zoning board meeting.

AQUATIC EXTENSION
Consider another land-use question! See the Aquatic WILD activity, "To Dam or Not To Dam."

EVALUATION
1. Describe zoning laws. Identify and describe possible effects and values of zoning laws. Consider potential positive and negative effects.
2. Find out how local zoning laws are passed. Write a short report describing how the activity "To Zone Or Not To Zone" is similar or different than what really happens.
3. Describe how citizens can get their opinions considered in land-use decision making processes.
4. Give an example of how a zoning law might be good for wildlife. Describe how citizens can get their opinions considered in land-use decision making processes.

LAND USE DECISION

Pleasant Valley is a ranching-logging community on the western slope of the Snow mountains. Silverton—a town of 20,000—is the trade center of the area. Cramer Lumber Company is expanding its operations. This will provide 250 new jobs, but housing is very limited. A 200-home subdivision has been proposed for an 80-acre plot of undeveloped land on the south edge of town. This forested area is bordered by Rattlesnake Creek on the west. Rattlesnake Creek provides excellent fishing for rainbow trout. Fifty-three species of birds have been sighted in this area, including some rare species. In the spring and fall, the area is used by migrating waterfowl and deer feed in the area. Many small watchable species such as ground squirrels and pocket gophers inhabit this land. This 80-acre plot is currently zoned for agriculture and forestry and would have to be rezoned as residential by a vote of the county commissioners. The subdivision would be on a central water system, but each home would have its own septic system.

Personal Data Cards

LEN OR LINDA OLSEN, REALTOR (COUNTY COMMISSIONER)

You started your business in Silverton five years ago. Your business is doing well, but you have difficulty relating to the "old timers" like Thompson. Your real estate company is not developing this property. You have some question regarding the credibility of the developer, but you generally vote in favor of development.

DAVID OR WANDA DRESSER, MERCHANT (COUNTY COMMISSIONER)

You are 46 and own a furniture store. You would like to sell furniture to all the new home owners. You can also see the value of the 80 acres left in a natural and undeveloped condition. You are wondering if there might be another site for the development of this housing area.

JACK OR JANET THOMPSON, RANCHER (COUNTY COMMISSIONER)

You are the third generation to run the "Rolling T" Cattle Company. You are proud to tell people that your grandfather was one of the first to settle in this valley. Your spread covers 800 acres and you have grazing rights to surrounding U.S. Forest Service land. You resent the increase in population of the area and, although you are involved in community affairs, you resent individuals moving into the area who do not share your values. Last winter, snowmobiles cut your fences three times and in one case your cattle wandered onto the highway and caused a traffic accident.

BOB OR BETSY HENDERSON, FARMER (COUNTY COMMISSIONER)

You own and operate a large farm near the south edge of town and adjacent to the 80-acre plot in question. You have been interested in the possibility of buying the land to add to your family's agricultural operations. You've a keen interest in the environment, making efforts to employ agricultural practices that benefit wildlife and minimize damage to other natural resources. Since you are an adjacent landholder, you may need to disqualify yourself from participation as a Commissioner in this meeting.

ELMER OR BERTHA WILLAS, RESIDENT

You are a 68-year old "old timer" living on the land proposed for the subdivision. You have lived on Cornwall's land for 45 years, built a home there with Cornwall's permission, and have raised seven children. You raise bees and chickens out back and your garden covers one-half acre. You are settled in the middle of the area proposed for the housing development and there is no question that you will have to be evicted and your house torn down. You have no legal claim to any of the land, but have nowhere else to go.

JAMES OR ERMA "FROSTY" WHITE, SNOWMOBILER

You are 30 years old and have just been elected president of the "Rattlers," the local snowmobile club, and you feel that you should defend their interests in the area. The cost of gas is high, and your club doesn't want to have to drive long distances to ride snowmobiles. You would like to open a snowmobile repair shop, but you might get a job at the new lumber mill.

TOM OR MARY BENNETT, PRESIDENT OF CHAMBER OF COMMERCE

This is your tenth year as president of the Chamber of Commerce. You own a grocery store in the middle of town. Your greatest concern is the weak business climate in your community. The Chamber recently hired Smith & Wittigen, a business consulting firm, to evaluate the retain potential of Pleasant Valley. Their findings indicate that the business community has overbuilt. Your profits and those of your fellow merchants have been steadily declining. You see this new lumber mill as the salvation of your business. You also have wondered about possible ways to improve the economy through increased tourism.

OSCAR OR JAN SPARROW, LOCAL AUDUBON PRESIDENT

You represent over 300 active Audubon members, and are director of the annual bird count competition. You have a list of 15 rare bird species found in the Rattlesnake Creek area. You are 37 years old and work at the lumber mill.

GEORGE OR ALICE LONG WINGS, NATIVE AMERICAN INDIAN LEADER

You have an interest in the sanctity of the area in question as it is an ancient ceremonial site for your tribespeople.

CHARLIE OR CHARLOTTE JACKSON, HUNTER

You are a 53-year old "old timer" and an avid hunter and fisher. You have four boys and hunting has always been an important family activity. You are an influential member of Ducks Unlimited, and the 80 acres proposed for development contains one of the prime duck hunting areas close to town.

WALLACE OR WILMA CRAMER, LUMBER MILL OWNER

You own the nearby lumber mill. Operations have expanded and you need inexpensive housing for new employees coming to the area. The wood milled is used locally and transported throughout the state. It provides an important source of income to the town.

MARTIN OR ETHEL HIGGINS, DEVELOPER

You are the largest developer in the area and can afford to buy the land outright. You will make a substantial profit if the housing that is needed for the lumber mill employees is built. You are successful and fairly competent, but you have been criticized more than once for a lack of attention to landscape detail and design.

HAROLD OR CORNELIA CORNWALL, LAND OWNER

You are a 63-year old retired business person. You want to sell your land, move to Palm Springs, and live happily ever after under sunny skies. You want cash but your asking price is very reasonable. You own the 80 acres of prime wild land south of town.

FRANK OR FRANCES STUDY, COLLEGE PROFESSOR

You teach at a nearby community college. You are an active member of several animal welfare organizations and are vocal in your opposition to hunting.

HARVEY OR GLADYS CROW, BANKER (COUNTY COMMISSIONER)

You are 50 years old, and, as a banker, are willing to finance new home loans. You are an art collector and former president of the local chamber of commerce. You also love birdwatching and fishing. You think the whole area south of town has economically valuable recreational potential but are concerned about protecting environmental quality.

DEADLY LINKS

OBJECTIVES

Students will: 1) give examples of ways in which pesticides enter food chains; and 2) describe possible consequences of pesticides entering food chains.

METHOD

Students become "hawks," "shrews," and "grasshoppers" in a highly involving physical activity.

BACKGROUND

People have developed pesticides to control organisms. Herbicides are used to control unwanted plants; insecticides to control nuisance insects, etc. Although these pesticides are useful to humans when properly used, they frequently end up going where they are not wanted. Many toxic chemicals have a way of persisting in the environment, and often become concentrated in unexpected and undesirable places—from food and water supplies to wildlife and sometimes people, too.

For example, a pesticide (a chemical—frequently synthesized from inorganic compounds—used to kill something identified as a "pest" under some conditions) called DDT used to be applied regularly to crops as a means of controlling insects that were damaging the plants or trees. Then it was discovered that DDT entered the food chain with damaging results. For example, fish ate insects that were sprayed by the chemical; hawks, eagles and pelicans ate the fish. The poison became concentrated in the birds—sometimes weakening and killing them directly, and over time resulting in side effects such as egg shells so thin that the eggs would not hatch, or were crushed by the parents in the nesting process. The impact on species, including the bald eagle and the brown pelican, has been well documented. Use of DDT has now been prohibited by law in the United States. DDT use is not prohibited worldwide. Resident animal populations in countries that still allow the use of DDT are at particular risk. Also, many species of animals that migrate between countries that permit DDT use and those that prohibit DDT are still at risk of DDT exposure. Even after the application of DDT is stopped, DDT and its by-products can impact the environment for decades.

People use other synthetic chemical pesticides in their homes, yards and gardens. Each targets a different organism. For instance, some kill cockroaches while others kill weeds. If used improperly, these substances can also be toxic to non-targeted animals such as honey bees and fish. Careful handling, application, and storage of these substances are important steps which can help prevent these substances from entering the food chain in the first place.

Damaging fertilizers as well as pesticides are used by many farmers as a part of the agricultural industry. Again, use of such chemicals—particularly the inorganic, synthesized compounds—can have varying side effects. For example, a pesticide may be sprayed or dusted on a crop. The pesticide may settle into the soil, or stay on the crop, until it is washed by rain or irrigation into other water sources like groundwater, lakes, streams, rivers and oceans. Testing the water after this has occurred typically does not show a particularly high concentration of these human-made chemicals—but testing the invertebrates (i.e., crayfish and shellfish) and fin-fish often does! Waterfowl and other species may also be affected—including human beings, if people eat contaminated fish or waterfowl,

Age: Grades 4-9
Subjects: Social Studies, Science, Physical Education
Skills: analysis, classification, comparing similarities and differences, computation, description, discussion, evaluation, generalization, kinesthetic concept development, synthesis
Duration: one 30 to 45-minute period
Group Size: minimum of ten students preferred
Setting: large playing area
Conceptual Framework Reference: I.C., I.C.3., I.C.4., I.D., II.B.2., II.B.3., II.B.4., III.B., III.B.1., III.B.2., IV.A.4., IV.C.3., VI.A., VI.A.2., VI.A.3., VI.A.4., VI.A.5., VI.B., VI.B.1., VI.B.2., VI.B.3., VI.C., VI.C.1., VI.C.6., VI.C.12., VI.C.13., VI.C.14., VI.C.15., VI.C.16., VI.D., VII.A.2., VII.A.4., VII.B., VII.B.1., VII.B.2., VII.B.3., VII.B.4., VII.B.5., VII.B.6., VII.B.7.
Key Vocabulary: pesticide, insecticide, herbicide, food chain, accumulate, toxic, chemicals, trade-offs, organic, inorganic
Appendices: Local Resources, Agencies and Organizations, Outdoors, Simulations

for example. In other words, wildlife and people become the concentrators of the pesticide because the chemicals do not pass out of their bodies but accumulate in their bodies over time.

Public pressure continues to force changes in the application and availability of pesticides. For example, there is now growing interest in integrated pest management. This is an approach to agriculture that considers the entire farm and garden ecosystem. Integrated pest management can include using a pest's predator as well as other biological controls to reduce crop damage. Integrated pest management can also include the selective use of naturally-occurring and synthetic pesticides as well as habitat manipulations. One concern with this approach concerns possible introduction of non-native species.

The major purpose of this activity is for students to recognize the possible consequences of accumulation of some pesticides in the environment.

MATERIALS

white and colored drinking straws, pipe cleaners, poker chips or any other material that students can easily pick up (NOTE: multi-colored, dry dog food works well and poses little environmental threat even if it is not all collected following the activity); 30 pieces per student is recommended in a proportion of two-thirds white to one-third colored pieces; one bag per grasshopper (approximately 18-20)

PROCEDURE

1. Tell the students that this is an activity about "food chains." If they are not familiar with the term, spend time in establishing a definition. (Food chain: a sequence or "chain" of living things in a community, based on one member of the community eating the member above it, and so forth; e.g., grasshopper eats plants like corn, shrews eat grasshoppers, hawks eat shrews.)
2. Divide the students into three groups. In a class of 26 students, there would be two "hawks," six "shrews," and 18 "grasshoppers." (Work with approximately three times as many shrews as hawks, and three times as many grasshoppers as shrews.) OPTIONAL: Have grasshoppers, hawks, and shrews labeled so they can be easily identified; e.g., arm ties for grasshoppers, red bandannas for "red-tail hawks," and brown arm ties or caps for shrews.
3. Hand each "grasshopper" a small paper bag or other small container. The container is to represent the "stomach" of whatever animal is holding it.
4. With the students' eyes closed, or otherwise not watching where you place the "food," distribute the white and colored straws (or whatever material you use) around in a large open space. Outside on a playing field if it is not windy or on a gymnasium floor will work; a classroom will also work if chairs and tables or desks can be moved back.
5. Give the students their instructions. The grasshoppers are the first to go looking for food. The hawks and shrews are to sit quietly on the sidelines watching the grasshoppers; after all, the hawks and shrews are predators, and are watching their prey! At a given sig-

nal, the grasshoppers are allowed to enter the area to collect food and place the food in their stomachs (the bags). The grasshoppers have to move quickly to gather food. At the end of 30 seconds, the grasshoppers are to stop collecting food.

6. The shrews are now allowed to hunt the grasshoppers. The hawks are still on the sidelines quietly watching the activity. The amount of time available to the shrews to hunt grasshoppers should take into account the size area in which you are working. In a classroom, 15 seconds may be enough time; on a large playing field, 60 seconds may be better. Each shrew should have time to catch one or more grasshoppers. Any grasshopper tagged or caught by the shrew, must give its bag of food to the shrew and then sit on the sidelines.

7. The next time period (from 15 to 60 seconds, or whatever time you set) is time for the hawks to hunt food. The same rules follow. Any shrews still alive may hunt for grasshoppers; grasshoppers are hunting for the food chips that represent corn or other plants; and the hawks are hunting for the shrews. If a hawk catches a shrew, the hawk gets the food bag and the shrew goes to the sidelines. At the end of the designated time period, ask all the students to come together in a circle, bringing whatever food bags they have with them.

8. Ask the students who are "dead," having been consumed, to identify what animal they are and what animal ate them. (If they are wearing labels, this will be obvious.) Next, ask any animals still alive to empty their food bags out onto the floor or on a piece of paper where they can count the number of food pieces they have. They should count the total number of white food pieces and total number of multi-colored food pieces they have in their food sacks. List any grasshoppers and the total number of white and multi-colored food pieces each has; list the number of shrews left and the number of white and multi-colored pieces each has; and finally list the hawks and the number of white and multi-colored food pieces each has.

9. Inform the students that there is something called a "pesticide" in the environment. This pesticide, DDT, was sprayed onto the crop the grasshoppers were eat-

ing in order to prevent a lot of damage by the grasshoppers. If there were substantial crop damage by the grasshoppers, the farmers would have less of their crop to sell, and some people and domestic livestock might have less of that kind of food to eat—or it might cost more to buy it because a smaller quantity was available. DDT been historically proven to accumulate in food chains and can stay in the environment for a long time. In this activity, all of the multi-colored food pieces represent the pesticide. All of the grasshoppers that were not eaten by shrews may now be considered dead, **if they have any multi-colored food pieces in their food supply.** Any shrews for which half or more of their food supply was multi-colored pieces would also be considered dead. The one hawk with the highest number of multi-colored food pieces will not die at this time; however, it has accumulated so much of the pesticide in its body that the egg shells produced by it and its mate during the next nesting season will be so thin that the eggs will not hatch successfully. The other hawks are not visibly affected at this time.

10. Talk with the students about what they just experienced in the activity. Ask them for their observations about how the food chain seems to work, and how toxic substances can enter the food chain, with a variety of results. The students may be able to give examples beyond those of the grasshopper—shrew—hawk food chain affected by the pesticide in this activity.

EXTENSIONS

1. Consider and discuss possible reasons for use of such chemicals. What are some of the trade-offs? What are some of the consequences?

2. Offer and discuss possible alternatives to uses of such chemicals in instances where it seems the negative consequences outweigh the benefits. For example, some farmers are successfully using organic techniques (e.g., sprays of organic, non-toxic substances; crop rotation; companion planting); biological controls (e.g., predatory insects); and genetic approaches (e.g., releasing sterile male insects of the pest species) in efforts to minimize damages to their crops.

3. Find out what research is going on to develop and test effects of pest control efforts—from effects of possibly toxic chemicals to non-toxic alternatives. With what impacts? Trade-offs? Potential?

4. Check newspapers for relevant local, national, or international examples of such issues.

AQUATIC EXTENSIONS

1. See the Aquatic WILD activities, "Deadly Waters" and "Plastic Jellyfish."

2. Show how pesticides can enter an aquatic food chain. Also show how pesticides can enter aquatic environments and end up in the food chains of terrestrial environments (mosquito larvae—fish—birds). Show how pesticides can enter the food chains in terrestrial environments and end up in aquatic environments (grasshoppers—small fish—large fish).

EVALUATION

1. Give examples of ways in which pesticides could enter a food chain.

2. Discuss two possible consequences of pesticides entering the food chain for each of the examples you gave above.

3. A group of ecologists studied the presence of a toxic chemical in a lake. They found the water had one molecule of the chemical for every one billion molecules of water. This is called one part per billion (1 ppb). The algae had one part per million (1 ppm) of the toxic chemical. Small animals, called zooplankton, had 10 ppm. Small fish had 100 ppm. Large fish had 1,000 ppm. How do you explain this increase in this toxic chemical to 1,000 ppm for the large fish? Use a drawing to help support your answer. The ecologists found the chemical was a pesticide which had been sprayed on cropland 100 miles away from the lake. How did so much of it get into the lake?

NO WATER OFF A DUCK'S BACK

OBJECTIVES

Students will: 1) identify ways oil spills can affect birds adversely; and 2) describe possible negative consequences to wildlife, people, and the environment from human-caused pollutants.

METHOD

Students conduct experiments using water, oil, hard-boiled eggs, detergent, and feathers.

BACKGROUND

The impacts of environmental pollution often are difficult to see. A major oil spill, however, provides dramatic evidence of potential impact to wildlife. Examples include damage to feathers, killing of embryos when oil seeps into eggs, suffocation of fish when gills are clogged, and death to marine and terrestrial animals by ingesting food and water contaminated by the oil. Oil soaked animals may try to clean themselves and, in so doing, ingest oil that often kills them.

People are involved in efforts to prevent oil spills and their consequences. They also are involved in efforts to "clean up" after such spills take place. Such actions are not always successful, and sometimes they have unfortunate consequences as well. For example, the process of using detergents to clean oil from the feathers of birds caught in spills may also damage the birds' feather structure and arrangement and thus the birds' wa-

terproofing. Birds may also be more susceptible to disease during this time of stress and may be weakened to the extent that it is more difficult for them to secure their necessary food and water. Obviously, the food and water sources may also be affected in quality.

Large oil spills account for just one way oil pollutes the environment. For example, many people who work on their own vehicles dispose of their waste oil improperly. They pour waste oil into storm drains, sewers or on the ground. Many people are surprised to learn that they and their neighbors can account for more pollution than large corporations.

Oil spills are just one example of the kinds of pollutants that can have adverse short- and long-term effects on wildlife, people and the environment. The impact of DDT on the food chain is well known, as another of many possible examples. DDT's influence on thinner egg shells in bald eagles and other birds is well documented, one more in a combination of factors which contribute to threatening, endangering and eliminating species.

The major purpose of this activity is for students to examine some of the possible consequences of human-caused pollution for wildlife, people and the environment.

Age: Grades 6-12
Subjects: Science, Mathematics, Social Studies, Language Arts, Home Economics
Skills: analysis, computation, discussion, drawing, estimation, generalization, graphing, observation
Duration: one to two 45-minute periods or longer
Group Size: small groups of three to four recommended
Setting: indoors
Conceptual Framework Reference: I.C., I.C.1., I.C.3., I.C.4., I.D., IV.C., IV.C.1., IV.C.3., IV.E., IV.E.4., IV.E.7., IV.E.10., V.A., V.B., VI.A., VI.A.2., VI.A.3., VI.A.4., VI.A.5., VI.B., VI.B.2., VI.B.3., VI.C.1., VII.A., VII.A.1., VI.A.2., VII.A.3., VII.A.4., VII.B., VII.B.1., VII.B.3., VII.B.4., VII.B.5., VII.B.6., VII.B.7.
Key Vocabulary: pollution, oil spill, trade-off
Appendices: Local Resources, Metric Chart

MATERIALS

cooking oil; shallow containers; eye dropper; hand lens; feathers (natural); liquid detergent solution (made with one part dishwashing liquid to 100 parts water); hard-boiled eggs

PROCEDURE

1. Divide the class into groups of three or four. Each group needs a shallow pan partially filled with water. Add one teaspoon of oil to the water. Observe the interaction of oil and water. Measure the area covered by the oil. There are 768 teaspoons in a gallon. Calculate how much area could be covered by one gallon of oil. Using this information, estimate the area that

© 1992 Council for Environmental Education

might be affected by an oil spill involving:

a. A tanker truck holding 8,000 gallons.

b. A ship holding 300,000 gallons.

c. A supertanker holding 83,000,000 gallons.

Discuss and compare estimates with other groups. Graph estimates and compute average figures.

2. Put enough oil in a small container to submerge three hard-boiled eggs. Add the eggs. Put the eggs under a good light and watch closely. Remove one egg after five minutes and examine it—before, during, and after peeling off the shell. Try to remove the excess oil from the outside before attempting to peel the egg. Remove the second egg after 15 minutes and the third egg after 30 minutes, repeating the procedure, examining each carefully. Discuss observations. What effect could oil have on the eggs of birds nesting near the water?

3. Examine a feather with a hand lens. Sketch what you see. Dip the feather in water for one or two minutes, and examine again with a hand lens. Sketch and compare to the original observations. Place the feather in oil for one or two minutes, and then examine with a hand lens, sketch, and compare with other sketches. Clean the feather in detergent, rinse in water, and dry it. Examine with a hand lens, sketch, and compare with previous sketches. Discuss changes in the feather after exposure to oil and then to detergents. What effect could these changes have on normal bird activity?

4. Discuss other possible effects on birds from an oil spill. Discuss possible impacts on other wildlife species, on humans, and on the environment. What trade-offs are involved? Do we have to choose between oil and birds, as well as other wildlife? What are some alternatives? What are other examples of human-caused pollutants that can have negative consequences for wildlife, people, and the environment? What is being done or can be done about these as well?

5. OPTIONAL: Ask each student to write a report, summarizing the findings of the experiment as well as making recommendations.

EXTENSIONS

1. A variety of oils—cooking oil, motor oil, crude oil—could be used, to produce effects to compare to the original experiment. Food coloring can be added to clear oils to observe the effects. Prior to using motor oil, crude oil, or similar products, you should have a plan for properly disposing of the waste materials. This includes the oil, polluted water and items used to clean the feathers. You can devise the plan. More oil is improperly placed in the environment by end users than commercial transporters. That means when it comes to oil pollution, ordinary people have a greater collective impact than oil shipping firms. You can use this opportunity to learn how to properly dispose of hazardous wastes in your own community. You can also research local laws pertaining to oil disposal.

2. Contact your local city or state environment department to determine what forms of pollution cause problems in your area. A local wildlife rehabilitator or wildlife pathologist can provide insight into common pollution problems for nearby wildlife. They may also be able to give information about the impact of improperly disposed of toxins on local wildlife populations.

AQUATIC EXTENSIONS

Find out what consequences there can be from oil spills for other species of aquatic wildlife, e.g., fish, marine mammals.

EVALUATION

1. How could an oil spill affect the success of birds nesting near the water?

2. Describe some possible effects of oil on a feather.

3. Explain why the effects of oil are different from those of water.

4. Describe some possible negative effects of three other human-caused pollutants on people, wildlife, and the environment.

KEEPING SCORE

OBJECTIVES

Students will: 1) describe cause and effect relationships that help and hinder wildlife in their community; and 2) recommend changes in their community that could benefit wildlife.

METHOD

Students investigate their neighborhoods for "cause and effect" relationships affecting wildlife; develop and use "community wildlife scorecards," and recommend actions to improve and/or maintain the quality of wildlife habitat in the community.

BACKGROUND

There are pleasant surprises to be found in discovering and exploring some of nature's secrets—and these are available in our own schoolyards, backyards, neighborhoods and communities. We sometimes forget that nature is all around us—in cities, suburbs, and agricultural areas—and not just in woods and lakes, high mountain meadows, deserts, rivers, skies and oceans.

This activity is designed to assist students in searching out these surprises, as well as to make them aware of any problems that may exist for wildlife in their near surroundings, particularly as a result of human actions.

Age: Grades 4-8
Subjects: Science, Social Studies, Language Arts, Mathematics
Skills: analysis, application, classification, computation, description, discussion, evaluation, observation, problem-solving, reporting, small group work, synthesis, writing (limited)
Duration: two to three 30 to 45-minute periods; time after school working individually or in teams
Group Size: small groups and individual activity
Setting: indoors and outdoors
Conceptual Framework Reference: I.A.2., I.B., I.B.2., I.C., I.C.1., I.C.3., I.C.4., I.D., II.A., II.B., II.B.2., II.C., II.D., II.E., II.F., III.A.1., III.B.3., III.B.4., IV.C., IV.C.1., IV.C.3, IV.D., IV.D.4, IV.E., IV.E.4, V.A., V.A.5, VI.A., VI.A.2., VI.A.2., VI.A.4., VI.A.5., VI.B., VI.B.1., VI.B.2., VI.B.3., VI.C., VI.C.12., VI.C.13., VI.C.15., VI.C.16., VI.D., VII.A., VII.A.1., VII.A.2., VII.A.3., VII.A.4., VII.B., VII.B.1., VII.B.2., VII.B.3., VII.B.4., VII.B.5., VII.B.6., VII.B.9.
Key Vocabulary: cause, effect, habitat
Appendices: Field Ethics, Outdoors, Observations and Inferences, Taking Action

---

Some of us live in areas where limited wildlife is in evidence. However, many of us forget to see wildlife around us, even when it is there. Sometimes it is easy to take birds, butterflies, squirrels and earthworms for granted! Frequently, we don't take into consideration the impact of our actions on the other living things around us. It is particularly easy to acquire a sort of "selective" vision that has us see aphids in our vegetable patch, for example, and not think about the impact on other life forms in the environment if we use a toxic spray to get rid of the aphids.

The major purpose of this activity is for students to increase their perceptions of cause and effect relationships affecting wildlife in their immediate communities, and to recommend some personal and community actions that could benefit wildlife.

MATERIALS

copies of scorecards; poster materials chalkboard or bulletin board for classroom display

PROCEDURE

1. Ask the students to go home after school and look for "cause and effect" relationships in their neighborhood or community that seem to help or hurt wildlife—and some that seem not to affect wildlife at all. Ask every student to come back to school the next day prepared to share at least one example.

2. Get a sampling of information from the students in a brief discussion of what they found. Encourage them to explain their basis for identifying "cause and effect." Consider the following:
   - What were some of the most surprising observations you made?
   - What kinds of actions are people taking that directly affect wildlife? Which, if any, of these actions seem harmful to wildlife? Which, if any, of these actions seem helpful to wildlife? Which, if any, seem to have no effect?
   - What, if any, problems affecting wildlife were identified? How do you know there are problems? If there are problems, are they apt to get

better or worse in the future? Are there any actions that can be taken—by individuals and by the community—to reduce or get rid of these problems?

3. Next ask the students to work in small groups of four to six students. They should share what they identified as cause and effect relationships and whether the effect hurts or helps wildlife in their community. They can add examples of cause and effect relationships that could help or harm wildlife, even if they did not actually see them happening in their community. They should pool their ideas, eliminating duplicates, and putting their cause and effect relationships on one list representing their group's ideas. Ask one person to report for each group and turn in the group's list.

4. Either the teacher or a small group of students can pool the ideas from all the groups, putting together one master "Community Wildlife Scorecard."

5. Provide each student or team of students with a copy of the "Community Wildlife Scorecard." Read through the scorecard together, making sure the students are clear about what they are looking for in each situation.

6. Decide where the students will be doing their observing and "scorekeeping." It might be on the school grounds. The activity works very well if the students each take their scorecards home with them, making their observations to and from school and after school in their own neighborhoods.

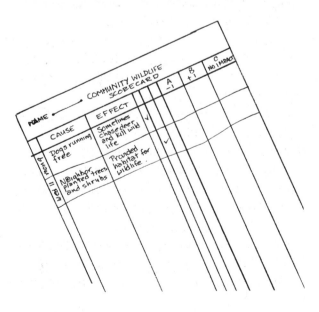

7. Ask the students to keep a score (tally) of each item they see—overnight, for a period of one week, or longer. (If a class cumulative scorecard is to be kept, prepare and post it in a conspicuous place—on a chalk board, poster board, or bulletin board, for example.)

8. At the end of the week—or whatever recordkeeping period is established—ask the students to tally and score their personal sightings. Subtract one point for every sighting of a cause and effect relationship that hurts wildlife; add one point for every sighting that helps wildlife; zero points for sightings with no impact.

9. Combine the personal scores and come up with a whole class score representing the "Community Wildlife Score."

10. Based on what they observed and recorded, ask the students what actions they think they could take as individuals and as a community to improve their "Community Wildlife Score." If the score is excellent already, what actions, if any, need to be taken to maintain the quality of their environment?

AQUATIC EXTENSION

Describe three actions that might be taken in your community which could benefit aquatic wildlife—explaining what would happen, and why it would be helpful.

EVALUATION

1. Identify and describe three kinds of wildlife habitat in your community and list three kinds of wildlife which could live in each habitat. Describe six actions taken by members of your community that impact the wildlife species you selected. Choose three activities that are harmful and three that are helpful.

2. Identify what seems to be the greatest short-term problem for wildlife in your community and the greatest long-term problem. Identify what might be done, if anything, to reduce or eliminate these problems. Predict the results of actions in the community that might affect wildlife.

3. If applicable, shade the map with three different colors. Use one color to show where there are more occurrences of things that harm wildlife than those that help wildlife. Use another color to show where harmful things and helpful things are found in approximately the same number. Use a third color to show areas where there are more helpful things than harmful things. What patterns do you see, if any? Explain those patterns.

4. Describe three actions taken by members of your community that are harmful to wildlife. Describe three actions that might be taken in your community which could benefit wildlife, explaining what would happen, and why it would be helpful. Identify what seems to be the greatest short-term problem for wildlife in your community, and the greatest long-term problem. Identify what might be done, if anything, to reduce or eliminate these problems.

DATE	CAUSE	EFFECT	HURTS	HELPS	NEITHER	A Subtract 1	B Add 1	C No Impact

COMMUNITY WILDLIFE SCORECARD

SUBTOTALS								

(Subtract Column A from Column B for Total Wildlife Score.)

Total Wildlife Score

WHEN A WHALE IS A RIGHT

OBJECTIVES

Students will: 1) describe general characteristics and status of whales; 2) recognize that international alliances affect wildlife; and 3) evaluate the possible impact of wildlife issues on alliances and other relationships between and among nations.

METHOD

Students hold a hypothetical meeting of the International Whaling Commission.

BACKGROUND

Whales are the largest animals on earth. There are approximately 80 known species of whales, which range in size from approximately four to almost one hundred feet in length, and from 160 pounds to 150 tons in weight. Whales are mammals, bearing live young. There has been some research to suggest that whales and other cetacea, including the dolphins, are creatures of such intelligence that—among other things—they have unusual capacities for communication.

Some species of whales have been hunted to the point of near-extinction. Out of concern for maintaining viable populations of whales, the International Whaling Commission, established by treaty, has been involved in regulation of harvesting activities. The Commission establishes regulations on the protection and hunting of whales. The purpose of the Commission is to preserve world whale stocks and to make possible the orderly development of the whaling industry. Among the important resolutions passed by the Commission are those prohibiting the sale of whaling equipment or technology to non-Commission members, forbidding the use of factory ships for whaling, and declaring most of the Indian Ocean a whale sanctuary until the end of 1989. The Commission adopted in 1982 a moratorium on commercial whaling beginning the end of 1985. However, at present, some countries are continuing to whale. (Source: *The Cousteau Almanac.* N.Y.: Doubleday & Company, 1981. p. 577.)

The Commission has no enforcement powers. Beyond economic sanctions and national laws by members, the Commission relies on voluntary adherence to its rules. World public opinion is an important force on the Commission and its member nations to make and enforce responsible conservation decisions.

The major purpose of this activity is for students to recognize that relationships between and among nations can affect wildlife.

MATERIALS

writing materials; research materials

PROCEDURE

1. Divide the students into four groups. One group will research the International Whaling Commission (IWC), one will research non-whaling nation members of the IWC, one will research whaling nation members of the IWC, and one will research whales.
2. Ask each group to conduct library research. Possible questions for each group might include:

International Whaling Commission

What is the International Whaling Commission? When, why and how was it established? Who are its members? What members are whaling nations? Are there any active whaling nations which are not members of

---

Age: Grades 7-12
Subjects: Social Studies, Language Arts, Environmental Problems, Science
Skills: analysis, application, debate, description, discussion, evaluation, generalization, public speaking, reading, reporting, research, small group work, synthesis, writing
Duration: two or three 45-minute periods; one homework assignment
Group Size: any; excellent for large group
Setting: indoors
Conceptual Framework Reference: II.A., II.A.1., II.A.2., II.A.3., II.A.4., II.B., II.C., II.C.1., II.C.2., II.C.3., II.D., II.F., IV.A., IV.F.4., IV.F.5., IV.F.11., V.A., V.A.2., V.A.3., VI.A.5., VI.B., VI.B.1., VI.B.2., VI.B.3., VI.B.6., VI.C., VI.C.1., VI.C.2., VI.C.4., VI.C.6., VI.C.7., VI.C.8., VI.C.12., VI.C.13., VI.C.15., VI.C.16., VI.D., VI.D.2., VI.D.3., VI.D.4., VII.B., VII.B.3.
Key Vocabulary: whale, cetacea, alliance, regulation, commission, harvest, subsistence, sanctuary, species
Appendices: Agencies and Organizations

---

the IWC? If so, what are their current practices affecting whales? What are the major reasons for and against continued whaling? Include economic, political, cultural, scientific and ethical considerations.

What positions do member nations tend to take on issues? For what reasons? What are the accomplishments of the IWC? What problems does the IWC face? What is the role of world opinion in affecting the activities of the IWC and its member and non-member nations? What recent recommendations and regulations has the IWC passed? How effective does the IWC seem to be in meeting its objectives? What other international agreements affect whales? Which countries participate in these agreements?

Non-whaling Nation Members of the IWC

Have these nations ever actively engaged in whaling? If yes, what are historic reasons for whaling among people of their nation? For what reasons are these nations now non-whaling nations? How did they vote on the moratorium decision of 1982? What, if any, national laws do they have involving whales?

Whaling Nation Members of the IWC

What are historic and contemporary reasons for whaling among people of their nation? What practices have they used and do they use in killing whales? What regulations, if any, do they support affecting killing of whales? How did they vote on the moratorium decision of 1982? What, if any, national laws do they have involving whales?

Whale Researchers

How many different kinds of whales exist today in the world? Have any whales become extinct? If yes, which? What are the characteristics of the different whale species? What is the status of each of these species? What is the reproductive rate and success of species? What population increase is potential? What food and other habitat needs do they have? What problems do they face? What species are most hunted, and for what purposes, historically and in the present? Which species are most scarce, which most abundant?

How intelligent might they be? What does the future hold for whales?

NOTE: Some students may want to research other related groups, e.g., commercial interests, subsistence hunters, preservationists, animal welfare interests, conservation organizations. There are a number of organizations and agencies interested in whale conservation which might be contacted for information. For example: American Cetacean Society, National Headquarters, PO Box 2639, San Pedro, CA 90731-0943; Animal Welfare Institute, PO Box 3650, Washington, D.C. 20007; Cousteau Society, Greenbriar Tower II, 870 Greenbriar Circle, Suite 402, Chesapeake, VA 23320; Greenpeace, 1436 U Street, NW, Washington D.C., 20009; National Marine Fisheries Service, U.S. Department of Commerce, NOAA, 1315 East-West Highway, Silver Spring, MD 20910.

3. After students have completed their research, set up the classroom to resemble a meeting hall. Hold a meeting of the IWC attended by scientific advisors and any guests, including other interest groups. Organize discussion and debate among the students, representing different interests, e.g, commercial interests, subsistence hunters, preservationists, animal welfare interests, conservation organizations.

4. The next task is to come up with a set of recommendations and regulations that the IWC, including its member whaling and non-whaling nations, can agree upon. This may be done through discussion by the whole class or by a subcommittee approach. If done by subcommittee, ask for volunteers to represent the IWC, with representatives of both whaling and non-whaling nations, to sit together to come up with a set of recommendations and regulations to present in written form to the rest of the class for review. Include other interest groups as well. Note whether this is actually how the IWC makes decisions.

5. Discuss any final recommendations. Evaluate the possible impact of wildlife issues on relationships between nations.

6. If you and the students feel it to be useful, you might send a copy of your set of recommendations to the International Whaling Commission for their review; or you might identify a member of the U.S.

Senate or House of Representatives who would be interested in your findings. Or, you might send your recommendations to the U.S. Commissioner to the IWC, NOAA, Department of Commerce, Washington D.C.

AQUATIC EXTENSION

Identify any other international bodies that have an influence on aquatic species of wildlife. Find out who these groups are, and what they do.

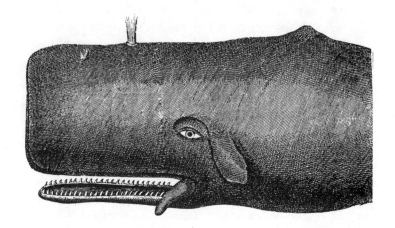

EVALUATION

1. List four basic characteristics of two different species of whales.

2. Name ten countries that are members of the International Whaling Commission. Indicate the countries which are whaling countries and list which species of whales they harvest. Explain how each country uses its harvested whales.

3. What is the purpose of the International Whaling Commission? Describe one action the Commission has taken to achieve its purpose. How are actions of the Commission enforced? What is your assessment of the Commission's importance and effectiveness?

4. Summarize your impressions of the impact of this issue—and other wildlife issues, if possible—on alliances and other relationships between and among nations.

NOTE: The name of this activity is not intended to imply that human use of whales is, or is not, a right. The title is a play on words, referring to the common name of one species of whale, the right whale. Students may want to investigate how the right whale was named, and discuss various interpretations of the meaning of "right" in this context.

PLANNING FOR PEOPLE AND WILDLIFE

OBJECTIVES

Students will: 1) describe considerations that are important in land-use planning for cities and other communities of people; 2) identify means by which negative impact on wildlife and other elements of the natural environment can be reduced in developing cities; and 3) describe actions that can be taken in some contemporary cities to enhance them as places in which both people and some wildlife can live.

METHOD

Students imagine and research what the area in which they live was like before a community was developed; design planned communities; and build and evaluate models of their community designs.

BACKGROUND

NOTE: This activity is used effectively to culminate a unit on the importance of land-use planning as well as to focus on issues affecting people, wildlife and environment.

Age: Grades 4-12
Subjects: Social Studies, Art, Science
Skills: analysis, application, comparing similarities and differences, discussion, drawing, evaluation, invention, media construction, psychomotor development, problem-solving, synthesis, visualization
Duration: minimum of five 45-minute periods
Group Size: any
Setting: indoors
Conceptual Framework Reference: I.A., I.A.1., I.A.2., I.A.3., I.A.4., I.B., I.C., I.C.1., I.C.2., I.C.3., I.C.4., I.D., IV.A., I.V.A.1., IV.A.2., IV.A.3., IV.A.4., IV.C., IV.D., IV.D.1., IV.D.2., IV.D.3., IV.D.4., IV.D.5., IV.D.6., IV.D.7., IV.E., IV.E.3., IV.E.4., IV.E.5., IV.E.7., IV.E.8., IV.E.10., IV.E.11., IV.F., IV.F.1., IV.F.2., IV.F.3., IV.F.4., IV.F.5., IV.F.6., IV.F.7., IV.F.8., IV.F.9., IV.F.11., V.A., V.B., V.B.1., V.B.2., VI.A., VI.A.2., VI.A.3., VI.A.4., VI.A.5., VI.B., VI.B.1., VI.B.2., VI.B.3., VI.B.4., VI.B.5., VI.B.6., VI.C., VI.C.1., VI.C.6., VI.C.12., VI.C.15., VI.C.16., VI.D., VI.D.1., VII.A., VII.A.1., VII.A.2., VII.A.3., VII.A.4., VII.B., VII.B.1., VII.B.2., VII.B.3., VII.B.4., VII.B.5., VII.B.6., VII.B.7.
Key Vocabulary: land-use planning, community, city
Appendices: Local Resources, Ecosystem, Taking Action, Simulated Field Trips

Cities have developed as people have clustered together for purposes of meeting their needs—from shelter to food to a sense of community. They have typically developed as a hub of transportation and commerce, again serving as a means by which people meet their day-to-day survival needs. The development of cities, however, has been a mixed blessing. The large concentration of people in a given area has displaced plants and animals that lived there previously and has given rise to problems unique to such crowded conditions. For example, varying forms of pollution accumulate in such centers, frequently with inadequate means for handling them—from products of industry to human waste.

Most cities are not the result of careful planning. Most have developed haphazardly, with attention to problems taking place when crises emerge. Crime, unemployment, poor housing, smog, depletion of water supplies, and contamination of water supplies by industrial and domestic waste disposal, energy consumption, transportation costs and land-use sprawl are all among the serious problems facing contemporary cities today.

People are faced with many important choices concerning how and where they will live. Many people in the United States are leaving the cities for suburban and rural life, bringing some of the same problems with them that encouraged them to leave the cities in the first place. New communities—large and small—are being developed. Some are the result of individual families moving into previously undeveloped areas; some are the result of business interests organizing to develop resources in an area and creating entirely new cities in the process. This is happening in areas throughout the planet. Whole areas of some large and old cities are decaying as they are abandoned; in some cities, re-development projects are taking place to try to improve the habitability of the old and dying neighborhoods.

Ethical questions arise as people make decisions about where and how they will live. Any development or re-development of an area has an impact on the plants and animals who do and can live there, as well as on any people who might live there. Sometimes the development can be of benefit, and sometimes of long-term harm. When such decisions are made, it seems prudent to plan for the impact of our actions as carefully and thoughtfully as possible.

The major purpose of this activity is for students to consider the importance of land-use planning in community maintenance, improvement, and development. The concepts can be applied when considering re-development of old cities, as well as building of new cities and alternative communities in which people can live and work.

MATERIALS

heavy cardboard or masonite; salt, flour and water to make salt clay for a model-building material; glue; toothpicks; natural materials like dried grass and construction paper for making buildings, roads, people, wildlife and other components of community; tempera paint, brushes; and any other materials available and useful in model-building

PROCEDURE

1. This is a "design a community" activity. Ask the students to close their eyes and picture the community in which they live. If they live in a city, or if there is a city nearby, ask them to picture how the city looks. Next ask them to try to picture what that area might have looked like before the city or community was built in that spot. What plants were common to the area? What animals? Was there water in the area? What was the topography of the land?
2. Ask for a committee of volunteers to find out more precisely what the land, vegetation, wildlife, etc., was like in their area before their community was built. If the students live in a rural area have them find out how the area has changed since the first settlers came to the area. Ask the committee to report back to the rest of the students with this information in approximately one week. Sources could include province, state, city, or county historical societies, libraries, etc. City, regional, and state or province land-use planning offices may also have such information.
3. Ask the committee to report back to the rest of the students. The committee should report both visually and verbally. For example, they should list the descriptive characteristics of the vegetation in the area, and identify the kinds of wildlife and the food and water sources upon which that wildlife depended. Ask the committee to describe their findings thoroughly enough that the rest of the students can clearly picture what the area looked like before a community was developed there. Also ask the committee to leave a visual record of the major information they found for the rest of the students to use as a reference.
4. Next, ask all of the students, including the committee members who did the background research, to divide into working groups of from two to four students. Tell each group that it is their task to develop a community in this natural area, given the background information the committee has provided. In designing their community, they should aim to **develop a community in which people live and work with the least possible negative impact on the existing vegetation, air quality, water, soil, and wildlife,** at the same time that the needs of the people are met as well. In order to do this, the students should consider the following, as well as factors they identify:
    - water sources, transportation, and treatment
    - economic base; e.g., industry, small business
    - kinds of housing, school, shopping areas, job sites
    - economical and recreational features; e.g., open space, green belts, parks
    - sewage and waste disposal and treatment
    - aesthetics
    - environmental safeguards

• means by which to effectively expand the number of people who can live in the community, if necessary, retaining minimum impact on the quality of the environment

5. Once each group has come up with a community development plan, review and discuss their plan with them.

6. Once their plans have been approved, provide the students with the necessary materials to build a model of their community. (See "Materials" above.)

7. Once all the groups have developed their models of the communities they have designed, have a "Model Community Design Show," with each of the groups explaining the design features of their community.

8. Discuss the advantages and disadvantages of each community design in detail. For example, include, "What if" questions, like, "What if a new school had to be built?", "What if there is a drought or severe winter, would it be necessary to take special measures to assist the wildlife?"

9. Return to the models after two weeks to a month and ask the students to reflect upon whether they would make any changes in their community designs, as if they had had the opportunity to "live" in their communities for a while and might now see the need to do some things differently.

10. Ask a local architect, city planner, wildlife biologist or other resource manager to visit the class in order to review and discuss the various model communities with the students who designed them.

EXTENSIONS AND VARIATIONS

1. Show photos of actual cities. Look for advantages and disadvantages of city life, under a variety of circumstances.

2. Get a map showing a community (preferably yours!) 15, 25, 50, 75, 150 years ago. Evaluate the planning—or lack of—that seems to have taken place, with what results.

AQUATIC EXTENSION

Ten years have passed. Your community has doubled in size. What measures, if any, have you taken to protect the availability and quality of water in the community? What impacts, if any, have there been to wildlife in the area as a result of this increase in population? What changes, if any, need to be made in order to protect the availability and quality of the water resources in this community for the next 25 years—for both people and wildlife?

EVALUATION

1. Name five important land uses to be consider in a community where people live.

2. For each of the previously mentioned considerations, list two ways that impact on the environment and wildlife can be reduced.

3. In most major cities, land-use planning has been non-existent, minimal or recent. Describe five methods that might be used to enhance the existence of a city's people and wildlife, with explanations for the methods you choose.

4. Make a plan to re-establish a once native wildlife species in your community. Choose an animal that is not extinct. Show how that plan will fit with the existing plan you already created for your community. Take into account both the habitat needs of the wildlife species and the needs of the community of people. Older students can consider relevant state and federal wildlife laws.

SECTION SEVEN
RESPONSIBLE
HUMAN ACTIONS

ETHI-THINKING

OBJECTIVES

Students will: 1) generate a list of activities done outside that are harmful to wildlife and the environment; 2) discuss reasons these activities are inappropriate; and 3) recommend alternate activities that are not harmful.

METHOD

Students list activities that might be harmful to wild plants and animals and use photos or drawings to picture, discuss, interpret and evaluate these activities.

BACKGROUND

NOTE: This activity can be used as an introduction to "Playing Lightly on the Earth."

The major purpose of this activity is for students to discriminate between outdoor activities that are harmful to wildlife and the environment and those which are not.

MATERIALS

art materials (crayons, construction paper, magazines for photos) to make discussion cards

PROCEDURE

1. Ask students to help you make a list of activities people do that seem harmful to wild plants and animals. Ask them to think about things they've seen or know about that might be harmful. Some of these things could be:
    - picking up baby wild animals in the environment (birds, fawns, etc.)
    - carving initials in trees
    - driving vehicles (cars, motorcycles) over fragile environments
    - removing plants from the environment, like digging up cactus
    - destroying bird nests
    - illegally killing, collecting, harassing, or possessing wildlife

2. Have students use cut-out photos or drawings to make these activities into cards showing pictures and describing what is happening. (Or, the teacher can prepare cards in advance, laminate, and use again.) Or, older students can dramatize the situation in skits, "commercials," songs, poems, etc.

3. Collect the cards. Count students off to make groups of four each. Hand out one card to each group and ask them to discuss (or present the skits, poems, etc.):
    - What is happening?
    - Does it harm wildlife? How?
    - Does it seem to be appropriate or inappropriate behavior? Why?
    - Is the person doing it having fun?
    - What else could he or she do that would satisfy his or her needs and interests without harming wildlife or the environment?

4. Ask each group to report to everyone else about: a) their feelings concerning what is happening in the outdoor activity shown in the picture; and b) their recommendation for an alternative activity the people could do that would not be harmful.

Age: Grades K-8
Subjects: Social Studies, Science, Art, Language Arts
Skills: analysis, application, description, discussion, drawing, evaluation, generalization, media construction, problem-solving, small group work, synthesis
Duration: one or two 20 to 40-minute periods
Group Size: any
Setting: indoors or outdoors
Conceptual Framework Reference: I.D., V.A., V.A.5., V.A.6., V.B.1., VI.A., VI.A.2., VI.A.3., VI.A.4., VI.A.5., VI.B., VI.B.1, VI.B.2., VI.B.3., VI.B.4., VI.B.5., VI.C., VI.C.1., VI.C.2., VI.C.12., VI.C.16., VII.A., VII.A.1., VII.A.2., VII.A.3., VII.A.4., VII.B., VII.B.1., VII.B.2., VII.B.3., VII.B.7.
Key Vocabulary: harm, wildlife
Appendices: Simulated Field Trips

EXTENSIONS

For Grades K-2:

Ask the students to draw pictures of things they know about or have seen happen that would hurt wild plants and animals. Ask them to describe what is happening in their drawing, and what could happen instead that would not be harmful.

For Older Students:

1. Choose something you or your family owns, like a car, television, refrigerator, etc. Imagine you are that object—and explore how you—from invention to garbage dump—affect wildlife!

2. Distinguish between actions that are harmful to individual plants and animals, and those which are harmful to large numbers of plants and animals. In what situations, if any, does it seem appropriate to harm a single animal or plant? In what situations, if any, does it seem appropriate to harm large numbers of animals or plants? In what situations, if any, does it seem inappropriate to harm a single animal or plant? In what situations, if any, does it seem inappropriate to harm large numbers of animals or plants? (Remember the definitions of wildlife and domesticated animals. Don't forget that wildlife includes, but is not limited to, insects, spiders, birds, reptiles, fish, amphibians and mammals.)

3. Sometimes it is difficult to decide what is harmful and what is not. Usually if something is against the law, it is harmful in some way. Sometimes actions may be legal or there simply may be "no law against it," and people differ in their judgment as to whether the actions are harmful or not. Sometimes we may recognize that some of our actions are harmful in some ways—like some of our choices for housing, transportation and consumer products in our daily lives—and we still take those actions because of our perceptions of the importance of our wants and needs. One way to examine wants and needs is to categorize them according to: Luxury, Useful But Not Necessary and Necessary for Survival. We begin to get into the area of personal value judgments. Think about personal ethics. What are ethics? How do we each make responsible decisions in our daily lives? (See "Enviro-Ethics" for an activity aimed at identifying a "Personal Code of Environmental Ethics.")

AQUATIC EXTENSIONS

1. Generate a list of activities that are sometimes or always harmful to aquatic species of wildlife and aquatic habitats. Discuss the ways these activities are harmful. Discuss ways these harmful activities can be prevented.

2. Identify at least five examples of things people can do in aquatic environments that are not damaging to populations of aquatic animals or the long-term health of aquatic habitats.

EVALUATION

1. Make a list of five things which people do that harm wildlife.

2. Make a list of five things which people do that harm wildlife habitat.

3. For each thing listed, describe what you can do about it.

4. Make a list of ten things which people do that help wildlife.

5. Choose ten magazine photographs of people doing things. Examine each photograph and evaluate the potential environmental impact from the activities of the people portrayed. Explain the reasoning for your evaluations. For activities you perceive to have a negative impact, suggest changes people could make to lessen their impact.

PLAYING LIGHTLY ON THE EARTH

OBJECTIVES

Students will: 1) distinguish between games that are damaging and not damaging to the environment; and 2) invent games with a benign effect on the environment.

METHOD

Students look for evidence of games that harm the environment; and then invent and play games with a benign effect on the environment.

BACKGROUND

Personal choices of all kinds can have an effect on the environment. Young people can look at the games they play outside and choose those which have little or no damaging impact on the environment, rather than those which leave scars—aesthetically and ecologically.

The major purpose of this activity is for students to become actively aware of the choices they make each time they play a game outside, and to consciously experience games that have a benign effect on the environment. The activity is designed for students to experience success, at a personal and immediate level, in maintaining and improving the quality of their own environments.

MATERIALS

access to going outside

Age: Grades K-8
Subjects: Social Studies, Physical Education, Science
Skills: analysis, comparing similarities and differences, evaluation, invention, psychomotor development, problem-solving, small group work, synthesis
Duration: one 30 to 45-minute period
Group Size: any
Setting: outdoors
Conceptual Framework Reference: I.D., VII.A., VII.A.1., VII.A.2., VII.A.3., VII.A.4., VII.B., VII.B.1., VII.B.2., VII.B.3., VII.B.7.
Key Vocabulary: game, harm
Appendices: Outdoors

PROCEDURE

1. Most of us like to play. In fact, playing is an important way to learn—as well as to have a good time. Ask the students to think of examples of ways to play outside that do no serious or permanent damage to the environment, and ways that are damaging. The damage might affect non-living things—like putting graffiti on cement walls. It might be damaging to plants and animals like carving initials on tree trunks. Both are damage. Are there any games we can play that do no damage? There may not be, but we can think about how much damage, how permanent it is, and what it affects.

2. Go outside on the school grounds and look for evidence of games that have damaged the environment. Ask students what could have caused the damage and how it might have been prevented.

3. Introduce the concept of playing games that do not seriously harm the environment.

4. Ask the students to work together in small groups—from two to seven or eight—to **invent** a game that does no serious harm to the environment, including the plants and animals living there. The students could also try to invent games that could make this a **better** environment in some ways. Give the students about 15 minutes to invent their games.

5. Ask each group to present their game to the other students. Play each of the games. Ask the students to talk about their feelings about the importance of playing games that do little if any damage to the environment.

EXTENSIONS

For Older Students:

Analyze a variety of kinds of recreation for their impact on wildlife, vegetation, other natural resources, etc.

EVALUATION

1. Keep a record of the games you play outside for one week. Identify which, if any, are harmful to the environment. For one week, or longer, play only games that do no harm to the environment.

2. Invent a game for younger children that does not harm the environment. Teach it to a younger child or group of children. Explain what the younger child or children learned about care for the environment.

NOISY NEIGHBORS

OBJECTIVES

Students will: 1) identify noise levels which can adversely affect people, domesticated animals and wildlife; and 2) recommend ways in which people can change some behaviors in order to reduce negative impacts from noise for people, domesticated animals and wildlife.

METHOD

Students conduct an investigation of noise levels in their community, generate and test hypotheses, and make recommendations.

BACKGROUND

People and wildlife are subject to similar environmental stresses. Loud noises, such as those from a motorcycle or snowmobile, a noisy group of people hiking, or new road or dam construction, can affect both humans and wildlife. People, domesticated animals and some wild animals living in metropolitan areas frequently learn to live with many loud noises. When animals in their natural habitat hear these and similar noises, they may react by running away, dying of the consequences of stress, or learning to adapt to these noises (as, for example, many animals in national parks have learned to do.)

Many students may know that animals have different hearing ranges than humans. They may know from personal experience that dogs and cats can hear things that humans cannot. Loud music is easier for humans to hear than a machine's high pitched whine, which may reach beyond our normal hearing range. Both sounds are real and although only one of them may be audible to us, both of them may be audible and disruptive to wildlife.

The major purpose of this activity is for students to recognize the effects that human-made noises can have on wild animals and to consider alternative behaviors which might have less damaging consequences.

MATERIALS

writing materials
OPTIONAL: decibel meter (many local zoning and code enforcement offices as well as state and local environment departments may have decibel meters that can be loaned to teachers or brought to the class for demonstration.

PROCEDURE

1. "What seems loud? What noises hurt your ears? Do any noises frighten or bother you?" Initiate a discussion about noise. What is noise? Noise to one person may be music to another.
2. Ask one or two students to volunteer to do some "fact-finding" and report back. Find out about noise ordinances. (Some communities have regulations about allowable noise levels.) Find out about recommended health standards for sound levels. What levels are considered harmful to human ears and with what consequences?
3. With this information about allowable and recommended noise levels, students can do a "sound search" of the community. If possible, get a decibel meter from a community agency to record decibel levels: around the school, shopping center, residential area, agricultural area, city park, entrance to national park or forest, etc. Look to see if there is any correlation between noise levels and numbers of people, domesticated animals and wildlife. If there are large numbers of people or animals in an area with high noise levels,

Age: Grades 7-12
Subjects: Social Studies, Environmental Problems, Science, Health
Skills: hypothesis formation and testing; interpretation of concepts, generalization, synthesis
Duration: minimum of two 45-minute periods
Group Size: any
Setting: indoors and outdoors
Conceptual Framework Reference: I.A.2., I.A.4., I.B., I.B.2., I.C., I.C.3., I.C.4., I.D., V.A., VI.A.3., VI.B., VI.B.1., VI.B.2., VI.B.3., VI.B.4., VI.B.5., VI.C., VI.D., VII.A., VII.A.1., VII.A.2., VII.A.3., VII.A.4., VII.B., VII.B.2., VII.B.7.
Key Vocabulary: stress, noise, decibel, ordinance, hypothesis, correlation, consequences, responsibility
Appendices: Local Resources

are they experiencing negative consequences, e.g., stress? How are they coping, with what effects? Ask the students to predict the impact of noise levels on people, domesticated animals, wildlife. Consider the sources and consequences of human-made noise. With wildlife, for example:

Recreation—backpackers, hunters, woodcutters, motorcycles, dune buggies, snowmobiles, all terrain vehicles

New Development—heavy construction equipment, automobiles

Mining—drilling, explosions, construction traffic Generate a few hypotheses and check them through research or consulting local authorities.

4. Generate a set of recommendations: What is the individual's responsibility toward noise control? Society's responsibility? What can students do personally— as individuals, groups, or families—to help increase and maintain an informed awareness and responsible behavior concerning the effects of noise on people, pets and wildlife?

EVALUATION

1. List four sources of noise that can often affect wildlife negatively. Describe the possible adverse effects.

2. Describe the process you used to formulate and test one hypothesis concerning the effects of noise.

3. Explain three things that could be done to reduce noise by people who are using wildlife habitats. What are you going to do personally to reduce the negative effects from noise on people, domesticated animals or wildlife?

RARE BIRD EGGS FOR SALE

OBJECTIVES

Students will: 1) identify reasons for and consequences of collecting wildlife and wildlife products; and 2) suggest and evaluate alternatives to collection to satisfy collection needs.

METHOD

Students participate in a debate.

BACKGROUND

People seem to collect everything—from rocks to stamps. Sometimes people collect wild and living creatures, both plants and animals. In some instances, these items are used for educational and research purposes. In other cases, as mementos of travel and memorable events. In other cases, they are acquired for their decorative and exotic values. In Victorian times, many homes were decorated with collections of stuffed birds, mounted butterflies, bird eggs and bird nests.

Age: Grades 7-12
Subjects: Language Arts (Speech, Debate), Social Studies (Psychology, Anthropology, Human Relations), Environmental Problems, Science
Skills: analysis, classification, debate, discussion, evaluation, public speaking, reporting, research
Duration: minimum of two to three 45-minute periods, depending upon extensiveness of research, and in-class time provided for research
Group Size: any, working in two teams to prepare for and present debate
Setting: indoors
Conceptual Framework Reference: I.D., II.A., II.B., II.C., II.D., II.E., II.E.1., II.E.2., II.E.3., II.F., V.A., V.A.5., V.B.1., VI.A., VI.A.1., VI.A.2., VI.A.5., VI.B., VI.B.1., VI.B.2., VI.B.3., VI.B.4., VI.B.5., VI.C., VI.C.1., VI.B.2., VI.C.6, VI.C.7., VI.C.12., VI.C.13., VI.C.15., VI.C.16., VI.D., VI.D.1., VI.D.2., VI.D.3., VI.D.4., VII.A., VII.A.1., VII.A.2., VII.A.3., VII.A.4., VII.B., VII.B.1., VII.B.2., VII.B.3., VII.B.4., VII.B.5., VII.B.6., VII.B.7.
Key Vocabulary: collector
Appendices: Local Resources, Field Ethics, Animals in the Classroom, Agencies and Organizations

As people's attitudes regarding wildlife shift so do their laws. In 1916 the Migratory Bird Treaty was signed between the United States and Great Britain acting for Canada. Among other things, the treaty prohibited collecting the bird eggs and nests of migratory birds. Over time, similar treaties have been signed with other countries.

Whenever an object—living or not—is moved or removed from its natural environment, there is an effect on that environment, if not on the object or organism. Some of these effects are more obvious than others. Moving a rock under which wildlife lives may not seem as radical a move as taking eggs from a phoebe's nest or collecting dragonfly naiads from a pond or capturing and mounting 100 species of butterflies.

Managers of protected wilderness and wildlife areas often admonish visitors to "take only pictures and leave only footprints." Unfortunately, many people feel that this applies only to protected areas. Not necessarily so. For example, the effects can be substantial on species and the environment when 30 student collectors pick their way through an area in search of things to bring back to school. Collecting bird nests, as one example, can have several impacts—particularly in cases where the birds return to use the same nest year after year.

The major purpose of this activity is for students to examine the reasons for and consequences of people's collecting tendencies, as well as to consider alternatives.

MATERIALS

reference materials

PROCEDURE

OPTIONAL: Use this activity as an extension to a visit to a local natural history museum with taxonomic collections and dioramas.

1. Ask students to brainstorm all of the kinds of collections they have seen or heard of that involve living or once-living organisms, as well as any artifacts or rare objects made of living or once-living organisms. Examples could include butterflies, seashells, coral, bird eggs, ivory artifacts, pine cones, wild animals in zoos, animals in research laboratories.

2. OPTIONAL: Think of possible reasons for collecting. (Categorize the examples of collections according to what purposes they might serve. Some examples may fit into more than one category.) The idea is to think of a range of possible purposes—such as education, research, decoration, profit motive as in selling the collectibles, memories, pets, or status.

3. Ask the students to divide into two working groups: one to speak for the reasons that collecting of such things **should be allowed,** and one to speak for the reasons that collecting of such things **should not be allowed**. After dividing within each team to research aspects of the topic, each team should organize its information for presentation in a debate format. Each team can have a principal spokesperson or captain who makes opening, transition and summary statements. That team captain can call on members of the team to provide specific information about pertinent topics as they arise during the debate. For example, a student on the "Reasons for Collecting" team might be an expert on the need for protecting genetic diversity by maintaining collections of wild animals in preserves and zoos. A student on the other team could be prepared to speak to the limitations of zoos and preserves that might outweigh the benefits. Both teams should consider consequences and alternatives, as well as include information about laws that already govern collecting, and areas where violations are serious problems. NOTE: The U.S. Fish and Wildlife Service is the agency in the United States that has legal responsibility for transportation of species between states and between the U.S. and other nations, as well as import and export of illegal wildlife and products. They can be contacted at: U.S. Fish and Wildlife Service, Interior Building, 1849 C Street NW, Room 3447, Washington, D.C. 20240. Tel. (202) 208-5634. Contact state or province authorities for local regulations.

4. Following the debate, ask the students to discuss their feelings about the subject, based on the information and experience they now have. Was it difficult to debate "for" or "against," given their personal attitudes? Did students find their attitudes changing? If so, how? Ask the students to look again at their earlier list of possible purposes for collecting, adding any additional purposes they may have identified as a result of their research. Discuss and evaluate whether they think each purpose is appropriate or inappropriate. If appropriate, identify under what circumstances. NOTE: Consensus is not necessary, except in areas where law prohibits collecting.

5. Finally, ask the students if they can come up with a list of alternatives for people who might want to "collect" things that seem to the students to be inappropriate. For example, the butterfly collector might try photography, the bird nest collector might try model-building of nests using raw materials like birds do.

EXTENSIONS AND VARIATIONS

1. If combining this activity with a trip to a local museum of natural history, do steps 1 and 2 as part of pre-trip preparation. Next go to the museum and do steps 3, 4, and 5. after the trip.

2. After step 2 above, ask students to copy the list they generated—marking those items they feel they could accept as reasons to collect. Each student should keep his or her list until later. After the debate (in step 4, above), ask the students to look at their lists—reflecting the points of view they held before the debate. Are some purposes for collecting no longer acceptable that seemed so before, and vice versa?

3. Throughout time, native people have collected and used natural resources for ceremonial, religious and cultural purposes. Should laws and guidelines for collecting living or once living organisms be different for native people? If yes, why? If no, why not?

AQUATIC EXTENSION

See the Aquatic WILD activity, "Turtle Hurdles." One of the factors that has contributed to the endangering of sea turtles is the illegal collection of sea turtle eggs.

EVALUATION

1. List three reasons why wildlife and wildlife products are collected by people. Identify and describe one situation in which you think that collection is inappropriate. Suggest and describe at least two alternatives a person might substitute.

2. Describe one way that collecting might contribute to the extinction of animal species. Describe one way that collecting might prevent a species from becoming extinct.

FLAMMULATED OWL
(Strigidae)

BELTED KINGFISHER
(Alcedinidae)

TAWNY FROGMOUTH
(Podargidae)

AUSTRALIAN OWLET-NIGHTJA
(Aegothelidae)

RAINBOW BEE-EAT
(Meropidae)

WHITE-BA
(Col

WHAT YOU WEAR IS WHAT THEY WERE

OBJECTIVES

Students will: 1) identify principal resources from which their clothing is made; 2) distinguish between renewable and nonrenewable natural resources; and 3) recognize environmental consequences of clothing preferences.

METHOD

Students draw, label and analyze their clothing according to the natural resources from which they are derived; and make personal judgments about appropriate uses of such natural resources based on criteria which they establish.

BACKGROUND

NOTE: "Make A Coat" is a similar activity for younger students.

In all but the most tropical of climates, people need an outside covering to keep warm. When ice floes receded after the last Ice Age about 10,000 years ago on the North American continent, people used fire for part of their warmth. Skins from wild animals were also used. Saber tooth tigers, bears, woolly mammoths and wolves were among the animals hunted for meat and clothing.

Age: Grades 7-12
Subjects: Social Studies, Science, Home Economics
Skills: analysis, classification, comparing similarities and differences, description, drawing, evaluation, kinesthetic concept development, listing, media construction, observation, psychomotor development, reporting, synthesis
Duration: one or two 45-minute periods
Group Size: any
Setting: indoors
Conceptual Framework Reference: II.A., II.B., II.C., II.D.1., II.D.2., II.D.3., II.D.4., II.E., II.E.1., II.E.2., II.E.3., II.F., IV.A., IV.A.4., IV.B., IV.B.1., IV.B.2., V.A., V.A.1., V.A.2., V.A.3., V.A.5., V.B.1., VI.B., VI.B.1., VI.B.2., VI.C., VI.C.7., VI.C.12., VI.C.15., IV.C.16., VI.D., VI.D.2., VI.D.3., VII.A., VII.A.1., VII.A.2., VII.A.3., VII.A.4., VII.B., VII.B.1., VII.B.2., VII.B.3., VII.B.4., VII.B.5., VII.B.6., VII.B.7.
Key Vocabulary: renewable, nonrenewable, natural resource
Appendices: Field Ethics (indirect)

American Indian tribes have used animals for food and covering, and some still do as a part of their present lifestyle. Elk, deer, bear, buffalo, seal and almost all animals killed for food also provided valuable skins for clothing.

When European settlers came to the North American continent, they brought with them a tradition of making clothing out of spun fibers such as linen and wool.

Today we have coats and other clothing made from many materials. We can divide the sources of these materials into two categories: **renewable and nonrenewable natural resources.** Definitions of renewable and nonrenewable natural resources are commonly used within the natural sciences. Use of these terms is intended to describe inherent biological attributes, not to imply value judgments.

Renewable natural resources are living things, with the capacity for regeneration. Trees and wildlife are examples of renewable natural resources. However, even renewable resources have limits. For example, although animals have the capacity for regeneration by mating and bearing offspring, they cannot do this if their habitat is destroyed, or if environmental or human-caused pressures are too great to permit successful reproduction.

Nonrenewable natural resources are non-living things. Minerals and fossils are examples of nonrenewable natural resources. Although such resources may be replenished over time by natural processes, the time span is enormously long as, for example, in the case of accumulations of fossils from which to derive products such as petroleum.

Cotton (from the cotton plant) and linen (from the flax plant) are two major clothing products derived from renewable natural resources—in this case, both from plants. Some clothing products come from animals. Wool, for example, comes from shearing the fleece off sheep, and does not require killing the animal. Other domesticated animals, like cattle, provide clothing products, like leather, and also provide food products. Geese and ducks provide feathers for down jackets.

In scientific terms, animals can be considered a renewable resource. In some cases, however, animal populations are endangered or threatened. In such cases, killing of these animals is forbidden by law. It is also illegal to hunt many animals that are not threatened. Of those animals that are hunted, they are hunted only under laws and regulations. Some people raise ethical questions as to the appropriateness of the use of animals, particularly wild ones, for products such as clothing, food, tools, medicines, cosmetics, jewelry and other ornaments.

Most synthetic clothing materials are derived from nonrenewable natural resources, like fossil-based petroleum products. Some people raise ethical questions as to the appropriateness of the use of nonrenewable resources such as fossil fuels, in consideration of questions such as their essentially finite availability as well as costs to humans, wildlife and the environment often derived from their mining and processing.

There are many aspects, aside from whether or not a resource is renewable, which are considerations in evaluating whether or not to use a particular material for clothing. For example, some materials (e.g., cowhide, petroleum-based synthetics) are derived as byproducts from the development of resources for other, primary purposes (e.g., food, energy). Other sources (e.g., furs) tend to be developed primarily or solely for manufacture of clothing. In addition, nonrenewable resources, such as fossil fuels, are used in obtaining, manufacturing and distributing clothes made from renewable as well as nonrenewable natural resources.

The pros and cons of appropriate uses of renewable and nonrenewable natural resources are difficult and complex—and may raise social, economic, ethical and political as well as biological questions. Even the concept that wildlife and other animals is a renewable resource raises ethical objections from some people who feel it encourages the treatment of wildlife as a commodity to be used like food crops such as corn, without regard for the animals themselves.

The major purpose of this activity is for students to distinguish, in scientific terms, between renewable and nonrenewable natural resources used as sources of clothing for people.

MATERIALS

drawing materials or notebook paper

PROCEDURE

1. Begin this activity with a discussion of where clothing comes from. Ask each student to look at what he or she is wearing. Using a piece of notebook or drawing paper, ask each student to draw a simple picture of himself or herself, including the major exterior clothing being worn—from top to toe. Ask them to label each piece of clothing according to the major thing or things it is made of (e.g., **cotton** shirt, **polyester** shirt, **leather** shoes).

2. Now, turn the discussion to the concept of natural resources. *Webster's New World Dictionary* defines natural resources as, "Those actual and potential forms of wealth supplied by nature." We define a resource as "a portion of an environment upon which people have placed or assigned value, or see as being available for use." Such definitions are intended to be descriptive, without intent to make moral or ethical judgments about the appropriateness or inappropriateness of use of portions of the environment which are designated as resources. Ask the students to define in scientific terms what might be considered **renewable natural resources**, and what might be considered **nonrenewable natural resources**. Using the brainstormed list of natural resources, put an "R" by those which can be considered renewable and an "N" by those which can be considered nonrenewable.

3. Returning again to their drawings, ask the students to label the clothing parts of their drawings according to the natural resources from which they are derived, also indicating whether the resources are renewable or nonrenewable.

4. OPTIONAL: Ask the students to divide renewable resources into plants and animals. Then ask the students to divide each of these categories into those which require killing the individual organism for use as a clothing resource contrasted with those which do not.

5. Discuss the students' findings. Consider questions such as:
- What kinds of impact do our preferences in clothing sources have on individual living organisms? On populations of organisms?
- What kinds of impact do our preferences in clothing sources have on different aspects of the cultural and natural environments, e.g., on local economies, international trade, cultural tradition, global resources, wildlife, wildlife habitat, agricultural lands, water quality, oil shale development?
- In our judgment—as individuals, or as a group—which sources of clothing seem to us to be most appropriate? Under what conditions?

Ask the students to establish some criteria for their judgments, explaining their reasoning.

EXTENSIONS

1. Inventory your clothes closet. Tally the number of garments per each natural resource. Make a personal graph showing proportions of cotton, polyester, leather, etc.

2. Write an environmental impact statement about the impact of your personal clothing preferences.

EVALUATION

In your opinion, would you have less impact on the environment if you tended to wear clothes made from renewable or nonrenewable resources. Why?

WATER'S GOING ON?!

OBJECTIVES

Students will: 1) record and interpret how much water they use in a day at school; and 2) make recommendations as to how they can save a significant percentage of that water.

METHOD

Students estimate and calculate water use in school and then design and try ways to conserve water.

BACKGROUND

Every molecule of water that was present when the earth's oceans were formed is still present today in one of water's three forms—as a gas, a liquid, or solid ice. Water molecules move at varying speeds through the water cycle. Water in its gaseous form may remain in the atmosphere for about nine days but it may stay frozen in the Antarctic ice cap for up to 10,000 years.

Most of the freshwater in the world is frozen in these polar ice caps. The largest part of what remains is groundwater—underground water that moves between layers beneath the earth's surface.

In the United States, approximately half of the water used is drawn from groundwater sources. This amounts to approximately 82 billion gallons a day of groundwater. Much of the groundwater used will not be returned to the groundwater system in the near future. Shallow groundwater may have a renewal rate of about 300 years, and deep groundwater (over 1,000 meters deep) may renew itself in about 4,600 years.

Age: Grades 5-9
Subjects: Mathematics, Social Studies, Science, Home Economics
Skills: analysis, application, computation, discussion, evaluation, generalization, observation, problem-solving, synthesis
Duration: two 30 to 45-minute periods
Group Size: any
Setting: indoors
Conceptual Framework Reference: I.D., V.B., V.B.1., VI.A., VI.B., VI.C., VI.D., VII.A., VII.A.1., VII.A.2., VII.A.3.
Key Vocabulary: conservation, water
Appendices: Local Resources, Metric Chart

This causes an ever-increasing drain on the groundwater supply. As groundwater dries up, stream flows are reduced. Ponds and marshes dry up and plant species die out. The groundwater remaining may also become contaminated by saltwater intrusion or by pollution, rendering it unfit to drink. All these results have obvious effects on wildlife, people, and the environment.

Most of the world's fresh water is used for irrigation, but if a majority of Americans practiced personal water conservation and water quality practices, it would make a real difference.

The major purpose of this activity is for students to become aware of the amount of water they use and waste each day at school, and to make recommendations for ways to conserve the water both at school and at home.

MATERIALS

chalkboard; paper and pencils; a variety of liquid measurement containers

PROCEDURE

1. Ask the students to estimate how much water each student uses each day in school. Have containers of different volumes for students to use for reference. Write their estimates on the chalkboard or on a chart. A chart may be made showing the class's estimates as follows:

Gallons	2	4	6	8	10	12
	X	X	XXX	XXX	XXX	XXX
		X	XXX	XXX	XX	
		X	XXX			

2. Ask the students to monitor their use of water for a day. They can time their drinks of water and record them in a notebook. Ask them to do the same for handwashing. They should also record the number of times they use the restrooms, etc.

---

3. As a class, calculate the amount of water used; e.g., run water from the fountain to a container for ten seconds and see how much water was used. Use this amount to calculate the amount per each drink that the students have recorded in seconds. Do the same for the sink faucets. Multiply a standard average of three gallons used per flush by the number of trips to the restroom. Have each student come up with an individual number of gallons used per day.

4. Compare the **estimates** of water use to the actual water used.

5. Add all the individual gallons of water used to arrive at a total for the entire class. Divide this amount by the number of students in the class. In this way, individual students can compare their individual usage against a class average to see if they are above or below average in their water use.

6. Ask the students if it would be possible to reduce the amount of water used, and if so, how. For example, cups could be used at the drinking fountain to reduce the amount of water that goes down the drain.

7. Put the students' suggestions into practice for a day or two. Then ask the students how water conservation practices changed what they did. What materials did they use or buy? Did their attitude change? How? Which changes in their behavior will they keep, as part of their personal lifestyles?

EXTENSIONS

1. Where does our water come from? How does it get here? Does our finding, transporting, and using water affect wildlife in any way? If so, how? After a discussion of the effects of water depletion and conservation on wildlife, draw two murals—one showing the effects of depletion and another the effects of conservation.

2. Monitor water use at home (showers, dishes, clothes washing, lawn watering, etc.)

3. Use this activity for paper and energy use and conservation.

4. Incorporate use of elementary statistics in this activity!

AQUATIC EXTENSION

Do this activity in combination with one or more Aquatic WILD activities—for example, "Alice in Waterland" and "How Wet Is Our Planet?"

EVALUATION

1. Estimate the number of gallons of water you personally use each day. Divide that usage into major categories. Present the data portraying your water use in the form of a graph.

2. What activity of yours requires the most water per year?

3. Describe and explain three ways you can decrease your use of water.

4. Describe and evaluate the seriousness of water problems you can identify which affect people and wildlife, now, and in the future.

WHAT DID YOUR LUNCH COST WILDLIFE?

OBJECTIVES

Students wiLL: 1) trace some foods from their source to the consumer; 2) identify the impact those foods and their processing have on wildlife and the environment in general; and 3) recommend, with explanations, some food habits that could benefit wildlife and the rest of the environment.

METHOD

Students trace food sources, diagram environmental impacts, and apply the knowledge they gain by making changes in some of their consumer choices.

BACKGROUND

NOTE: Especially for younger students, this activity makes a nice summary companion to "What's For Dinner?"

Most of us make lifestyle choices each day that have some impact on wildlife and the environment. Many of those impacts are indirect, and therefore we are not as aware of them as we might be. The choice of foods we eat, for example, is an area with many implications for wildlife and the environment.

The places and ways in which foods are grown has impact. For example, we know that loss of habitat is one of the most critical problems facing wildlife.

> **Age:** Grades 4-12
> **Subjects:** Social Studies, Language Arts, Science, Home Economics, Vocational Agriculture
> **Skills:** analysis, application, classification, comparing similarities and differences, discussion, drawing, evaluation, media construction, problem-solving, synthesis, visualization, writing (limited)
> **Duration:** one to three 45-minute periods
> **Group Size:** any
> **Setting:** indoors
> **Conceptual Framework Reference:** I.D., III.B., III.B.1., III.B.2., IV.C., V.A., V.A.1., V.B., V.B.1., VI.A., VI.A.2., VI.A.3., VI.A.4., VI.B., VI.B.1., VI.B.2., VI.B.3., VI.C., VI.C.16., VI.D., VI.D.1., VII.A., VII.A.1., VII.A.2., VII.A.3., VII.A.4., VII.B., VII.B.1., VII.B.3., VII.B.7.
> **Key Vocabulary:** organic, inorganic, source, renewable, nonrenewable, impact
> **Appendices:** Taking Action

Habitat may be lost to agricultural use or development as well as to industrial, commercial, and residential uses. Given that people need food, the ways in which we grow that food—and the ways we care for the land in the process—are very important. Farmers can take measures to maintain and improve wildlife habitat as they grow and harvest their crops. They can pay attention to the impact of their growing practices. Both inorganic and organic fertilizers are commonly used in industrial agriculture. These compounds may run off or leach into water supplies. In lakes, for example, this run-off may contribute to a huge increase in the growth of plant nutrients such as algae. This excess growth can act as a pollutant, poisonous to aquatic animal life such as fish, amphibians, arthropods, and insects.

Use of insecticides and herbicides also affects the environment, including wildlife. Obviously, if pesticides kill and eliminate the food source for wildlife, the wildlife either leaves or dies. Indirect effects can include accumulation of pesticides in the bodies of animals such as predatory birds, fish and mammals, including people.

Not all of the impact is due to some farmers' practices, however. Certainly the transportation, processing, packaging and marketing industries are involved as well. Questions about the natural resources involved in getting the food from its source of origin to the consumer are critically important. One example is increased exploration for and development of fossil fuels used to transport the food from growing site to consumer, used often to fuel the processing, and frequently used in the packaging, as in the case of fossil fuel-derived plastics.

Ethical considerations can also be raised concerning the impact upon individual animals and plants by the methods used to produce food for people, as well as choices of which foods to eat. If the students have concern about adopting lifestyle habits that can be healthful to themselves at the same time they have less impact on wildlife and the environment, they can look at the food they eat as one place to begin.

The major purpose of this activity is to provide a means for students to begin that process.

MATERIALS
writing and drawing materials

PROCEDURE
1. Select a processed food item. Identify the item's ingredients. In a discussion with students, trace the item's ingredients all the way back to their origins. Include where and how they grew or were formed and how they were harvested, processed, transported, packaged and made available to the consumer.
2. Ask the students to generate a list of foods they either brought or bought for lunch. Be sure to include any packaging materials the foods came in.
3. Ask each student to pick one food to trace all the way back to its origins, including where and how it grew, was harvested, was processed (if it was!), was transported, was packaged and was made available to the consumer—the student. Ask the students to make simple flow diagrams of the path the food takes. (The students may want to do some research at this point to get some additional information.)
4. Next ask the students to add drawings of possible and likely impacts to wildlife and the environment along the path their food took to get to them.
5. Ask the students to report back to their class-mates—using their diagrams as a visual aid as they describe the path taken by their food and its impact to wildlife and the environment along the way.
6. Ask the students to discuss and summarize their findings.
7. Ask each student to think of one change he or she could make in his or her own lunch-time eating habits that would be likely to have a beneficial—or at least less harmful—effect on wildlife and the environment. Describe the reasoning for this change and evaluate its consequences. If, after examination, each change seems in fact to be helpful, suggest that the students try making their changes for a week. At the end of the week, ask the students to report back. Were they able to stick with the change? What happened? If they did-n't make the change, why not? Did they forget? If they did make the change, did they find themselves

making or thinking about any other possible changes? If yes, what were they?

EXTENSIONS
1. Map the **energy** used to grow and get the food to you.
2. Include impact on other specified natural resources along the way.
3. Distinguish between renewable and nonrenewable resources.

AQUATIC EXTENSION
If it is not already obvious, do this activity again asking the question, "What Did Your Lunch Cost Aquatic Wildlife?" Think of whole populations of species of aquatic animals and aquatic habitats.

EVALUATION
1. Trace the possible course of a container of milk served in your school back to its probable source. What impact does this journey have on wildlife?
2. Name three food habits that could reduce negative impacts to wildlife and the environment. Explain the reasoning behind your suggestions.

FLIP THE SWITCH FOR WILDLIFE!

OBJECTIVES

Students will: 1) trace the route of electrical energy from source to use; 2) describe impacts on wildlife and the environment derived from various kinds of energy development and uses; and 3) evaluate the impact on wildlife and the environment as a result of their own energy-use practices.

METHOD

Students illustrate the route of energy from its sources to human use, including environmental impacts along its path; and then invent and try ways to make beneficial impacts on wildlife through their personal energy-use practices.

BACKGROUND

Electrical energy comes from a variety of sources. Your local electric utility can provide information about the source of your community's electricity. In the United States, a little less than 56% of electrical energy is produced from coal, 21% from nuclear, 10% from hydroelectric sources, 9% from natural gas and 4% from petroleum. Geothermal, wood, waste, solar and wind account for less than one half of one percent of the United States' electrical energy production.

In obtaining the energy to fuel our power plants, we affect wildlife in both positive and negative ways. We may build a hydroelectric dam that supplies energy and forms a lake good for fish, blocks runs of other fish, and in the process floods valuable wildlife habitat for land animals. A power line through a forest may improve the habitat for some species and degrade it for others.

The major purpose of this activity is for students to compare the various sources of electrical energy as well as learn the positive and negative impacts on wildlife from each of these sources, including those they use each day.

MATERIALS

writing and drawing materials

PROCEDURE

1. Ask the students the question, "What effects, if any, do we have on wildlife when we turn on a light switch?" Let them discuss the question and form an opinion. (Older students can generate hypotheses.) As a way of testing their ideas (or hypotheses), assign groups of three or four to research where their electricity comes from, identifying all steps from the light switch back to the land and how they think each step along the way might affect wildlife. Also assign groups to research alternative technologies (e.g., solar, geothermal, tidal, wind power). NOTE: This activity is excellent as an extension to energy source activities already underway with students.

2. Ask the students within each group to draw and label their "power pathway" on a large sheet of paper. For example, coal would travel from the strip mine or tunnel by truck to the processing plant, then by train to the power plant, over the electric power lines to their house and their light switch. Have the students label points along the way where wildlife could be positively or negatively affected.

3. When the students have completed their power paths, have them show them to the rest of the class. You can then discuss the following questions with them:

Age: Grades 5-12
Subjects: Science, Social Studies, Language Arts
Skills: analysis, application, comparing similarities and differences, discussion, drawing, evaluation, media construction, problem-solving, reporting, research (hypothesis formation and testing), small group work, synthesis, visualization, writing (limited)
Duration: one to three 45-minute periods, depending on student prior knowledge of energy sources
Group Size: any
Setting: indoors
Conceptual Framework Reference: I.D., V.B., V.B.1., VI.A., VI.A.2., VI.A.3., VI.A.4., VI.A.5., VI.B., VI.C., VI.D., VII.A., VII.A.1., VII.A.2., VII.A.3., VII.A.4., VII.B., VII.B.1., VII.B.2., VII.B.3., VII.B.4., VII.B.5., VII.B.7.
Key Vocabulary: energy, development, generator, technology
Appendices: Local Resources, Taking Action

- What kind of effects on wildlife do we have when we turn on a light switch? Are they positive or negative? Can any of them reasonably be changed?
- Which type of fuel source do you think would have the greatest negative impact on wildlife? Which the least? Why? Which the greatest positive impact on wildlife? Why?
- How could we minimize the negative impacts?
- Why don't we use the source of power with the least impact to a greater degree?
- Which energy sources cost the least to develop and use? Which provide more jobs? Which seem to have the least negative overall impact on the environment?
- What trade-offs are involved? Are there any reasonable solutions? If yes, describe some possibilities. With what consequences?
- How can each of us help wildlife and the environment through our energy habits?

4. Ask each student to think of at least one constructive thing to do for wildlife that involves energy and its use—and do it!

EXTENSIONS

1. Create a large mural on butcher paper of a natural area complete with wildlife, trees, mountains, rivers, etc., but no human development. After completing the mural, brainstorm a list of things that would happen if a much needed energy source (e.g., coal, oil, uranium, water) was discovered in that area. Draw pictures of these activities and facilities with one picture for each item listed. When all the pictures are completed, place them in appropriate places on the mural. For example, put the pictures where you think they should go if you were an energy developer. You can pin, tack, or tape the pictures onto the paper. Discuss the positive and negative impacts the "new development" will have on the environment and wildlife and create a list of these effects. Now, re-develop the energy source and see if you can come up with ways that the development can have less impact on the environment and still get the energy needed at an affordable cost.

2. See if a similar situation exists in your area.

AQUATIC EXTENSION

If not already addressed, do the activity again examining the possible positive and negative consequences for aquatic wildlife and aquatic habitats as a result of energy use practices and sources of energy used.

EVALUATION

1. Trace energy from a burning light bulb back to the sun using two different pathways.

2. Describe two ways that wildlife and/or habitat might be affected by each of the following electric energy development and uses: hydroelectric dam, nuclear generating plant, coal generating plant, oil generating plant, wind generating plant, tidal generating plant, active or passive solar facility.

ETHI-REASONING

OBJECTIVES

Students will: 1) examine their own values and beliefs related to wildlife and other elements of the environment; 2) listen to and respect the rights of others to maintain different values and beliefs; and 3) evaluate possible actions they might take that have impact on wildlife and the environment.

METHOD

Students read, discuss, make judgments and write about hypothetical dilemmas concerning wildlife and/or natural resources.

BACKGROUND

This activity is designed to give students the opportunity to examine their own values and beliefs as they relate to wildlife and other elements of the environment. It is not the intent of this activity to prescribe "right" and "wrong" answers for the students. One exception is in the areas where information about laws is conveyed.

There are variations from state to state in laws affecting wildlife and the environment. Each state has an official public agency that is legally responsible for caring for most wildlife within the state. This agency can be contacted in your state to request general information about laws affecting most wildlife in your area. For example, it is legal to hunt and fish for some animals in all states; however, what animals and under what conditions are specified by laws and regulations for which

the state wildlife agency is responsible. There are also federal regulations affecting wildlife. The U.S. Fish and Wildlife Service can be contacted for information about such laws. For example, federal law protects all birds of prey—eagles, hawks and owls—from shooting or any other intentional cause of death, injury, or harassment. All threatened and endangered species are protected by law. Songbirds are protected by law; that is, it is against the law to intentionally harm songbirds. It is also generally illegal to possess birds' nests, eggs and feathers, even those found lying on the ground. It is generally against the law to pick up the carcass of an animal which has been killed by a vehicle along the highway or road. Instead, local wildlife authorities should be notified. In many cases, it is against the law to take an injured wild animal home to care for it. For example, birds of prey cannot be cared for by private citizens unless those citizens have a permit to do so. There are many laws, and they are complex. Again, it is useful and important to contact local authorities about the laws protecting and affecting wildlife in your area.

Whether right or wrong, questions of law can be separated from questions of ethics. At a personal level, an individual's choices as to what seem right or wrong for him or her in terms of values and behaviors may be described as a personal code of ethics. Hunting, for example, is controversial for some people from an eth-

Age: Grades 5-12
Subjects: Social Studies, Science, Language Arts
Skills: analysis, application, discussion, evaluation, problem-solving, small group work, synthesis, writing
Duration: one 30 to 45-minute period
Group Size: any; small groups of two to four students recommended
Setting: indoors or outdoors
Conceptual Framework Reference: I.D., V.A., V.B., V.B.1., VI.B., VI.B.1., VI.B.2., VI.B.4., VI.B.5., VI.C., VI.C.1., VI.C.2., VI.C.7., VI.C.12., VI.C.16., VII.A., VII.A.1., VII.A.2., VII.A.3., VII.A.4., VII.B., VII.B.1., VII.B.2., VII.B.3., VII.B.4., VII.B.7.
Key Vocabulary: dilemma, responsibility
Appendices: Local Resources

ical point of view. Some people say that even though hunting is legal, it is unethical, because a human being is taking the life of a wild animal. Others believe hunting to be a responsible and ethical form of recreation, acquiring food, or animal population control. These differences of belief may be sincerely held. Whether or not a person chooses to hunt is a personal choice dictated by one's personal ethics. Conflicts arise, however, when a person motivated by one set of ethics tries to force his or her ethics on others through activities such as arguments, harassment, or legislative action.

It is the major purpose of this activity to provide students with an opportunity to come to their own judgments about what they think are the most responsible and appropriate actions to take in situations affecting wildlife and the environment.

MATERIALS
copies of "dilemma cards"

PROCEDURE
1. From the attached pages the teachers should copy and cut up the dilemma cards. Other dilemmas could be written that are more specific to problems in your area. Students could also be involved in the process of creating the dilemma cards, with each student responsible for one card. Dilemmas can be left entirely open-ended, with no options suggested for consideration.
2. Divide the class into groups of four, and give each group a stack of dilemma cards. Place them face down at the center of the group.
3. The first student draws a card from the top of the stack. The student studies the situation, decides what he or she should do, and formulates his or her reasons.
4. When the student is ready—typically in less than two minutes—the student reads the situation and the options aloud to the rest of the group. The student gives the decision he or she has chosen and describes the reasoning involved. In turn, each of the other members of the group is invited to comment on the dilemma and what he or she would do in the situation. The discussion of each dilemma by the members of the

group should take about five minutes. The person whose dilemma is being discussed should have the opportunity to ask questions of the other members of the group and to offer clarification about his or her decision. The discussion gives the students experience in having ideas examined by peers and is intended to remind the students of the need to take personal responsibility for decision-making. It is not necessary and may not be desirable for the students to reach consensus; there are legitimately ranging views of the most appropriate and responsible actions to take in many situations. The purpose is to provide students with an opportunity to examine, express, clarify and take responsibility for their own reasoning.
5. The card is then returned to the bottom of the stack and the next student selects a card from the top of the stack. Continue this process until all students have had the opportunity to express their decision and rationale about a dilemma.

EXTENSIONS AND VARIATIONS
1. Here are a few other general topics around which dilemma cards could be created: abandoning pets to fend for themselves to try to find new homes; impact of pets on wildlife, such as cats catching wild birds and dogs chasing deer; use of pesticides in gardens; live Christmas trees versus artificial; acid rain; picking wild flowers and fruit; feeding wildlife around your home, etc.
2. Adapt this to a debate format!
3. Write and discuss your own dilemmas!

EVALUATION
Choose a dilemma. Write a short paragraph on the positive and negative effects of all the options listed for that dilemma. Indicate what additional information, if any, is needed in order to make a responsible and informed decision. Give two opposing and convincing arguments for how to respond to this dilemma. Identify what you judge to be the most responsible decision; explain your reasoning. Explain how someone else could reach a different, yet valid, opinion with the same information.

Dilemma Card

A deer herd has grown so large during the past ten years that many of the deer appear to be starving. The herd is severely damaging the habitat, eliminating much of the vegetation that the animals use for food or shelter. There is a disagreement within your community as to what course of action is best to take. You are personally opposed to hunting. A limited legal hunt has been proposed in order to reduce the size of the herd in this area. Should you:

- Investigate and consider the situation to see what, in your judgment, seems to be the most humane and reasonable solution, including the feasibility of options such as moving some of the deer to other areas, understanding that they still may not survive;
- attempt to identify the causes of this population increase and propose action to return the system to a balance;
- allow the habitat degradation to continue and the deer to starve;
- leave it to the state wildlife agency to work with the landholder to arrive at a solution;
- other.

Dilemma Card

You are a homeowner in an area directly above a suburban city. The local government officials have proposed the diversion of a small stream from the property of several of the homeowners above the city, including yours, to power a hydro-electric system, benefitting the entire city. As a homeowner, you are concerned with losing the aesthetic values of this stream from your property. You are also concerned about the effect the removal of this stream will have on the fish and aquatic habitat. Another concern is that your property may lose some of its value for resale. You realize that your city needs to supply electric power to all its citizens as cost effectively as possible. Should you:

- hire a lawyer and prepare to sue the city for loss of property value;
- form a coalition of homeowners to meet with city planners and explore possible alternatives;
- sell your property before the project is begun;
- decide the needs of the city are more important than either the consequences to you personally or the ecological costs;
- other.

Dilemma Card

Your family owns a 500-acre farm. A tributary to a high-quality fishing stream runs along the boundary of your property. The nitrogen- and phosphorous-based fertilizer which your family uses to increase crop production is carried into the stream by rain run-off. This type of fertilizer is increasing algae growth and adversely affecting the fish population in both the tributary and the main stream. Your farm production is your sole source of income, but your family has always enjoyed fishing and doesn't want to lose the fish from the streams. Should you:

- change fertilizers even though it may reduce crop yield;
- allow a portion of your land along the stream to grow wild thus establishing a buffer zone (riparian area);
- investigate the possibility of gaining a tax exemption for the land you allowed for a buffer zone;
- do nothing;
- other.

Dilemma Card

You are a farmer. You've been studying and hearing about farming practices like leaving edge areas for wildlife and organic pest control. Although these practices may improve your long-term benefits, they may reduce your short-term profits. You are already having trouble paying your taxes and keeping up with expenses. Should you:

- sell the farm;
- keep studying farming practices but make no changes for now;
- try a few methods on some of your acreage and compare the results with other similar areas on your land;
- other.

Dilemma Card

You are fishing at a secluded lake and have caught seven fish during your first day at the lake. Now, on the second day, the fishing has been great and you have caught five fish in the first hour, all of which are bigger than yesterday's fish. The law allows you to possess 12 fish. Should you:

- continue to fish and keep all the fish;
- dispose of the smaller fish you caught yesterday and keep the big ones to stay within your limit;
- have fish for lunch;
- quit fishing and go for a hike;
- other.

Dilemma Card

You are finally able to build the home your family has dreamed about. After reviewing the plans for your home, you realize that you cannot include all the features you had planned for, due to rising construction costs. You must decide which one of the following you will include:

- solar heating;
- recreation room with fireplace;
- hot tub and sauna;
- greenhouse;
- other.

Dilemma Card

You are a member of a country club that has recently voted to build a wildlife farm to raise animals for members to hunt. You are not a hunter, you think that hunting is only okay to do in the wild and you are opposed to the building of the wildlife farm. Should you:

- stay in the club and do nothing;
- stay in the club and speak out strongly against the subject;
- resign from the club;
- other.

Dilemma Card

You are an influential member of the community. On your way home from work, you are stopped by a police officer and cited for having excessive auto emissions. Should you:

- use your influence to have the ticket invalidated;
- sell the car to some unsuspecting person;
- work to change the law;
- get your car fixed and pay the ticket;
- other.

Dilemma Card

You are on a field trip with your class to the zoo. Although you know that feeding of the animals by zoo visitors is prohibited, some of your friends are feeding marshmallows to the bears. Should you:

- tell them that feeding marshmallows may harm the bears and ask them to stop;
- report their behavior to the nearest zoo keeper;
- ask the teacher to ask them to stop;
- not do anything;
- other.

Dilemma Card

You are on a picnic with your family and you see another family leaving to go home, without having picked up their own trash. It is clear the other family is going to leave litter all around. Should you:

- move quickly and ask them to pick up their trash before they leave;
- wait for them to leave and pick up the trash for them;
- do nothing;
- other.

Dilemma Card

You are walking in the woods and come upon a young fawn. There is no sign of the fawn's mother. Should you:
- leave it where it is;
- move it to a sheltered area;
- take it home;
- other.

Dilemma Card

You love children and would like to have a large family. You are aware, however, of the world's population projections for the future. Should you:
- plan to have a large family anyway;
- decide not to have children;
- limit yourself to one or two children;
- other.

Dilemma Card

You have found a young screech owl which you have managed to raise to maturity. You have been told that you cannot keep the owl any longer because keeping it without the proper permit is in violation of state and federal laws. Should you:
- offer it to your local zoo;
- keep it as a pet;
- call the fish and wildlife agency and ask their advice;
- determine whether it could survive in the wild and, if it appears it could, release it in a suitable area;
- other.

Dilemma Card

You are out in the woods with a friend when you spot a hawk perched on a high limb. Before you realize what is happening, your friend shoots the hawk. An hour later, you are leaving the woods and are approached by a state wildlife officer who tells you a hawk has been illegally shot and asks if you know anything about it. Should you:
- deny any knowledge of the incident;
- admit your friend did it;
- make up a story implicating someone else;
- say nothing, but call the fish and wildlife officer later with an anonymous phone tip;
- other.

Dilemma Card

You are president of a large corporation. You are very interested in pollution control and have had a task force assigned to study the pollution your plant is creating. The task force reports that you are barely within the legal requirements. The plant is polluting the community. To add the necessary equipment to reduce pollution would cost so much that you have to fire 50 employees. Should you:
- add the equipment and fire the employees;
- not add the equipment;
- wait a few years to see if the cost of the equipment will drop;
- hire an engineering firm to provide further recommendations;
- other.

Dilemma Card

You have purchased a beautiful ten-acre property in the mountains to build a summer home. One hillside of the property has a beautiful view of the valley and lake below and is your choice for your homesite. However, you discover there is an active bald eagle nest site on that hillside. The bald eagle is sensitive to disturbance around its nest tree and is a protected species. Bald eagles are highly selective in choosing nest sites and usually return to the same nest year after year. Should you:
- select a different site on the property to build your home;
- sell the property;
- chop down the tree and build your home;
- other.

314

WILD BILL'S FATE

OBJECTIVES
Students will: 1) identify sources of information concerning legislation affecting wildlife; and 2) compare differing social and political viewpoints concerning legislation.

METHOD
Students investigate pending legislation affecting wildlife.

BACKGROUND
NOTE: See "Know Your Legislation: What's In It For Wildlife" for a similar activity.

State governments make decisions that affect wildlife. At the same time, protecting and managing the wildlife of any state is the responsibility of a state agency—usually a state wildlife department. Issues affecting wildlife are complex. Legislation affecting wildlife is no exception.

Some proposed laws directly affect wildlife. Other laws considered by a state legislature may have a strong effect on wildlife, although the laws may not relate directly to wildlife.

Age: Grades 7-12
Subjects: Social Studies (Government), English, Environmental Problems
Skills: analysis, evaluation, reading, reporting, research, small group work, writing
Duration: two initial class periods (45-minutes each), then on-going out-of-class work with occasional in-class reporting for several months
Group Size: whole class in small groups of four to six
Setting: indoors
Conceptual Framework Reference: II.A., II.B., II.C., II.C.2., II.C.3., II.D., II.E., II.F., IV.E., IV.E.11., IV.F., IV.F.1., IV.F.2., IV.F.3., IV.F.4., IV.F.5., IV.F.6., IV.F.7., IV.F.8., IV.F.9., IV.F.11., V.A., V.A.5., V.A.6., V.B., V.B.1., V.B.2., VI.B., VI.B.1., VI.B.2., VI.B.3., VI.B.4., VI.B.5., VI.C., VI.C.1., VI.C.2., VI.C.6., VI.C.12., VI.C.13., VI.C.16., VII.B., VII.B.2., VII.B.3., VII.B.4., VII.B.5., VII.B.6., VII.B.7.
Key Vocabulary: bill, law, legislation, legislature, amendment
Appendices: Local Resources

In this activity, students can study the legislative process while inquiring into wildlife issues. When state legislatures meet, the public can learn what bills are under consideration. Usually, it is possible to contact the "bill" room at the state legislature. To find out what bills are specifically important to wildlife, contact your state wildlife agency and ask for the legislative liaison. Wildlife-oriented private groups and organizations will also be watching the legislature and can also be asked to help identify wildlife-related bills. The major purpose of this activity is for students to recognize that there is a legislative process that affects wildlife.

MATERIALS
writing materials; telephone; stamps

PROCEDURE
1. First, appoint one or two students to contact the state legislature—when it is in session—to find out what bills have been introduced that affect wildlife. One or two other students should contact the state agency responsible for management of wildlife. Another one or two students should contact representatives of a diverse and representative range of organizations interested in wildlife which might have information about any pending legislation; for example, such groups could include American Humane Association, Defenders of Wildlife, Humane Society of the United States, International Association of Fish and Wildlife Agencies, National Audubon Society, National Rifle Association, National Wildlife Federation, Sierra Club, The Wildlife Society, Wildlife Management Institute.
2. These small groups of wildlife scouts should then prepare a report for the rest of the class, summarizing their findings. They should prepare a list of the bills under consideration, with a short paragraph of information about each, including the issues behind each bill.

3. The entire class should then divide itself into small groups of four to six students, and each group should select one piece of legislation to review and understand.

4. Each team should keep an information file on the bill they are studying which includes: 1) the legislative bill number and title; 2) when it was introduced in the legislature, by whom and where; 3) its route to and through committees; 4) when it passes through the house or senate; and 5) when it is signed into law, or if not signed into law, what happens to it. (A status sheet is usually published on a daily basis when a legislature is in session.) Pay particular attention to amendments. Amendments to the original bill may drastically alter the intent. See if amendments improve or hamper the intent, and attempt to determine if an amendment is intended to improve, or actually to "kill" the legislation.

5. Each team of students should prepare a list of questions they have about their bill: for example, those groups that were contacted initially simply to find out what legislation was pending would be appropriate sources of additional information at this time. Before the students, or a representative of each group, contact any organization or individual—make sure you go over their questions in advance. You want to make sure that the students are adequately prepared to impose on these people for information. Secondly, you may want to make sure that one group is not contacted by five or six groups of your students, and another group not contacted at all. In addition to the legislative liaison at the state wildlife agency and members of private conservation groups, students might also contact people such as the person who introduced the legislation; a representative of local business interests, as appropriate; and people "on the street" who may or may not know about the proposed legislation.

6. Students should report periodically (once a week) on the status of the legislation they are studying, its progress, and the issues affecting it.

EXTENSION

Debate contrasting viewpoints concerning the proposed legislation. See whether the final disposition of the legislation matches the students' conclusions.

AQUATIC EXTENSIONS

1. Focus on water-related legislation. Identify any possible effects on aquatic wildlife and aquatic habitats if the legislation is passed.

2. Write a letter to a legislator expressing your personal opinion about proposed legislation affecting aquatic wildlife. Include at least three statements which you can support with evidence in order to convey your reasons for your perspective concerning the proposed legislation.

EVALUATION

1. Identify one bill which has been introduced into your state legislature that will affect wildlife. Describe it. Explain its major purpose. Offer and support your opinion as to whether this bill should be passed.

2. Describe two opposing viewpoints, if any, affecting wildlife that relate to this bill.

3. Explain any possible unanticipated consequences from passage of this bill.

4. Identify two stages where you or other members of the public could influence the bill's passage or defeat. Describe what actions citizens might take at those steps.

KNOW YOUR LEGISLATION: WHAT'S IN IT FOR WILDLIFE?

OBJECTIVES

Students will: 1) describe the legislative process in which a bill becomes law; 2) identify points at which private citizens can have an impact on the legislative process; and 3) evaluate the effectiveness of the legislative process from the perspective of their personal experience.

METHOD

Students actively participate in the legislative process.

BACKGROUND

NOTE: See "Wild Bill's Fate" for a similar activity.

Students can learn about the political process by getting involved at a "grass-roots" level. Voting, letter-writing and lobbying are among the direct ways used by adults to communicate their opinions to their governmental representatives. Young people can prepare themselves for their voting rights and responsibilities by monitoring the legislative process—specifically following a bill of interest to them in its course toward becoming a law. This activity is best done over a one to two month or longer period. The students should select a local wildlife or other environmental issue of interest to them with related legislation pending. Be sure that the students tackle a piece of legislation that is worth the effort.

Real life—rather than simulated—experiences are important in learning these concepts and skills. Although role-play and simulation activities can be useful, they do not come as close to teaching students that they can have an impact in policy making. Instructional benefits to students from this activity will vary depending on their own interest and abilities, access to governing groups and amount of time available to work on this project.

The major purpose of this activity is to give students real-life experience in studying and participating in the legislative process. They are given an opportunity to have an impact on issues of concern to them.

HELPFUL HINTS from a classroom teacher who has successfully done this activity with students!
1. You **will** make an impact. Four or five letters on a legislator's desk get attention. This type of campaign will be taken seriously.
2. Your students will really learn how a bill progresses—important knowledge in a democracy where citizens have rights and responsibilities.
3. You **might** actually assist in getting the bill enacted into law—and make an impact for the good of wildlife and the environment that will last a long time.
4. You **might not** get your bill through. Most pieces of legislation take three to five years to get through the legislature. It typically takes that long for a bill to get serious attention and for the legislators to acquire sufficient information to consider its importance. If your bill doesn't pass, don't be discouraged. You can ask your students to join forces with next year's class in the same project. Their impact may not bring about the passage of a bill in one year, but it will hasten the time when the bill is finally passed.
5. Be leery about working on an appropriations bill. Bills that require money are a lot harder to get passed.
6. This is a lot of work. Be sure you and your students choose a piece of legislation that is worth the effort.

Age: Grades 7-12
Subjects: Social Studies (Government, Civics), Science, Environmental Problems, Language Arts
Skills: analysis, application, comparing similarities and differences, description, discussion, evaluation, interview, listing, public speaking, problem-solving, reading, reporting, research, small group work, synthesis, writing
Duration: five 30 to 45 minute-periods to start the project, 45 minutes every two weeks, 15-minute updates each week
Group Size: any
Setting: indoors
Conceptual Framework Reference: II.C., II.C.2., II.C.3., V.A., V.A.5., V.A.6., V.B., V.B.1., V.B.2., VI.B.6., VI.C., VI.C.1., VI.C.2., VI.C.6., VI.C.12., VI.C.16., VII.A., VII.B., VII.B.1., VII.B.2., VII.B.3., VII.B.4., VII.B.5., VII.B.6., VII.B.7.
Key Vocabulary: legislation, legislature, bill, law
Appendices: Taking Action, Agencies and Organizations, Local Resources

---

MATERIALS

copy of a bill being considered in local legislature; butcher or poster paper; marking pens; writing materials

PROCEDURE

Day One

1. Ask your students if they know of any laws which affect wildlife and the environment. They may be able to give a few examples. Initiate a discussion about how such laws become laws. Where do they come from and how are they passed into law?

2. Ask for students to volunteer to contact local people about any legislation presently being considered that would affect wildlife or other aspects of the environment. One student could call the state wildlife agency and ask to speak to someone responsible for information about proposed legislation. Another could call a federal agency with responsibilities affecting wildlife. Another student could call a private organization—like a local chapter, affiliate, or representative of the American Humane Association, Defenders of Wildlife, Humane Society of the United States, National Audubon Society, National Rifle Association, National Wildlife Federation, The Wildlife Society, or Wildlife Management Institute—for information about proposed legislation they might be concerned about and working on. Industry can also provide valuable information. For example, the government affairs office of a large corporation might be able to assist. Check with the students before they make their calls or send letters. Stress that they make their requests clearly, concisely and courteously. Ask the students to be prepared to report back within two weeks about what they have learned. If possible, by that time the students should have copies of proposed legislation for review by other members of the class.

Day Two

3. Ask the students who contacted local people about proposed legislation to report to the rest of the class. After hearing the reports, ask the entire class to decide what one piece of proposed legislation they are most interested in finding out more about—by following its route through the legislature to possible passage.

Day Three and On

4. Once the students have selected the legislation they are interested in following, these are the next main steps:

A. Know Your Legislation. Give each student a copy of the proposed legislation. Divide the class into committees. Ask each committee to take a section of the legislation, read it, interpret it to the best of their ability and report back to the whole class. Ask each committee to outline their reports visually and verbally on a large piece of butcher paper for presentation in front of the class.

B. Writing the Position Paper. Ask the students to decide which areas of the legislation they wish to support with specific positions. Again, ask the students to work in committees to do research, bringing back information and expert opinions to substantiate their positions. All the information and concerns should then be compiled into a class position paper they will use to present their points of view to the legislators and allied groups.

C. Get in Touch with Your Representative or Senator. Next, ask each student to write a letter to his or her state legislator. At least one copy of the students' position paper should be included with their letters. Be sure to check these letters for grammar and spelling errors—they have to be perfect!

D. Student "Eagle-Eye." Ask the class to appoint a student "Eagle-Eye" to be the contact person with the legislator's office. If possible, the student should introduce himself or herself in person or by phone to the legislator or aide and express the class' wish to keep track of this bill. It is the responsibility of the student "Eagle-Eye" to:

  • contact the legislator's office twice a week to determine where the bill is in the process, and whether it has picked up any amendments
  • keep a flow chart on the progress of the bill. This flow chart can be placed on a large piece of butcher paper on a bulletin board for the class to follow.

E. Student "Reach-Outs." The class already may have identified allied groups that might have an interest in this bill, e.g., when students volunteered at the beginning of the project to contact people for information about proposed legislation. Ask the students to appoint one class member to each group identified. It will be the responsibility of these student "Reach-Outs" to contact, in person, the president or legislative chairperson of the local allied group for which they are the contact. Explain this class project, and give them a copy of the position paper. Student "Reach-Outs" are to keep their allied groups informed, and—when the legislation reaches a critical point—student "Reach-Outs" will contact the allied group leader, asking that they contact their general membership to write or call their local legislators about the bill. Keep a list of who is "reached."

F. Keep Your Eye on the Ball! Student "Zero-In."
Ask the class to appoint another student to have the responsibility of finding out what committees this bill will probably be assigned to. Wildlife bills usually go to the Natural Resource Committee, and to the Appropriations or Ways and Means Committee if they cost money. The student "Zero-In" should get a list of committee members and their districts from the legislature's Information Desk. Ask the student "Zero-In" to list and display the names of these committee members and their districts. The student "Zero-In" should also keep in constant contact with the student "Eagle-Eye" in case the bill is relegated to some other committee unexpectedly.

G. Student "Watchdog." Each committee member on the student "Zero-In'"s list should be assigned to a student "Watchdog." Each "Watchdog" is to write his or her committee member a letter stating the class position and including a copy of the position paper. Keep track of who is contacted, when and how. It is the responsibility of each student "Watchdog" to call his or her respective legislator's office a couple of days before the bill goes into that committee to reaffirm the position of the students. Again, stress courtesy and clarity on the part of the students in making these calls. Student "Watchdogs" can also encourage relatives and friends who live in their committee member's district or write or call the legislator and voice their opinions. Student "Watchdogs" should also work with student "Reach-Outs" to contact the allied group leaders who live in their legislator's district.

H. Zero Hour—What to do when the bill is about to go into full Committee or before the full House or Senate! You have your organization in place, so it is time for the students, their friends, relatives and allied groups to write or call (get the toll-free number for them) the legislators who will be making the decisions—making one last effort to make their views known.

I. Get the Results! The bill may or may not pass. In either case, the students have acquired valuable information and developed first-hand skills in working within the established political processes affecting wildlife and the environment.

EXTENSIONS AND VARIATIONS

1. Draft your own proposed legislation; debate it in a mock classroom legislature. Submit it for consideration to your state legislator or the appropriate committee!

2. Distinguish between **laws** and **regulations**. Regulations may have the same powers and penalties as laws—and may not. Look at similarities and differences. Obtain copies of state wildlife laws and regulations. They are normally free from the state wildlife agency.

AQUATIC EXTENSIONS
Pick legislation related to aquatic species or aquatic habitats.

EVALUATION

1. List five stages in the passage of a bill where citizens can influence the outcome. List the stages in order. Assume the bill begins in a House of Representatives. Briefly describe how citizens can have input.

2. What are three good places to go for information about legislation affecting wildlife, natural resources and the environment?

3. How can a citizen find out the status of a bill that is being considered for legislation?

4. What impact does the legislative process have on people's perceptions and actions affecting wildlife and its habitat? Based on your experience, what suggestions, if any, would you like to make to improve the effectiveness of the legislative process? What are its strongest, most valuable features? What are its weakest, most negative features? What is your assessment of its overall importance?

5. What advice would you offer other students who want to influence the passage of legislation?

ACTION FLOWCHART FOR
"KNOW YOUR LEGISLATION" ACTIVITY

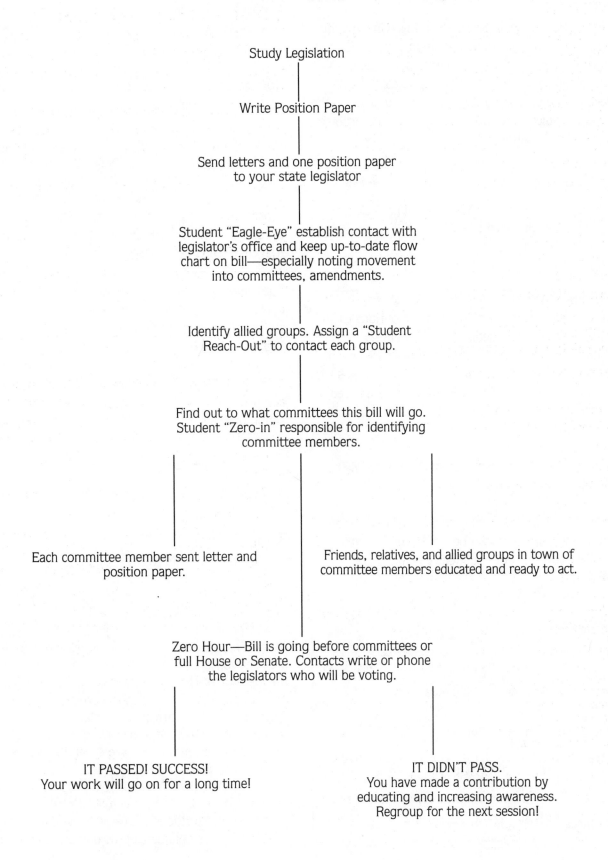

Study Legislation

Write Position Paper

Send letters and one position paper
to your state legislator

Student "Eagle-Eye" establish contact with
legislator's office and keep up-to-date flow
chart on bill—especially noting movement
into committees, amendments.

Identify allied groups. Assign a "Student
Reach-Out" to contact each group.

Find out to what committees this bill will go.
Student "Zero-in" responsible for identifying
committee members.

Each committee member sent letter and
position paper.

Friends, relatives, and allied groups in town of
committee members educated and ready to act.

Zero Hour—Bill is going before committees or
full House or Senate. Contacts write or phone
the legislators who will be voting.

IT PASSED! SUCCESS!
Your work will go on for a long time!

IT DIDN'T PASS.
You have made a contribution by
educating and increasing awareness.
Regroup for the next session!

CAN DO!

OBJECTIVES

Students will: 1) identify a problem involving wildlife on their own school grounds; 2) suggest and evaluate alternative means by which to either solve the problem or at least improve the situation; 3) successfully undertake the project; and 4) analyze and describe the process by which they successfully solved the problem or improved the situation.

METHOD

Students select a school environmental project; conduct research; make plans; and follow procedures to accomplish the project.

BACKGROUND

Each of us can make constructive contributions to improving the environment in which we live. Sometimes our actions can improve the environment for people, sometimes for wildlife, and sometimes for both. Sometimes our effectiveness can be improved if we work with other people—sharing ideas, information and skills.

A working knowledge of the following terms will be useful to students in this activity:

Problem A difficult situation to be improved, or an opportunity to make things better. Problems can't always be "solved," but situations can usually be improved.

Age: Grades 2-9
Subjects: Social Studies, Language Arts, Science
Skills: analysis, application, description, discussion, evaluation, invention, listing, public speaking, problem-solving, small group work, synthesis, writing
Duration: minimum of three 45-minute periods
Group Size: any
Setting: outdoors and indoors
Conceptual Framework Reference: I.D., IV.A., IV.A.1., IV.A.2., IV.A.3., IV.A.4., IV.C., IV.D., IV.D.1., IV.D.2., IV.D.3., IV.D.4., IV.D.5., IV.D.6., IV.E., IV.E.4., IV.E.5., IV.E.9., IV.E.10., IV.F.11., VI.B.7., VII.A., VII.A.2., VII.A.3., VII.B., VII.B.1., VII.B.5., VII.B.6.
Key Vocabulary: problem, authority, compromise, constructive, realistic, effective, alternatives
Appendices: Taking Action, Outdoors

Authority An individual or group of people with the power to make changes.

Compromise A way to settle a problem in which both "sides" usually give a little.

Given that it is important for young people to learn that they "can do" for people, wildlife and the environment—use your judgment in the course of this activity to assist students in selecting a project that is realistic, constructive and possible. If not, the students may experience an activity that contributes to their thinking that they "can't do."

The major purpose of this activity is to provide students an opportunity to experience success in taking constructive actions to improve the environment for people and wildlife.

NOTE: See "Taking Action" beginning on page 354 for additional tips on involving students in environmental action projects.

MATERIALS

writing materials

PROCEDURE

1. Ask the students to think of some ways in which they could improve areas of the school grounds as a home for wildlife. They might generate a list of activities on their school grounds that have a negative impact on wildlife. The list might include litter that poses a hazard for some kinds of wildlife; a muddy area that birds use for water but that has been recommended for blacktopping to minimize dust and mud; a proposed pesticide spraying that will not only kill the "pest" but perhaps affect other plants and animals; removal of a tree that presently helps contribute to cleaning the air, produces oxygen, and serves as a food and shelter source for varying kinds of wildlife, etc.
2. Looking at the list of possible problems and suggestions for ways to improve wildlife habitat at school—ask the students to select one they think they could realistically handle and do something construc-

tive about. If there is difficulty in deciding which one, and reasonable support has been offered for each, the students might vote to decide. Students could also make speeches in support of the project they want to tackle in hopes of swaying the class vote.

3. Once the project has been selected, ask the students to work alone or in small groups to begin to generate ideas for possible solutions to the problem and ways to implement the project. Each individual or small group could come up with a plan, including a written description and illustrations or sketches of how it will work, and how it can be accomplished.

4. Ask the groups to present their plans to the rest of the students. Students may ask questions for clarification. Once all the plans have been presented, ask the students to select the plan that seems most: a) constructive; b) realistic; c) helpful to wildlife; and d) apt to make a lasting contribution.

5. Also ask the students to select one or more alternative plans, in case their first choice is not acceptable to authorities at the school.

6. Once a plan, with alternatives for "back up," has been selected—ask the students to select a delegation to present their proposal to the school principal or whomever the appropriate authority would be. Remember janitors, groundskeepers, school board, etc.—anyone who would be physically and/or officially involved. A practice session before the students and any interested parents or other groups of students would be helpful. At the practice session, the student delegation would make their presentation as they plan to before the principal, janitor, etc.—responding to any questions from their audience that might be raised.

7. The students should make an appointment to present their proposal, make the presentation, and report back to their classmates. If their plan is accepted, they should make sure they know who to contact next in order to successfully complete their project. Making sure they have all necessary permissions secured, the students should proceed to successfully accomplish their project. If their plan, including alternatives, is not accepted, have the students identify the reasons why. Have them find out exactly what people objected to in their original plan. The students can then respond to those objections with alternative proposals. Creating an alternative plan may require further research, careful interviews and time.

8. Once accomplished, ask the students to analyze their results. Did things work out like they wanted them to? Were there any surprises? Any unforeseen problems? How might they have been any more effective?

AQUATIC EXTENSION

Pick a problem to solve that involves water as a component of habitat on the school grounds!

EVALUATION

A nature center near your school reports a smaller bluebird population than there used to be. People are taking bluebird nest boxes down from trees and breaking them. The nature center director says there is no money to pay for security guards or to make repairs. Make a plan for helping the bluebirds.

IMPROVING WILDLIFE HABITAT IN THE COMMUNITY

OBJECTIVES

Students will: 1) apply their knowledge of wildlife by describing essential components of habitat in an arrangement appropriate for the wildlife they identify; and 2) evaluate compatible and incompatible uses of an area by people and specified kinds of wildlife.

METHOD

Students design and accomplish a project to improve wildlife habitat in their community.

BACKGROUND

NOTE: See "Can Do." Its scope is the school; the scope of "Improving Wildlife Habitat" is the community. "Keeping Score" can be helpful in identifying community needs for habitat improvement, used prior to this activity. See "Taking Action" beginning on page 354 for additional tips on involving students in environmental action projects.

This activity provides an opportunity for students to evaluate and apply much of what they have learned about wildlife and its needs.

The major purpose of this activity is to provide stu-

dents with experience in looking at their own communities; applying knowledge and skills they have acquired; evaluating; and experiencing the possibilities of enhancing their communities as places within which both people and wildlife can live suitably.

MATERIALS

writing and drawing materials; poster or butcher paper; OR, model making materials, like plaster of Paris, clay, small replicas of animals, etc.

PROCEDURE

1. Ask students whether their community could benefit from improved areas for wildlife habitat. If yes, this activity provides a process for helping to make such improvements. If a need is identified, the scope of such a project is a major decision. Habitat improvement projects can be large or small. If a project from this activity is actually to be implemented:
   - It should be within the scope and means of the students to experience success with it; and
   - It should clearly be of benefit to wildlife and the community.
2. After general discussion, ask the students to divide into groups of four or five. Give each group the task of beginning a design for a habitat improvement project. The project should involve native plants and animals, and make a contribution to the community. Provide time for the students to discuss and make decisions about:
   - What will be its purpose?
   - What animals will it serve? Will people be able to visit? Will it be for plants and animals only? What plants and what animals? If people can visit, what will they be allowed to do? What won't they be allowed to do?
   - What positive contributions might this improved wildlife habitat area make to the community? What possible problems could arise, if any?
   - What costs will be involved? Who will pay? How?

Age: Grades 4-12
Subjects: Science, Social Studies, Art, Mathematics, Language Arts
Skills: analysis, application, description, discussion, drawing, evaluation, invention, media construction, problem-solving, small group work, synthesis, visualization
Duration: one or two 45-minute class periods if hypothetical; much more time if project is to be implemented
Group Size: any
Setting: indoors (and outdoors, optional)
Conceptual Framework Reference: I.D., IV.A., IV.A.1., IV.A.2., IV.A.3., IV.A.4., IV.C., IV.C.1., IV.C.2., IV.C.4., IV.D., IV.D.1., IV.D.2., IV.D.3., IV.D.4., IV.D.5., IV.D.6., IV.E., IV.E.4., IV.E.5., IV.E.7., IV.E.8., IV.E.9., IV.E.10., IV.E.11., IV.F.11., V.A., V.B., V.B.1., V.B.2., VII.A., VII.A.1., VII.A.2., VII.A.3., VII.A.4., VII.B., VII.B.1., VII.B.2., VII.B.3., VII.B.5., VII.B.6., VII.B.7.
Key Vocabulary: habitat, improvement
Appendices: Taking Action, Local Resources

- Where will the area be? How large will it be?
- What are the habitat needs of any animals who will live there? What species of animals can live in the size land are that is available? (Some animals need more room than others and if you are to have a self-sustaining system, you will need a population in an area large enough for successful breeding over time.)
- What herbivores and carnivores might be needed? Predators? Prey? What specific kinds of plants (herbs, shrubs, trees, grasses, etc.) are needed and in what arrangement?
- What will be the water sources? How will air and water quality be maintained?
- What kinds of programs, if any, will be necessary to maintain the area once it has been improved?
- Who must be contacted in order for this project to be undertaken? What permissions would be needed? From whom?
- In balance, is it a good idea—for wildlife, the environment and the people who live in this community?

OPTIONAL: Make a site visit.

3. Ask each of the groups to prepare the following: a) a written description of their habitat improvement project, including its location, characteristics, inhabitants and purposes; and b) a map or model to scale of the area. The map or model can include:

- habitat components for various species
- wildlife living in the area, in their appropriate locations
- bodies of water, natural or made by people
- major areas of vegetation and a key to type
- major landmarks; e.g., rock outcropping, roosts for birds, bare ground, meadows, brush, low trees, high trees
- major food sources and types; e.g., berry patch for birds, prairie dog village for coyotes or birds of prey
- areas developed for human access

4. Ask each group to display their plans. After all the students have had an opportunity to read the background information and see the map or model of each habitat improvement project, ask the students to talk about what they learned in the process of creating these designs. They can include discussion of problems they encountered, what seemed realistic and what did not, etc. In discussion—and based on their observations of the various proposed projects—ask the students to summarize what seemed to be the most important things to remember about designing such an area (e.g., size appropriate to wildlife, diversity, native elements, appropriateness to community wants and needs).

EXTENSIONS

1. Consider the feasibility of designing and implementing one or more of these projects for your community. Do have a local wildlife specialist, and appropriate local officials, etc., landowners, zoning authorities, critique and cooperate with any proposed project before you get underway with it. Make sure the project is worthy, feasible and legal—and then proceed!

2. Tie your habitat improvement project into an existing network of habitat improvement projects. Contact your local wildlife or Project WILD office and find out if any adopt-a-stream, backyard habitat, or school site habitat improvement programs are taking place in your area. If there are none, the people at the Project WILD office may be able to refer you to a national program that could provide you and your students with ideas and assistance.

AQUATIC EXTENSION

Pick a habitat improvement project directly related to aquatic wildlife and aquatic habitats!

EVALUATION

1. Rate the following uses of an area as either compatible or incompatible for people and wildlife:

- houses being built 200 feet from a heron rookery;
- picnic tables set up in an area heavily populated by squirrels;
- snowmobile trails through a deciduous forest;
- swimming beach at a local lake.

Think of your own examples. What could be done to make each of these uses more compatible for both people and wildlife?

2. Draw a picture or design a blueprint of a community in which people have taken actions to improve the environment for both people and wildlife. Explain some of the features of the plan. Compare similarities and differences between the plan and the characteristics of your own community.

ENVIRO-ETHICS

OBJECTIVES

Students will: 1) distinguish between actions that are harmful and beneficial to the environment; and 2) evaluate the appropriateness and feasibility of making changes in their own behaviors related to the environment.

METHOD

Students develop and use a "Personal Code of Environmental Ethics."

BACKGROUND

Ethics are derived from our guiding moral principles. They are influenced by age, gender, culture, family and religion. Between the ages of ten and 18, many people go through profound moral growth. During that time, they typically not only develop the mental reasoning abilities to grapple with moral issues, they also find themselves in more and more situations where they have to make their own decisions. Ethics extend into many areas including how people treat wildlife and the rest of the environment.

As students become more informed about wildlife and topics associated with the environment, as well as the range of viewpoints surrounding them, they may experience shifts in their environmental ethics. Superficial understandings will probably lead to superficial ethical decisions. Having some accurate information about wildlife and human impacts on the environment will tend to help students reach more responsible decisions

concerning wildlife and the environment upon which all life depends.

Class discussions related to ethics should be designed to respect the student's right to privacy and non-participation. Teachers should also review and follow any school policies related to teaching about ethics. Many teachers have incorporated environmental ethics into drug prevention and other health programs. Developing ethical standards in one area can serve as a bridge to developing them in others.

The major purpose of this activity is to provide students with the encouragement and opportunity to examine their own lifestyles in light of their impacts on wildlife and the environment.

MATERIALS

none needed

PROCEDURE

1. Involve the students in discussion about the impact each of us has each day on aspects of the environment—from using electricity to make breakfast to putting on clothes that were derived from some natural resources and transported to us by some means, to use of the varied products we choose and employ each day, to our choices of recreation and entertainment. We are consumers, and our impact is formidable.

2. Have each student identify someone who has done something that benefited wildlife and the environment. It could be someone famous like Teddy Roosevelt or Rachel Carson or someone who might not be known by very many people at all. Ask what personal beliefs or values might that person hold (or have held) about the environment?

3. Next, ask each student to identify something that they have done to help wildlife and the environment that they did not have to do. Ask why they chose to perform that task voluntarily. Talk about what "ethic or "ethical standard" guided their decision. Explain that complex issues, like most wildlife and other environmental issues, contain a wide range of valid ethical positions.

Age: Grades 6-12
Subjects: Language Arts, Social Studies, Science, Home Economics
Skills: analysis, application, comparing similarities and differences, description, discussion, evaluation, invention, problem-solving, reporting, synthesis, writing (optional)
Duration: one or two 30 to 45-minute periods
Group Size: any
Setting: indoors or outdoors
Conceptual Framework Reference: I.D., V.A., V.B.1., VI.A., VI.B., VI.B.2., VI.B.3., VI.B.4., VI.B.5., VI.C., VII.A., VII.A.1., VII.A.2., VII.A.3., VII.A.4., VII.B., VII.B.1., VII.B.2., VII.B.3., VII.B.6., VII.B.7.
Key Vocabulary: ethics, responsibility, lifestyle
Appendices: Field Ethics, Animals in the Classroom

4. Have the students brainstorm a list of the daily impacts each of us has on the environment. This can include our use of water, electricity and fossil fuels; the impacts caused by the production and manufacture of our food and clothing; and the environmental consequences of our recreation and entertainment choices.

5. Discuss how all living things impact the environment. Ask how some human environmental impact is different than the impact caused by other living things. Discuss how ethics can influence human impact on wildlife and the environment. Ask how a personal code of environmental ethics might have guided the people who were identified as having done something for wildlife and the rest of the environment. Now ask the students how they think a personal code of environmental ethics might guide them as they make decisions about the daily impacts they just listed.

6. Ask each student to work alone to devise a "Personal Code of Environmental Ethics." This code may be written or not. Emphasize the importance of the code being for the person who creates it. The code should take into consideration daily actions that are harmful to the environment and those which are beneficial. The students should consciously create their code based on actions they believe are beneficial, or at least not harmful, to elements of the environment. We will always have some impact; we can make choices about the kinds of impacts we make, their extensiveness, etc.

7. Ask for any volunteers to share their "Personal Code of Environmental Ethics." They might share the entire code or a segment of it. They might describe the thinking that went into the decisions they made in constructing their code. Students might illustrate a part of their code—if they chose not to write it—to convey a major idea. Encourage the students to ask each other questions about the codes, in the spirit of learning more about each person's priorities, but not in a judgmental approach. The purpose is for each student to evaluate his or her own priorities, in a responsible consideration of day-to-day actions that affect the environment, without being actively critical of another student's approach to the same problem. In this way, each student is simply encouraged to take responsibility for his or her own actions.

8. Encourage the students to try using their codes, keeping track of how easy or difficult it is for them to live by them. "Progress reports" are appropriate, again in the spirit of each person paying attention to his or her own actions, and bearing responsibility for them.

VARIATIONS AND EXTENSIONS

1. Reflect for a few minutes on your daily life. In fact, close your eyes and follow yourself through a typical day. What natural resources do you use? What choices do you make that have an impact on the environment? What choices do you make that have an impact on wildlife and its habitat? What choices do you make that have an impact on other people, here and elsewhere on the planet? If you could, what things—if any—would you change about your daily life in order to have a more beneficial, or less harmful, impact on the environment? What things—if any—do you already do that you think are helpful, or at least not harmful, to the environment? Brainstorm ten words that come to mind when you think of actions and behaviors you value. Create a sentence, paragraph, or poem that might capture the essence of your own "Personal Code of Environmental Ethics."

2. Develop a "life map." It could include where you want to live, whether you want a family, what kind of home, transportation, food sources, job, recreation, etc. Look at the costs and benefits of your choices—for you personally, other people in your community, wildlife, other natural resources, etc.

3. Revisit this activity several times throughout the year. It can serve as a starting point for numerous classroom activities. NOTE: Students can establish their own or class ethical guidelines for a variety of experiences. For example, students can establish guidelines related to having animals in the classroom, going on field trips, or using electricity and paper in the classroom.

4. Locate and study ethical codes issued by various environmental organizations.

EVALUATION

1. List five environmental issues.

2. List one way that you directly or indirectly contribute to an environmental problem.

3. Identify, describe and evaluate one way you could lessen your role in contributing to an environmental problem.

4. Make at least one change in your lifestyle that will reduce your role in contributing to an environmental problem.

LIST OF AGENCIES AND ORGANIZATIONS

The following list is not intended to be comprehensive. It includes federal agencies with responsibilities involving wildlife which are referenced in Project WILD activities. State wildlife agencies may be contacted directly in each state. The organizations are also listed in one or more Project WILD activities, tend to have national memberships or scope, and can be contacted for information. The organization list as a whole represents a range of views concerning wildlife-related issues. Project WILD encourages teachers and students to contact a **range** of organizations, supporting instruction for informed decision making. It is recommended that requests be as specific as possible, be mailed on behalf of a class rather than each individual student submitting a request and be sent with a stamped self-addressed envelope for return of materials. Only ask for what you think you want and will use—and try to allow two to three weeks time for a response.

FEDERAL AGENCIES

Bureau of Land Management
Interior Building
1849 C Street NW
Washington, DC 20240
(202) 452-5128

Cooperative Extension Service
US Department of Agriculture
14th & Independence Avenue, SW
Washington, DC 20250-0900
(202) 720-3029

National Marine Fisheries Service
US Department of Commerce, NOAA
1315 East-West Highway
Silver Spring, MD 20910
(301) 713-2370

National Park Service
Interior Building
PO Box 37127
Washington, DC 20013-7127
(202) 208-4747

Natural Resources Conservation Service
PO Box 2890
Washington, DC 20013
(202) 720-4525

US Army Corps of Engineers
HQ USACE (CECW-ON)
20 Massachusetts Avenue, NW
Washington, DC 20314-1000
(202) 761-0011

US Department of Agriculture
Office of Public & Media Outreach
412A Jamie Whitten Building
Washington, DC 20250
(202) 720-2798

US Environmental Protection Agency
Environmental Education Division
Mail Code 1707
401 M Street SW
Washington, DC 20460
(202) 260-4965

US Fish and Wildlife Service
Media Services
Main Interior Building
1849 C Street NW, Rm 3447
Washington, DC 20240
(202) 208-5634

US Fish and Wildlife Service
Publications Unit
4401 N. Fairfax Drive
Mail Stop 130 Webb
Arlington, VA 22203
(703) 358-1711

USDA Forest Service, CF
Natural Resource Conservation Education
PO Box 96090 (4 SE)
Washington, DC 20090-6090
(202) 205-1545

REGIONAL OFFICES OF FEDERAL AGENCIES

Environmental Protection Agency

Environmental Protection Agency
Env. Ed. Program, Region 1
JFK Federal Building
Mail Stop-RPM
Boston, MA 02203
(617) 565-3404

Environmental Protection Agency
Env. Ed. Program, Region 2
290 Broadway, 26th Floor
New York, NY 10007
(212) 637-3671

Environmental Protection Agency
Env. Ed. Program, Region 3
841 Chestnut Street
Mail Stop-3EA20
Philadelphia, PA 19107
(215) 566-5120

Environmental Protection Agency
Env. Ed. Program, Region 4
345 Courtland Street, NE
Atlanta, GA 30365
(404) 347-3004

Environmental Protection Agency
Env. Ed. Program, Region 5
77 West Jackson Blvd.
Mail Stop-PI-19J
Chicago, IL 60604
(312) 353-3209

Environmental Protection Agency
Env. Ed. Program, Region 6
1445 Ross Avenue
Mail Stop-6X
Dallas, TX 75202-2733
(214) 665-6444

Environmental Protection Agency
Env. Ed. Program, Region 7
726 Minnesota Avenue
Kansas City, KS 66101
(913) 551-7003

Environmental Protection Agency
Env. Ed. Program, Region 8
1 Denver Place
999 - 18th Street, Suite 500
Mail Stop-80EA
Denver, CO 80202-2405
(303) 293-1113

Environmental Protection Agency
Env. Ed. Program, Region 9
75 Hawthorne Street
Mail Stop-E2
San Francisco, CA 94105
(415) 744-1581

Environmental Protection Agency
Env. Ed. Program, Region 10
1200 Sixth Avenue
Mail Stop EXA-142
Seattle, WA 98101-9797
(206) 553-1207

USDA Forest Service

USDA Forest Service
Alaska Region
PO Box 21628
Juneau, AK 99802-1628
(907) 586-8863

USDA Forest Service
100 Matsonford Road
Northeastern Area—S & PF
5 Radnor Corporate Center, Suite 200
Radnor, PA 19087-4585
(610) 975-4111

USDA Forest Service
Eastern Region
310 West Wisconsin Avenue, Room 500
Milwaukee, WI 53203
(414) 297-3693

USDA Forest Service
Intermountain Research Station
Federal Building
324 - 25th Street
Ogden, UT 84401-2310
(801) 625-5412

USDA Forest Service
Northern Region
PO Box 7669
Missoula, MT 59807-7669
(406) 329-3511

USDA Forest Service
Pacific Northwest Region
333 Southwest 1st Avenue
PO Box 3623
Portland, OR 97208-3623
(503) 326-3592

USDA Forest Service
Public Affairs Office
Pacific Southwest Region
630 Sansome Street
San Francisco, CA 94111
(415) 705-2874

USDA Forest Service
Rocky Mountain Region
PO Box 25127
Lakewood, CO 80225
(303) 275-5350

USDA Forest Service
Southern Region
1720 Peachtree Road, NW
Atlanta, GA 30309
(404) 347-2384

USDA Forest Service
Southwestern Region
517 Gold Avenue, SW
Albuquerque, NM 87102
(505) 842-3292

ORGANIZATIONS

American Cetacean Society
National Headquarters
PO Box 2639
San Pedro, CA 90731-0943
(310) 548-6279

American Fisheries Society
5410 Grosvenor Lane
Bethesda, MD 20814-2199
(301) 897-8616

American Humane Association
63 Inverness Drive East
Englewood, CO 80112
(303) 792-9900

American Society of Mammalogists
School Education Partnership
c/o Dr. Thomas Tomasi
Department of Biology
Southwest Missouri State University
9091 South National Avenue
Springfield, MO 65804-0095

American Sport Fishing Association
1033 N. Fairfax Street, Suite 200
Alexandria, VA 22314
(703) 519-9691

Animal Protection Institute
2831 Fruit Ridge Rd.
Sacramento, CA 95820
(916) 731-5521

Animal Welfare Institute
PO Box 3650
Washington, DC 20007
(202) 337-2333

Atlantic Cetacean Research Center
PO Box 1413
Gloucester, MA 01930
(508) 283-3296

Center for Coastal Studies
59 Commercial Street, Box 1036
Provincetown, MA 02657
(508) 487-3622

Center for Marine Conservation
1725 DeSales Street NW, Suite 600
Washington, DC 20036
(202) 429-5609

Cetacean Research Unit
Box 159
Gloucester, MA 01930
(508) 281-6351

Cetacean Society International
PO Box 953
Georgetowne, CT 06829
(203) 544-8617

Cousteau Society
870 Greenbriar Circle, Suite 402
Chesapeake, VA 23320
(804) 523-9335

Defenders of Wildlife
1101 14th Street NW, Suite 1400
Washington, DC 20005
(202) 682-9400

Ducks Unlimited
1 Waterfowl Way
Memphis, TN 38120
(901) 758-3825

Earth Island Institute
300 Broadway, Suite 28
San Francisco, CA 94133
(415) 788-3666

Fund for Animals
200 W. 57th Street
New York, NY 10019
(212) 246-2096

Future Fisherman Foundation
1033 N. Fairfax Street, Suite 200
Alexandria, VA 22314
(703) 519-9691

Greenpeace
1436 U Street, NW
Washington, DC 20009
(202) 462-1177

International Association of Fish and
Wildlife Agencies
444 North Capitol Street NW,
Suite 544
Washington, DC 20001
(202) 624-7890

International Whaling Commission
The Red House
135 Station Road
Histon, Cambridge CB4 4NP
England

Izaak Walton League of America
707 Conservation Lane
Gaithersburg, MD 20878-2983
(301) 548-0150

National Association for Humane and
Environmental Education
Humane Society of the United States
PO Box 362
East Haddam, CT 06423
(203) 434-8666

National Association of Conservation
Districts
PO Box 855
League City, TX 77574-0855
(713) 332-3402

National Audubon Society
700 Broadway
New York, NY 10003
(212) 979-3000

National Rifle Association
Wildlife Management Division
11250 Waples Mills Road
Fairfax, VA 22030
(703) 267-1000

National Wildlife Federation
1400 - 16th Street NW
Washington, DC 20036-2266
(202) 797-6800

New England Aquarium
Central Wharf
Boston, MA 02110
(617) 973-5200

Safari Club International
4800 West Gates Pass Road
Tucson, AZ 85745
(602) 620-1220

Sierra Club
730 Polk Street
San Francisco, CA 94109
(415) 776-2211

The Nature Conservancy
1815 N. Lynn Street
Arlington, VA 22209
(703) 841-5300

The Wilderness Society
900 - 17th Street NW
Washington, DC 20006
(202) 833-2300

The Wildlife Society
5410 Grosvenor Lane, Suite 200
Bethesda, MD 20814
(301) 897-9770

Wildlife Management Institute
1101 - 14th Street NW, Suite 801
Washington, DC 20005
(202) 371-1808

GLOSSARY

abiotic: a non-living factor in an environment; e.g., light, water, temperature.

adapted, adaptation: the process of making adjustments to the environment. For example, forests develop only where soil types, moisture, and sunlight are balanced to the proper degree. Desert plants have made adjustments so as to be able to live under intense sunlight, on poor quality soils, and with much reduced water supply.

aerate: to supply with air or oxygen; to supply the blood with oxygen as in the function of lungs; to supply running water with additional oxygen as when a stream runs over falls or rapids, or when wind creates waves on a lake.

aesthetic: relating to or dealing with the beautiful. An aesthetic value relates to the value placed on beauty.

aestivation: dormancy, typically seasonal.

amphibian: an animal that typically lives in an aquatic habitat breathing by gills as young, and primarily in a terrestrial habitat breathing by lungs and through moist glandular skin as adult, e.g., frog.

anadromous fish: those fish that spend the greater share of their lives in salt water but migrate into fresh water streams for reproduction; salmon, shad, bass and others that migrate from the sea up a river to spawn.

animal community: animals of various species living within a certain habitat, each occupying a specific position in this particular environment; directly parallel and related to plant communities. For example, in a desert area, a coyote, jackrabbit, gopher, snake, elf owl, gecko, scorpion and cactus wren may be part of an animal community.

annual: a plant that completes its life cycle from seedling to mature seed-bearing plant during a single growing season and then dies.

annual turnover: the rate of replacement of individual animals in a population. Birds, such as quail, may have a 70 percent turnover annually. This means that only 30 percent of the birds alive at the beginning of one year are still alive at the end of the year. The reproductive capability of a species will match the mortality, or turnover, rate.

anthropomorphism: the attribution of human characteristics to non-humans, especially animals. Biologists recognize that animals may exhibit emotions and behavior patterns resembling those of humans. Anthropomorphism is generally used to refer to a fictionalized portrayal of animals found in many children's books, cartoons, etc.

aquatic: growing, living in, or frequenting water.

arboreal: tree dweller.

bag limit: the maximum number of animals allowed to be taken by an individual in regulated fishing or hunting. For example, an angler may catch ten fish; a deer hunter may kill one deer per year. These are bag limits.

behavior: what an animal does.

biennial: a plant that lives for two growing seasons, producing only leaves during the first season, flowers and seeds during the second.

big game: a term designating larger hunted species, such as deer, elk, moose, bear and bighorn, as opposed to "small game," such as rabbits, woodchucks, squirrels, doves and quail, or "nongame," such as songbirds and birds of prey. In many states, species are legally designated as big game, small game or nongame.

biodegradable: the property of a substance that permits it to be broken down by microorganisms into simple, stable compounds such as carbon dioxide and water.

biodiversity: a term used to represent the variety of life forms in a given area.

biologist: a person who studies living organisms and their relationship to one another.

biome: a large geographic area with somewhat uniform climatic conditions; a complex of communities characterized by a distinctive type of vegetation and maintained under the climatic conditions of the region.

biosphere: the part of the earth's crust, water and atmosphere where living organisms can subsist.

biota: the animal and plant life of a region or period.

biotic community: commonly the living organisms in a given community. It includes all plant and animal life within the community. The non-living parts are considered the abiotic parts of the community.

biotic potential: the capacity of a population of animals or plants to increase in numbers under optimum environmental conditions.

blind: a hiding place for observing.

bounty: a reward or payment for removing certain species of animals felt to be harmful. Use of bounties is slowly going out of practice.

breeding: a series of complex behavioral interactive patterns from courtship to rearing of young which are necessary for the continuation of a species.

broadleaf: the term describing a plant with widebladed leaves, such as an oak or maple; generally refers to flowering trees in contract to conifers.

brood: the offspring of a bird or mammal.

browse: a general term, commonly used in wildlife management to signify brushy plants utilized by deer, elk, or cattle as feed; to eat the twigs and leaves of woody plants.

burrowing: spending a portion of life under ground.

canopy: layer formed by the leaves and branches of the forest's tallest trees.

carnivore: a meat eater.

carrion: the bodies of dead animals, usually found in nature in the process of decay; not "fresh" meat.

carrying capacity: a wildlife management term for an equilibrium expressed by the availability of habitat components and the number of animals in a given area. In general ecological usage, carrying capacity is the dynamic equilibrium established between any life form and its environment. It is frequently expressed as a number indicating the population of any given animal a given area can support. Carrying capacity varies throughout the year. The population number varies from year to year, dependent upon conditions within the habitat such as rainfall.

cast: to regurgitate indigestible prey remains.

chaparral: in wildlife work, the term describing brushy areas where manzanita, ceanothus, cliffrose, scrub oak, skunk brush and others are the predominant vegetative types. The term originates from the Spanish and referred to thorny bushes and is also the source of the word "chaps," a part of the cowboy costume. Chaps were originally called "chaparreras," with the word later shortened by Anglo cowboys.

climatic: the average condition of the weather as defined by temperature, precipitation and wind velocities; the environmental conditions relating to weather.

climax: the final stage of plant or animal succession; when environmental conditions have been stable long enough for an area to develop a semi-permanent biome. For example, rock crumbles and pioneering plants begin to grow in the sandy soil. As they add mulch and humus, other plants follow—from grasses to shrubs to pine forest. If climatic conditions and soil types are appropriate, the climax species could be the pine forest. Animal types would follow this pattern of succession, ending perhaps with squirrels, porcupines and Stellar's jays as climax species.

coloration: a genetically-controlled pattern or markings which protects an individual organism.

community: an association of organisms—plant and animal—each occupying a certain position or ecological niche, inhabiting a common environment and interacting with each other; all the plants and animals in a particular habitat that are bound together by food chains and other interrelations.

competition: when two or more organisms have the potential for using the same resource. May be inter- or intraspecific.

conifer: a plant that bears its seeds in cones; usually refers to needleleaf trees, although some needleleaf, such as yew, do not bear cones.

coniferous: refers to cone-bearing. A coniferous forest is one composed of pines, firs, or spruces.

conservation: the use of natural resources in a way that assures their continuing availability to future generations; the wise and intelligent use or protection of natural resources. (See "preservation.")

consumer: the first part of an ecosystem is the nonliving substance; the second part consists of those organisms which are called "producers" or food makers; part three of this system is called the "consumer" because it utilizes the producer for its food; it may in turn be used as food by a secondary consumer. A rabbit is a primary consumer. A fox would be a secondary consumer.

consumptive use: in general terms related to wildlife, any use which involves activity resulting in the loss of wildlife. Examples may be the death of an individual animal as in hunting, fishing and trapping. Consumptive use may include indirect impacts of activities such as habitat loss or alteration. (See "non-consumptive use.")

courtship: a behavior pattern which ensures mating with a suitable partner of the correct species at the correct time.

cover: the vegetation, debris and irregularities of the land that provide concealment, sleeping, feeding, and breeding areas for wildlife.

covey: a small flock or group, often a family group, of birds such as quail.

crepuscular: active at dawn and dusk.

dabbling ducks: ducks which frequent shallow marshes, ponds and rivers and "tip up" to feed. They feed with body above water and take off vertically when startled; also called "puddle ducks." (See "diving ducks.")

deciduous: referring to trees, those that annually shed their leaves; regarding animal teeth, those commonly called "milk teeth."

decomposer: those organisms (bacteria, fungi) which convert dead organic materials into inorganic materials; a plant or animal that feeds on dead materials and causes its mechanical or chemical breakdown.

depredation: the act of preying upon, usually in relation to wildlife damage to people's crops or animals.

desert scrub: arid environments with irregular winter rainfall, summer rainfall or biseasonal rainfall; highly varied plantlife, with leafless, drought deciduous, or evergreen species of trees, shrubs, herbs and grasses, yuccas, agaves and cacti.

display: an observable behavioral pattern that carries a specific message. The message may be inter- or intraspecific.

diurnal: active by daylight; the opposite of nocturnal.

diversity: variety.

diving ducks: ducks which prefer deep water as in lakes

and bays. They feed by diving below the surface and take wing from a running start.

domesticated: referring to animals, those which humans have tamed, kept in captivity and bred for special purposes. All domesticated animals have their origins in wild ancestors. Cattle used for food and other products; sheep for wool and other products; as well as dogs, cats, birds, and fish commonly kept as pets are all examples of domesticated animals.

dominant species: plant or animal species which exert major controlling influence on the community. Removal of dominant species results in important changes in the community. Generally dominants have the greatest total biomass represented by total numbers or weight.

ecological niche: the role played by an organism in a biological community; its food preferences, requirements for shelter, special behaviors, and the timing of its activities (e.g., nocturnal or diurnal). The ecological niche of an organism has little to do with **where** it is found but much more to do with its **function** or role, e.g., predator, decomposer, and with **how** it performs that function.

ecologist: a scientist who studies the interrelations of living things to one another and their environment.

ecology: the study of the relation of organisms or groups of organisms to their environment; or the science of the interrelations between living organisms and their environment.

ecosystem: a natural unit that includes living and nonliving parts interacting to produce a stable system in which the exchange of materials between the living and nonliving parts follows closed paths; all living things and their environment in an area of any size with all linked together by energy and nutrient flow.

edge effect: the tendency of wildlife to use the areas where two vegetative types come together forming an edge; where rabbits, for example, concentrate in an area where brush land and meadow land meet because of the diversity of food, shelter and other habitat components provided by the edge.

endangered: an "endangered" species is one which is in danger of extinction throughout all or a significant portion of its range. (A "threatened" species is one that is likely to become endangered.)

environment: the total of all of the surroundings—air, water, vegetation, human element, wildlife—that has influence on you and your existence, including physical, biological and all other factors; the surroundings of a plant or animal including other plants and animals, climate and location.

ethics: a personal or social moral code.

eutrophication: enrichment of soils and water due to fertilization, sewage, effluent or other waters that carry a high plant-nutrient component.

evergreen: a plant that does not lose all of its leaves at one time. Among trees, some broadleaf species, such as live oak, remain green all year, but most North American evergreens are coniferous.

exotic: in conservation language, this refers to a foreign plant or animal—one that has been introduced into a new area. Examples could be the "wild" burro or the ring-necked pheasant.

extinction: the condition of having been removed from existence. An animal or plant facing extinction is one in danger of vanishing from our world.

feral: used in wildlife as referring to domesticated animals gone wild; e.g., wild burros, goats, cats, dogs.

finite: having bounds or limits; capable of being counted or measured; the opposite of infinite.

flyway: fly routes established by migratory birds.

food chain: the transfer of food energy from the source in plants through a series of animals, with repeated eating and being eaten. For example, a green plant, a leaf-eating insect, and an insect-eating bird would form a simple food chain. Any one species is usually represented in several or many food chains.

food web: an interlocking pattern of food chains.

forage: refers to vegetation taken naturally by herbivorous animals, both wild and domesticated.

forbs: an important part of wildlife habitat. In wildlife usage, forbs are weeds and herbs; low growing, annual or perennial, herbaceous plants.

forest floor: the layer of decomposing material that covers the soil in a forest.

forest management: the practical application of scientific, economic and social principles to the administration of a forest for specified objectives.

forest region: an extensive area of a continent in which the climax forest associations are closely similar. The major forest regions of North America are West Coast Forest, Western Forest, Central Hardwood Forest, Tropical Forest, Northern Forest, and Southern Forest.

game animal: legal designation for animals which may be managed and hunted only under regulation.

grassland: a vegetative community in which grasses are the most conspicuous members.

grazer: a herbaceous organism that consumes primarily grasses.

habitat: the arrangement of food, water, shelter or cover and space suitable to animals' needs. It is the "life range" which must include food and water, as well as escape cover, winter cover, cover to rear young and even cover in which to play.

hardwood: a deciduous or broadleaf tree; the wood from such trees.

harvest: the intentional gathering of plants, animals and other natural resources for use, especially renewable resources; a human intervention in a life cycle in order to use a resource. In wildlife management, hunting is considered a form of harvest in which individual animals are killed.

herb: any flowering plant or fern that has a soft, rather than woody, stem.

herb layer: the layer of soft-stemmed plants growing close to the forest floor.

herbivore: a plant eater.

hibernation: the act of passing the winter, or a portion of it, in a state of sleep; a torpid or resting state.

home range: the area in which an animal travels in the scope of normal activities; not to be confused with territory.

hunter: a person or animal who searches for wildlife with the intent of catching or killing it.

hunting: the act of a person or animal who hunts.

hunting pressure: the numbers, amount or concentration of hunters in a specific area and upon a specific animal.

indigenous: a naturally occurring species.

inorganic: not living.

insectivorous: refers to insect eaters.

interaction: the relationship of one organism to another; the action of one population affecting the growth or death rate of another population. One population may eat members of the other populations, compete for food, excrete harmful wastes or otherwise interfere with the other population. Some interactions are positive, some negative and some are completely neutral.

interdependencies: the interrelationships of wildlife with one another and with the various elements of their environment.

invade: to enter, to encroach upon, to spread over into. In wildlife usage, this usually refers to when an organism is removed from a community and another organism spreads over into this community.

inventory: in wildlife terms, the process of identifying and counting animals.

key plant species: those plant species which are used to indicate the general condition of a habitat. For example, when plants show overuse, the animals may have exceeded the carrying capacity of the habitat.

license: in wildlife terms, a legal permit, e.g., to hunt, fish, trap, transport, keep captive wildlife or perform taxidermy.

lichen: algae and fungus growing together in a symbiotic relationship.

life cycle: the continuous sequence of changes undergone by an organism from one primary form to the development of the same form again.

limiting factors: influences in the life history of any animal, population of animals, or species; e.g., food, water, shelter, space, disease, predation, climatic conditions, pollution, hunting, poaching and accidents. When one or more of these exceeds the limit of tolerance of that animal, population of animals or species, it then becomes a limiting factor; it then directly affects the well-being of that animal and may result in the animal or animals' death. Limiting factors may result from causes in nature as well as human activities.

litter: the number of young born per birthing.

management: in general terms related to wildlife, the intentional manipulation or non-manipulation of habitat and/or the organisms within the habitat. (See "wildlife management.")

microclimates: the climates of specific small areas. Microclimates are the tiny contrasts to the general climate of the area. A deep, narrow, shadowed canyon—cool and damp—might be a microclimate within a desert mountain range. The shady side of a huge boulder, or the area immediately surrounding a tiny spring, or the north side of a city building would be classified as microclimates.

microhabitat: a small habitat within a larger one in which environmental conditions differ from those in the surrounding area. A hole in a tree trunk or an animal carcass is a microhabitat within the forest.

microorganism: an organism microscopic in size, observable only through a microscope.

migratory: in wildlife usage, birds or other animals which make annual migrations; i.e., travel distances in seasonal movements. Migrations may be great, or very short, depending upon the species.

mitigate: to make up for; to substitute some benefit for losses incurred.

mixed forest: a forest that includes both coniferous and deciduous trees.

monoculture: the raising of a crop of a single species, generally even-aged.

mortality rate: the death rate; usually expressed in deaths per thousand.

mulching: to add materials to soil in order to protect from cold, to reduce evaporation, to control weeds or to enrich the soil. Common materials could be sawdust, bark, leaves.

multiple-use: a term referring to a system of management in which lands and waters are used for a variety of purposes. The uses are not necessarily simultaneous but are intended to be compatible. For example, a tract of forest land can serve as a home for wildlife, provide clean air and water, be a place for recreation, be used to grow and harvest trees for products, and be aesthetically pleasing, all at the same time.

multiple-use forestry: any practice of forestry fulfilling two or more objectives of management.

mutualism: a close association between two different species whereby each species derives some benefit. The yucca plant and the yucca moth each benefit from their relationship.

natal: related to birth or being born.

natural selection: a process in nature resulting in the survival and perpetuation of only those forms of plant and animal life having certain favorable characteristics that enable them to adapt best to a specific environment.

needleleaf: bearing needlelike leaves.

niche: see "ecological niche."

nitrogen-fixation: the conversion of elemental nitrogen from the atmosphere to organic combinations or to forms readily utilizable in biological processes; normally carried out by bacteria, living symbiotically in legumes or by free-living soil bacteria.

nocturnal: active by night; the opposite of diurnal.

nonconsumptive use: in general terms related to wildlife, any use which does not directly kill wildlife, e.g., most forms of birdwatching, photography, hiking and other pursuits involving activity as well as vicarious forms such as movie, television and gallery viewing of wildlife. (See "consumptive use.")

nongame: all wildlife species which are not commonly hunted, killed or consumed by humans, such as songbirds and raptors.

nonrenewable resource: nonliving resources such as rocks and minerals; resources which do not regenerate themselves; substances such as petroleum, coal, copper and gold which, once used, cannot be replaced—at least not in this geological age. (See "renewable resource.")

omnivore: an animal that eats both plant and animal materials.

organic matter: chemical compounds of carbon combined with other chemical elements and generally manufactured in the life processes of plants and animals. Most organic compounds are a source of food for bacteria and are usually combustible.

organism: a living thing; a form of life composed of mutually dependent parts that maintain various vital processes.

parasite: an organism that lives by deriving benefit from another organism, usually doing harm to the organism from which it derives benefit.

parasitic: to be a parasite on. Mistletoe is a parasite growing on trees.

pelage: body covering on a mammal.

perennial: a plant that lives for several years and usually produces seeds each year.

pesticide: any chemical preparation used to control populations of organisms, including plants and animals, perceived to be injurious.

pinch period: that period of an annual cycle when the factors necessary for life are least favorable.

plankton: those organisms suspended in an aquatic habitat which control their own movements; usually microscopic, including bacteria, algae, protozoans, rotifers, larvae, and small crustaceans. Phytoplankton are the plant plankton; zooplankton are the animal species.

plant communities: an association of plants, each occupying a certain position or ecological niche, inhabiting a common environment and interacting with each other. Dominant plants usually define the community, e.g., a spruce-fir community.

pollution: harmful substances deposited in the air or water or land, leading to a state of dirtiness, impurity, unhealthiness.

population: the number of a particular species in a defined area.

population inventory: a measure of the current density of a species of animal or plant.

prairie: a grassland community.

predaceous: a predaceous animal is a predator who kills and eats other animals.

predation: the act of preying upon.

predator: an animal that kills and eats other animals.

prescribed burning: the planned application of fire to natural fuels with the intent to confine the burning to a predetermined area.

preservation: protection which emphasizes nonconsumptive values and uses, including no direct use by humans, contrasted with conservation which emphasizes both consumptive and nonconsumptive values and uses. (See "conservation.")

prey: animals that are killed and eaten by other animals.

primary producers: green plants which are able to manufacture food from simple organic substances.

rain shadow: an area on the leeward side of a mountain barrier that receives little rainfall.

range: see "home range", the land upon which animals live; an area grazed by livestock and/or wildlife.

rangeland: all lands, including forest land, that produce native forage in contrast to land cultivated for agricultural crops or carrying a dense forest.

raptor: pertaining to eagles, hawks and owls; birds which are predatory, preying upon other animals.

rare: referring to wildlife species not presently in danger but of concern because of low numbers.

recreation: entertainment, frequently implying activity in the out-of-doors.

reintroduction of species: a wildlife management technique where a species is reintroduced into historic range; replanting of animals in areas where they had become extinct.

renewable resource: living resources, such as plants and animals, which have the capacity to renew themselves when conditions for survival are favorable. (See "nonrenewable resource.")

resident wildlife: animals which are residents to a specific area on a year-round basis as opposed to migratory.

resource: a portion of an environment upon which people have placed or assigned value or see as being available for use.

savanna: a parklike grassland with scattered trees or clumps of trees.

scavenger: an organism that habitually feeds on refuse or carrion. A coyote is a part-time scavenger; a dermestid beetle is a full-time scavenger.

scrub: low, woody vegetation composed principally of shrubs.

season: a period of time, usually when something specific occurs; for example, any of four times of year characterized by differences or changes, as in plant growth and temperature. In wildlife management or conservation terms, that time when hunting, fishing or trapping is permitted for a particular species.

sere: the series of communities that follow one another in a natural succession, as in the change from a bare field to a mature forest.

shelter: cover; cover from elements, for natal activity, to travel in, for breeding, for bedding, etc.; varies depending upon species.

skink: any of a family of small, smooth-scaled lizards.

slough: an inlet from a river; backwater; tideflat; a creek in a marsh.

small game: a term designating smaller hunted species, such as rabbits, woodchucks, squirrels, doves and quail, as opposed to big game such as deer, elk, moose, bear and bighorn, or "nongame" such as songbirds and birds of prey. In many states, species are legally designated as big game, small game or nongame.

snag: a standing dead tree from which the leaves and most of the branches have fallen; typically important as wildlife habitat.

social limits: the saturation point of a species in an environment; how much crowding an individual will accept; varies widely with species.

softwood: a coniferous tree; a common but not strictly accurate term; the wood of many conifers is harder than that of some so-called hardwood trees.

spawning: the act of producing or depositing eggs; usually refers to fish.

species: a population of individuals that are more or less alike and that are able to breed and produce fertile offspring under natural conditions; a category of biological classification immediately below the genus or subgenus.

state wildlife agency: the state agency that has the legal responsibility for management of some or all wildlife, including habitat protection, restoration and alteration; planning; land acquisition; research; education; information; endangered species; consumptive uses; nonconsumptive programs; regulations; and usually law enforcement.

static: showing little change, usually used in reference to a population or to a condition of habitat.

stewardship: related to the environment, the concept of responsible caretaking; based on the premise that we do not own resources but are managers of resources and are responsible to future generations for their condition.

stress: usually thought of as a physical factor that applies to detrimental pressure to an organism or population. A drought period would apply a stress to a plant community and thereby to an animal population and this would perhaps inhibit reproduction rather than eliminating the species.

succession: the orderly, gradual and continuous replacement of one plant or animal by another.

symbiosis: a close living relationship between organisms.

symbiotic: the characteristic of symbiosis.

terrestrial: ground dweller.

territory: the concept of "ownership" or dominance over a unit of habitat; an area defended by an animal against others of the same species; used for breeding, feeding or both. Many species of wildlife are territorial. Best known are certain birds and wolves.

territorial imperative: the instinctive compulsion to gain and defend a territory. Many zoologists believe this drive to be more compelling and persuasive than the sexual urge.

threatened: in wildlife terms, a species present in its range but in danger because of a decline in numbers.

tree: a woody plant 12 or more feet (four or more meters) tall with a single main stem (trunk) and a more or less distinct crown of leaves.

transplant: in wildlife terms, an animal moves to a new area.

understory: the layer of plants growing under another higher layer of plants, e.g., grass, weeds and brush under forest trees.

vegetation: the mass of plants that covers a given area. Flora, a term often wrongly used interchangeably with vegetation, is a list of the species of plants that compose the vegetation.

veldt: South African grassland, with scattered trees.

viable: capable of living, growing and developing.

waterfowl: water birds, usually ducks, but including shore and wading birds, geese, etc.

wild: not tamed or domesticated, living in a basically free condition. A wild animal provides for its own food, shelter and other needs in an environment that serves as a suitable habitat.

wildlife: animals that are not tamed or domesticated; may be small organisms only visible to humans if seen through a microscope or as large as a whale. Wildlife includes, but is not limited to, insects, spiders, birds, reptiles, fish, amphibians and mammals, if non-domesticated.

wildlife manager: a person who manages wildlife habitat, and/or other related human activities.

wildlife management: the application of scientific knowledge and technical skills to protect, preserve, conserve, limit, enhance, or extend the value of wildlife and its habitat.

woodland: a wooded area in which the trees are often small, short bowled and open grown; farm woodland—any wooded area that is part of a farm.

yard up: to gather in a sheltered area in winter; used typically in reference to deer, moose, etc.

zero population growth: the maintenance or holding of population numbers at a fixed level so as to obviate increase.

This glossary is primarily designed for reference and background information. Occasionally, terms are defined within an activity and are not repeated here. Key vocabulary for activities is usually defined here, especially if it is specific to wildlife and understanding of natural systems. This "Glossary" is compiled from four principal sources. The majority of the terms and definitions are reprinted with few changes from *Multidisciplinary Wildlife Teaching Activities*, developed and edited by William R. Hernbrode. (Columbus, Ohio; ERIC Clearinghouse for Science, Mathematics, and Environmental Education, 1978). The next largest group of entries is derived from the "Glossary" which appears in the *Project Learning Tree Supplementary Activity Guide for Grades K through 6*, and *Grades 7 through 12*. (Washington D.C.: American Forest Institute, 1977). A number of entries are adapted or reprinted from *Wildlife Aid No. 2*. (Portland, Oregon: U.S. Forest Service, R-6, June 1965). Additional entries are based on the contributions of the Project WILD Management Committee, staff, and reviewers. All "Glossary" materials derived from previously published sources are adapted and/or reprinted with the permission of the copyright holder. We extend our thanks to those organizations and individuals for their assistance.

CONCEPTUAL FRAMEWORK

This framework serves as the conceptual basis for activities in Project WILD. Each activity in the materials is designed to correspond to one or more points in this outline. Sometimes the correspondence is direct; that is, the activity is designed to teach the underlying concepts. In other instances, the relationship is indirect; that is, the reference to the conceptual framework is made to provide additional background information for the instructor.

I.   AWARENESS AND APPRECIATION OF WILDLIFE
A.   Humans and wildlife have similar basic needs.
1.   All forms of life depend upon water, oxygen, nutrients and/or sunlight in some combination.
2.   All living things are affected by and interact with their environment.
3.   Either directly or indirectly, plants support nearly all forms of animal life, including humans.
4.   Wildlife has habitat needs that are much like those of humans, although these needs are satisfied in different ways.
B.   Humans and wildlife share environments.
1.   Wildlife is present in or on nearly all areas of the earth's surface.
2.   Over a period of time, humans and wildlife must adjust or adapt to the environment, alter the environment, or perish.
3.   Wildlife is all around us even though we may not actually see, hear, or otherwise sense its presence.
4.   Wildlife varies from microscopic forms to those over 100 feet in length and occurs in a variety of forms, colors and shapes.
C.   Humans and wildlife are subject to many of the same environmental conditions.
1.   Both humans and wildlife depend on their habitats.
2.   Habitat is composed of many integrated components including food, water, shelter or cover, space and the arrangement of these in relation to each other.
3.   The health and well-being of both humans and wildlife are dependent upon the quality of the natural environment.
4.   Environmental change in its various forms affects all life.
D.   Humans have far greater ability to alter or adjust to environments than does wildlife; thus, humans have a responsibility to consider effects of their activities on other life forms.

II.   HUMAN VALUES AND WILDLIFE
A.   Wildlife has aesthetic and spiritual values.
1.   The aesthetic and spiritual values humans place on wildlife vary from person to person and culture to culture.
2.   Human and wildlife relationships are expressed through myths, religious teachings and writings, symbols, ceremonies and other activities.
3.   Humans may find peace and inspiration through study and observation of wildlife, or simply through knowledge of its existence.
4.   Human appreciation of wildlife is often expressed through art, music, drama, dance, literature, photography and other means of creative expression.
B.   Wildlife has ecological and scientific values.
1.   Wildlife interacts with its environment and thereby affects the functioning of the ecological system.
2.   Wildlife may be used as a barometer of overall environmental quality.
3.   Study of the interaction of wildlife and its environment, past and present, helps humans to better understand ecological systems and the effect of human activities on those systems.
4.   Study of the physiology, behavior and needs of wildlife can yield insight into some of the physiology, behavior and needs of humans.
C.   Wildlife has social and political values.
1.   Historically, wildlife affected the development, movement and size of human societies.
2.   Wildlife questions and issues have influenced alliances and conflicts between and within communities, societies, states and nations.
3.   Wildlife issues can affect national, regional and local political activities.
D.   Wildlife has commercial and economic values.
1.   The distribution and abundance of wildlife can affect the economy of an area.
2.   Throughout history, humans have utilized wildlife for food, shelter, clothing and other products.
3.   Human use of wildlife directly and indirectly creates job opportunities for people.
4.   Some wildlife provides products of commercial value to humans.
E.   Wildlife has consumptive and non-consumptive recreational values.
1.   Wildlife-based recreation is of major importance to many millions of Americans.
2.   Consumptive wildlife-based activities, such as hunting and fishing, provide U.S. and Canadian citizens with millions of days of outdoor recreation each year.

3. Non-consumptive activities, such as wildlife photography, painting, feeding and observation also provide millions of days of recreation annually.
   F. Wildlife has intrinsic value, although humans often only recognize values based upon human wants and needs.

III. *WILDLIFE AND ECOLOGICAL SYSTEMS*
   A. Each environment has characteristic life forms.
      1. The environment, created and shaped by natural forces and modified by humans, determines what life forms can occupy it.
      2. Each species occupies a niche within the range of environments in which it is found.
      3. All life forms show adaptations to the environments in which they live.
   B. All living elements of an ecological system are interdependent.
      1. Plants and animals in ecological systems live in a web of interdependence in which each species contributes to the functioning of the overall system.
      2. Food webs and energy chains illustrate the interrelationships of all living things.
      3. In a naturally functioning ecosystem, life forms and environmental factors interact to keep wildlife populations in a long-term dynamic equilibrium with each other and with their habitats.
      4. Diverse plant communities tend to support diverse wildlife communities.
      5. Some wildlife populations exhibit cyclic patterns over time.
      6. Natural laws are ultimately as binding on human populations as on wildlife.
   C. Variation and change occur in all ecological systems.
      1. All forms of life, including wildlife, are affected by changes in their environments.
      2. Wildlife numbers and species compositions are not static but are constantly changing.
      3. There is a trend of continuous replacement of one natural community of life by another.
      4. Natural events and human activities affect the rate and direction of succession.
   D. Adaptation is continuous within all ecological systems.
      1. Each habitat is suitable only to those life forms that have adapted, over a number of generations, to its ecological conditions.
      2. Wildlife adapts to its environment in ways that enable it to survive and maintain its numbers.
      3. Wildlife species differ in their ability to adapt to changes in their habitat.
      4. Species with very specific habitat requirements tend to be less able to adjust to environmental change.
      5. Isolated ecosystems such as lakes or islands may develop specialized life forms, thus making these systems more vulnerable to environmental change.
   E. Living things tend to reproduce in numbers greater than their habitat can support.
      1. A population tends to increase in size until limited by one or more factors.
      2. Various mortality factors, such as disease, predation, climatic conditions, pollution, accidents and shortages of life's necessities, will cause a percentage of any population to die each year.
   F. Each area of land or water, and ultimately the planet, has a carrying capacity of plants and animals.
      1. Carrying capacity is determined by climatic, geological, biological and/or behavioral factors along with human activities.
      2. Carrying capacity may vary from season to season and year to year.
      3. Carrying capacity affects and is affected by wildlife behavior.
      4. The numbers, health and distribution of wildlife are related to carrying capacity.
      5. Carrying capacity limitations can result in competition between and among domestic animals, wildlife and humans.

IV. *WILDLIFE CONSERVATION*
   A. Management of resources and environments is the application of scientific knowledge and technical skills to protect, preserve, conserve, limit, enhance or extend the value of a natural resource, as well as to improve environmental quality.
      1. All resource and environmental management practices are limited in their scope and effectiveness.
      2. Wise resource and environmental management can improve the quality of life for wildlife and humans.
      3. Wildlife management practices are limited in their ability to benefit wildlife.
      4. Philosophies, objectives and practices of various types of resource management are sometimes incompatible with each other and therefore conflicts and tradeoffs may occur.
   B. Wildlife is one of our basic natural resources, along with water, air, minerals, soil and plant life.
      1. Nonrenewable natural resources are those which are available on a finite basis, such as minerals and fossil fuels.
      2. Wildlife and other renewable natural resources can replenish themselves independently or with human assistance.
   C. Good habitat is the key to wildlife survival.
      1. Wildlife is affected by changes in the quality, quantity and distribution of its habitat.
      2. For a wildlife population to sustain itself there must be suitable habitat to support a viable breeding population, not just a few individuals.

3. Most species that are endangered or threatened became so from natural or human-caused changes in their habitat and their inability to adapt or adjust to such changes.
4. Successful reintroduction of wildlife into formerly occupied range may be possible but only if suitable habitat is available.

D. Wildlife resources can be managed and conserved.
   1. Wildlife can be managed to alter its value to humans.
   2. Humans have learned management principles by observing natural forces and events through experimentation and research.
   3. Conservation of wildlife involves wise and varied uses as well as protection.
   4. The diversity and numbers of wildlife present in an area often reflect the nature of human use of that habitat.
   5. Habitat management is often the best way to help threatened or endangered species.
   6. Management of one species will affect other species in a community.
   7. For management purposes, wildlife has often been divided into categories such as game, nongame, endangered, threatened, furbearers and commercial.

E. Wildlife conservation practices depend on a knowledge of natural laws and the application of knowledge from many disciplines.
   1. Wildlife management practices generally developed in a progressive sequence, beginning with regulations, followed by predator control, creation of refuges, stocking programs and habitat management.
   2. Systematic inventory of wildlife populations did not become a common practice until the 1930s, although journals of early explorers reflect considerable variation in historic population levels.
   3. Nongame species have recently begun to receive greater and more specific management attention.
   4. Scientific knowledge of all aspects of wildlife, including biological and social, is limited but growing.
   5. Wildlife managers use a variety of techniques in management programs, such as information, education and regulations involving people; as well as inventory, damage control, habitat management, stocking, artificial propagation, transplanting and direct manipulation of wildlife populations.
   6. Regulated harvest of some wildlife is a management technique.
   7. Regulations are necessary for wildlife conservation but cannot substitute for good habitat or maintain a species whose habitat has been depleted or destroyed.
   8. Some wildlife species are not native but have been introduced to the area they presently occupy. Such introductions create changes ranging from beneficial to harmful.
   9. Adding members to a community or subtracting members from it affects other members of the community.
   10. Acquisition, protection, improvement and restoration of habitat are considered to be the most beneficial long-range management techniques for wildlife.
   11. Wildlife management programs are based on both biological and social-political considerations.

F. In the United States, wildlife is considered to be a public resource. Ownership of land or water alone does not secure ownership of wildlife on that land or in that water as it does in some other countries.
   1. Primary responsibility for most wildlife conservation programs in the U.S. is delegated to governmental agencies.
   2. States are generally considered to have a greater responsibility for wildlife conservation programs than the federal government.
   3. State wildlife agencies are legally responsible for managing most wildlife on public and private lands within their geographic jurisdictions.
   4. Federal agencies, in cooperation with state agencies, are legally responsible for managing wildlife affecting national interest such as most threatened and endangered species and migratory wildlife.
   5. Private organizations, industrial interests and individual citizens also conduct wildlife conservation activities.
   6. Privately owned lands continue to provide significant amounts of habitat for wildlife.
   7. Funds provided by consumptive users, not general tax dollars, are the primary source of income for most state wildlife management programs and some federal programs.
   8. Most wildlife exists on land or in waters that are not directly controlled by state or federal wildlife management agencies.
   9. Wildlife agencies manage not only wildlife but also the activities of people who use wildlife.
   10. Wildlife agencies employ persons with a variety of scientific training and vocational skills. Competition for jobs in the wildlife field is keen and applicants must usually have a college degree.
   11. Citizens can become involved in the management of wildlife, habitat and the environment by direct participation in the political process or through local, state, national or international organizations.

V. *CULTURAL AND SOCIAL INTERACTION WITH WILDLIFE*
   A. Human cultures and societies, past and present, affect and are affected by wildlife and its habitat.
      1. All livestock and pet animals were domesticated and developed from wildlife species as humans sought to provide themselves with food, shelter, medicines and companionship and to satisfy other needs or wants.
      2. Human societies and cultures developed in various ways partly because environmental factors produced different types of plants and animals in different places.
      3. Members of some cultures still depend on wildlife to supply a portion of their requirements for food, shelter and clothing.

4. Creative portrayal of wildlife through art, literature, dance, music and drama is an historic as well as contemporary means of expressing human relationships with wildlife.
5. Societies and subgroups within a society may have different attitudes toward wildlife and its uses, formed and transmitted by family, community and other social groups in a variety of ways.
6. Social attitudes toward wildlife and habitat are affected by the content of various communications media such as books, television, radio, movies and magazines.

B. Societies develop programs and policies relating to wildlife and its habitat through a variety of social mechanisms.
1. Some of the values, ethics and historical traditions of societies are reflected in their treatment of wildlife and other resources.
2. Wildlife management programs and policies are developed largely through political, social, economic and scientific processes.
3. Other nations and governments have different policies and philosophies relating to wildlife ownership and protection and to habitat management.

VI. *WILDLIFE ISSUES AND TRENDS: ALTERNATIVES AND CONSEQUENCES*
A. Human impacts on wildlife and its habitat are increasing worldwide.
1. Demand for wildlife tends to be greater than the supply available.
2. Human intervention in the environment continues to change plant and animal distribution, diversity and abundance.
3. Increasing human populations and technologies often require space and activities that are detrimental to wildlife and its habitat.
4. Loss and degradation of habitat is considered the greatest problem facing wildlife today.
5. Human activities are accelerating the rate at which wildlife becomes threatened, endangered and extinct.

B. Issues involving wildlife and its habitat are a product of social and cultural trends.
1. Cultural differences and priorities continue to cause conflicts concerning wildlife.
2. Modernization continues to separate people from direct contact with the natural world. This affects their actions and attitudes toward wildlife.
3. Economic trends plus increased human population and mobility have important influences on wildlife and its habitat.
4. Recreational trends affect wildlife and its habitat.
5. More leisure time and growing pursuit of outdoor activities are increasing the pressures on wildlife and habitat.
6. Political trends affect wildlife and other natural resources.

C. Current wildlife issues and trends are complex and involve alternatives and consequences.
1. Public interest and involvement in wildlife continues to grow.
2. Many wildlife issues involve conflicts between different interest groups.
3. Historically when conflict between recreational and commercial harvest of a wildlife species became severe, the commercial use has been eliminated.
4. Native American Indians and other groups at times disagree over certain uses of and rights to wildlife.
5. Charging an access fee to hunt, fish, camp, recreate, or trap on private land is becoming a more common practice.
6. Wildlife interest groups are making increasing use of the judicial, legislative and regulatory systems in seeking their objectives.
7. Whether uses of wildlife should be consumptive or non-consumptive is of concern to increasing numbers of people.
8. Among consumptive groups, conflicts often involve how, when and how much wildlife populations are used.
9. Funding for state wildlife agencies historically has been derived from consumptive user fees.
10. The levels and methods by which wildlife interest groups should fund wildlife programs are continuing issues.
11. Recent concerns are that policies are influenced by funding sources rather than from a wider constituency.
12. Various groups interested in wildlife represent a wide range of philosophies and ethics concerning wildlife and how best to ensure its long range health and viability.
13. Questions exist concerning efforts to save endangered species for their present and future scientific, biological, aesthetic, economic, social and intrinsic values.
14. Controversy exists between some state and federal agencies over the responsibility for management of various wildlife species.
15. Philosophies and practices in wildlife management have been both supported and criticized by individuals as well as public and private organizations.
16. The value placed on wildlife is commonly an issue in resource management decisions because value is often intangible and varies from person to person.

D. Many problems, issues and trends involving wildlife in other parts of the world are similar to those in this country.
1. Wildlife habitat loss as a result of natural trends or human activities is a condition common among nearly all nations.

2. Consumptive uses of wildlife have been excessive in some settings and continue as a persistent problem in parts of the world.
3. Commercial sale of wildlife and wildlife products is controversial and has worldwide implications.
4. Many wildlife species regularly move across national boundaries, making adoption of international agreements necessary along with formation of international agencies and organizations to ensure protection and management of these species.

VII. *WILDLIFE, ECOLOGICAL SYSTEMS AND RESPONSIBLE HUMAN ACTIONS*
   A. Each person as an individual and as a member of society affects the environment.
      1. Individual and community lifestyle decisions, including recreational choices, transportation options, housing selections, vocation, food, clothing and energy use, affect wildlife directly and indirectly.
      2. Personal and community conservation practices, plus social, cultural and economic values, affect environmental programs and activities.
      3. Wildlife depletion and habitat destruction can be changed by the development and adoption of alternative human lifestyles and social expectations.
      4. In determining responsible and ethical actions in relation to wildlife and the environment, individuals must separate desires from actual needs.
   B. Responsible environmental actions are the obligation of all levels of society, starting with the individual.
      1. Human activities increasingly determine which species of plants and animals will flourish and which will decline or disappear.
      2. All users of wildlife must respect the rights and property of others, consider effects on the habitat and observe rules and regulations relating to wildlife.
      3. It is the responsibility of citizens, government and industry to avoid waste and destructive exploitation of natural resources, including wildlife.
      4. Prosecution for violations relating to wildlife and other natural resources often reflects the community's perception of the importance of those resources.
      5. Public decisions that affect wildlife and the environment are made through social and political processes designed to represent the wishes of the society.
      6. Individuals can influence public processes by voting, demonstrating, lobbying, seeking office and supporting compatible interest groups.
      7. Private decisions that affect wildlife and the environment are made through personal judgments. Each person makes such decisions on a daily basis, including use of time and energy, consumer choices, vocational and leisure time activities.

METRIC CONVERSION CHART

SYMBOL	WHEN YOU KNOW	MULTIPLY BY	TO FIND	SYMBOL
		LENGTH		
in	inches	2.5	centimeters	cm
ft	feet	30.0	centimeters	cm
yd	yards	0.9	meters	m
mi	miles	1.6	kilometers	km
cm	centimeters	.4	inches	in
m	meters	3.3	feet	ft
m	meters	1.09	yards	yd
km	kilometers	0.6	miles	mi
		AREA		
in^2	square inches	6.5	square centimeters	cm^2
ft^2	square feet	0.09	square meters	m^2
yd^2	square yards	0.84	square meters	m^2
mi^2	square miles (640 acres)	2.6	square kilometers	km^2
a	acre (43.560 sq.ft.)	0.4	hectares	h
cm^2	square centimeter	0.16	square inches	in^2
m^2	square meter	10.8	square feet	ft^2
m^2	square meter	1.2	square yards	yd^2
km^2	square kilometer	0.4	square miles	mi^2
h	hectare	2.5	acres	a
		MASS		
oz	ounces (avoirdupois)	28	grams	g
lb	pound	0.45	kilograms	kg
	short tons (2,000 lbs.)	0.9	tonnes (metric ton)	t
g	grams	0.035	ounces (avoirdupois)	oz
kg	kilograms	2.2	pounds	lb
t	tonnes	1.1	short tons (2,000 lbs.)	t
		VOLUME		
tsp	teaspoons	5.0	milliliters	ml
Tbsp	tablespoons	15.0	milliliters	ml
fl oz	fluid ounces	30.0	milliliters	ml
c	cups (liquid)	0.24	liters	l
pt	pints (liquid)	0.47	liters	l
qt	quarts (liquid)	0.95	liters	l
gal	gallons	3.8	liters	l
ft^3	cubic feet	0.03	cubic meters	m^3
yd^3	cubic yards	0.76	cubic meters	m^3
ml	milliliters	0.2	teaspoons	tsp
ml	milliliters	0.07	tablespoons	Tbsp
ml	milliliters	0.03	fluid ounces	fl oz
l	liters	4.2	cups (liquid)	c
l	liters	2.1	pints (liquid)	pt
1	liters	1.06	quarts (liquid)	qt
1	liters	0.26	gallons	gal
m^3	cubic meters	35.0	cubic feet	ft^3
m^3	cubic meters	1.3	cubic yards	yd^3
		TEMPERATURE		
F	degrees Fahrenheit	(9/5 x C) + 32	decrees Celcius	C
C	degrees Celsius	5/9 x (F-32)	degrees Fahrenheit	4.92

GUIDELINES FOR RESPONSIBLE USE OF ANIMALS IN THE CLASSROOM

An NSTA Position Statement

These guidelines are recommended by the National Science Teachers Association (NSTA) for use by science educators and students. They apply, in particular, to the use of nonhuman animals in instructional activities planned and/or supervised by teachers who teach science at the precollege level.

Observation and experimentation with living organisms give students unique perspectives of life processes that are not provided by other modes of instruction. Studying animals in the classroom enables students to develop skills of observation and comparison, a sense of stewardship, and an appreciation for the unity, interrelationships and complexity of life. This study, however, requires appropriate, humane care of the organism. Teachers are expected to be knowledgeable about the proper care of organisms under study and the safety of their students.

These are the guidelines recommended by NSTA concerning the responsible use of animals in a school classroom laboratory:

- Acquisition and care of animals must be appropriate to the species.
- Student classwork and science projects involving animals must be under the supervision of a science teacher or other trained professional.
- Teachers sponsoring or supervising the use of animals in instructional activities—including acquisition, care, and disposition—will adhere to local, state, and national laws, policies, and regulations regarding the organisms.
- Teachers must instruct students on safety precautions for handling live animals or animal specimens.
- Plans for the future care or disposition of animals at the conclusion of the study must be developed and implemented.
- Laboratory and dissection activities must be conducted with consideration and appreciation for the organism.
- Laboratory and dissection activities must be conducted in a clean and organized work space with care and laboratory precision.
- Laboratory and dissection activities must be based on carefully planned objectives.
- Laboratory and dissection objectives must be appropriate to the maturity level of the student.
- Student views or beliefs sensitive to dissection must be considered; the teacher will respond appropriately.

—Adopted by the
NSTA Board of Directors
in July, 1991

Published by the National Science Teachers Association
1840 Wilson Boulevard
Arlington, VA 22201

THE FIRST CLASSROOM IS OUTDOORS: USE IT!

Modern schooling places many demands on teachers and students alike. In the urgency for teachers to teach more and faster, there is a growing assumption that the building classroom is the only place where legitimate learning can take place. The result of this tendency is increasingly to abandon the out-of-doors. In our view, this is a mistake.

The *Project WILD Activity Guide* and the *Project WILD Aquatic Education Activity Guide* all have numerous activities that are enhanced by being conducted in the out-of-doors. Our experience as well as the results of many research studies show that effective learning is often heightened in natural settings. The most fundamental reason for teaching in the out-of-doors whenever possible when using Project WILD is that nature itself is the subject. The natural context—the living world and people's interactions with it—is the subject for most Project WILD activities. The schoolground, a nearby park, a pond, a small stream, a vacant lot, and sites visited on extended field trips may all serve to enhance learning when incorporated within instructional experiences. It seems increasingly important, in this urbanized age where much information comes to us vicariously and abstractly, to make sure that students have meaningful, first-hand experiences with the living world.

Such natural explorations lead students to understand and remember important concepts. With confidence gained first hand in relatively small scale, local field experiences—students can more effectively embrace ideas that involve wildlife in the global ecosystem.

Another benefit gained from outdoor experience is that it provides foundational experiences for lifelong learning. More and more leisure activities take advantage of outdoor settings. Birdwatching, hiking, camping, photography, drawing and sketching, and more athletic sports like skiing, snorkeling, and running are all becoming increasingly popular. Students who are grounded in outdoor studies are more apt to continue active learning past school.

Using the out-of-doors as a natural classroom can take many forms. It may be as simple as using the windows and windowsills of the building classroom to observe what's outside. We encourage the active use of schoolgrounds as legitimate and appropriate places for study of concepts. Urban settings in the community as well as city parks can offer a variety of opportunities. Getting outside does not require the capacity to drive distances to undeveloped forests and open spaces.

FIELD ETHICS

The question of whether to collect some objects from natural settings—either temporarily or permanently—is difficult to answer. Such decisions are left to individual teachers and their students. We do, however, urge thoughtful decision-making about the process. We urge caution and respect for the living environment. In most cases, we urge no collecting at all—and recommend instead simply leaving the natural environment as it is found, with as little impact from students in the process of learning as possible. There are times, however, when it may seem appropriate and so instructionally powerful that some limited forms of collecting are desired. If so, we recommend involving students in the process of deciding whether, what and how to collect.

Collecting for instructional purposes can take a variety of forms. Sometimes it involves going outside to the schoolgrounds and picking up fallen leaves on an autumn day. Sometimes it involves collecting human-made litter from a park. Sometimes it involves using a net and examining organisms found in pond water.

If any collecting is to be done, students should begin with a respect for the environment. You should determine in advance what laws may apply. Involve your students in deciding what, if anything, to collect. Have them decide in advance how much is appropriate. By involving students in the process of deciding whether and what to collect, they are more likely to develop an ethic which considers their impact on ecosystems. This kind of thoughtful decision-making about the consequences of our actions is an important, lifelong skill.

The following ethic was developed by a class of sixth graders in Illinois:

1. We should obey all laws protecting plants and animals.
2. We should ask the owner before we take anything.
3. We should only collect an animal if we know we can keep it alive long enough to learn from it.
4. We should not collect things that will hurt us.
5. We should only collect something if there are a lot of them in that place.
6. We should only collect something if we can learn something very important about it.

Obviously, any collecting for instructional purposes should leave the environment as little changed as possible. It should not significantly damage wildlife or its habitat. Where possible, any thing collected from the environment for instructional purposes should be returned to the environment in the location in which it was found at the conclusion of the activity.

We also need to consider an ethic that goes beyond the collecting issue. We can affect living things in other ways too. For example, just by walking over fragile areas outdoors or observing animals under certain conditions, we can destroy or disturb organisms. When we leave a trail, we can kill plants and animals. When we walk on rocks, we can remove new soil and crush mosses and lichens if they are present. When we walk along the banks of a pond or stream, vegetation can be affected. When we leave traces of aquatic vegetation on a shore, they can change the beauty and ecology of an area.

We cannot decide what is ethical and appropriate for teachers and students who are using Project WILD. We can encourage every learner to pay attention to the consequences of actions. We do urge thoughtful decision-making and responsible behavior—not just as an outcome or goal of Project WILD—but as a path to take in the process of learning.

OBSERVATIONS AND INFERENCES: WHAT'S THE DIFFERENCE?

Learning how to be observant and how to make inferences are two important skills. They are two of the skills that students can develop when participating in some of the Project WILD instructional activities. Since many students seem to confuse observations and inferences, let us distinguish between the two.

Observations are descriptions of characteristics or attributes—for example, of objects, processes, or events. Inferences are judgments or interpretations about such things as objects, processes, or events.

If a student sees a fish in the water and he or she describes the coloration, length, width, thickness, mobility, fin pattern, scale configuration, and eye characteristics—that student is making an observation.

If a student sees a fish darting about near some fish eggs in the water and says it is a female fish protecting a nest, he or she has made an inference.

Observations are objective in the sense that what is said about objects, processes or events usually can be agreed upon by any observer. Descriptions of such characteristics as measurements, weights, color, fin patterns, etc., may usually be the same for any observer—while inferences, derived from judgments or interpretations, go beyond descriptions.

For many students, the act of labeling something becomes an end in itself. For example, a student may observe a fish and identify it as a trout. Observationally, the student may be seeing an animal of about ten inches in length with a body two inches thick and three inches deep that lives in an aquatic environment. Inferentially, the student may decide that the fish is protecting a nest. Inferences go beyond objective information of the kind obtained by observation and involve efforts to determine cause and effect relationships with other elements.

Inference requires students to use observations in combination with information they may be missing in order to establish what are intended to be informed cognitive leaps—or inferences.

Typically in scientific study, observations are gathered. Later, when patterns begin to emerge, the process of inference begins. The distinction between these two modes of inquiry becomes especially important when we consider how willingly some tend to come to conclusions on the basis of inferences with no grounding in observational experience. At best such inferences reflect guessing and at worst superstition and prejudice. Learning the skills of observation adds richness to the data base from which inferences are made. As students learn these skills of observation, mature inferences tend to emerge, which in turn lead to hypothesis and theory in science.

GUIDELINES FOR INTERVIEWING PEOPLE

To some extent, everyone in a community is an expert on something. Perhaps your students will want to know what something in the community looked like 20 or 40 years ago. They may want to speak with some long-living residents. An interview can provide a powerful piece of oral history—or it can be an intrusion into the life and privacy of a person. If students are sent out to interview people, some guidelines are useful.

Students should have an introductory letter on school stationery explaining what they are doing, who they are, and asking for cooperation and assistance—with thanks in advance.

Interviews should be planned in advance, at least in terms of outlining major questions to be asked. Students should be taught to conduct a professional interview, and to keep the interview focused on the purposes of the research. For example, students should listen and record their subject's responses. Rather than the students using the time of the interview to expound their own views on the topic, their task is to learn the subject's views. The subject should at all times be treated with dignity and respect. If any form of recording is desired, the people being interviewed should be asked in advance for their permission and should be told what will be done with the information. If you want to quote the person being interviewed by name, then the person should be given the opportunity to see the written proceedings of the interview, review any excerpts to be used, or review the recording before any class or public use of the information takes place. If any public opinion surveys or other forms of interviews in public places are planned, students should be supervised by adult helpers. People who might be concerned (shop keepers, mall managers, etc.) should be asked in advance and informed about the project and its purposes. If people do not want to be interviewed, thank them politely for their time and let them proceed with their business. As a general principle, it is recommended that any interviews to be conducted by students be arranged in advance by their teacher. An in-class trial run or practice session using role-playing techniques with students acting parts and other students serving as constructive critics of their performances can be effective preparation for actually conducting interviews.

LOCAL RESOURCES

In the course of exploring activities in Project WILD, you may find that local resource people would be of great assistance to you and your students. Some of the topics covered in Project WILD activities address areas in which most people do not have extensive background or experience. No one can be an expert in everything. We can celebrate the expertise of various people in our communities by inviting them to contribute their special knowledge and understanding to our students. Most experts are busy people, however—that's one characteristic of how they got to be experts in their field. They have focused their energy and time on knowing more about their subject and, frequently, care passionately about it. If we respect their commitment to their field, we need to make sure that we use their time well. To do this, we need to prepare our students and ourselves before we invite experts to speak to classes, send students to interview them, or take field trips to special facilities. Here are a few basic suggestions that may help you with this process.

BASIC SUGGESTIONS

Have the students explore the question of who might have special knowledge to contribute to a particular activity or topic.

One of the important skills that students can learn is, "How can we find out?" Part of this may involve asking someone who knows more than we do, possibly a lot more. Students can go on a "treasure hunt" for potential experts. Where could they find someone who knows about local water quality—in the local city health department? in the state water commission? in the Office of the Environment? Are there citizen groups that are interested in the topic? Do they publish any resource materials? Do the local colleges and universities have people on their faculties with expertise in this area? Develop a list of "leads," possible avenues to explore in order to identify the experts on a topic in your area.

Develop a plan for approaching the agencies or organizations where "experts" may be found.

Once the students have decided where experts might be found, they will need to decide how to approach these institutions in order to actually get the names of some people who might be speakers, lead field trips or be interviewed. Some governmental agencies, for example, have public affairs departments—and these departments might be the best place to start. Some public libraries have information librarians who specialize in this sort of task and may know who to approach. Some universities and colleges publish speakers lists which include topics that faculty are willing to speak about. Local businesses may also have people who are experts. Again, the public affairs departments may be good places to start. Sometimes you may be referred directly to the resource person. In case this happens, consider the next suggestion—found below—before you undertake this part of the search.

Once you have identified some potential resource people, develop a strategy for determining whether they would be willing to act as experts for your class, and, if so, how they would like to work.

As a teacher, you may want to go and speak with resource persons first before you actually have them come to your class. This is usually a good idea. Sometimes, when you explain the questions in which your class has an interest, or what the topic of your study is, the experts may suggest that they really do not feel themselves to be the best choice to address the topic. They may suggest someone else. Some experts are not comfortable speaking to large groups of people, especially young students. They may want to talk to a small group, or even one student, who can take the information back to the rest of the class. Some may not be able to get away from their work to visit your school during the day. In that case, you may want to consider whether a field visit would be possible for the class. The expert may suggest other sources of information—books, magazines, or films, for example. If the resource person is willing to work directly with students, either with whole classes or with smaller groups or individuals, find out what preparation the expert would like, and what conditions. Would they like written questions from the class beforehand so that they can think about them in advance? Would they be willing to be audio or videotaped? Would they be willing to be written up in the school or local newspaper? A visit to town by some experts is news! If they are coming to your school, what sort of special equipment will they need (slide projector, overhead, etc.)? If the class will take a field trip to visit the resource person at his or her office, laboratory, business, or home, what should the class know in advance? Are any special clothes required? How long will the visit be? Where should the group report in order to start the visit? Attention to this kind of detail can make the trip more productive, effective, and appropriate.

Decide on students who will act as recorders, hosts or hostesses and moderators. Brief the class about the roles each of these people will serve as well as the responsibilities and expectations for behavior that you have for all of the students.

Resource people coming to a school for the first time may be quite uncertain about simple things—beginning with how to find the school. For example, you may want to send a map in advance. When a guest arrives at the school, a student can meet and conduct the visitor to the classroom—asking if he or she wants assistance with any materials, etc. A letter to the resource person in advance will help to verify the details of the arrangements to which you have mutually agreed. If student interviewers will visit the resource person, they should have a letter of introduction and they should be well briefed about how to interview the person. Students who leave the schoolgrounds to interview people should see themselves as representing the school and your class in particular. They will want to leave a good impression. Whether guests come to school or students visit resource people in the community—the importance of courteous, considerate, and responsible behavior should be stressed.

Do your advance work on the topic.

Resource people usually do not mind giving their time to people they think can use it well. If you and the class have done some homework on the subject, you are more likely to ask intelligent questions and be able to understand what the expert has to offer. This advanced preparation is strongly recommended in any circumstance. It is especially important in order to make the best use of a field trip to a complex facility—for example, a sewage treatment plant in the community or a fish hatchery.

Remember that a little consideration and hospitality go a long way.

Resource people can become lifelong supporters of your school and its programs, or lifelong critics. Which will happen not only depends upon things like the suggestions offered here, but on small but important things like thanking them at the time of their visit (or your visit) and following up with a letter. If the class uses the information from the resource person in some special way, a picture or samples of the work sent to the resource person can be appropriate and helpful. If the local media produce an article, send along a copy to your expert. Do not expect nor demand large amounts of additional time from the experts, but do let them know that their expertise was appreciated and how it was used.

HINTS FOR USING SIMULATED FIELD TRIPS

A simulated field trip is a powerful way for students to create vivid experiences in their mind's eye. Many older people remember when the major form of entertainment was radio. With radio and its absence of visual images, many listeners were forced to create mental pictures of the way various characters looked and acted. It was common for listeners to see landscapes, cities, and any number of exotic settings. Often one hears teachers and parents claim that radio helped make students more creative as it required the listeners to stretch their imaginations. Many neuroscientists concur.

Research has shown that, with their eyes closed, people activate parts of their brain-mind systems that are often left unstimulated. When we picture things in our minds, we call parts of our brains into activity that are unused in reading or writing. Studies show skill in picturing things in our minds enhances our ability to enrich reading and to increase skill and imagination in writing. The capacity to remember concepts, words, names and ideas is enhanced. Dramatic results have been achieved when these approaches are combined with medicine. In many instances, life-threatening illnesses have been reversed and overcome.

The use of simulated field trips for instructional purposes is promising to become one of the most effective educational strategies of the past two decades. The following guidelines provide a basic, useful approach to the use of simulated field trips as a teaching tool.

1. Ask the students to lay aside all pens, pencils, books, etc.
2. Instruct the students to sit in a comfortable and relaxed position with their eyes closed.
3. Wait until you see a general state of relaxation before beginning.
4. Using a steady and paced reading or speaking style, begin offering the students the narrative. Remember to speak slowly and steadily. If you want the students to create rich mental pictures, you must allow them time to do so. It takes about as much time to observe mental images as it does to carefully review actual physical settings.
5. Once the narrative is finished, invite the students to review all of the images they saw in their minds. Again, try to allow enough time for an adequate visual review—and remember, the review takes time.
6. After an adequate time for mental review (at least one minute and possibly two minutes), ask the students to open their eyes.
7. Begin discussing the simulated field trip in terms of the instructional purpose for its use.

In some cases, the process serves simply to provide a visual review of some of the students' past experiences. At other times, you are providing stimuli for the students to create original images. In any case, it is important to realize that there are no mistakes in mental images. What a student pictures is real. The images are data. If students create images that are inconsistent with what you expected, consider the images to represent differing perspectives rather than wrong answers. Try to honor and nour-ish variety as a means to add richness to the topics being explored.

In addition to serving as a powerful and effective way to explore and remember concepts, regular use of simulated field trips also tends to relax students. When relaxed, they will frequently be more productive in all academic areas—including scoring higher on standardized achievement tests.

USING SIMULATIONS FOR INSTRUCTIONAL PURPOSES

An educational simulation is an instructional activity that models aspects of the real world to teach one or more concepts. Simulations—especially those that involve students in kinesthetic learning experiences—are used frequently in Project WILD.

"Hooks and Ladders," a salmon simulation, and "How Many Bears Can Live in This Forest," an activity about limiting factors, are examples. In conducting simulations for instructional purposes, it is important to remember that the activity can take on a life of its own. The students can get so involved in the role they are playing that they forget to relate the objects, events, and processes to what they represent in nature.

Students of all ages may tend to get competitive when they are responsible for capturing or escaping the animals depicted in an activity. Often antic and energetic physical behavior results. During such activity, the students identify subjectively with the role they are playing. This identification is important and should be encouraged as part of the powerful learning that is possible through simulations. Yet it is also important to link the subjective experience with the objective concepts that are central to each activity.

Distinguish between what is realistic and what is not realistic about the simulation. Simulations, by definition, are simple representations of more complex natural interactions. Teachers should point this out to students and help them understand how the simulation is like and not like the real situation.

Simulations always leave out some elements that exist in nature. They simplify in order to make a point. Make sure that the students are clear about the point.

A GUIDE TO THE ECOSYSTEM CONCEPT

Many hundreds of books and many thousands of research articles have been written in the field of ecology. There are also many fine textbooks. This short description of a complex and sophisticated field cannot, by its brief nature, do anything more than provide a summary of a few major concepts. However, the *Project WILD Activity* Guides contain a number of activities that are designed to invite students of all ages to ask questions about how ecosystems work. To address these questions, teachers do not need to be professional ecologists, nor do you need an extensive background in biology or wildlife management. You will need a basic set of concepts that will help you work with your students. This section of the appendices is designed to help teachers develop a few simple and powerful ecological concepts with students.

THE ECOSYSTEM

The word ecosystem combines two words: ecology and system. It connects the idea of **eco**, the household of nature, with that of **system**, a set of interactions over time among living and nonliving elements of the household. Ecologists have offered a number of different definitions of this concept over the last three or four decades. One of the problems that many teachers encounter with the term is the question of how big is an ecosystem? Some have seen photos of the earth from space and have heard the entire planet referred to as an ecosystem. This ecosystem is termed the global ecosystem or biosphere.

An ecosystem is really a term that represents an idea more than a place or set of things. When children set up a wide mouth jar in the classroom with pond water, a few small animals, and some plants in it, and cap the bottle tightly, they have established an ecosystem. The jar contains biotic and abiotic elements. The biotic elements are all the living things in the jar: plants, snails, microbes, etc. The abiotic elements are the nonliving elements: air, water, rocks, and bottom debris. Even here it is often difficult to distinguish between living (biotic) and nonliving (abiotic) things. Some biologists would define the abiotic components as those elements in the system that are not of biological origin. Problems arise here too when one considers that some of the carbon dioxide gas was produced by animals and some of the oxygen, if not all of it, by plants. This

little ecosystem in a jar will quickly turn into a gooey mess unless the children place the bottle in the light—but not in direct sunlight. The system in the bottle is not going to operate without a source of energy—namely light energy. If there are not too many animals and other non-green organisms in the jar, the bottle can be tightly sealed, even "air tight," and may operate as a self-contained environment for many years. It will slowly change over time. Some organisms will die and be decomposed. Slow hatching eggs or spores may develop and germinate. The acidity of the water may change. The color of the water may change and absorb more heat and light. The system will undergo a life cycle of its own, slowly aging and changing. The term ecosystem is a convenience. We can draw an imaginary line around a section of the larger world and decide to treat its elements separately from the rest—and call it an ecosystem. When we describe how the organisms in the system behave; how they interact, grow, adapt; what they eat; how long they live; what happens to them when they die; what they require to stay healthy or to reproduce; we are dealing with the way in which the household system operates—and we are thinking SYSTEM-atically. We are finding connections. Often the connections between elements of a system are subtle and hard to see or understand. Quite frequently, this is because they take a long time to happen. The life cycle of some organisms in an ecosystem in the forests of the west coast of North America is 300 to 500 years. In an average human lifespan, we might see little change in those forests. But the life cycle of an ecosystem in a pond that dries up during the summer and is frozen in the winter might be 12 months. Life cycles in a jar of microbes might be measured in hours.

When the term ecosystem is used in Project WILD, it describes a system in which there are living organisms, nonliving components, and a primary source of energy. In most systems, the primary source of energy is the sun. We could establish organisms in various environments but unless there was an appropriate balance or set of relations among them, the system would quickly or slowly go into crisis and die. Many students and teachers have seen examples of changed systems when they have cleaned out refrigerators or discovered last month's uneaten lunch in the bottom of their lockers.

One ecosystem that is often studied in school is the pond. Pond is not a word that is typically used with a precise definition. It is like the word ecosystem in many ways. In some parts of the world, a pond is a small body of fresh water, usually a very small body of water. In other places though a pond can be a lake quite reasonable in size and depth. In some countries, ponds can be small bays with narrow entrances to the ocean. Here we use the term to refer to small, shallow, freshwater bodies of water.

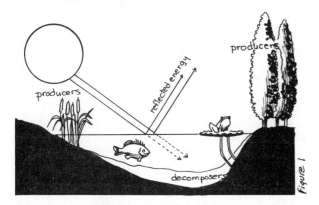

Figure 1 shows a "typical" pond. While this is greatly oversimplified, it shows the basic elements of any ecosystem. There is the sun—the energy source. The sun is the "engine" driving the rest of the system. There are the green plants and animals. The green plants are direct "sun catchers." The wonderful process of capturing some of the sun's energy is known as photosynthesis—**photo** (light) and **synthesis** (assembly, connection, manufacture). The energy of the sun is stored in the form of chemical bonds in molecules. Photosynthesis magically stores solar energy by assembling complex molecules with six carbon atoms from building blocks of one carbon (CO_2) and water. The animals cannot do this trick. They rely on the green plants to catch solar energy and to use it to assemble food materials. The green plants are the food factories in natural systems. They are called producers. The plants also provide oxygen as a byproduct of this process, but use carbon dioxide and water as raw materials.

Not all animals eat plants directly. Those that eat plants and only plants are known as herbivores or primary consumers. They are one step away from being sun catchers. Animals that eat other animals are two steps away from the sun, so they are often called secondary consumers or carnivores (meat eaters). The sequence gets more complex if we add animals that prey on other meat eaters: tertiary consumers (three steps away from the sun). *Figure 2* illustrates some of these relationships.

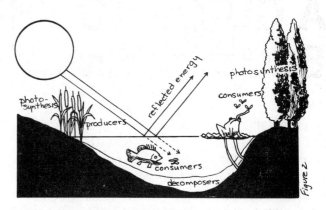

If we make a diagram linking some of these organisms as producers and consumers, we illustrate a food chain. *Figure 3* shows a very simple food chain that might be associated with a pond. In this diagram the eagle eats the fish that eats the frog. In turn the frog eats spiders and the spiders eat insects.

But this food chain is not an ecosystem. Some things are missing. There are no direct sun catchers (producers)—no green plants capable of photosynthesis. The eagle cannot capture energy from the sun directly. It is an least three steps away from the sun's input of energy. In its tadpole stage, the frog eats plant material. The insect might feed on plant nectar, or its larval stage might eat leaves. The food chain describes only a portion of the connections in the pond ecosystem. If we made the diagram more complex, we would produce a food web. It would include all the producers and consumers in the pond, or as many as we can identify. It would introduce a net set of special consumers—the decomposers. They are the garbage collectors of nature. They do not trap solar energy directly, because they are not green and therefore cannot perform photosynthesis. They break down a wide variety of materials into simpler compounds. They produce CO_2 and release needed elements into the system. Without these recyclers, the entire ecosystem would gradually run down. Imagine a forest in which none of the fallen trees, branches, dead animals, and leaves ever rotted. Soon it would be impossible to move through it and nothing new could grow. Decomposition is a creative activity. Without some decomposition in ponds, the accumulation of materials falling to the bottom would result in the pond's rapidly becoming so shallow that it would no longer be a pond.

As a general principle, students need to understand that both energy and materials constantly circulate in all ecosystems. Plants, through the process of photosynthesis, are the major point of entry into the natural system of the sun's energy. However, that energy does work in ecosystems in other ways a well. Solar heating of the atmosphere and oceans produces the flow of winds and the great patterns of air circulation in the atmosphere. The absorption of solar energy in the oceans is expressed in the flow of ocean currents. In a way, the entire planet is a great solar-powered engine. All materials cycle—some slowly, and some quickly.

CO_2, for example, is a byproduct of respiration in plant and animal cells. The carbon of CO_2 is used by green plants in photosynthesis and becomes the building block of many biological molecules, including sugars, proteins, and fats. Once assembled into these materials, the carbon may be taken in by animals when they eat food materials—whether from plant or animal sources. Food is both a source of energy and a source of raw materials for biological construction.

The carbon cycle is one of the great cycles in natural systems. Nitrogen, water and elements such as phosphorus are also involved in cycles. The passage of materials along food chains and through cycles is responsible for the concentration effect of chemicals such as pesticides. Small amounts of pesticide molecules passed along a food chain may accumulate when they reach the top consumer, whether that be an eagle or a human. Sometimes animals like the humpback whale may "shorten" the steps between the input of solar energy and themselves by feeding directly on millions of small animals and plants that are closer to the source of solar energy. *See Figure 4.*

Thus an ecosystem may be viewed as a set of elements, living and nonliving, interacting over time, within a defined locale. Ecologists attempt to define ecosystems in terms of sets of elements that normally interact with each other. At a global level, all the elements on the plant interact. The rain that falls today on the plains may have evaporated yesterday from the leaf of a tree in the coastal forest. But in practical terms, for the purposes of studying and understanding the interactions among organisms in the environment, it is useful to draw boundaries around certain groups of organisms which are normally interacting in a relatively direct way, as a community or neighborhood grouping. This may be considered an ecosystem.

Within these biological neighborhoods, it is possible to assign organisms both an "address," describing their typical location in space; and an "occupation," or role which they play in the system. An organism's address is its "habitat." The occupation of an organism in an ecosystem is called its "niche." For many people, the term niche seems to describe a location, a type of space, but as the term is used by ecologists it applies to the organism's roles or activities in the system. This has frequently been a source of confusion.

There are many different aquatic ecosystems. Within those systems, there are a variety of zones. Figure 5 illustrates some of the zones that can be found in a typical pond ecosystem. There are organisms occupying the edge or margins of the pond. These are said to be in the littoral zone. There are others that float and drift in the water itself. These are planktonic organisms and may be plants or animals. There are still others that live on the bottom and in the sediments. And

PLANKTON

Figure 4

THE SURFACE FILM

BENTHIC ZONE
bottom sediments

PLANKTONIC ZONE
the floaters and drifters

LITTORAL ZONE
the edge

Figure 5

there are those, like water striders, that inhabit the narrow zone comprised of the actual water surface film. Sometimes organisms inhabit different zones at different stages i their lives. It is important to explore a variety of zones in different habitats because students will encounter quite different sets of organisms in different zones. Often people tend to overlook some zones—possibly because they do not seem very interesting or attractive. Who wants to spend time sifting through the muck on a pond bottom when their dip nets are filled with interesting things found in the water or on the rushes at the shore line? But, in order to develop an understanding of the diversity of life forms that inhabit an ecosystem, we need to explore the whole range of addresses where they might be found.

TIPS ON STUDYING ECOSYSTEMS

A major purpose in having students study ecology is for them to develop an awareness and understanding of relationships. This entails developing the ability to see systems, sets of interactions; and thinking about how they have changed, and might still change with time. It entails beginning to understanding living systems as complex mosaics in which all the parts fit together to make a whole. The removal of one small, apparently unimportant, component can often have major consequences.

It is convenient for teachers to start small with your students. Making miniature ecosystems in jars and plastic bags can start students thinking about what elements are needed in order to keep an ecosystem healthy. Asking students to create drawings connecting things from nature to as many other things (themselves included) as they can also promotes thinking about interactions. A dead leaf floating on the surface of a pond might be seen as simple litter until—by drawing connections in as many directions and dimensions as possible—the student starts to see it as food, as a habitat, and as a former trap for the sun's energy. The student begins to appreciate the role of apparently inert and dead material.

Often we get caught up in the appreciation of individual organisms. They are often strange, beautiful, or somehow humorous. We want to know as much about them as we can. But the next step in developing ecosystematic thinking is to try to appreciate the role played by the organism in the community of which it is a part. Is this a predator, or is it prey? Ultimately all organisms are "food," even if for microbes. Does one organism provide a home for other organisms? Is it a sun catcher, a trapper of solar energy? It is an important part of the debriefing of many of the activities in Project WILD to ask students to think about these connections, and ultimately to connect themselves to the system as well.

Naming is often both an asset and an obstacle to the study of natural systems. When students go to a community, they want to know the names of the organisms they encounter. This is a good time to learn to recognize some plants and animals. But often it is enough to appreciate differences and similarities, and even for students to assign names of their own making to the things they see. Do not let a lack of detailed knowledge of names discourage study. Instead, use this as an opportunity to pose the, "How can we find out?" questions. Emphasize the characteristics of plants and animals and their interactions, rather than losing sight of those attributes in a quest to label the parts. Finally, it is often a powerful experience for students to visit and revisit a natural setting at various seasons of the year. Spring is an ideal season to study ponds and streams. But it is a mistake for students to think of nature as dead, or even as largely dormant, in the winter. Seasonal changes are important to the economy of nature. Ecosystems change over time. The changes of the seasons are an important expression of continuing natural change in natural systems. So, if the opportunity presents itself, have students follow an ecosystem—perhaps a pond, stream, lake, or river—throughout the seasons from late summer to fall, through winter and into spring and summer. School-grounds can provide useful opportunities of this kind. Some schools have also adopted a local pond or stream and have made it the focus of studies by classes over many years. If the past data are saved, students can appreciate what is happening to their local ecosystems.

TAKING ACTION
Involving Students In Environmental Action Projects

The following is adapted from Project WILD's *TAKING ACTION: An Educator's Guide to Involving Students in Environmental Action Projects*, published by Western Regional Environmental Education Council, Inc., in cooperation with World Wildlife Fund. Intended for educators of grades 5–12, this guide describes how to plan, implement, and evaluate effective environmental action projects. It also includes ways to connect action projects to all areas of the curriculum; a thorough description of more than 30 student action projects from around the United States; a list of action related Project WILD activities; and a bibliography of action resources. For more information or to order this guide, please contact the national office of Project WILD, 5430 Grosvenor Lane, Suite 230, Bethesda, MD 20814-2142, *phone* (301) 493-5447, *email* natpwild@igc.apc.org.

RECIPE FOR ACTION

Combine one bunch of students with equal amounts of solid planning, positive attitude, and creative thinking. Fortify mixture with dashes of guidance (as needed) and allow it all to blend. As excitement comes to a boil, add liberal quantities of encouragement. Throw in pinches of patience, flexibility, and persistence at regular intervals, and sprinkle entire combination with an atmosphere of fun. When recipe bears fruit, share results with others. Serves all involved—and serves them well. Continue to serve indefinitely.

You don't have to be a gourmet cook to get good results with this basic recipe for successful environmental action. All you need is a little inspiration and some comprehensive how-to information.

WHAT IS AN ACTION PROJECT?
We've defined environmental action projects as any activities that get students involved in tackling an environmental issue or problem, or that aim at improving an environmental setting. They are often most successful when they're focused on the local community.

The enhancement of outdoor habitats and the development of natural sites within a community are great advertisements for your students' efforts. Projects can also work on a much broader scope—raising money to adopt sea turtles, for example, or trying to change company policies that damage rainforests.

An action project can be as simple or complex as you want to make it: as straightforward as putting up a community bulletin board of environmental current events, or as involved as developing and implementing a community plan for oil collection and recycling. However complex, most action projects will fit into a variety of educational settings. Many educators find that action education blends well with their regular teaching duties, while others choose to make it the basis for after-school sessions. Action learning is effective in nonformal settings, too. Nature centers, zoos, aquariums, and scouting programs all have strong potential for action projects.

WHO CAN DO ACTION PROJECTS?
Students of all ages can take part in environmental action projects. However, it's critical to match the complexity of the tasks to the abilities of students. On the one hand, older students can get involved in issues that require research, issue analysis, in-depth discussion, careful planning, and follow-up. They might lobby on specific issues at the local, state, or national level; set up river monitoring activities; or conduct community education initiatives. On the other hand, younger students should begin with projects that don't involve heated controversy, long-term commitments, or complex solutions. Picking up litter, writing a letter about an environmental concern, or planting a butterfly garden is an excellent starting point for younger students.

APPROACHES TO ENVIRONMENTAL ACTION

Teach It!—The Educate and Inform Approach
Projects that focus on teaching others about environmental issues, such as older students mentoring younger students, conducting community education programs, writing and putting on plays, writing and performing songs and poems, conducting workshops with school or community groups, and so forth.

Make the Case—The Persuasive Approach
Projects designed to convince people to support a certain course of action or point of view. Activities include creating posters or brochures, conducting debates, writing letters to the editor, giving speeches, and distributing public service announcements.

Be on the Money—The Economic Approach
Strategies that encourage consumers to shop with the environment in mind, as well as projects that raise money to support specific organizations, programs, or individuals working on environmental issues. Activities might include promoting environmentally friendly products, asking for cash donations or in-kind donations of time and materials from businesses and community groups, or applying for grants from corporations or government agencies.

Get Physical—The "Ecomanagement" Approach
Projects that physically improve the environment, such as planting trees, landscaping school grounds, cleaning up neighborhood parks or streams, or building bird and bat houses. Zoos, nature centers, and other community landowners may allow nature sites on their property.

Make Decisions—The Political Action Approach
Projects that focus on political action. Activities could include speaking at a public hearing, meeting with an elected representative to discuss specific legislation, testifying before lawmakers, circulating petitions and fliers, writing letters to the editor, or campaigning for candidates.

Become Legal Eagles—The Courtroom Approach
Projects that attempt to create change through legislation, or that take legal action against an individual, corporation, community, or government agency. Although most projects that involve primary and secondary students will not involve actual legal action, many projects can educate youngsters about existing laws and the workings of the legal system.

"Approaches" adapted with permission from *Investigating and Evaluating Environmental Issues and Actions*, by Harold R. Hungerford et al. 1992. Stipes Publishing Co., 10–12 Chester St., Champaign, IL 61820.

SEVEN STEPS TO ACTION

Here are some basic steps that will help your students get action projects off the ground. Although we've listed them in a specific order, it's important to note that planning and implementing a project is not always a clear-cut, linear process. In some cases, students will investigate an issue, discuss it, begin to work on it, and then change their strategy as they use new information. They might decide to narrow their focus or switch projects after realizing that the potential solutions are beyond their capabilities. This zig-zagging is a normal part of the learning process and needs to happen whenever students get involved with environmental action projects. With that in mind, adapt these steps to fit your own needs.

1. Bone Up on Project Topics
Before your students decide which environmental projects to pursue, they need to become informed about the possibilities. One way to do this is to have students collect a pool of information from newspapers and magazines, interview community members and parents, or contact organizations and government agencies that focus on environmental issues. Then have them share their findings in a series of environmental

current events sessions. You might even set up a "Hot Topics" bulletin board.

Another important step in this initial process, if you can organize it, is to arrange for students to get out and see local environmental problems firsthand. A field trip to a stream in need of cleanup is much more powerful than reading about water pollution. Even if students eventually select a problem that's occurring thousands of miles from their community, the exposure to concerns in their own backyard will be an important learning experience.

Remember that action projects don't necessarily have to address something that is widely perceived as a problem or issue. Many projects focus on things like enhancing a neighborhood habitat (constructing nesting platforms in a wetland, planting vegetation to stabilize soil, and so forth), or making a unique environment more accessible (building an observation blind near a pond, developing natural history interpretive signs along a community trail, and so forth).

2. Create a List of Possibilities

Once the students' search has highlighted a number of potential topics, have them work in groups to come up with a list of the most interesting or worthwhile ones. Then have them come up with a list of projects to address all or part of each topic. Select a group member to be in charge of recording ideas.

It might be helpful to explain that environmental topics can be very broad and there are almost always several project possibilities for each topic. For example, water quality in the community might encompass pollution in a local river, lead in the city water system, leaks in a landfill, and many other topics. Projects might include monitoring the pollution levels in the river over time and presenting data to the city council, conducting an education campaign about lead in the city's drinking supply, or developing a recycling plan to reduce the pressure on a landfill. Have students list the topic they would most want to tackle. Then they can brainstorm specific projects that might help the situation. They could list any additional information they'll need to evaluate each project.

3. Narrow the Choices

Once groups have selected the issues and projects they are most interested in, they need to evaluate and narrow their choices. There are a number of ways you can help them. For each project listed, the groups should realistically address what they might accomplish and what problems the project might solve.

If one of the project ideas is to create a city park in a vacant lot or to restore a park, the students might ask these questions:
- *Why is it important for the city to have a park?*
- *What problems would be addressed with the development of a park?*
- *How would different people in the community feel about the park?*
- *Who might support or oppose a project like this?*
- *Who will benefit from the park? Why?*
- *What costs and obstacles are in the way?*

In this case, the students might be addressing the problem of a lack of green space in their city. But by discussing options, they might decide that a park is not the only solution to the problem. Planting trees and flowers throughout the city or passing a new ordinance to limit development might be other options.

Encourage students to discuss the feasibility of each possibility as you ask specific questions that help them think about the details of accomplishing certain tasks. Students may want to develop criteria to help them first select a project and then decide how they will determine the most appropriate solution. How much time will the project take? How complex is it? What resources are needed? Whom will they need to talk to?

Sometimes it's difficult for students to decide among local, national, and global projects. Although each will provide learning opportunities, an advantage of a local project is that students will learn more about how their own community works. They'll also be more likely to see real results. To begin with, focus on one or two small-scale projects. A large-scale project may become too time-consuming or discouraging and lose its impact.

4. Become Experts and Pick a Project

By this point, students should have narrowed the list to the top three to five projects. Now they need to select the one project to work on. The more your students know about specific possibilities, the better equipped they'll be to develop a realistic action plan.

Give them adequate time to research, and encourage the use of libraries, interviews with experts, surveys, newspaper articles, local TV news, and so on. Afterward, organize presentations or class discussions designed to help students demonstrate their knowledge. Invite experts or resource people in to discuss problems, find potential solutions, and help evaluate ideas.

Students may need to come up with a list of questions about the issue or project, and then work in groups to find the answers. Of course, the questions will vary, but whatever the topic, students should become well versed in the various perspectives. Understanding and respecting different points of view will enable them to reassess and clarify their own positions. That, in turn, will allow them to discuss their project more confidently, and may eventually lead to solutions that everyone can live with.

As students approach their final decision, have each group present a case for one or more of the projects that the group feels strongly about Then hold a group vote. Or have a large group discussion and try to reach consensus. The important thing is to let students have as much say in the decision-making process as possible. At the end, group members should have chosen a project that they think is both interesting and doable.

5. Create an Action Plan

Once students have done their research and selected a project, help them get started on their action plan by asking, "What do you hope you'll be able to accomplish by doing this project?" After students share their answers with the group, then guide them in coming up with a goal for the project and specific, concrete objectives that need to be accomplished along the way.

Remind the students to keep the goal and objectives in mind as they work in groups to fill out a planning sheet (see "Mapping Your Action Project," p. 218). A large-format task and time line chart may help the groups keep track of responsibilities and deadlines. If you've decided to let each group take on its own project, you should adapt this process to fit small group work.

As the students work on their action plan, guide them toward realistic objectives. One of the most common problems for students is thinking too big. Help them focus and simplify the project by discussing the responses to the questions on their planning sheet and by asking them to really consider hard questions. ("How will you raise that much money?" "Is it realistic to think you can spend every weekend working on this project?" "How might you tackle a smaller, but more possible, piece of the problem?")

MAPPING YOUR ACTION PROJECT

1. What environmental problem will your project focus on?

2. Briefly describe the goal of your project and your strategy to accomplish this goal.

3. What are the specific objectives that will help you reach your overall goal?

4. What are the approximate starting and ending dates of your project?

5. List the tasks that need to be accomplished to meet each objective. Include a tentative completion date for each task, the names of people responsible, the supplies and equipment needed, any funding needed, and ideas about where you might get materials and funding.

6. Write down the names of people and organizations that may be able to provide you with useful information, specific skills or expertise, or other help.

7. List ideas for how to publicize and generate support for your project.

8. Describe how you will measure your success.

6. Put the Plan into Action

As students get started, explain that their projects will work best if they keep careful records of what they've done, when they did it, whom they've contacted, and so on. They'll also need to keep track of who's doing what to make sure crucial tasks are being completed and to avoid duplicating efforts.

It's important that students take stock of the project periodically to see if they're on target and to make modifications if necessary. Remind them that it's OK to rethink their goals and objectives and revise their plan of action in light of new information or unexpected obstacles.

To build support for action projects, publicize any successes and showcase the ways that action learning promotes educational goals and addresses community priorities. There are many ways to let others know what students have done—holding a community awards event, getting a reporter from the local newspaper or TV station to cover a project, or sending out public service announcements (PSAs). Have students brainstorm ways to publicize their work.

7. Assess, Generalize, and Apply

As a project draws to an end, guide students in assessing the project itself, as well as their feelings about the experience (see "Ideas for Measuring Success," p. 359).

It's important for students to evaluate the success of each project and to think about improvements for the next time. It's also important that they look beyond the immediate impact to more long-term, broad-scale gains—skills, knowledge, and attitudes that they can apply to other aspects of their lives. Discussions can include issues such as empowerment, citizenship, and community service. A group discussion will give students a chance to reflect on their own feelings and attitudes by giving them the opportunity to listen to what others say about the project and the experiences they have had.

IDEAS FOR MEASURING SUCCESS

Taking time to really evaluate an action project helps students understand what they've accomplished and allows them to recognize how their project has facilitated their personal growth.

Assessing Student Knowledge:

■ Keep a video or photo log of project highlights. After the project is completed, use the video or photo scrapbook as a springboard for discussions in which students share their feelings about the experience and what they learned.

■ Collect memorabilia (articles about the project, newspaper photos, students' own photos, planning schedules, and so on) to create an action project scrapbook that students can sign and write comments in.

■ Ask students whether they've changed their thinking or behaviors as a result of the project. Have them write essays describing those changes and what they think prompted them.

■ Have students keep a journal to record feelings about the project, its progress, and its setbacks, and to keep notes about working with others. After the project, have students share parts of their journals with the group and discuss their feelings.

■ Have students evaluate other members of their group, as well as themselves. Before they do, give students pointers on positive, constructive feedback and focus the session on specific points, such as contribution to the project, effort, conflict resolution approach, and so on.

■ Have community members who were involved in the project assess student performances. You can develop an assessment form or have students conduct short interviews.

Assessing Project Success:

■ Have students describe how well they think their project accomplished the objectives they outlined at the start.

■ Have students conduct surveys, field studies, or interviews to assess the success of their completed project. What worked? What didn't and why?

■ Evaluate how the students planned for ongoing maintenance and sustainability of the project.

■ Have community members and others who were involved in the project assess project outcome.

SOME TIPS TO KEEP IN MIND

Encourage student ownership and initiative.
The more your students are involved in the project, the more they'll get out of it. To the extent possible, allow them to make their own decisions (which problem to focus on, how to conduct the project, and how to share results). Of course, you will be involved in decisions by (among other things) helping students evaluate the pros and cons of each choice. You can gauge how much direction makes the most sense, but, ultimately, the students should feel as though they're charting their own course.

Encourage parents and other community members to buy into the project.
Conflict can sometimes surface when students interact with community members and parents who don't agree with a specific activity or who don't feel that action projects are an appropriate educational approach. In many cases, you can diffuse this response by discussing projects with parents and community members beforehand and by explaining how environmental action projects enhance educational goals.

Keep your opinions in perspective.
We all have our own ideas, beliefs, and opinions about environmental issues. Part of being an effective environmental educator is allowing everyone to have the chance to openly express his or her opinions, no matter how different they may be from our own. Many educators recommend that teachers hold back on sharing their opinions so students have a chance to discuss the issues, to research material, and to form their own ideas about how they feel. It is also critical for educators to keep students on track and focused on the facts. Emotionally charged debate and hotly contested points of view can obscure the real facts and divert students' attention from the issue under scrutiny.

Encourage student cooperation, compromise, and understanding.
Have your students work in small groups as much as possible. Besides the well-documented educational benefits of cooperative learning, group work offers a taste of real-life problem solving. Point out that finding solutions to environmental problems is rarely a solitary endeavor. Teams of people—scientists, politicians, concerned citizens—often arrive at a plan of action together. Ideally, each person brings his or her own perspectives and talents to the process, and the results reflect the strengths of those human resources. Multiple perspectives encourage thoughtful debate, boost critical thinking skills, and allow students to make informed choices—especially if opinions are accompanied by reliable information.

Help students evaluate their methods and change their plans if necessary.
Being able to adapt—or even totally change directions if something isn't working—is a plus when it comes to solving problems. From time to time over the course of a project, have the students step back, assess the overall scheme, and evaluate their methods. Ask if they think things are running as smoothly as they expected. If they think there's room for improvement, ask what might be done to adjust the situation. In some cases, problem-solving teams can brainstorm ways to deal with the snags and setbacks encountered along the way.

Encourage specific methods for evaluating success as the project develops. Students might keep journals and record what they think is going well and what seems to need change. They can also survey community members to get reactions to the project plan and progress. Likewise, periodic check-ups for reactions from colleagues, teachers, or other students can be valuable.

Help students appreciate the value of their work.
It's important for students to know that their project, no matter how small, is significant. Too often all of us feel that there's nothing we can do to solve an environmental problem, or that whatever we can do isn't enough. Assure youngsters that every action counts. Even if the students' actions don't seem to have much effect right away, the long-term results can be very important. For example, if a project designed to help consumers choose environmentally friendly products fails to make big changes in consumer purchases, students will have learned a lot about the issue, and brought public attention to bear—perhaps they will have inspired others to take up the cause.

EVALUATING AND ASSESSING STUDENT LEARNING

There are a variety of ways to evaluate and assess student competence. Many teachers are seeking ways to show that their students can go beyond the recitation of facts. They are asking their students to demonstrate a mastery of higher order thinking skills in the context of their classroom activities. Project WILD is designed to assist teachers as they assess various levels of student learning.

Each Project WILD activity suggests at least one way to evaluate student learning. These suggestions are found at the end of each activity under the heading, "Evaluation." An activity's evaluation assesses for what was described in that activity's "Objective" section. Some of the suggested evaluations assess student understanding of factual information. Many of the evaluations ask students to demonstrate a theoretical or applied conceptual understanding.

When suggested evaluations do not meet your needs, consider using some of the generic evaluation techniques listed here.

Dramatization. Students role play or act out an activity's key concepts. This can also be done using finger or hand puppets.

News Reporting. Students pretend they are news reporters and give a 30-second report about what took place during an activity and what about it was significant.

Signalling. A class is asked a series of questions. All students signal their own response by holding their thumbs either pointed up for "yes" or down for "no."

Journal Writing. Students write and illustrate their own personal version of what they learn and do throughout an activity.

Visual Representation. Students draw, paint or otherwise create an image that conveys an activity's central ideas.

Teaching Students teach the activity's concepts to peers or younger students.

Position Statements. Students write from a specific point of view. (For example: What a rabbit's point of view might be regarding camouflage.)

Self Described Outcomes. Students are asked open-ended questions that allow them to describe, either in written or verbal form, what they learned. (For example: "Describe three things you learned about while doing this activity.")

Real World Examples. Students find examples of an activity's concepts in their community, or in the media, and then report those examples to the rest of the class.

Game Making. Students make games that involve the activity's facts and concepts. (For example: Students make and play a trivia-style board game where players move around a gameboard by correctly answering questions.)

Peer Testing. Students write assessment questions for each other, then evaluate their peer's responses.

ACTIVITIES BY GRADE	Found on Page	Kindergarten	Grade 1	Grade 2	Grade 3	Grade 4	Grade 5	Grade 6	Grade 7	Grade 8	Grade 9	Grade 10	Grade 11	Grade 12
What's Wild?	2	•	•	•	•									
Animal Charades	4					•	•	•	•	•	•	•	•	•
Bearly Born	6					•	•	•	•					
Ants on a Twig	10				•	•	•	•	•	•	•			
Color Crazy	12	•	•	•	•	•	•	•						
Interview a Spider	14						•	•	•	•				
Grasshopper Gravity	16			•	•	•	•	•	•					
Wildlife Is Everywhere	20	•	•	•	•									
Microtrek Treasure Hunt	22					•	•	•						
Stormy Weather	26					•	•	•	•	•				
The Beautiful Basics	30		•	•	•	•	•	•	•	•	•	•	•	•
Everybody Needs a Home	32	•	•	•	•									
Habitat Lap Sit	34					•	•	•	•	•				
Habitracks	36		•	•	•	•								
What's That, Habitat?	38		•	•										
Habitat Rummy	40					•	•	•	•					
My Kingdom for a Shelter	46						•	•	•	•	•			
What's for Dinner	48				•	•	•	•	•					
Litter We Know	50					•	•	•						
Tracks!	52					•	•	•	•					
Habitrekking	56								•	•	•	•	•	•
Spider Web Geometry	58											•	•	•
We're in This Together	60										•	•	•	•
Learning to Look, Looking to See	62	•	•	•	•	•	•	•	•	•				
Wild Words...A Journal Making Activity	66					•	•	•	•	•	•	•	•	•
Animal Poetry	70					•	•	•	•					
Museum Search for Wildlife	72				•	•	•	•						
Let's Go Fly a Kite	74					•	•	•						
Eco-Enrichers	76								•	•	•	•	•	•
Seed Need	78						•	•						
Environmental Barometer	80				•	•	•							
Make a Coat!	82	•	•	•	•	•	•	•	•					
Drawing on Nature	86								•	•	•	•	•	•
Photos Keep It Happening!	88								•	•	•	•	•	•
Wild Edible Plants	90								•	•	•	•	•	•
Wildlife as Seen on Coins and Stamps	92								•	•	•	•	•	•
Wildlife Bibliography	94								•	•	•	•	•	•
What Bear Goes Where?	98	•	•	•	•									
Graphanimal	100		•	•	•	•	•							

ACTIVITIES BY GRADE

Activity	Found on Page	Kindergarten	Grade 1	Grade 2	Grade 3	Grade 4	Grade 5	Grade 6	Grade 7	Grade 8	Grade 9	Grade 10	Grade 11	Grade 12
Urban Nature Search	102					•	•	•	•	•	•			
Good Buddies	104					•	•	•	•					
Forest in a Jar	108	•	•	•	•	•	•	•						
Pond Succession	110					•	•	•	•	•	•			
The Thicket Game	112	•	•	•	•	•	•	•						
Adaptation Artistry	114					•	•	•	•	•	•			
Seeing is Believing... Or the Eyes Have It!	116	•	•	•	•	•	•	•						
Surprise Terrarium	118	•	•	•	•									
Polar Bears in Phoenix?	120			•	•	•	•	•	•	•	•	•	•	•
Quick Frozen Critters	122					•	•	•						
Classroom Carrying Capacity	126	•	•	•	•		•							
Muskox Maneuvers	130					•	•	•	•	•	•			
How Many Bears Can Live in This Forest?	134				•	•	•	•	•	•	•			
Visual Vocabulary	138					•	•	•	•					
Rainfall and the Forest	140						•	•	•	•				
Owl Pellets	144				•	•	•	•	•					
Oh Deer!	146					•	•	•	•	•	•	•	•	•
Birds of Prey	150											•	•	•
Carrying Capacity	152								•	•	•	•	•	•
I'm Thirsty!	154								•	•	•	•	•	•
Time Lapse	156								•	•	•	•	•	•
Which Niche?	158								•	•	•	•	•	•
Who Fits Here?	160								•	•	•			
Turkey Trouble	164											•	•	•
Wildwork	168	•	•	•	•	•	•	•	•	•	•	•	•	•
Here Today, Gone Tomorrow	170						•	•	•	•	•	•	•	•
Who Lives Here?	174					•	•	•	•	•	•			
Planting Animals	176					•	•	•	•	•	•			
Smokey Bear Said What?	178					•	•	•						
Fire Ecologies	182								•	•	•	•	•	•
Checks and Balances	186							•	•	•	•	•	•	•
The Hunter	190						•	•	•	•	•	•	•	•
Wildlife Research	198								•	•	•	•	•	•
Bird Song Survey	200										•	•	•	•
Deer Crossing	202								•	•	•	•	•	•
Riparian Zone	206								•	•	•	•	•	•
Who Pays for What?	212								•	•	•	•	•	•
A History of Wildlife Management	216								•	•	•	•	•	•
Lobster in Your Lunchbox	222					•	•	•	•					

ACTIVITIES BY GRADE

Activity	Found on Page	Kindergarten	Grade 1	Grade 2	Grade 3	Grade 4	Grade 5	Grade 6	Grade 7	Grade 8	Grade 9	Grade 10	Grade 11	Grade 12
First Impressions	224	•	•	•	•	•	•	•						
And the Wolf Wore Shoes	226			•	•	•	•							
Saturday Morning Wildlife Watching	228	•	•	•	•	•	•	•						
Cartoons and Bumper Stickers	230							•	•	•	•	•	•	•
Does Wildlife Sell Cigarettes?	232							•	•	•	•	•	•	•
The Power of a Song	234							•	•	•	•	•	•	•
Wildlife in National Symbols	238					•	•	•	•	•	•			
Changing Attitudes	240						•	•	•	•	•	•		•
Philosophical Differences	242								•	•	•	•	•	•
Wildlife Issues	244								•	•	•	•	•	•
Pro and Con	250								•	•	•	•	•	•
Too Close for Comfort	254	•	•	•	•	•	•	•						
Shrinking Habitat	258					•	•	•	•					
Migration Barriers	262					•	•	•						
Cabin Conflict	264								•	•	•	•	•	•
To Zone or Not to Zone	266							•	•	•	•			
Deadly Links	270					•	•	•	•	•	•			
No Water off a Duck's Back	274							•	•	•	•	•	•	•
Keeping Score	276					•	•	•	•	•				
When a Whale Is a Right	280								•	•	•	•	•	•
Planning for People and Wildlife	284					•	•	•	•	•	•	•	•	•
Ethi-Thinking	290	•	•	•	•	•	•	•	•					
Playing Lightly on the Earth	292	•	•	•	•	•	•	•	•	•				
Noisy Neighbors	294								•	•	•	•	•	•
Rare Bird Eggs for Sale	296								•	•	•	•	•	•
What You Wear Is What They Were	300								•	•	•	•	•	•
Water's Going on?!	304						•	•	•	•	•			
What Did Your Lunch Cost Wildlife?	306					•	•	•	•	•	•	•		
Flip the Switch for Wildlife	308						•	•	•	•	•	•	•	•
Ethi-Reasoning	310						•	•	•	•	•	•	•	•
Wild Bill's Fate	316								•	•	•	•	•	•
Know Your Legislation	318								•	•	•	•	•	•
Can Do!	322			•	•	•	•	•	•	•	•			
Improving Wildlife Habitat	324					•	•	•	•	•	•	•	•	•
Enviro-Ethics	326							•	•	•	•	•	•	•

ACTIVITIES BY SUBJECT

This is intended only as a guide for finding activities by subject. It is not a comprehensive listing of the subject areas within which a Project WILD activity may be used. Please be encouraged to incorporate and adapt activities for use in subject areas not listed.

Activities are listed in alphabetical order.

ANTHROPOLOGY
Changing Attitudes; Enviro-Ethics; The Hunter; Photos Keep It Happening!; Rare Bird Eggs for Sale; Too Close for Comfort; We're in This Together!; What You Wear is What They Were; When a Whale is a Right; Wild Edible Plants; Wildlife as Seen on Coins and Stamps; Wildlife in National Symbols

ART
Adaptation Artistry; Color Crazy; Drawing on Nature; Ethi-Thinking; Everybody Needs a Home; Improving Wildlife Habitat in the Community; Learning to Look, Looking to See; Let's Go Fly a Kite; Litter We Know; Make a Coat!; Museum Search for Wildlife; My Kingdom for a Shelter; Planning for People and for Wildlife; Planting Animals; Pond Succession; Rainfall and the Forest; Seeing is Believing; Smokey Bear Said What?; Spider Web Geometry; Time Lapse; Tracks!; What Bear Goes Where?; What's Wild?; What's That, Habitat?; Wild Edible Plants; Wildlife in National Symbols

BIOLOGY
Adaptation Artistry; Ants on a Twig; Bearly Born; Bird Song Survey; Birds of Prey; Carrying Capacity; Checks and Balances; Deadly Links; Deer Crossing; Drawing on Nature; Eco-Enrichers; Fire Ecologies; Good Buddies; Grasshopper Gravity; Habitat Rummy; Habitat Lap Sit; Habitrekking; Here Today, Gone Tomorrow; How Many Bears Can Live in This Forest?; The Hunter; I'm Thirsty!; Improving Wildlife Habitat in the Community; Keeping Score; Muskox Maneuvers; My Kingdom for a Shelter; No Water Off a Duck's Back; Noisy Neighbors; Oh Deer!; Owl Pellets; Photos Keep It Happening!; Planning for People and Wildlife; Polar Bears in Phoenix?; Pond Succession; Rainfall and the Forest; Shrinking Habitat; Too Close for Comfort; Tracks!; Turkey Trouble; Urban Nature Search; What You Wear is What They Were; What's For Dinner?; When a Whale is a Right; Which Niche?; Who Fits Here?; Wildlife Research

BUSINESS EDUCATION
Does Wildlife Sell Cigarettes?; Rare Bird Eggs for Sale; What Did Your Lunch Cost Wildlife?; Who Pays for What?; Wildwork

CAREER EDUCATION
Checks and Balances; History of Wildlife Management; What Did Your Lunch Cost Wildlife?; Which Niche?; Wildwork

CHEMISTRY
Deadly Links; Eco-Enrichers; Fire Ecologies; No Water Off a Duck's Back

CIVICS
Cabin Conflict; Changing Attitudes; Deer Crossing; Here Today, Gone Tomorrow; History of Wildlife Management; Know Your Legislation; Philosophical Differences; Rare Bird Eggs for Sale; Riparian Zone; To Zone or Not to Zone; When a Whale Is a Right; Who Pays for What?; Wild Bill's Fate; Wildlife as Seen on Coins and Stamps

COMMUNICATIONS
Can Do!; Cartoons and Bumper Stickers; Changing Attitudes; Does Wildlife Sell Cigarettes?; Drawing on Nature; Enviro-Ethics; History of Wildlife Management; Know Your Legislation; Learning to Look, Looking to See; Noisy Neighbors; Philosophical Differences; Photos Keep It Happening!; Power of a Song; Pro and Con: Consumptive and Non-consumptive Uses of Wildlife; Rare Bird Eggs for Sale; Riparian Zone; Time Lapse; To Zone or Not to Zone; Too Close for Comfort; We're in This Together!; When a Whale is a Right; Which Niche?; Wildlife Issues: Community Attitude Survey; Wildlife Research

COMPOSITION
Adaptation Artistry; Cartoons and Bumper Stickers; Changing Attitudes; Enviro-Ethics; Grasshopper Gravity; Habitrekking; History of Wildlife Management; Know Your Legislation; No Water Off a Duck's Back; Philosophical Differences; Urban Nature Search; We're in This Together!; Who Pays for What?; Wild Bill's Fate; Wild Edible Plants; Wildlife Issues: Community Attitude Survey; Wildlife Research

DEBATE
Pro and Con: Consumptive and Nonconsumptive Uses of Wildlife; Rare Bird Eggs for Sale

DRAMA
Animal Charades; Ants on a Twig; Cabin Conflict; Deadly Links; Ethi-Reasoning; How Many Bears Can Live in This Forest?; Muskox Maneuvers; Photos Keep It Happening!; Riparian Zone; Time Lapse; To Zone or Not to Zone; Visual Vocabulary; When a Whale is a Right

EARTH SCIENCE
Eco-Enrichers; Fire Ecologies; Pond Succession; Rainfall and the Forest

ECONOMICS
Does Wildlife Sell Cigarettes?; Know Your Legislation; Lobster in Your Lunch Box; Pro and Con: Consumptive and Nonconsumptive Uses of Wildlife; Rare Bird Eggs for Sale; What Did Your Lunch Cost Wildlife?; Which Niche?; Who Pays For What?; Wildlife as Seen on Coins and Stamps; Wildwork

ENGLISH

Animal Poetry; Animal Charades; Cartoons and Bumper Stickers; Does Wildlife Sell Cigarettes?; Enviro-Ethics; Interview a Spider; Learning to Look, Looking to See; Philosophical Differences; Planting Animals; Power of a Song; Pro and Con: Consumptive and Nonconsumptive Uses of Wildlife; Rare Bird Eggs for Sale; Stormy Weather; Visual Vocabulary; Who Lives Here?; Wild Words: A Journal-Making Activity; Wildlife Issues: Community Attitude Survey

THESE ADDITIONAL ACTIVITIES MAY ALSO BE USED IN ENGLISH CLASSES:

Adaptation Artistry; Ants on a Twig; Bird Song Survey; Cabin Conflict; Can Do!; Changing Attitudes; Deer Crossing; Ethi-Reasoning; Ethi-Thinking; Flip the Switch for Wildlife!; Good Buddies; Grasshopper Gravity!; Habitrekking; Here Today, Gone Tomorrow; History of Wildlife Management; The Hunter; Improving Wildlife Habitat in the Community; Keeping Score; Know Your Legislation; No Water Off a Duck's Back; Riparian Zone; Spider Web Geometry; Time Lapse; To Zone or Not to Zone; Too Close for Comfort; Urban Nature Search; We're in This Together!; What Did Your Lunch Cost Wildlife?; What's for Dinner?; When a Whale is a Right; Which Niche?; Who Pays for What?; Wild Bill's Fate; Wild Edible Plants; Wildlife in National Symbols; Wildlife Research

English Composition

Adaptation Artistry; Cartoons and Bumper Stickers; Changing Attitudes; Enviro-Ethics; Grasshopper Gravity; Habitrekking; History of Wildlife Management; Know Your Legislation; No Water Off a Duck's Back; Philosophical Differences; Urban Nature Search; We're in This Together!; Who Pays for What?; Wild Edible Plants; Wild Bill's Fate; Wildlife Issues: Community Attitude Survey; Wildlife Research

ENVIRONMENTAL PROBLEMS

Cabin Conflict; Changing Attitudes; Deadly Links; Deer Crossing; Enviro-Ethics; Ethi-Reasoning; Ethi-Thinking; Flip the Switch for Wildlife!; Habitrekking; Here Today, Gone Tomorrow; History of Wildlife Management; How Many Bears Can Live in This Forest?; Improving Wildlife Habitat in the Community; Keeping Score; Know Your Legislation; No Water Off a Duck's Back; Noisy Neighbors; Planning for People and for Wildlife; Polar Bears in Phoenix?; Rare Bird Eggs for Sale; Riparian Zone; Shrinking Habitat; To Zone or Not to Zone; Too Close for Comfort; Turkey Trouble; Water's Going On?!; We're in This Together!; What You Wear is What They Were; What Did Your Lunch Cost Wildlife?; When a Whale is a Right; Who Pays for What?; Wild Bill's Fate; Wild Edible Plants; Wildlife Issues: Community Attitude Survey; Wildlife Research

GEOGRAPHY

Here Today, Gone Tomorrow; Photos Keep It Happening!; Planning for People and for Wildlife; Polar Bears in Phoenix?; Pond Succession; Rainfall and the Forest; Riparian Zone; Shrinking Habitat; What You Wear is What They Were; What Did Your Lunch Cost Wildlife?; What's For Dinner?; When a Whale is a Right; Who Fits Here?; Wild Edible Plants; Wildlife as Seen on Coins and Stamps; Wildlife in National Symbols

GEOMETRY

Spider Web Geometry

GOVERNMENT

Cabin Conflict; Changing Attitudes; Deer Crossing; Here Today, Gone Tomorrow; History of Wildlife Management; Know Your Legislation; Philosophical Differences; Rare Bird Eggs for Sale; Riparian Zone; To Zone or Not to Zone; When a Whale is a Right; Who Pays for What?; Wild Bill's Fate; Wildlife as Seen on Coins and Stamps; Wildlife in National Symbols

HEALTH

Beautiful Basics; Deadly Links; Keeping Score; Lobster in Your Lunch Box; No Water Off a Duck's Back; Noisy Neighbors; Too Close for Comfort; What's For Dinner?; Wild Edible Plants

HISTORY

Cabin Conflict; Changing Attitudes; Fire Ecologies; Here Today, Gone Tomorrow; History of Wildlife Management; Photos Keep It Happening!; Planning for People and for Wildlife; Planting Animals; Pond Succession; Pro and Con: Consumptive and Nonconsumptive Uses of Wildlife; Rare Bird Eggs for Sale; When a Whale is a Right; Who Lives Here?; Wild Edible Plants; Wildlife as Seen on Coins and Stamps; Wildlife in National Symbols

HOME ECONOMICS

Deadly Links; Enviro-Ethics; Lobster in Your Lunch Box; Make a Coat!; No Water Off a Duck's Back; Water's Going On?!; What You Wear is What They Were; What Did Your Lunch Cost Wildlife?; What's For Dinner?; Wild Edible Plants

HUMAN RELATIONS

Changing Attitudes; Enviro-Ethics; Ethi-Reasoning; Noisy Neighbors; Philosophical Differences; Rare Bird Eggs for Sale; To Zone or Not to Zone; Too Close For Comfort; Which Niche?; Wildwork

LANGUAGE ARTS

Adaptation Artistry; And The Wolf Wore Shoes; Animal Charades; Animal Poetry; Ants on a Twig; Beautiful Basics; Bird Song Survey; Cabin Conflict; Can Do!; Cartoons and Bumper Stickers; Changing Attitudes; Classroom Carrying Capacity; Color Crazy; Deer Crossing; Does Wildlife Sell Cigarettes?; Enviro-Ethics; Ethi-Reasoning; Ethi-Thinking; Everybody Needs a Home; First Impressions; Flip the Switch for Wildlife!; Good Buddies; Graphananimal; Grasshopper Gravity; Habitracks; Habitrekking; Here Today, Gone Tomorrow; History of Wildlife Management; The Hunter; Improving Wildlife Habitat in the Community; Interview a Spider; Keeping Score; Know Your Legislation; Learning to Look, Looking to See;

Litter We Know; Lobster in Your Lunch Box; Make a Coat!; Microtrek Treasure Hunt; Museum Search for Wildlife; Noisy Neighbors; No Water Off a Duck's Back; Philosophical Differences; Planting Animals; Polar Bears in Phoenix?; Pond Succession; Power of a Song; Rare Bird Eggs for Sale; Riparian Zone; Saturday Morning Wildlife Watching; Seeing is Believing; Smokey Bear Said What?; Spider Web Geometry; Stormy Weather; Surprise Terrarium; Thicket Game; Time Lapse; To Zone or Not to Zone; Too Close for Comfort; Urban Nature Search; Visual Vocabulary; We're in This Together!; What Did Your Lunch Cost Wildlife?; What's That, Habitat?; What's Wild?; When a Whale is a Right; Which Niche?; Who Pays for What?; Who Lives Here?; Wild Bill's Fate; Wild Words; Wildwork; Wild Edible Plants; Wildlife in National Symbols; Wildlife Issues: Community Attitude Survey; Wildlife Research

LIFE SCIENCE

Adaptation Artistry; Ants on a Twig; Bearly Born; Bird Song Survey; Birds of Prey; Carrying Capacity; Checks and Balances; Deadly Links; Deer Crossing; Drawing on Nature; Eco-Enrichers; Fire Ecologies; Good Buddies; Grasshopper Gravity; Habitat Rummy; Habitat Lap Sit; Habitrekking; Here Today, Gone Tomorrow; How Many Bears Can Live in This Forest?; I'm Thirsty!; Improving Wildlife Habitat in the Community; Keeping Score; Muskox Maneuvers; My Kingdom for a Shelter; No Water Off a Duck's Back; Noisy Neighbors; Oh Deer!; Owl Pellets; Photos Keep It Happening!; Planning for People and for Wildlife; Polar Bears in Phoenix?; Pond Succession; Rainfall and the Forest; Shrinking Habitat; Too Close for Comfort; Tracks!; Turkey Trouble; Urban Nature Search; What You Wear is What They Were; What's for Dinner?; When a Whale is a Right; Which Niche?; Who Fits Here?; Wild Edible Plants; Wildlife Research

MATHEMATICS

Bearly Born; Bird Song Survey; Birds of Prey; Carrying Capacity; Checks and Balances; Environmental Barometer; Graphananimal; Grasshopper Gravity; How Many Bears Can Live in This Forest?; The Hunter; I'm Thirsty!; Improving Wildlife Habitat in the Community; Keeping Score; Let's Go Fly a Kite; Litter We Know; Lobster in Your Lunch Box; Make a Coat!; No Water Off a Duck's Back; Oh Deer!; Seed Need; Spider Web Geometry; Turkey Trouble; Water's Going On?! Wildlife Issues: Community Attitude Survey

MUSIC

Power of a Song

PHILOSOPHY

Cabin Conflict; Changing Attitudes; Deer Crossing; Does Wildlife Sell Cigarettes?; Enviro-Ethics; Ethi-Reasoning; Ethi-Thinking; Grasshopper Gravity; Philosophical Differences; Playing Lightly on the Earth; Power of a Song; Pro and Con: Consumptive and Nonconsumptive Uses of Wildlife; Rare Bird Eggs for Sale; Too Close for Comfort; What Did Your Lunch Cost Wildlife?; What You Wear is What They Were; Wildlife Issues: Community Attitude Survey; Wildlife in National Symbols; Wildlife Research

PHOTOGRAPHY

Photos Keep It Happening!; Time Lapse

PHYSICAL EDUCATION

Deadly Links; Habitat Lap Sit; How Many Bears Can Live in This Forest?; Muskox Maneuvers; Oh Deer!; Playing Lightly on the Earth; Quick Frozen Critters; Thicket Game

PSYCHOLOGY

Changing Attitudes; Enviro-Ethics; Ethi-Reasoning; Philosophical Differences; Rare Bird Eggs for Sale; Too Close for Comfort; We're in This Together!; Wildlife as See on Coins and Stamps; Wildlife in National Symbols; Wildlife Research

READING

And the Wolf Wore Shoes

SCIENCE

Adaptation Artistry; And the Wolf Wore Shoes; Animal Charades; Animal Poetry; Ants on a Twig; Bearly Born; Beautiful Basics; Bird Song Survey; Birds of Prey; Cabin Conflict; Can Do!; Carrying Capacity; Changing Attitudes; Checks and Balances; Classroom Carrying Capacity; Color Crazy; Deadly Links; Deer Crossing; Drawing on Nature; Eco-Enrichers; Environmental Barometer; Enviro-Ethics; Ethi-Reasoning; Ethi-Thinking; Everybody Needs a Home; Fire Ecologies; First Impressions; Flip the Switch for Wildlife!; Forest in a Jar; Good Buddies; Graphananimal; Grasshopper Gravity; Habitat Lap Sit; Habitat Rummy; Habitracks; Habitrekking; Here Today, Gone Tomorrow; History of Wildlife Management; How Many Bears Can Live In This Forest?; The Hunter; I'm Thirsty!; Improving Wildlife Habitat in the Community; Interview a Spider; Keeping Score; Know Your Legislation; Learning to Look, Looking to See; Let's Go Fly a Kite; Litter We Know; Lobster in Your Lunch Box; Make a Coat!; Microtrek Treasure Hunt; Migration Barriers; Muskox Maneuvers; My Kingdom for a Shelter; No Water Off a Duck's Back; Noisy Neighbors; Oh Deer!; Owl Pellets; Photos Keep It Happening!; Planning for People and for Wildlife; Planting Animals; Playing Lightly on the Earth; Polar Bears in Phoenix?; Pond Succession; Pro and Con: Consumptive and Nonconsumptive Uses of Wildlife; Quick Frozen Critters; Rainfall and the Forest; Rare Bird Eggs for Sale; Seed Need; Seeing is Believing; Shrinking Habitat; Smokey Bear Said What?; Spider Web Geometry; Stormy Weather; Surprise Terrarium; Thicket Game; Time Lapse; To Zone or Not to Zone; Too Close for Comfort; Tracks!; Turkey Trouble; Urban Nature Search; Visual Vocabulary; Water's Going On?!; We're in This Together!; What Bear Goes Where?; What Did Your Lunch Cost Wildlife?; What You Wear is What They Were; What's for Dinner?; What's That, Habitat?; What's Wild?; When a Whale is a Right; Which Niche?; Who Fits Here?; Who Lives Here?; Wild Edible Plants; Wild Words; Wildlife is Everywhere!; Wildlife in National Symbols; Wildlife Issues: Community Attitude Survey; Wildlife Research; Wildwork

SOCIAL STUDIES

Cabin Conflict; Can Do!; Cartoons and Bumper Stickers; Changing Attitudes; Classroom Carrying Capacity; Deadly Links; Deer Crossing; Does Wildlife Sell Cigarettes?; Environmental Barometer; Enviro-Ethics; Ethi-Reasoning; Ethi-Thinking; Fire Ecologies; Flip the Switch for Wildlife!; Grasshopper Gravity; Habitracks; Habitrekking; Here Today, Gone Tomorrow; History of Wildlife Management; How Many Bears Can Live in This Forest?; The Hunter; Improving Wildlife Habitat in the Community; Keeping Score; Know Your Legislation; Learning to Look, Looking to See; Litter We Know; Make a Coat!; Microtrek Treasure Hunt; Migration Barriers; Museum Search for Wildlife; No Water Off a Duck's Back; Noisy Neighbors; Oh Deer!; Philosophical Differences; Photos Keep It Happening!; Planning for People and for Wildlife; Playing Lightly on the Earth; Polar Bears in Phoenix?; Pond Succession; Power of a Song; Pro and Con: Consumptive and Nonconsumptive Uses of Wildlife; Rainfall and the Forest; Rare Bird Eggs for Sale; Riparian Zone; Saturday Morning Wildlife Watching; Seed Need; Shrinking Habitat; Smokey Bear Said What?; Stormy Weather; Time Lapse; To Zone or Not to Zone; Too Close for Comfort; Urban Nature Search; Water's Going On?!; We're in This Together!; What Did Your Lunch Cost Wildlife?; What You Wear is What They Were; What's That, Habitat?; When a Whale is a Right; Which Niche?; Who Pays for What?; Who Fits Here?; Wild Bill's Fate; Wild Edible Plants; Wildlife as Seen on Coins and Stamps; Wildlife in National Symbols; Wildlife Issues: Community Attitude Survey; Wildlife Research; Wildwork

SOCIOLOGY

Changing Attitudes; Ethi-Reasoning; Noisy Neighbors; Rare Bird Eggs for Sale; To Zone or Not to Zone; Too Close for Comfort; We're in This Together!; What You Wear is What They Were; When a Whale is a Right; Wildlife as Seen on Coins and Stamps; Wildlife in National Symbols; Wildlife Research

SPEECH

Cabin Conflict; Pro and Con: Consumptive and Nonconsumptive Uses of Wildlife; Rare Bird Eggs for Sale; Riparian Zone; To Zone or Not to Zone; We're in This Together!; When a Whale is a Right; Which Niche?; Wildlife Issues: Community Attitude Survey

VOCATIONAL AGRICULTURE

Checks and Balances; What Did Your Lunch Cost Wildlife?

WORLD GEOGRAPHY

Here Today, Gone Tomorrow; Photos Keep It Happening!; Pond Succession; Rainfall and the Forest; Rare Bird Eggs for Sale; Shrinking Habitat; Too Close for Comfort; What You Wear is What They Were; When a Whale is a Right; Wild Edible Plants; Wildlife as Seen on Coins and Stamps; Wildlife in National Symbols

WORLD HISTORY

Here Today, Gone Tomorrow; Photos Keep It Happening!; Pond Succession; Rare Bird Eggs for Sale; When a Whale is a Right; Wildlife as Seen on Coins and Stamps; Wildlife in National Symbols

TOPIC INDEX

The following is an alphabetical listing of topics included in Project WILD activities. This is not a comprehensive listing; that is, it does not list every possible topic. It does however include topics that might be included in an elementary course of study in a variety of subject areas. Activities are listed in alphabetical order, not according to the degree to which they emphasize the topic. We hope this serves to assist in your curriculum planning as you integrate Project WILD activities into existing courses of study and other instructional programs.

ADAPTATION
Adaptation Artistry; Birds of Prey; I'm Thirsty; Muskox Maneuvers; Owl Pellets; Polar Bears In Phoenix?; Quick Frozen Critters; Rainfall and the Forest; Seeing Is Believing; Surprise Terrarium; Thicket Game; Tracks!; Time Lapse; What Bear Goes Where?; Which Niche?; Who Fits Here?

ADVERTISING
Does Wildlife Sell Cigarettes?; Power of a Song

AESTHETIC VALUES OF WILDLIFE
Animal Poetry; Bird Song Survey; Cabin Conflict; Cartoons and Bumper Stickers; Does Wildlife Sell Cigarettes?; Drawing on Nature; Fire Ecologies; First Impressions; Here Today, Gone Tomorrow; Let's Go Fly a Kite; Migration Barriers; Museum Search for Wildlife; Photos Keep It Happening!; Planning for People and for Wildlife; Power of a Song; Pro and Con: Consumptive and NonConsumptive Uses of Wildlife; Rare Bird Eggs for Sale; Shrinking Habitat; To Zone or Not to Zone; Too Close for Comfort; Who Pays for What; Wildlife as Seen on Coins and Stamps; Wildlife in National Symbols; Wild Words: A Journal-Making Activity

AESTIVATION
Birds of Prey

AGRICULTURE
Deadly Links; Fire Ecologies; What Did Your Lunch Cost Wildlife?; What You Wear is What They Were; Wild Edible Plants

BASIC SURVIVAL NEEDS
Ants on a Twig; Bearly Born; Beautiful Basics; Birds of Prey; Carrying Capacity; Checks and Balances; Classroom Carrying Capacity; Deadly Links; Deer Crossing; Everybody Needs a Home; Flip the Switch for Wildlife!; Habitat Rummy; Habitat Lap Sit; Habitracks; Habitrekking; Here Today, Gone Tomorrow; How Many Bears Can Live in This Forest?; Improving Wildlife Habitat in the Community; Interview a Spider; Lobster in Your Lunch Box; Migration Barriers; My Kingdom for a Shelter; Noisy Neighbors; Oh Deer!; Owl Pellets; Polar Bears in Phoenix?; Quick Frozen Critters; Rainfall and the Forest; Shrinking Habitat; Spider Web Geometry; Stormy Weather; Too Close for Comfort; Tracks!; Turkey Trouble; We're In This Together!; What You Wear is What They Were; What Bear Goes Where?; What's for Dinner?; What's That, Habitat?; When a Whale Is a Right

CAMOUFLAGE
Color Crazy; Quick Frozen Critters; Surprise Terrarium; Thicket Game

CAREER EDUCATION
History of Wildlife Management; Which Niche?; Wildwork

CARRYING CAPACITY
Carrying Capacity; Checks and Balances; Classroom Carrying Capacity; Flip the Switch for Wildlife!; How Many Bears Can Live in This Forest?; Improving Wildlife Habitat in the Community; Oh Deer!; Planting Animals; Rainfall and the Forest; Shrinking Habitat; Too Close for Comfort

CHANGE
Birds of Prey; Carrying Capacity; Checks and Balances; Classroom Carrying Capacity; Deadly Links; Deer Crossing; Eco-Enrichers; Fire Ecologies; Flip the Switch for Wildlife!; Forest in a Jar; History of Wildlife Management; How Many Bears Can Live In This Forest?; Improving Wildlife Habitat in the Community; Oh Deer!; Planning for People and for Wildlife; Planting Animals; Pond Succession; Shrinking Habitat; Smokey Bear Said What?; Time Lapse; To Zone or Not to Zone; Turkey Trouble; Who Lives Here?

COMMENSALISM
Good Buddies

COMMERCIAL VALUES OF WILDLIFE
Does Wildlife Sell Cigarettes?; Fire Ecologies; First Impressions; Lobster in Your Lunch Box; Make a Coat!; Power of a Song; Pro and Con: Consumptive and Nonconsumptive Uses of Wildlife; Rare Bird Eggs for Sale; What You Wear is What They Were; When a Whale is a Right; Who Pays for What?; Wildlife Bibliography; Wildlife in National Symbols

COMMUNICATIONS
And the Wolf Wore Shoes; Cabin Conflict; Can Do!; Cartoons and Bumper Stickers; Changing Attitudes; Checks and Balances; Does Wildlife Sell Cigarettes?; Enviro-Ethics; Ethi-Reasoning; First Impressions; History of Wildlife Management; Improving Wildlife Habitat in the Community; Know Your Legislation; Migration Barriers; Philosophical Differences; Planning for People and for Wildlife; Power of a Song; Riparian Zone; Saturday Morning Wildlife Watching; To Zone or Not to Zone; What Did Your Lunch Cost Wildlife?; Wild Bill's Fate; Wildlife as Seen on Coins and Stamps; Wildlife in National Symbols; Wildlife Issues: Community Attitude Survey

COMMUNITY ATTITUDES
Cabin Conflict; Can Do! Changing Attitudes; Enviro-Ethics; Ethi-Reasoning; Ethi-Thinking; Fire Ecologies; Flip the Switch for Wildlife; History of Wildlife Management; The Hunter; Improving Wildlife Habitat in the Community; Know Your Legislation; Philosophical Differences; Pro and Con: Consumptive and Nonconsumptive Uses of Wildlife; Rare Bird Eggs for Sale; Riparian Zone; Shrinking Habitat; To Zone or Not to Zone; Water's Going On?!; We're In This Together!; What Did Your Lunch Cost Wildlife?; Who Pays for What?; Wildlife Issues: Community Attitude Survey

COMPONENTS OF HABITAT

Ants on a Twig; The Beautiful Basics; Bird Song Survey; Everybody Needs a Home; Habitat Rummy; Habitat Lap Sit; Habitracks; Habitrekking; Improving Wildlife Habitat in the Community; Oh Deer!; Owl Pellets; Polar Bears in Phoenix?; Rainfall and the Forest; Shrinking Habitat; Spider Web Geometry; We're in this Together!; What Bear Goes Where?; What's That, Habitat?

CONCEPT REVIEW

Visual Vocabulary

CONFLICTING POINTS OF VIEW REGARDING NATURAL RESOURCE ISSUES

Cabin Conflict; Cartoons and Bumper Stickers; Changing Attitudes; Checks and Balances; Deer Crossing; Does Wildlife Sell Cigarettes?; Ethi-Reasoning; Fire Ecologies; History of Wildlife Management; The Hunter; Improving Wildlife Habitat in the Community; Know Your Legislation; Migration Barriers; No Water Off a Duck's Back; Philosophical Differences; Power of a Song; Pro and Con: Consumptive and Nonconsumptive Uses of Wildlife; Rare Bird Eggs for Sale; Riparian Zone; Saturday Morning Wildlife Watching; Shrinking Habitat; Smokey Bear Said What?; To Zone or Not to Zone; What Did Your Lunch Cost Wildlife?; When a Whale is a Right; Who Pays for What?; Wild Bill's Fate; Wild Edible Plants; Wildlife Issues: Community Attitude Survey;

CONSERVATION

Cabin Conflict; Can Do!; Cartoons and Bumper Stickers; Checks and Balances; Deadly Links; Deer Crossing; Does Wildlife Sell Cigarettes?; Enviro-Ethics; Ethi-Reasoning; Ethi-Thinking; Fire Ecologies; Flip the Switch for Wildlife!; Here Today, Gone Tomorrow; History of Wildlife Management; The Hunter; I'm Thirsty!; Improving Wildlife Habitat in the Community; Keeping Score; Know Your Legislation; Lobster in Your Lunch Box; Migration Barriers; No Water Off a Duck's Back; Planning for People and for Wildlife; Planting Animals; Playing Lightly on the Earth; Rare Bird Eggs for Sale; Riparian Zone; Shrinking Habitat; Smokey Bear Said What?; To Zone or Not to Zone; Too Close for Comfort; Water's Going On?!; What Did Your Lunch Cost Wildlife?; What You Wear is What They Were; When a Whale Is a Right; Who Lives Here?; Who Pays for What?; Wild Edible Plants

CONSUMPTIVE/NONCONSUMPTIVE

The Hunter; Pro and Con: Consumptive and Nonconsumptive Uses of Wildlife; Who Pays for What?

CROWDING

Deer Crossing; Planning for People and for Wildlife; Shrinking Habitat; Too Close for Comfort

CYCLES

Birds of Prey; Checks and Balances; Deadly Links; Deer Crossing; Fire Ecologies; Forest in a Jar; Oh Deer!; Pond Succession; Rainfall and the Forest; Smokey Bear Said What?; Wild Edible Plants

CULTURE

Cabin Conflict; Can Do!; Cartoons and Bumper Stickers; Changing Attitudes; Deadly Links; Deer Crossing; Does Wildlife Sell Cigarettes?; Enviro-Ethics; Ethi-Reasoning; Ethi-Thinking; Fire Ecologies; Flip the Switch for Wildlife!; History of Wildlife Management; Improving Wildlife Habitat in the Community; Keeping Score; Know Your Legislation; Lobster in Your Lunch Box; No Water Off a Duck's Back; Philosophical Differences; Planning for People and for Wildlife; Playing Lightly on the Earth; Polar Bears in Phoenix?; Power of a Song; Pro and Con: Consumptive and Nonconsumptive Uses of Wildlife; Rare Bird Eggs for Sale; Riparian Zone; To Zone or Not to Zone; Water's Going On?!; We're In this Together!; What You Wear is What They Were; When a Whale Is a Right; Who Pays for What?; Wild Work; Wild Bill's Fate; Wild Edible Plants; Wildlife as Seen on Coins and Stamps; Wildlife Bibliography; Wildlife Issues: Community Attitude Survey; Wildlife Research

DEFINITIONS OF WILD AND DOMESTICATED ANIMALS

Animal Charades; Interview a Spider; Lobster in Your Lunch Box; What's Wild?

DEPENDENCE ON PLANTS

Checks and Balances; Deadly Links; Deer Crossing; Eco-Enrichers; Fire Ecologies; Habitrekking; Improving Wildlife Habitat in the Community; Lobster in Your Lunch Box; Oh Deer!; Rainfall and the Forest; Riparian Zone; Shrinking Habitat; Smokey Bear Said What?; What Did Your Lunch Cost Wildlife?; What You Wear is What They Were; What's for Dinner?; Who Fits Here?; Wild Edible Plants

ECOLOGICAL VALUES OF WILDLIFE

Cabin Conflict; Eco-Enrichers; Environmental Barometer; Fire Ecologies; First Impressions; Good Buddies; Here Today, Gone Tomorrow; History of Wildlife Management; Lobster in Your Lunch Box; Migration Barriers; Owl Pellets; Planning for People and for Wildlife; Planting Animals; Pond Succession; Rare Bird Eggs for Sale; Seed Need; Shrinking Habitat; Spider Web Geometry; To Zone or Not to Zone; Too Close for Comfort; When a Whale is a Right; Which Niche?; Who Lives Here?; Wild Edible Plants

ECONOMICS

Checks and Balances; Does Wildlife Sell Cigarettes?; Flip the Switch for Wildlife!; Improving Wildlife Habitat in the Community; Make a Coat!; Migration Barriers; No Water Off a Duck's Back; Planning for People and for Wildlife; Power of a Song; Shrinking Habitat; To Zone or Not to Zone; Water's Going On?!; What Did Your Lunch Cost Wildlife?; What's For Dinner?; Wildwork

ECOSYSTEMS

Birds of Prey; Carrying Capacity; Fire Ecologies; Rainfall and the Forest; Riparian Zone; Who Fits Here?

ENDANGERED (RARE, THREATENED AND EXTINCT) SPECIES

Deadly Links; Here Today, Gone Tomorrow; History of Wildlife Management; Planting Animals; Polar Bears in Phoenix; Rare Bird Eggs for Sale; Too Close For Comfort; When a Whale Is a Right; Who Fits Here?

ENERGY

Flip the Switch for Wildlife!; Lobster in Your Lunch Box; Migration Barriers; Planning for People and for Wildlife; Water's Going On?!; What Did Your Lunch Cost Wildlife?

ENVIRONMENTAL IMPACT STATEMENT

Migration Barriers

ENVIRONMENTAL PROBLEMS

Cabin Conflict; Deadly Links; Deer Crossing; Habitrekking; Know Your Legislation; Noisy Neighbors; Philosophical Differences; Rare Bird Eggs for Sale; Riparian Zone; We're in This Together!; When a Whale Is a Right

ENVIRONMENTAL QUALITY

Deadly Links; Habitrekking; Keeping Score; Noisy Neighbors; We're in This Together!

EVIDENCE OF WILDLIFE

Bird Song Survey; Environmental Barometer; Graphananimal; Habitrekking; Keeping Score; Owl Pellets; Spider Web Geometry; Surprise Terrarium; Too Close for Comfort; Tracks!; Urban Nature Search

FIRE

Fire Ecologies; Smokey Bear Said What?

FOOD CHAIN

Birds of Prey; Deadly Links; Owl Pellets; Shrinking Habitat; What Did Your Lunch Cost Wildlife?

GAME/NONGAME

History of Wildlife Management; Pro and Con: Consumptive and Nonconsumptive Uses of Wildlife; Rare Bird Eggs for Sale

HABITAT (APPLICATION; SEE COMPONENTS OF HABITAT FOR INTRODUCTION)

Bird Song Survey; Birds of Prey; Cabin Conflict; Can Do!; Carrying Capacity; Checks and Balances; Classroom Carrying Capacity; Deadly Links; Ethi-Thinking; Flip the Switch for Wildlife!; Here Today, Gone Tomorrow; History of Wildlife Management; How Many Bears Can Live in This Forest?; Improving Wildlife Habitat in the Community; Keeping Score; Migration Barriers; Oh Deer!; Planning for People and for Wildlife; Planting Animals; Polar Bears in Phoenix?; Rainfall and the Forest; Shrinking Habitat; To Zone or Not to Zone; Turkey Trouble; What Did Your Lunch Cost Wildlife?; When a Whale is a Right; Who Lives Here?

HABITAT IMPROVEMENT

Cabin Conflict; Can Do!; Checks and Balances; Environmental Barometer; Fire Ecologies; Flip the Switch for Wildlife!; History of Wildlife Management; Improving Wildlife Habitat in the Community; Keeping Score; Planning for People and for Wildlife; Shrinking Habitat; Smokey Bear Said What?; Who Pays for What?

HABITAT LOSS

Cabin Conflict; Carrying Capacity; Checks and Balances; Classroom Carrying Capacity; Deer Crossing; Fire Ecologies; Flip the Switch for Wildlife!; History of Wildlife Management; How Many Bears Can Live in This Forest?; Improving Wildlife Habitat in the Community; Keeping Score; Migration Barriers; My Kingdom For a Shelter; No Water Off a Duck's Back; Oh Deer!; Planning for People and for Wildlife; Planting Animals; Riparian Zone; Shrinking Habitat; Smokey Bear Said What?; To Zone or Not to Zone; Too Close for Comfort

HERBIVORES, CARNIVORES, OMNIVORES

Deadly Links; Owl Pellets; Shrinking Habitat

HISTORICAL VALUES OF WILDLIFE

Cabin Conflict; Cartoons and Bumper Stickers; Changing Attitudes; First Impressions; Here Today, Gone Tomorrow; History of Wildlife Management; The Hunter; Lobster in Your Lunch Box; Make a Coat!; Migration Barriers; Museum Search for Wildlife; Planning for People and for Wildlife; Polar Bears in Phoenix?; Power of a Song; Pro and Con: Consumptive and NonConsumptive Uses of Wildlife; Shrinking Habitat; To Zone or Not to Zone; Too Close for Comfort; What You Wear is What They Were; When a Whale Is a Right; Who Pays for What?; Wildlife Bibliography; Wildlife as Seen on Coins and Stamps; Wildlife in National Symbols

HUMAN RESPONSIBILITIES AND WILDLIFE

Cabin Conflict; Can Do!; Cartoons and Bumper Stickers; Changing Attitudes; Checks and Balances; Deadly Links; Deer Crossing; Does Wildlife Sell Cigarettes?; Enviro-Ethics; Ethi-Reasoning; Ethi-Thinking; Fire Ecologies; First Impressions; Flip the Switch for Wildlife!; Grasshopper Gravity; History of Wildlife Management; The Hunter; Improving Wildlife Habitat in the Community; Keeping Score; Know Your Legislation; Litter We Know; Lobster in Your Lunch Box; Migration Barriers; No Water Off a Duck's Back; Noisy Neighbors; Planning for People and for Wildlife; Planting Animals; Playing Lightly on the Earth; Polar Bears in Phoenix?; Power of a Song; Rare Bird Eggs for Sale; Riparian Zone; Saturday Morning Wildlife Watching; Shrinking Habitat; Smokey Bear Said What?; To Zone or Not to Zone; Too Close for Comfort; What You Wear Is What They Were; What Did Your Lunch Cost Wildlife?; When a Whale Is a Right; Who Pays for What?; Wild Bill's Fate; Wild Edible Plants; Wildlife Research

HUMOR

Cartoons and Bumper Stickers; Saturday Morning Wildlife Watching

HUNTING

Changing Attitudes; Checks and Balances; Classroom Carrying Capacity; Deer Crossing; Ethi-Reasoning; History of Wildlife Management; The Hunter; Philosophical Differences; Pro and Con: Consumptive and Nonconsumptive Uses of Wildlife; When a Whale is a Right; Who Pays for What?

INTERDEPENDENCE

Birds of Prey; Can Do!; Checks and Balances; Deadly Links; Deer Crossing; Enviro-Ethics; Fire Ecologies; Flip the Switch for Wildlife!; Forest in a Jar; Good Buddies; How Many Bears Can Live in This Forest?; Improving Wildlife Habitat in the Community; Keeping Score; Migration Barriers; No Water Off a Duck's Back; Oh Deer!; Owl Pellets; Planning for People and for Wildlife; Planting Animals; Polar Bears in Phoenix?; Pond Succession; Quick Frozen Critters; Rainfall and the Forest; Rare Bird Eggs for Sale; Riparian Zone; Shrinking Habitat; Smokey Bear Said What?; Thicket Game; To Zone or Not to Zone; Too Close for Comfort; Tracks!; Urban Nature Search; Water's Going On?!; What Did Your Lunch Cost Wildlife?; Which Niche?; Who Lives Here?; Wild Edible Plants

INTERNATIONAL ALLIANCES

Rare Bird Eggs for Sale; When a Whale is a Right; Wildlife Bibliography

INTRINSIC VALUE

Grasshopper Gravity; Here Today, Gone Tomorrow; The Hunter; Keeping Score; Make a Coat!; Pro and Con: Consumptive and Nonconsumptive Uses of Wildlife; Rare Bird Eggs for Sale; What You Wear is What They Were; When a Whale is a Right; Wild Bill's Fate; Wild Words; Wildlife Research

INTRODUCED SPECIES

Lobster in Your Lunch Box; Planting Animals; Turkey Trouble; Who Lives Here?

INVENTORY

Bird Song Survey

LAND DEVELOPMENT

Deer Crossing; Flip the Switch for Wildlife!; Migration Barriers; Planning for People and for Wildlife; Riparian Zone; Shrinking Habitat; To Zone or Not to Zone

LAND USE

Birds of Prey; Cabin Conflict; Can Do!; Deer Crossing; Flip the Switch for Wildlife!; Improving Wildlife Habitat in the Community; Keeping Score; Migration Barriers; Planning for People and for Wildlife; Playing Lightly on the Earth; Riparian Zone; Shrinking Habitat; To Zone or Not to Zone; Too Close for Comfort; What Did Your Lunch Cost Wildlife?

LAND USE PLANNING

Birds of Prey; Cabin Conflict; Can Do!; Deer Crossing; Improving Wildlife Habitat in the Community; Migration Barriers; Planning for People and for Wildlife; Riparian Zone; Shrinking Habitat; To Zone or Not to Zone

LEGISLATION

Know Your Legislation; Wild Bill's Fate

LIMITING FACTORS

Checks and Balances; Deadly Links; Here Today, Gone Tomorrow; How Many Bears Can Live in This Forest?; The Hunter; Improving Wildlife Habitat in the Community; Muskox Maneuvers; Oh Deer!; Planting Animals; Quick Frozen Critters; Rainfall and the Forest; Shrinking Habitat; Too Close for Comfort; Turkey Trouble

LITERATURE

And the Wolf Wore Shoes; Animal Poetry; The Hunter; Wild Words

MANAGEMENT OF HABITAT

Cabin Conflict; Can Do!; Carrying Capacity; Cartoons and Bumper Stickers; Checks and Balances; Classroom Carrying Capacity; Deadly Links; Deer Crossing; Fire Ecologies; Flip the Switch for Wildlife!; Here Today, Gone Tomorrow; History of Wildlife Management; The Hunter; Improving Wildlife Habitat in the Community; Migration Barriers; No Water Off a Duck's Back; Planning for People and for Wildlife; Planting Animals; Polar Bears in Phoenix?; Shrinking Habitat; Smokey Bear Said What?; To Zone or Not to Zone; Too Close for Comfort; What Did Your Lunch Cost Wildlife?; Who Lives Here?

MANAGEMENT TECHNIQUES

Bird Song Survey; Can Do!; Cartoons and Bumper Stickers; Checks and Balances; Deadly Links; Deer Crossing; Cabin Conflict; Fire Ecologies; History of Wildlife Management; The Hunter; Improving Wildlife Habitat in the Community; Migration Barriers; No Water Off a Duck's Back; Planning for People and for Wildlife; Planting Animals; Pro and Con: Consumptive and Nonconsumptive Uses of Wildlife; Shrinking Habitat; Smokey Bear Said What?; To Zone or Not to Zone; Too Close for Comfort; Turkey Trouble

MIGRATION

Bird Song Survey; Deer Crossing; Migration Barriers

MUSIC

Power of a Song

MUTUALISM

Good Buddies

NATIONAL SYMBOLS

Wildlife as Seen on Coins and Stamps; Wildlife in National Symbols

NATIVE AMERICAN INDIANS

The Hunter; Philosophical Differences; When a Whale is a Right; Wild Edible Plants

NATIVE/NON-NATIVE SPECIES

Here Today, Gone Tomorrow; Lobster in Your Lunch Box; Planting Animals; Who Lives Here?; Wild Edible Plants

NEWSPAPER

Cabin Conflict; Cartoons and Bumper Stickers; Does Wildlife Sell Cigarettes?; Interview a Spider; Wildlife Issues: Community Attitude Survey

SEASONS
Deer Crossing; Wild Edible Plants

SEED DISPERSAL
Seed Need

SIMILARITIES AND DIFFERENCES BETWEEN PEOPLE, WILDLIFE AND DOMESTICATED ANIMALS
And the Wolf Wore Shoes; Ants on a Twig; Bearly Born; Beautiful Basics; Carrying Capacity; Deadly Links; Everybody Needs a Home; Habitat Lap Sit; Habitracks; Habitrekking; How May Bears Can Live in this Forest?; I'm Thirsty!; Noisy Neighbors; Saturday Morning Wildlife Watching; Shrinking Habitat; Stormy Weather; Too Close for Comfort; We're In This Together!; What's For Dinner?; What's That, Habitat?; Which Niche?

SOIL
Eco-Enrichers; Fire Ecologies

STEREOTYPES
And the Wolf Wore Shoes; Does Wildlife Sell Cigarettes?; First Impressions; Saturday Morning Wildlife Watching; Wildlife in National Symbols

STOCKING
History of Wildlife Management; Who Pays for What?

SUCCESSION
Fire Ecologies; Forest in a Jar; Pond Succession

SYMBIOSIS
Good Buddies

SYMBOLS
Wildlife as Seen on Coins and Stamps; Wildlife in National Symbols

TELEVISION
Does Wildlife Sell Cigarettes?; Saturday Morning Wildlife Watching; Wildlife Issues: Community Attitude Survey

TERRITORY
Bird Song Survey

TOXIC SUBSTANCES
Deadly Links; No Water Off a Duck's Back; What Did Your Lunch Cost Wildlife?

URBAN
Bird Song Survey; Can Do!; Deer Crossing; Eco-Enrichers; Environmental Barometer; Enviro-Ethics; Ethi-Thinking; Flip the Switch for Wildlife!; Habitracks; Habitrekking; Improving Wildlife Habitat in the Community; Keeping Score; Litter We Know; Microtrek Treasure Hunt; Migration Barriers; My Kingdom for a Shelter; Noisy Neighbors; Planning for People and for Wildlife; Playing Lightly on the Earth; Pro and Con: Consumptive and Nonconsumptive Uses of Wildlife; Shrinking Habitat; Spider Web Geometry; To Zone or Not to Zone; Urban Nature Search; Water's Going On?!; We're in This Together!; Which Niche?; Who Lives Here?; Wildlife is Everywhere!

VARIETY OF WILDLIFE
Adaptation Artistry; And the Wolf Wore Shoes; Animal Poetry; Ants on a Twig; Bearly Born; Bird Song Survey; Birds of Prey; Color Crazy; Eco-Enrichers; Environmental Barometer; Fire Ecologies; Graphananimal; Habitrekking; Here Today, Gone Tomorrow; How Many Bears Can Live in This Forest?; I'm Thirsty!; Improving Wildlife Habitat in the Community; Interview a Spider; Keeping Score; Lobster in Your Lunch Box; Museum Search for Wildlife; Muskox Maneuvers; My Kingdom for a Shelter; Owl Pellets; Polar Bears in Phoenix?; Rainfall and the Forest; Seeing Is Believing; Spider Web Geometry; Surprise Terrarium; Tracks!; What Bear Goes Where?; When a Whale is a Right; Which Niche?; Who Fits Here?; Wildlife as Seen on Coins and Stamps; Wildlife in National Symbols

WATER
I'm Thirsty!; No Water Off a Duck's Back; Rainfall and the Forest; Riparian Zone; Water's Going On?!; When a Whale is a Right

WILDLIFE AS AN INDICATOR OF ENVIRONMENTAL QUALITY
Deadly Links; Deer Crossing; Environmental Barometer; Habitrekking; Keeping Score; Litter We Know; No Water Off a Duck's Back; Noisy Neighbors; Owl Pellets; Shrinking Habitat; Too Close for Comfort; Tracks; Wildlife Research

ZOOS
Polar Bears in Phoenix?; Rare Bird Eggs for Sale

INDOORS OR OUTDOORS

Most activities can be conducted outdoors. However, this listing is designed to indicate those activities tending to require an outdoor setting or at least a large open area.

INDOORS

Adaptation Artistry; And the Wolf Wore Shoes; Animal Charades; Animal Poetry; Bearly Born; Beautiful Basics; Birds of Prey; Cabin Conflict; Can Do!; Carrying Capacity; Cartoons and Bumper Stickers; Changing Attitudes; Checks and Balances; Classroom Carrying Capacity; Color Crazy; Deer Crossing; Does Wildlife Sell Cigarettes?; Eco-Enrichers; Enviro-Ethics; Ethi-Reasoning; Ethi-Thinking; Everybody Needs a Home; First Impressions; Flip the Switch for Wildlife!; Forest in a Jar; Good Buddies; Graphananimal; Grasshopper Gravity; Habitat Lap Sit; Habitat Rummy; Here Today, Gone Tomorrow; History of Wildlife Management; The Hunter; I'm Thirsty!; Improving Wildlife Habitat in the Community; Interview a Spider; Know Your Legislation; Learning to Look, Looking to See; Lobster in Your Lunch Box; Make a Coat!; Migration Barriers; Museum Search for Wildlife; No Water Off a Duck's Back; Owl Pellets; Philosophical Differences; Planning for People and for Wildlife; Planting Animals; Polar Bears in Phoenix?; Pond Succession; Power of a Song; Pro and Con: Consumptive and Nonconsumptive Uses of Wildlife; Rainfall and the Forest; Rare Bird Eggs for Sale; Riparian Zone; Saturday Morning Wildlife Watching; Seeing is Believing; Shrinking Habitat; Smokey Bear Said What?; Stormy Weather; Surprise Terrarium; To Zone or Not to Zone; Too Close for Comfort; Turkey Trouble; Visual Vocabulary; Water's Going On?!; We're in This Together!; What Bear Goes Where?; What Did Your Lunch Cost Wildlife?; What You Wear is What They Were; What's for Dinner?; What's That, Habitat?; What's Wild; When a Whale is a Right; Which Niche?; Who Fits Here?; Who Lives Here?; Who Pays for What?; Wild Bill's Fate; Wildlife Bibliography; Wildlife as See on Coins and Stamps; Wildlife in National Symbols; Wildlife Issues: Community Attitude Survey; Wildlife Research; Wildwork

OUTDOORS

Animal Poetry; Ants on a Twig; Bird Song Survey; Can Do!; Deadly Links; Drawing on Nature; Environmental Barometer; Fire Ecologies; Grasshopper Gravity; Habitracks; Habitrekking; How Many Bears Can Live in This Forest?; Keeping Score; Learning to Look, Looking to See; Let's Go Fly a Kite; Litter We Know; Microtrek Treasure Hunt; Muskox Maneuvers; My Kingdom for a Shelter; Noisy Neighbors; Oh Deer!; Photos Keep It Happening!; Playing Lightly on the Earth; Quick Frozen Critters; Seed Need; Shrinking Habitat; Spider Web Geometry; Thicket Game; Time Lapse; Tracks!; Urban Nature Search; Wild Edible Plants; Wild Words: A Journal-Making Activity; Wildlife is Everywhere!

CROSS REFERENCE BY SKILLS

The following is a listing of major skills which Project WILD activities have been designed to teach or develop. The list is not intended to be comprehensive; most activities teach additional skills. Activities may also be adapted to emphasize additional and different skills.

ANALYSIS

Adaptation Artistry; And the Wolf Wore Shoes; Animal Charades; Ants on a Twig; Bearly Born; Beautiful Basics; Birds of Prey; Cabin Conflict; Can Do!; Carrying Capacity; Cartoons and Bumper Stickers; Changing Attitudes; Checks and Balances; Classroom Carrying Capacity; Deadly Links; Deer Crossing; Does Wildlife Sell Cigarettes?; Eco-Enrichers; Environmental Barometer; Enviro-Ethics; Ethi-Reasoning; Ethi-Thinking; Everybody Needs a Home; Fire Ecologies; First Impressions; Flip the Switch for Wildlife!; Forest in a Jar; Graphananimal; Grasshopper Gravity; Habitat Rummy; Habitracks; Habitrekking; Here Today, Gone Tomorrow; History of Wildlife Management; How Many Bears Can Live in This Forest?; The Hunter; Improving Wildlife Habitat in the Community; Keeping Score; Know Your Legislation; Litter We Know; Lobster in Your Lunch Box; Make a Coat!; Microtrek Treasure Hunt; Migration Barriers; Museum Search for Wildlife; Muskox Maneuvers; No Water Off a Duck's Back; Owl Pellets; Philosophical Differences; Planning for People and for Wildlife; Planting Animals; Playing Lightly on the Earth; Polar Bears in Phoenix?; Pond Succession; Power of a Song; Pro and Con: Consumptive and Non-consumptive Uses of Wildlife; Quick Frozen Critters; Rainfall and the Forest; Rare Bird Eggs for Sale; Riparian Zone; Saturday Morning Wildlife Watching; Seed Need; Seeing is Believing; Smokey Bear Said What?; Spider Web Geometry; Thicket Game; To Zone or Not to Zone; Tracks!; Urban Nature Search; Water's Going On?!; We're in This Together!; What Bear Goes Where?; What Did Your Lunch Cost Wildlife?; What You Wear is What They Were; What's for Dinner?; What's That, Habitat?; When a Whale is a Right; Which Niche?; Who Fits Here?; Who Pays for What?; Wild Bill's Fate; Wild Edible Plants; Wildlife as Seen on Coins and Stamps; Wildlife Bibliography; Wildlife in National Symbols; Wildlife is Everywhere!; Wildlife Issues: Community Attitude Survey; Wildlife Research; Wildwork

APPLICATION

Adaptation Artistry; And the Wolf Wore Shoes; Bird Song Survey; Can Do!; Classroom Carrying Capacity; Deer Crossing; Drawing on Nature; Eco-Enrichers; Enviro-Ethics; Ethi-Reasoning; Ethi-Thinking; Flip the Switch for Wildlife!; Forest in a Jar; Good Buddies; Habitat Rummy; Habitrekking; Improving Wildlife Habitat in the Community; Keeping Score; Know Your Legislation; Microtrek Treasure Hunt; Migration Barriers; Museum Search for Wildlife; My Kingdom for a Shelter; Oh Deer!; Planning for People and for Wildlife; Polar Bears in Phoenix?; Pond Succession; Rainfall and the Forest; Seeing is Believing; Shrinking Habitat; Surprise Terrarium; Thicket Game; Time Lapse; To Zone or Not to Zone; Tracks!; Urban Nature Search; Visual Vocabulary; Water's Going On?!; We're in this Together!; What Bear Goes Where?; What Did Your Lunch Cost Wildlife?; When a Whale is a Right; Which Niche?; Wild Words: A Journal-Making Activity; Wild Edible Plants; Wildlife Issues: Community Attitude Survey; Wildlife Research

APPLICATION OF GEOMETRIC PRINCIPLES

Spider Web Geometry

CLASSIFICATION

And the Wolf Wore Shoes; Ants on a Twig; Beautiful Basics; Bird Song Survey; Deadly Links; Does Wildlife Sell Cigarettes?; Eco-Enrichers; Environmental Barometer; Good Buddies; Graphananimal; Grasshopper Gravity; Habitat Rummy; Habitracks; Here Today, Gone Tomorrow; Keeping Score; Litter We Know; Lobster in Your Lunch Box; Make a Coat!; Microtrek Treasure Hunt; Philosophical Differences; Rare Bird Eggs for Sale; Saturday Morning Wildlife Watching; Seed Need; Seeing is Believing; Smokey Bear Said What?; Urban Nature Search; We're in This Together!; What You Wear is What They Were; What Bear Goes Where?; What Did Your Lunch Cost Wildlife?; What's for Dinner?; What's Wild?; Which Niche?; Who Fits Here?; Who Lives Here?; Wild Edible Plants; Wildlife as Seen on Coins and Stamps; Wildlife Bibliography; Wildlife Issues: Community Attitude Survey; Wildlife Research

COMPARING SIMILARITIES AND DIFFERENCES

And the Wolf Wore Shoes; Ants on a Twig; Bearly Born; Beautiful Basics; Bird Song Survey; Birds of Prey; Carrying Capacity; Changing Attitudes; Classroom Carrying Capacity; Deadly Links; Deer Crossing; Eco-Enrichers; Environmental Barometer; Enviro-Ethics; Everybody Needs a Home; First Impressions; Flip the Switch for Wildlife!; Forest in a Jar; Grasshopper Gravity; Habitat Rummy; Habitracks; Habitrekking; The Hunter; Know Your Legislation; Migration Barriers; Oh Deer!; Owl Pellets; Philosophical Differences; Planning for People and for Wildlife; Playing Lightly on the Earth; Polar Bears in Phoenix?; Pond Succession; Pro and Con: Consumptive and Nonconsumptive Uses of Wildlife; Rainfall and the Forest; Saturday Morning Wildlife Watching; Seed Need; Seeing is Believing; Shrinking Habitat; Smokey Bear Said What?; Stormy Weather; To Zone or Not to Zone; Tracks!; Urban Nature Search; What Bear Goes Where?; What Did Your Lunch Cost Wildlife?; What You Wear is What They Were; What's That, Habitat?; Which Niche?; Who Fits Here?; Who Pays for What?; Wild Edible Plants; Wildlife as Seen on Coins and Stamps; Wildlife Bibliography; Wildlife in National Symbols; Wildlife Research

COMPUTATION

Bearly Born; Birds of Prey; Checks and Balances; Deadly Links; Eco-Enrichers; Environmental Barometer; Graphananimal; Grasshopper Gravity; How Many Bears Can Live in This Forest?; I'm Thirsty!; Keeping Score; Litter We Know; Lobster in Your Lunch Box; No Water Off a Duck's Back; Spider Web Geometry; Turkey Trouble; Water's Going On?!; Who Pays for What?; Wildlife Issues: Community Attitude Survey

DEBATE

Pro and Con: Consumptive and Nonconsumptive Uses of Wildlife; Rare Bird Eggs for Sale; When a Whale is a Right

DESCRIPTION

Adaptation Artistry; Animal Poetry; Ants on a Twig; Bird Song Survey; Birds of Prey; Cabin Conflict; Can Do!; Carrying Capacity; Classroom Carrying Capacity; Color Crazy; Deadly Links; Eco-Enrichers; Enviro-Ethics; Ethi-Thinking; First Impressions; Forest in a Jar; Grasshopper Gravity; Habitrekking; History of Wildlife Management; The Hunter; Improving Wildlife Habitat in the Community; Interview a Spider; Keeping Score; Know Your Legislation; Learning to Look, Looking to See; Make a Coat!; Microtrek Treasure Hunt; Migration Barriers; Muskox Maneuvers; My Kingdom for a Shelter; Oh Deer!; Pond Succession; Pro and Con: Consumptive and Nonconsumptive Uses of Wildlife; Quick Frozen Critters; Riparian Zone; Seed Need; Seeing is Believing; Shrinking Habitat; Smokey Bear Said What?; Spider Web Geometry; Stormy Weather; Thicket Game; Time Lapse; To Zone or Not

to Zone; Urban Nature Search; We're In This Together!; What Bear Goes Where?; What You Wear is What They Were; When a Whale is a Right; Which Niche?; Who Lives Here?; Wild Edible Plants; Wild Words: A Journal-Making Activity; Wildlife Research; Wildwork

DISCUSSION

Adaptation Artistry; And the Wolf Wore Shoes; Ants on a Twig; Bearly Born; Beautiful Basics; Bird Song Survey; Cabin Conflict; Can Do!; Cartoons and Bumper Stickers; Classroom Carrying Capacity; Deadly Links; Deer Crossing; Does Wildlife Sell Cigarettes?; Drawing on Nature; Eco-Enrichers; Environmental Barometer; Enviro-Ethics; Ethi-Reasoning; Ethi-Thinking; Everybody Needs a Home; Fire Ecologies; Flip the Switch for Wildlife!; Forest in a Jar; Grasshopper Gravity; Habitat Lap Sit; Habitracks; Habitrekking; Here Today, Gone Tomorrow; History of Wildlife Management; How Many Bears Can Live in This Forest?; The Hunter; I'm Thirsty!; Improving Wildlife Habitat in the Community; Interview a Spider; Keeping Score; Know Your Legislation; Learning to Look, Looking to See; Let's Go Fly a Kite; Litter We Know; Lobster in Your Lunch Box; Make a Coat!; Microtrek Treasure Hunt; Museum Search for Wildlife; Muskox Maneuvers; No Water Off a Duck's Back; Oh Deer!; Philosophical Differences; Planning for People and for Wildlife; Planting Animals; Polar Bears in Phoenix?; Pond Succession; Power of a Song; Quick Frozen Critters; Rainfall and the Forest; Rare Bird Eggs for Sale; Riparian Zone; Saturday Morning Wildlife Watching; Seeing is Believing; Shrinking Habitat; Smokey Bear Said What?; Surprise Terrarium; Thicket Game; To Zone or Not to Zone; Turkey Trouble; Urban Nature Search; Water's Going On?!; What Did Your Lunch Cost Wildlife?; What's for Dinner?; What's That, Habitat?; When a Whale is a Right; Which Niche?; Who Fits Here?; Who Lives Here?; Who Pays for What?; Wild Edible Plants; Wild Words: A Journal-Making Activity; Wildlife as Seen on Coins and Stamps; Wildlife Bibliography; Wildlife is Everywhere!; Wildlife Issues: Community Attitude Survey; Wildlife Research; Wildwork

DRAWING

Adaptation Artistry; Bearly Born; Birds of Prey; Color Crazy; Drawing on Nature; Ethi-Thinking; Everybody Needs a Home; Flip the Switch for Wildlife!; Forest in a Jar; Improving Wildlife Habitat in the Community; Migration Barriers; No Water Off a Duck's Back; Planning for People and for Wildlife; Polar Bears in Phoenix?; Pond Succession; Spider Web Geometry; What Did Your Lunch Cost Wildlife?; What You Wear is What They Were; What's for Dinner?; What's That, Habitat?; Wild Edible Plants; Wild Words: A Journal-Making Activity

ESTIMATION
Bearly Born; No Water Off a Duck's Back

EVALUATION
Birds of Prey; Cabin Conflict; Can Do!; Carrying Capacity; Cartoons and Bumper Stickers; Changing Attitudes; Checks and Balances; Classroom Carrying Capacity; Deadly Links; Deer Crossing; Does Wildlife Sell Cigarettes?; Environmental Barometer; Enviro-Ethics; Ethi-Reasoning; Ethi-Thinking; Fire Ecologies; Flip the Switch for Wildlife!; How Many Bears Can Live in This Forest!; The Hunter; I'm Thirsty!; Improving Wildlife Habitat in the Community; Keeping Score; Know Your Legislation; Litter We Know; Make a Coat!; Migration Barriers; Muskox Maneuvers; Philosophical Differences; Planning for People and For Wildlife; Playing Lightly on the Earth; Polar Bears in Phoenix?; Power of a Song; Pro and Con: Consumptive and Nonconsumptive Uses of Wildlife; Quick Frozen Critters; Rare Bird Eggs for Sale; Riparian Zone; Saturday Morning Wildlife Watching; Shrinking Habitat; Smokey Bear Said What?; To Zone or Not to Zone; Too Close for Comfort; Water's Going On?!; What Did Your Lunch Cost Wildlife?; What You Wear is What They Were; When a Whale is a Right; Who Lives Here?; Who Pays for What?; Wild Bill's Fate; Wild Edible Plants; Wildlife in National Symbols; Wildlife Issues: Community Attitude Survey; Wildlife Research

GENERALIZATION
Ants on a Twig; Bearly Born; Birds of Prey; Carrying Capacity; Color Crazy; Deadly Links; Drawing on Nature; Eco-Enrichers; Ethi-Thinking; Everybody Needs a Home; Fire Ecologies; First Impressions; Forest in a Jar; Grasshopper Gravity; Habitat Lap Sit; Habitrekking; How Many Bears Can Live in This Forest?; I'm Thirsty!; Interview a Spider; Microtrek Treasure Hunt; Migration Barriers; Museum Search for Wildlife; Muskox Maneuvers; No Water Off a Duck's Back; Noisy Neighbors; Oh Deer!; Owl Pellets; Quick Frozen Critters; Rainfall and the Forest; Riparian Zone; Seeing is Believing; Shrinking Habitat; Stormy Weather; Surprise Terrarium; Thicket Game; To Zone or Not to Zone; Urban Nature Search; Water's Going On?!; We're in This Together!; What Bear Goes Where?; What's That, Habitat?; When a Whale is a Right; Which Niche?; Who Lives Here?; Who Pays for What?; Wildlife as Seen on Coins and Stamps; Wildlife is Everywhere!; Wildlife Research

GRAPHING
Bearly Born; No Water Off a Duck's Back; Oh Deer!

HYPOTHESIS FORMATION AND TESTING
Birds of Prey; Carrying Capacity; Flip the Switch for Wildlife!; Noisy Neighbors; Too Close for Comfort; Wildlife in National Symbols

INFERENCE
Classroom Carrying Capacity; Deer Crossing; I'm Thirsty!; Photos Keep It Happening!; Seeing is Believing; Too Close for Comfort; Wildlife as Seen on Coins and Stamps

INTERPRETATION OF CONCEPTS
Noisy Neighbors; Turkey Trouble

INTERVIEW
Changing Attitudes; History of Wildlife Management; Interview a Spider; Know Your Legislation; We're in This Together!; Which Niche?; Wildlife Issues: Community Attitude Survey

INVENTION
Adaptation Artistry; Animal Poetry; Can Do!; Color Crazy; Drawing on Nature; Enviro-Ethics; Forest in a Jar; Habitrekking; Improving Wildlife Habitat in the Community; Let's Go Fly a Kite; Make a Coat!; Photos Keep It Happening!; Planning for People and for Wildlife; Playing Lightly on the Earth; Polar Bears in Phoenix?; Seeing is Believing; Spider Web Geometry; Time Lapse; Visual Vocabulary; Wildlife Issues: Community Attitude Survey; Wildlife Research

KINESTHETIC CONCEPT DEVELOPMENT
Animal Charades; Ants on a Twig; Carrying Capacity; Classroom Carrying Capacity; Deadly Links; Drawing on Nature; Eco-Enrichers; Graphananimal; Habitat Lap Sit; How Many Bears Can Live in This Forest?; Muskox Maneuvers; Oh Deer!; Quick Frozen Critters; Seed Need; Shrinking Habitat; Thicket Game; Urban Nature Search; Visual Vocabulary; What You Wear is What They Were

LISTENING
Power of a Song; Which Niche?

LISTING
And the Wolf Wore Shoes; Beautiful Basics; Can Do!; Carrying Capacity; Classroom Carrying Capacity; First Impressions; Graphananimal; Grasshopper Gravity; Here Today, Gone Tomorrow; How Many Bears Can Live in This Forest?; Know Your Legislation; Learning to Look, Looking to See; Lobster in Your Lunch Box; Microtrek Treasure Hunt; Polar Bears in Phoenix?; Seed Need; Smokey Bear Said What?; Urban Nature Search; We're in This Together!; What Bear Goes Where?; What You Wear is What They Were; What's for Dinner?; Which Niche?; Wildlife Bibliography; Wildlife Research; Wildwork

MAPPING
Bird Song Survey; Habitracks

MATCHING PAIRS
Good Buddies

MEASUREMENT
Spider Web Geometry

MEDIA CONSTRUCTION
Adaptation Artistry; Bearly Born; Bird Song Survey; Color Crazy; Drawing on Nature; Ethi-Thinking; Flip the Switch for Wildlife!; Forest in a Jar; Graphananimal; Habitat Rummy; Habitrekking; Improving Wildlife Habitat in the Community; Let's Go Fly a Kite; Litter We Know; Lobster in Your Lunch Box; Make a Coat!; Migration Barriers; My Kingdom for a Shelter; Photos Keep It Happening!; Planning for People and for Wildlife; Planting Animals; Polar Bears in Phoenix?; Pond Succession; Seeing is Believing; Smokey Bear Said What?; Spider Web Geometry; Time Lapse; What Bear Goes Where?; What Did Your Lunch Cost Wildlife?; What You Wear is What They Were; What's Wild?; What's For Dinner?; Who Fits Here?; Wild Edible Plants; Wild Words: A Journal-Making Activity; Wildlife in National Symbols

OBSERVATION
Adaptation Artistry; And the Wolf Wore Shoes; Animal Charades; Ants on a Twig; Bird Song Survey; Birds of Prey; Carrying Capacity; Cartoons and Bumper Stickers; Classroom Carrying Capacity; Color Crazy; Does Wildlife Sell Cigarettes?; Drawing on Nature; Eco-Enrichers; Environmental Barometer; Fire Ecologies; Graphananimal; Grasshopper Gravity; Habitracks; Habitrekking; How Many Bears Can Live in This Forest?; Keeping Score; Learning to Look, Looking to See; Litter We Know; Make a Coat!; Microtrek Treasure Hunt; Migration Barriers; Museum Search for Wildlife; Muskox Maneuvers; My Kingdom for a Shelter; No Water Off a Duck's Back; Oh Deer!; Photos Keep It Happening!; Polar Bears in Phoenix?; Pond Succession; Quick Frozen Critters; Saturday Morning Wildlife Watching; Seed Need; Seeing is Believing; Shrinking Habitat; Spider Web Geometry; Surprise Terrarium; Thicket Game; Urban Nature Search; Visual Vocabulary; Water's Going On?!; What Bear Goes Where?; What You Wear is What They Were; What's Wild?; Wild Words: A Journal-Making Activity; Wildlife as Seen on Coins and Stamps; Wildlife is Everywhere!

PHYSICAL INTERPRETATION OF CONCEPTS
Animal Charades

PROBLEM SOLVING
Adaptation Artistry; Birds of Prey; Can Do!; Deer Crossing; Enviro-Ethics; Ethi-Reasoning; Ethi-Thinking; Flip the Switch for Wildlife!; Improving Wildlife Habitat in the Community; Keeping Score; Know Your Legislation; Let's Go Fly a Kite; Litter We Know; Microtrek Treasure Hunt; Photos Keep It Happening!; Planning for People and for Wildlife; Playing Lightly on the Earth; Polar Bears in Phoenix?; Turkey Trouble; Visual Vocabulary; Water's Going On?!; What Did Your Lunch Cost Wildlife?; Wildlife Research

PSYCHOMOTOR DEVELOPMENT
Carrying Capacity; Eco-Enrichers; Forest in a Jar; Graphananimal; How Many Bears Can Live in This Forest?; Let's Go Fly a Kite; Make a Coat!; Muskox Maneuvers; Oh Deer!; Planning for People and for Wildlife; Planting Animals; Playing Lightly on the Earth; Quick Frozen Critters; Seeing is Believing; Thicket Game; Tracks!; Visual Vocabulary; What Bear Goes Where?; What You Wear is What They Were

PUBLIC SPEAKING
Cabin Conflict; Can Do!; Changing Attitudes; Know Your Legislation; Pro and Con: Consumptive and Nonconsumptive Uses of Wildlife; Rare Bird Eggs For Sale; To Zone or Not to Zone; When a Whale is a Right; Which Niche?; Who Lives Here?; Wildlife Issues: Community Attitude Survey

READING
And the Wolf Wore Shoes; Bearly Born; Beautiful Basics; Birds of Prey; Cartoons and Bumper Stickers; Color Crazy; Deer Crossing; Does Wildlife Sell Cigarettes?; Graphananimal; Grasshopper Gravity; Habitat Rummy; Habitracks; The Hunter; Interview a Spider; Know Your Legislation; Microtrek Treasure Hunt; Spider Web Geometry; Visual Vocabulary; When a Whale is a Right; Which Niche?; Who Fits Here?; Who Lives Here?; Wild Bill's Fate; Wildlife as Seen on Coins and Stamps; Wildlife Bibliography; Wildlife Issues: Community Attitude Survey; Wildlife Research

REPORTING
Adaptation Artistry; Changing Attitudes; Deer Crossing; Eco-Enrichers; Enviro-Ethics; Fire Ecologies; First Impressions; Flip the Switch for Wildlife; Good Buddies; Keeping Score; Know Your Legislation; Migration Barriers; Pro and Con: Consumptive and Nonconsumptive Uses of Wildlife; Rare Bird Eggs for Sale; Riparian Zone; Saturday Morning Wildlife Watching; To Zone or Not to Zone; What You Wear is What They Were; When a Whale is a Right; Which Niche?; Who Lives Here?; Wild Bill's Fate

RESEARCH

Changing Attitudes; Eco-Enrichers; Fire Ecologies; First Impressions; Flip the Switch for Wildlife!; Forest in a Jar; Good Buddies; Habitrekking; History of Wildlife Management; Interview a Spider; Know Your Legislation; My Kingdom for a Shelter; Planting Animals; Pro and Con: Consumptive and Nonconsumptive Uses of Wildlife; Rare Bird Eggs for Sale; Riparian Zone; Smokey Bear Said What?; Spider Web Geometry; To Zone or Not to Zone; We're in This Together!; When a Whale is a Right; Which Niche?; Who Fits Here?; Who Lives Here?; Who Pays for What?; Wild Bill's Fate; Wild Edible Plants; Wildlife as Seen on Coins and Stamps; Wildlife Bibliography; Wildlife in National Symbols; Wildlife Issues: Community Attitude Survey; Wildlife Research; Wildwork

SMALL GROUP WORK

And the Wolf Wore Shoes; Ants on a Twig; Can Do!; Ethi-Reasoning; Ethi-Thinking; First Impressions; Flip the Switch for Wildlife!; Good Buddies; Habitat Lap Sit; Habitat Rummy; Habitracks; Habitrekking; Improving Wildlife Habitat in the Community; Keeping Score; Know Your Legislation; Litter We Know; Microtrek Treasure Hunt; Migration Barriers; Muskox Maneuvers; Playing Lightly on the Earth; Pond Succession; Pro and Con: Consumptive and Nonconsumptive Uses of Wildlife; Saturday Morning Wildlife Watching; Seeing is Believing; Smokey Bear Said What?; Visual Vocabulary; When a Whale is a Right; Which Niche?; Who Fits Here?; Wild Bill's Fate; Wildlife Bibliography; Wildlife Issues: Community Attitude Survey

SYNTHESIS

Adaptation Artistry; Animal Poetry; Can Do!; Deadly Links; Deer Crossing; Drawing on Nature; Enviro-Ethics; Ethi-Reasoning; Ethi-Thinking; Fire Ecologies; Flip the Switch for Wildlife!; Habitracks; Habitrekking; Here Today, Gone Tomorrow; History of Wildlife Management; Improving Wildlife Habitat in the Community; Keeping Score; Know Your Legislation; Litter We Know; Make a Coat!; Migration Barriers; Noisy Neighbors; Philosophical Differences; Photos Keep It Happening!; Planning for People and for Wildlife; Planting Animals; Playing Lightly on the Earth; Polar Bears in Phoenix?; Pond Succession; Pro and Con: Consumptive and Nonconsumptive Uses of Wildlife; Rainfall and the

Forest; Riparian Zone; Saturday Morning Wildlife Watching; Seeing is Believing; Shrinking Habitat; Smokey Bear Said What?; Time Lapse; To Zone or Not to Zone; Tracks!; Visual Vocabulary; Water's Going On?!; We're in This Together!; What Bear Goes Where?; What Did Your Lunch Cost Wildlife?; What You Wear is What They Were; When a Whale is a Right; Which Niche?; Who Pays for What?; Wild Edible Plants; Wildlife Bibliography; Wildlife Issues: Community Attitude Survey; Wildlife in National Symbols; Wildwork

VISUALIZATION

Animal Poetry; Drawing on Nature; Everybody Needs a Home; Flip the Switch for Wildlife!; Improving Wildlife Habitat in the Community; Migration Barriers; Planning for People and for Wildlife; Planting Animals; Polar Bears in Phoenix?; Pond Succession; Smokey Bear Said What?; Stormy Weather; Time Lapse; Visual Vocabulary; What Did Your Lunch Cost Wildlife?; Wild Edible Plants; Wild Words: A Journal-Making Activity

WRITING

Adaptation Artistry; Animal Poetry; Ants on a Twig; Bearly Born; Can Do!; Changing Attitudes; Color Crazy; Eco-Enrichers; Ethi-Reasoning; Fire Ecologies; First Impressions; Flip the Switch for Wildlife!; Graphananimal; Grasshopper Gravity; Habitat Rummy; Habitrekking; History of Wildlife Management; Interview a Spider; Keeping Score; Know Your Legislation; Lobster in Your Lunch Box; Microtrek Treasure Hunt; Philosophical Differences; Planting Animals; Seed Need; Spider Web Geometry; Time Lapse; To Zone or Not to Zone; Urban Nature Search; We're in This Together!; What Did Your Lunch Cost Wildlife?; What's for Dinner?; What's That, Habitat?; When a Whale is a Right; Which Niche?; Who Fits Here?; Who Pays for What?; Wild Bill's Fate; Wild Edible Plants; Wild Words: A Journal-Making Activity; Wildlife Bibliography; Wildlife as Seen on Coins and Stamps; Wildlife Issues: Community Attitude Survey; Wildlife Research

PROJECT EVALUATION

Project WILD has undergone thorough evaluation of a variety of forms. The purpose has been to develop as well-conceived and tested a supplementary instructional resource as possible.

DEVELOPMENT OF PROJECT WILD ACTIVITY GUIDES

Expert Review

All of the instructional activities in Project WILD, as well as the conceptual design reflected in the Curriculum Framework, have been reviewed for educational soundness, balance and content accuracy. The initial instructional activities were written primarily by classroom teachers. Reviewers throughout each stage of the project's development have included classroom teachers, university faculty, resource agency personnel, wildlife biologists, representatives of private conservation groups, school administrators, curriculum developers, environmental education specialists, representatives of private industry, citizen volunteers and others. Results of this review process were used in editing and improving the Project WILD instructional materials throughout the program's development.

Pilot Test

Of the literally hundreds of instructional activities developed for possible use in Project WILD, a core group was selected and refined for use in the preliminary pilot test version of the materials. Each of the instructional activities which appears in the final Project WILD materials was tested by classroom teachers to ensure its quality and appropriateness. Some revisions—from major to minor—were made in each of the activities, and a few were discarded entirely. This entire process was developed and implemented by a respected team of researchers.

Field Test

Following the year of the pilot test of the original Project WILD activities, a major field test was designed and conducted to determine the effectiveness of the materials when used by teachers with their students. Again, this study was developed and implemented by a knowledgeable and esteemed team of researchers. The field test was conducted in three states, in three demographic areas (urban, suburban and rural) and across all elementary and secondary grade levels during one full school year. Two hundred fifty-nine teachers and more than 6000 students were involved. The results indicate that Project WILD has a definite impact on teachers and students. Students showed significant gains in learning and developed attitudes toward wildlife that are consistent with the goals of Project WILD. Teachers generally found the activities stimulating and worthwhile in their classes and were able to integrate them into their curricula. A direct relationship was evidenced between the number of Project WILD instructional activities used by the teachers and student gains in knowledge and attitudes. Project WILD was effective in urban, suburban and rural areas.

IMPLEMENTATION OF PROGRAM

The Project WILD Activity Guides are provided to educators free of charge in instructional workshops that average seven hours in length. Participant feedback from these workshops is regularly monitored. Two major surveys of uses have been conducted—one in 1986 and one in 1990—to determine the extent to which the Project WILD materials are used after workshops, under what conditions, with what results. The results are outstanding. For example, the data indicate that approximately 80% of the participants in Project WILD workshops actually use the materials with students after the workshop. More than 35 million students have been taught with Project WILD to date. More than 95% of teachers using Project WILD report that their students have taken action to benefit wildlife and the environment as a result of Project WILD.

CONTINUING EVALUATION

Project WILD will be monitored and evaluated on an on-going and long-term basis in order to ensure its quality and effectiveness as well as to make revisions and additions to the program as needed.

ACKNOWLEDGEMENTS

Project WILD is made available as the result of the concerned and dedicated efforts of literally hundreds of thousands of people.

It is not possible to individually thank and credit all of those who have assisted—including the thousands of students in kindergarten through high school classrooms who participated in the pilot and field test stages of the project's development.

We would like to make special mention of the contributions of the American Forest Institute, cosponsor of Project Learning Tree with the Council for Environmental Education. Project Learning Tree's record of quality and success led directly to the development, and subsequent availability, of Project WILD.

We would also like to acknowledge the generous support made possible through the contributions of the International Association of Fish and Wildlife Agencies, as well as the other Associate Sponsors and Contributors to the Project.

With chagrin and apologies as we recognize that we will inadvertently omit the names of many for whom we would wish acknowledgement, we would like to thank the following.

Project WILD Program Committee
Peggy Cowan, Michelle Mauthe Harvey, Arva J. Jackson, John Kimball, Nancy Rolli, Max Peterson; ex-officio—Josetta Hawthorne, Donna Asbury.

Founding WREEC Members and Former Members
Tina Allen, LaMar Allred, Bill Andrews, Steve Andrews, Tony Angell, Kerry Baldwin, Meyer Bogost, Bob Briggs, Frank Bryce, Carol Bylsma, Tom Cates, Peggy Cowan, Kurt Cunningham, Bill Dillinger, Dave Eckert, George Ek, Bob Ellis, Edward Eschler, Dr. Bill Futrell, John Gahl, John George, Donna Gleisner, B.K. Graham, Dr. Gary Hall, Cliff Hamilton, Rob Harper, Russ Hartford, John Hawkins, Dick Hess, Mark Hilliard, Don Hollums, Rhonda Hunter, Beverly Isenson, Dr. Richard Kay, David A. Kennedy, Donn Kesselheim, Joanna P. Lackey, Marc Lame, Mike Lang, Dolores Moulton Larson, Dale Lashnits, Dr. Mary Jo Lavin, Bob Lawson, Don MacCarter, Carl Masaki, Colleen Matt, Susan McLane, Terry Messmer, Jennifer Meyer, Gini Mitchell, Cheryl Mollohan, Pat Murphy, Stu Murrell, Perry Olson, Sam Ornelas, Dr. Richard Peterson, Dr. Al Ramirez, Mike Reed, Ray Remund, David Rice, Dave Sanger, Rudolph

J. H. Schafer, Dolores Scott, Daphne Sewing, Bud Smith, Darleen Stoner, Elena Tarailo, Ray Thiess, Vivienne Torgeson, Vince Vandre, Joe Vogler, Robert Warren, Shann Weston, Chris Williams, Don Winslow, Mary Ellen Wolfe, Vince Yannone, Terry Zubchenok; Josetta Hawthorne, Executive Director.

Former Project WILD Management Committee
Gene Allen, Kerry Baldwin, Bob Briggs, Carol Bylsma, Dr. Cheryl Charles, Edward Eschler, Dr. Tom Fitzgerald, John Gahl, Cliff Hamilton, William F. Hammond, William R. "Bob" Hernbrode, Dr. Richard Kay, Dr. Clifford E. Knapp, Joanna Lackey, Dolores Moulton Larson, Dr. Don Lundstrom, Don MacCarter, Dr. Milton McClaren, Dr. Lewis Nelson, Jr., Perry Olson, Tim Provan, Rudolph J. H. Schafer, Daphne Sewing Dr. Jerry Tucker, Shann Weston, Terry Wilson, Don Winslow, Dr. Dennis Yockers.

Reviewers of Project WILD Curriculum Framework
The Project WILD Curriculum Framework was reviewed by hundreds of individuals, representing a range of organizations including conservation groups, natural resource agencies, private industry, public education and private education. We regret not being able to list these many individuals and organizations by name, but appreciate their substantial contributions to the overall accuracy and quality of the framework which formed the basis for the development of the Project WILD instructional materials. We would like to especially acknowledge Mr. Cliff Hamilton for his exceptional effort and skill in serving as general editor of the final framework.

FIRST EDITION
Project WILD Writing Conference Participants
Alaska: Dolores Moulton, Edward Eschler, Lew Nelson, Kris Kantola, Sue Matthews, Paul Arneson, Eric Morris, Wendell Shiffler, Nancy Murphy, Peter Buck, Sue Quinlan, Walter Suomela, Hal Neace, Sister Bridget M. Connor, Judy Hauck, Cheryl Charles; *Arizona:* Rosemary Elkins, Jean Fields, Patty Horn, Cleo Scheyli, Eloise Babcock, Valerie Davison, Ann Motley, Peggy Griego, Judith Enz, Kitty Fischer, Mary Howell, Dean Holland, Bob Hernbrode, Kerry Baldwin, Joanna Lackey, Jerry Tucker, Wendy Greenberg, Cheryl Charles, Gerry Hernbrode, Jim Hudnall, Tanna Baldwin; *California:* Rudy Schafer, Augie Scornaienchi, Larry Rose, Anne Manolis, Evelyn Cormier, Phyllis Shuck, Molly Whiteley, Carolie Sly, Marlynn Kaake, Jan Rensel, Bob Flasher, Steve Wilkes, Martin Abrams, Otis McCain, John Mackenzie, Juanita Gex, Olina Gilbert, Mary Rodgers, Susan

de Treville, Dolores Moulton, Cheryl Charles, Rocky Rohwedder; *Colorado:* Russell Skillings, Glenn McGlathery, Paul Bauman, Jeff Brigham, Sue Miller, Evaline Olson, Carol Bergevin, Kathy Williams, James Jackson, Cheryl Charles, Kerry Baldwin, Bud Smith, Gene Carroll, Jack Anderson, Helen Davis, Cliff Hamilton, Roxy Pestello, William Turner, Stu Murrell, John Ernst, Kris Gabrielson, Robin Hernbrode, Joanna Lackey, George Ek, Sandy Sanborn, Dave Perry, Bill Huntley, Dr. Norma Livo, Kathy Kelley, Bill Haggerty; *Idaho:* Marjorie Reinecker, Nancy Christensen, Royce Williams, Glendon Jones, Bob Humphries, Mary Lynn Popplewell, Begie Hatmaker, Joanna Lackey, Bob Hernbrode, Cheryl Charles, Jerry Tucker, Lewis Nelson, Cliff Hamilton, Edward Eschler, Richard Kay, Ray Remund, Stu Murrell, Ben Peyton, Harry Mills, Bob Nisbitt, Lea Williford, Shelley Davis, Creed Noah, Dennis Cartwright, Cindy Teipner, Joe Vogler, Connie Gilman, Lyn Fleming.

Field Test Teachers and Administrators
Teachers, administrators and students in school districts in the states of Colorado, Virginia and Washington assisted in the formal field testing of the Project WILD materials. The confidentiality of the testing process requires that we not identify the participating personnel and districts. We extend our grateful thanks to all of those involved for their assistance.

Pilot Teachers, Students and Administrators
Teachers, administrators and students in school districts in the states of Washington and Arizona assisted in the formal pilot testing of the Project WILD materials. We thank each of these people for their dedicated and generous assistance. In particular, we would like to acknowledge the coordination and support provided by Lynn Olson, Principal, La Center, Washington; and Dick Clark, Science Supervisor, Washington Public Schools, Phoenix, Arizona. In addition, we would like to thank the following individual teachers for providing a wealth of valuable information that was used to improve and revise the Project WILD materials: Becky Staley, Jacque Sniffen, E. Helledy, Nancy Schmidt, M. Little, Virginia Barton, Bonnie Lock, M. Bruder, Robert Ryan, Sandy Mraz, Kitty Whitlaw, Gary Wallace, Karen Atkins, M. Balkenbush, M. Dollar, Mr. Gissell, Brenda Pierce, Charri Strong, Albert L. Pitzer, Tom Lutz, J. Gallagher, M. Kelbourn, M. Mitchell, Mary Anne French, Mr. Allison, Mr. Schoenborn, Mary Cowan, Diana Smiley, Tom Kennedy, Lea Hamlet, M. Russell, M. Christofanelli, K. Klaas, M. Bergmann, W. Hart, M. Pruitt, Doris Rankin, Mary Flanders, T. Kreuser, Shirley Corn, B. Charles Dorsey, Lydia Whitey, Sandy Stanley, M. Schmidli, Linda Lee Tatro. If we have inadvertently omitted anyone who assisted, please let us know, and we will make the appropriate corrections in the next printing of these materials.

Special Personnel and Materials Assistance   Alameda County Office of Education (California), Alaska Department of Fish and Game, American Humane Association, Arizona Department of Game and Fish, Boulder Valley Public Schools (Colorado), California Department of Game and Fish, Colorado Department of Education, Colorado Division of Wildlife, Defenders of Wildlife, Hawksong Associates, Idaho Department of Game and Fish, Montana Office of the Superintendent of Public Instruction, National Audubon Society, National Wildlife Federation, New Mexico Department of Game and Fish, Ohio Department of Natural Resources, Oregon Department of Fish and Wildlife, Pennsylvania Game Commission, U.S. Forest Service, U.S. Fish and Wildlife Service, Utah Department of Natural Resources, Virginia Department of Education, Washington Department of Game, Washington Office of the Superintendent of Public Instruction, Wyoming Department of Game and Fish.

Principal Contributing Editors and Authors, in Addition to Writing Conference Participants   Kerry Baldwin, Liz Caile, Dr. Cheryl Charles, Judy Dawson, Dr. Lyn Fleming, Dr. Gary Hall, Cliff Hamilton, Bob Hernbrode, Dr. Richard Konicek, Dr. Ben Peyton, Joanna Prukop Lackey, Dr. Don Lundstrom, Ernie McDonald, Dolores Moulton, Dr. Lew Nelson, Jan Rensel, Bob Samples, Rudy Schafer.

Evaluation   Pilot Testing: Dr. Ben Peyton, Principal Investigator; Dr. Lyn Fleming, Associate; Field Testing: Dr. Lyn Fleming, Director; Dr. Rick Kroc, Dr. Ben Peyton, Dr. Norris Harms, Contributing Consultants; Dr. Gene Glass, Dr. Mary Lee Smith, Dr. Kenneth Hopkins, Technical Assistance.

Additional Special Assistance   Tom Charles, Harry Mills, Tony Angell, Donna Szuhy, Dale Crider, Linda Crider, Dick Draney, Bob Flasher, Marlynn Kaake, Jim Gladson, Jim Graban, Bill Hammond, Tex Hawkins, John Herrington, Dick Hess, Larry Littlebird, June McSwain, Dr. Jake Nice, Jim Phillips, Augie Scornaienchi, Jan Rensel, Bob Samples, Robin Hernbrode, Chris Wille, Irene Shelver, Bill Shelver, Stician Samples, Dr. Tom Fitzgerald, Perl Charles, Mattie Charles, Teresa Auldridge, George Ek, Dave Boynton, Dr. Judith Enz, Dr. Jon Hooper, David A. Kennedy, Craig Thompson.

Reviewers of Pilot Materials   Carlton Owen, June McSwain, Lester DeCoster, Rocky Rohwedder, Bob Flasher, Dore Zwingman, Janet Sheldon, Bev Wu, Larry Malone, Linda DeLucchi, Bill Bolar, Kerri Lubin, Joy Crupper, Dr. Jim Armitage, Phyllis Clarke, Tina Yeager, Wanda Headrick, David Yeager, Tiajuana Cochnauer, Shirley J. Wright, Dana Bowyer, Dean Williams, Ron Hamilton, Nancy Christensen, Pam Aikins, Jim Carlson, Ernie McDonald, Bob Samples, Dr. Gary Hall, Cliff Hamilton, Bob Hernbrode, Dr. Lew Nelson, Dr. Ben Peyton, Vince Vandre.

Copy Editing Assistance and Additional Technical Review, First Edition   Dick Hess; Former Chief, Information and Education, Colorado Division of Wildlife.

Principal Editor   Dr. Cheryl Charles.

SECOND EDITION: 1992 UPDATE
Coordinators/Editors   Dan Shaw and Mary Stuever, Seldom Seen Expeditions, Inc.

Principal Editor   Dr. Cheryl Charles, Hawksong Associates.

Editorial Assistants   Judy Dawson and Janet Rasmussen, Hawksong Associates.

Small Group Reviews   Dr. Hans Anderson, Louise Ashman, Richard Baumfalk, Susan Beck, Mark Bennett, Nancy Brown, Becky Brown, Nancy Caldwell, Sam Carmen, Amy Chandler, Laurie Christie, Barbara Church, Jane Cleaves, Rodger Coombs, Phil Cooper, Randy Cotten, Clif Daniels, Shelly Davis, Jerry deBin, Elizabeth DelVerne, Alvin Diamond, Jo Dodds, Ed Donovan, Carolyn Dunmore, Miriam Dunne, Linda Eastwood, Mary Beth Eberwein, Jim Edwards, Kathy Farr, Beth Fasnacht, Jack Finger, Carl Finstad, TC Floy, Susan Foote-Martin, Terri Franklin, Nancy Franz, Connie Gahl, John Gahl, Warren Gartner, Rick Gilchrist, Susan Gilchrist, Alan Gray, Robert Griffin, Corey Hall, Lynn Haralson, Kerry Harkins, Bonnie Helzer, Mel Hickman, Earl Hodil, Carol Holden, Jean Holland, Douglas Housskeeper, Susan Ilgner, Elizabeth Javrin, Jan Jose, Twila Kadel, Michael Kamen, Marti Kane, Michael Karmen, Jeff Kiefer, Julie King, Judy Klippel, Sherry Klosiewski, Bill Koehler, Jackie Lane, Tim Lemon, Chris Martin, Jim McCollough, Jack McNeel, Cathy Meyer, Brenda Miller, Carrie Morgan, Tim Morgan, Margha Mulling, Stu Murrell, Jim Nelson, Deb Neuenschwander, Rod Nichols, Mike Overton, Rod Parker, Deborah Patton, Barbara Pietrucha, Mark Pochon, Polly Powell, Teresa Prather, Christine Raabe, Anna Radue, Barbara Reed, Marian Rendall, Ken Riddleberger, John Russell, Dave Sanger, Nancy Schneider, Ann Seppenfield, M. Sharp, Art Shomo, James Slater, Theresa Stabo, Caroline Sweigart, Jean Terry, Tracey Thompson, Mary Todd, Barbara Tucker, Kenneth Uhlhorn, Al Van Hoey, Karen Van Norman, Linda Walbruch, Bob Waller, Dave Wanisko, Jennifer Warwick, Luann Waters, Linda Watters, Brenda Weiser, Donna White, Frank Williams, Don Winslow, Shirley Wright, Julie Yamamoto, Dr. Dennis Yockers, Kathie Zager, Dean Zimmerman, Darci Zolman.

Draft Reviewers   Miriam Dunne, John Gahl, Barbara Gigar, Suzie Gilley, Maggie Hachmeister, Ellie Horwitz, Dr. Cliff Knapp, Don MacCarter, Chris Martin, Colleen Matt, Cheryl Mollohan, Ken Riddleberger, Larry Sarner, Nancy Schneider, Daphne Sewing, Art Shomo, Dr. Cindi Smith-Walters, Heidi Solper, Jo Temte, Brenda Weiser, Carl Wolfe, Dr. Dennis Yockers.

Independent Comments   Elaine Almeida, Bette Anderson, Paul Beckwith, Carol Beyna, Judy Binger, Sue Bogacz, Evelyn Bologna, Evelyn Boring, Gail Bouslog, Gerry Bryan, Sandra Buck, Sara Campbell, Susan Chambers, Rick Chase, Dorothy Chavez, James Colman, Michael Countess, Kelly Countouris, Ellen Cunningham, Jan Davis, Patrick DeSantis, Barbara Dunbar, LuAnne Folks, Janene Fowler, J. Frey, Sharon Giza, Jim Goodwin, Andy Greif, Karen Grimes Cooper, Linda Gruberski, Karen Hangrove, Linda Harris, Jean Harris, Bob Hernbrode, Earl Hodil, Kathie Holden, Mary Jane Holmes, Bonielee Hooper, Karen Hostetter, Mary Hurst, Jodi Jenkins, Laura Jodice, Jeffrey Keidel, Janice Kesler, Pat Knighten, Pat Lang, Mickey Larkins, Gretchen Leuenberger, Haile Macurdy, Barbara Marshall, Roy Martin, Dale Mason, Beth McCanley, Shalon McCart, Jim McCullough, Terry McLaughlin, Mary Melican, Justine Menci, Patricia Mercker, Cathy Meyer, Debra Miller, Suzanne Miller, Susan Miller, Matt Miller, Sterling Miller, Gerald Mohr, Marie Monfredo, Fran Morris, Jane Moynihan, Kim Mumper, Tom Nelson, Dorcas Newkirk, Connie O'Brien, Helen Panagiotopoulos, Lynette Parkhurst, Deborah Poti, Earl Richardson, Dolores Ringdahl, Wanda Rowland, Linda Sand, Larry Sarner, Rachel Schneider, Mary Shapiro, Art Shomo, Lisa Silverman-Gent, Rick Sinnott, Lucy Slinger, Marlies Smith, Cecil Buckey Smith, Dean Smith, Jacquelyn Sparrow, David St. Clair, Paula St. Clair, Catherine Stefanides, Michael Stephan, Regina Stovall, Jack Turner, Dennis Unkenholz, Larry Vanderlinden, Jane Vollmer, Mary Frances Wagner, Dave Walters, Arthur Washburn, Kenneth Watkins, Elizabeth White, Ellen Wilken,

Debbi Wilkinson, Tim Williams, Laurie Woodall, Jill Yeager, Eileen Yost, Janice Young, Cathy Zazanis, Judy Zeider, Sue Zimmerman, Nancy Zuschlag.

Graphic Design   Bob Samples, Hawksong Associates.

Cover Design   Susie Duckworth, Duckworth Illustration and Graphic Design.

Artwork   All drawings are by Bob Samples unless otherwise acknowledged or public domain.

Photographs   Photographs remain the property of the contributing photographer.

Arizona Game and Fish Department—p. 166, Pat O'Brien; p. 217; p. 295, Pat O'Brien.

Beedle, Butch; J.C. McKenna Middle School, Wisconsin—p. 357.

Burcham, Milo—p. 286.

California Department of Fish and Game—p. 55, Trey Bonetti; p. 185, Paul Wertz; p. 219; p. 277, Jennifer Meyer; p. 310; p. 354; p. 356.

Colorado Game, Fish and Parks Department—p. 29, George D. Andrews.

Dunleavy, Tom; Fishburn Park School, Virginia—p. 73.

Florida Department of Environmental Services—p. 257.

Henry, George B.; Friendsville Elementary School, Tennessee—p. 355.

Idaho Department of Fish and Game—p. 201, Stu Murrell.

Joy, Diane—p. 244.

Kennedy, Clinton A.; Cascade Senior High, Idaho—p. 206.

Knight, Frank—p. 303.

La Hart, Dr. David—p. 87; p. 159.

MacCarter, Don—p. 95, top.

Meyer, Maggie; Lakes Elementary, Wisconsin—p. 358.

Mississippi Museum of Natural Science—p. 25; p. 65; p. 208.

National Marine Fisheries Service—p. 291, A. Lawhead.

NEBRASKAland Magazine/Nebraska Game and Parks Commission—p. 195.

New Jersey Division of Fish, Game and Wildlife—p. 188; p. 199, Laurie Pettigrew.

New Mexico Game and Fish Department—p. v, Don L. MacCarter; p. vi, p. vii, p. 1; p. 47; p. 71; p. 179.

New York State Department of Environmental Conservation—p. 33; p. 68.

Ohio Division of Wildlife—p. 3, Ron Keil; p. 19, Alvin E. Staffam; p. 20, Ron Keil; p. 31, Ron Keil; p. 35, Ron Keil; p. 39, Ron Keil; p. 58, Ron Keil; p. 114, Ron Keil; p. 125, Alvin E. Staffam; p. 161, Ron Keil; p. 247, Ron Keil; p. 253, Ron Keil; p. 315, Ron Keil; p. 323, Ron Keil.

Oregon Department of Fish and Wildlife—p. 49; p. 174.

Pennsylvania Game Commission—p. 122, J.E. Osman; p. 205, J.E. Osman; p. 255, J.E. Osman.

Rocky Mountain Elk Foundation—p. 155.

Samples, Bob—pp. iv, xiv, 13, 20, 40, 45, 59, 60, 67, 77, 81, 95 bottom, 97, 113, 119, 124, 127, 129, 143, 145, 157, 163, 171, 175, 211, 213, 215, 221, 223, 224, 229, 234, 235, 239, 249, 259, 260, 263, 264, 273, 289, 297, 305, 307, 309, 336.

U. S. Fish and Wildlife Service—p. 14; p. 50, W.H. Julian; p. 121; p. 227; p. 271; p. 283; p. 301.

Williams, Lovett—p. 165.

Project WILD
5430 Grosvenor Lane, Suite 230
Bethesda, MD 20814-2142
Phone (301) 493-5447
Fax (301) 493-5627
Email natpwild@igc.apc.org
Web http://eelink.umich.edu/wild/

CEE STAFF
Josetta Hawthorne, Donna Asbury
Michele Campbell, Mike Kaspar

ALPHABETICAL LISTING